Mathematics and Computing:

with *FORTRAN Programming*

Mathematics and Computing:

with *FORTRAN* Programming

WILLIAM S. DORN
Thomas J. Watson Research Center
International Business Machines Corporation
Yorktown Heights, New York

HERBERT J. GREENBERG
Chairman, Department of Mathematics
University of Denver
Denver, Colorado

John Wiley & Sons, Inc.   *New York*   *London*   *Sydney*

Preface

This book is written for the student who has completed two or three years of high school mathematics — algebra, geometry, and perhaps trigonometry. It can be the basis for a one-year mathematics course which has the computer as its focal point. Portions of the book can also be used for a one-semester course.

Selected topics in intuitive calculus and in finite mathematics, including linear equations and inequalities, logic and probability, are covered. The student is introduced to computing and computer programming in the context of these mathematical disciplines while using a computer to solve typical problems.

The mathematical material has been selected with a view toward exploiting the computer to extend the student's knowledge of mathematics. The emphasis has been placed on problems and algorithms for their solution and not on formal proofs of precisely stated theorems. When a theorem is applicable, however, it is pointed out to the reader and in many cases a proof of the theorem is outlined.

A course taught from this text will be transitional between the usual high school mathematics courses and more advanced subjects in mathematics. The student's assignments, therefore, will consist of more reading and thought and less repetitive exercise solving. The exercises are meant to be both challenging and instructive.

Such a course might be considered introductory to the study of more advanced mathematics. It might also be considered to be an appropriate and useful terminal course for liberal arts, social science, or business school students. In addition, this book may be used as a supplement for courses in computer programming, and thus provide the student with the relevant mathematics for the solution of meaningful problems on a computer. Often a student takes a course in programming only to find that the only problems he can solve with his new skills are trivial ones that he could just as readily solve by hand or with a desk calculator. The fields of probability, logic, linear algebra, and calculus provide the mathematical material necessary for formulating and solving meaningful problems and therefore for writing meaningful programs for a computer.

The use of the computer as a mathematical tool allows the student to solve problems, develop insights, and make discoveries that otherwise would not be possible. Consider first the student for whom the material in this book is introductory to more advanced courses. For example, consider the pre-calculus student who has at hand an algorithm and has written a computer program for summing a specific type of infinite series. Suppose he also has an algorithm and a program for computing the slope of a curve. Given the series for sin x and cos x, he is able (for the first time!) to calculate these functions and the slope of the sine curve. He is led to make a discovery: the slope of the sine function appears to be the cosine function. His experience, extended by the computer, leads to interesting and nontrivial conjectures. Though it may be beyond his immediate mathematical ability to verify these conjectures, nevertheless the experience gives him the understanding and appreciation that will prepare him to use the techniques he will acquire later.

On the other hand, there is the student whose formal mathematical training ends with a course taught from this material. He will have obtained an intuitive understanding of the processes and ideas of the calculus from having carried out the solution of problems such as the one described in the preceding paragraph. It is our contention that this student's understanding of the ideas of the calculus will be deeper and better retained than that of a student who has had a traditional calculus course and nothing more.

The example outlined above and others like it are left to the student to carry out himself. Such exercises prepare him for the more formal aspects of the calculus. Here, however, the approach to the calculus is intuitive and problem-oriented. Besides computing slopes, the student will learn to sketch curves, compute areas, sum infinite series, and find numerical solutions to nonlinear equations.

In addition to the basic ideas and processes of the calculus, the material covered in this book includes linear systems of equations and inequalities with optimization, logic, Boolean algebra, and elementary probability. In all of them, applications are emphasized, and the computer is used to carry out the solution of problems with appropriate algorithms.

Chapters 1 and 2 discuss the solution of linear equations and linear inequalities. Linear programming, the most powerful tool now used for the solution of finite optimization problems, is introduced, and the student learns the classical simplex method for solving them.

Chapter 3 discusses elementary FORTRAN programming, although the student will already have encountered some FORTRAN in the first two chapters. Chapters 4 through 7 are concerned with intuitive calculus.

Chapter 4 presents the notion of the derivative by the calculation of the speed of a moving object. Here for the first time in this text the student encounters a process that has no end and is introduced to the idea of convergence of such never-ending algorithms.

In Chapter 5 the student learns how to find the solution of nonlinear equations by using never-ending algorithms. In particular, he learns how to calculate square roots and cube roots and how to estimate the accuracy of his results.

Chapter 6 is concerned with finding the sum of an infinite number of terms. The student will learn that, although computers may be used to evaluate these sums to a prescribed accuracy, they cannot be used to find out whether such an infinite number of terms has a sum. These discussions lead to methods for evaluating the number π and for computing trigonometric tables.

Chapter 7 introduces the concept of the integral by the calculation of areas. Other applications of the integral are also discussed and practical numerical techniques are developed.

In the chapter on logic (Chapter 8) the student will find a discussion of Boolean algebra and truth tables. Here the use of a computer permits the evaluation of more complicated and meaningful truth tables than is otherwise possible. It also permits the analysis and design of practical switching circuits, which provide the student not only with a deeper understanding of logic but also with realistic applications of this powerful mathematical tool.

The final chapter (Chapter 9) on probability, introduces the modern concepts of sample spaces, events, trees, and stochastic processes. The theoretical discussions are reinforced by the study and use of random number generators and Monte Carlo methods. After having analyzed the rather complicated game of dice, the student uses the Monte Carlo method to verify and test his results by simulating thousands of such games on a computer. Such practice deepens the student's understanding of probability and moreover provides him with the means for investigating more complex problems.

We believe that the student can best be motivated by confronting him with meaningful problems whose solutions demonstrate the power of the mathematics he is learning. Consequently, each topic is introduced in terms of a problem, which is reduced to a mathematical statement, and the student is then taught the mathematical ideas and techniques that allow him to solve it.

In this way the central role of mathematics and mathematicians in the reduction of complex situations to mathematical statements and the use of mathematical procedures (or algorithms) to solve these mathematical statements is constantly emphasized.

In order to exploit the computer successfully, the student is taught the use of flow charts and some elementary programming very early in the book (Chapters 1 and 3). The computer language is FORTRAN. However, it is necessary to discuss only a very small portion of the FORTRAN language. Indeed, the only computer programming covered is that required to solve the mathematics problems encountered — no more, no less. Consequently, everything in this book applies to any and all versions of FORTRAN and can be used on any computer with a FORTRAN compiler. A list of more than 70 such computers is given in Appendix E. It is to be emphasized that computer programming is not the objective of this book. It is merely a happy by-product.

The student who wishes to learn all the capabilities that FORTRAN can provide for him should supplement this book with one of the standard texts on FORTRAN. Two excellent examples are *A Guide to FORTRAN Programming,* which covers the FORTRAN II language, and *A Guide to FORTRAN IV Programming.* Both were written by Daniel D. McCracken and are published by John Wiley and Sons.

Besides programming, the student also learns the numerical analysis appropriate to each topic. Particular attention is paid to the limitations inherent in numerical computation on a digital computer. A thorough discussion of floating-point arithmetic is given, and the reader encounters some unexpected facts, such as the nonassociativity of addition, when using this arithmetic in a computer. Analysis of errors is introduced wherever possible, and its importance is emphasized.

Finally, the student is made aware of the history of mathematics to the present day by the liberal use of footnotes which summarize the contributions and events in the lives of famous mathematicians and scientists. All of these men were selected because their names are associated with the subject matter of the book. It is interesting to note that of the twenty-six scientists who are referenced, five are alive today and seven others live, or have lived, in the twentieth century.

The entire text may be and has been used for a full-year course. However, selected chapters may be employed as the basis for two separate one-semester courses. The material on the calculus may be omitted by selecting Chapters 1, 2, 3, 8, and 9. These chapters provide a one-semester introduction to linear algebra with inequalities, logic, and probability as well as computer programming. On the other hand, a one-semester intuitive calculus course which includes an introduction to computing can be taught from Chapters 1, 3, 4, 5, 6, and 7, in which case much of linear algebra and all of the logic and probability will be passed over.

A large number of problems are presented both at the end of each chapter and scattered throughout the book. Those in the text are intended to raise questions and stimulate discussion. They are designed to test and further the student's understanding and to lead him into the succeeding material. All should be completed by every student.

The exercises at the close of each chapter are of three types. First are the simple numerical examples that give the student practice in the mechanics of the methods he has learned. Second are the problems that require the student to create a mathematical model of some physical situation and to test and increase his understanding of the mathematical ideas presented in the chapter. Finally, there are problems that allow the student to discover for himself additional results, concepts, and techniques of mathematics.

Although it is not necessary for a school to have a computer, classes should have access to equipment with a FORTRAN compiler — for example, the IBM 1620. It is estimated that each student will require about two to three hours of computer time during the entire school year. If a computer larger or smaller than a 1620 is used, the time should be appropriately scaled up or down.

The students should see the computer at least once or twice and on those occasions be able to load cards and watch the entire operation. Most of the time, however, the computing can be done in the students' absence — on the evening shift at a nearby university or at a local firm if a computer is not available at the school.

An ideal solution is to have a typewriter-like device called a "terminal" at school and to connect it by telephone lines with a large central computer. Many computing centers have equipment that can accommodate such devices now and more will be able to do so as time goes on. It performs most of the functions of the computer to which it is attached at only a fraction of the former's cost because many terminals can be served by one computer. In this way these terminals have the added advantage of introducing the student to a phase of computer use that is becoming more and more prevalent in university and industrial environments.

If a complete computer system is available rather than a terminal connected to a remote computer, keypunch and accounting machines should also be provided for the students' use at or near the school. The students should punch cards themselves at least once and could do all of their own keypunching (15 to 30 minutes a week on the average). The accounting machine is used only to provide them with a printed list of their punched cards (5 minutes a week per student). Each student may be expected to consume 1000 punched cards over the year's time. The keypunch and the accounting machine should be capable of printing all the symbols used by FORTRAN. If a typewriter and a remote computer are used, the typewriter replaces the keypunch, accounting machine, and cards.

A preliminary edition of this book was tested in high schools and colleges during 1965 and 1966. Then the material was revised and the present edition was prepared. An instructor's manual is also published. It includes further explanatory material and answers to all the exercises.

It is a pleasure to acknowledge some of those who assisted us in the preparation of this book. Miss Carol E. Shanesy of IBM Research carefully read all of the final manuscript and solved all of the exercises. Her suggestions and criticisms were invaluable. Mr. Abraham M. Glicksman of the Bronx High School of Science read the preliminary edition and made many constructive suggestions which helped to shape the final version of the text. To both of these people we owe a considerable debt of gratitude. Mr. Andrew Hathaway and Mr. Bernard Capuano of Greenwich High School, Connecticut, taught classes in 1965 and 1966, using the preliminary edition. They and their students were of great assistance to us in revising the original manuscript. Finally, we express our appreciation to Mrs. Angela Maxey, who typed the first draft, Mrs. Nina Hogan, who typed the preliminary edition, and Miss Lauren Hyland, who typed the final manuscript and the instructor's manual.

We also have drawn inspiration and guidance from many other sources, including other textbooks. They are so numerous that it is impossible to acknowledge all of them. The best we have been able to do is to mention a few of those who helped us and to hope that the many others will understand our gratitude even though it remains unexpressed.

William S. Dorn
Herbert J. Greenberg

Yorktown Heights, New York
Denver, Colorado
April 1967

Contents

Mathematics and Computing:

with *FORTRAN Programming*

CHAPTER ONE

Linear Equations—Finding a Solution

1.1 The Chemistry Exam Problem

There you are in the middle of a chemistry examination. You really understand all the questions and how to answer them. But one thing is stopping you from putting the answers down on paper — *you've forgotten the formula for changing Fahrenheit temperature to centigrade temperature.* Time is running out and all you can recall is that it looked somewhat like

$$C = \tfrac{9}{5}(F + 32)$$

or was it ⅝? And, oh yes, you remember that water freezes at 0°C and 32°F and that it boils at 100°C and 212°F. Can we use this information to find the formula you need? Let's see.

First we check your formula to see if it works for the freezing point. We put $F = 32$ into the formula and get $C = 115.2. \ldots$ Obviously something is wrong. If the formula had -32 in it instead of $+32$, then, when $F = 32$, it would produce $C = 0$. Perhaps it should be

$$C = \tfrac{9}{5}(F - 32)$$

Now let's check the boiling point. When $F = 212°$, $C = 324°$ (not 100° as it should be). Again the formula is wrong.

You could keep guessing and correcting to find the answer, but there is a more systematic way of going about solving our problem. First we notice that it is the constants in the formula, namely, ⅝ and $+32$, that are in doubt. If we let the constants be unknown quantities, the formula can be written

$$C = aF + b \tag{1}$$

where a and b are constants to be found. Whatever those numbers a and b are, they must work for the freezing point and boiling point of water because the formula must be true for all temperatures.

1

When water is freezing, $C = 0°$ and $F = 32°$. Putting $C = 0$ and $F = 32$ in (1), we find that a and b must be numbers such that

$$0 = 32a + b \tag{2}$$

On the other hand, when water boils, $C = 100°$ and $F = 212°$; thus, from (1) we find that

$$100 = 212a + b \tag{3}$$

Equations (2) and (3) are two simultaneous linear equations for two unknowns, a and b.[1] Solving (2) for b, we obtain

$$b = -32a \tag{4}$$

Putting this value for b in (3) gives

$$100 = 212a - 32a$$

which is the same as

$$100 = 180a$$

Therefore,

$$a = \frac{100}{180} = \frac{5}{9}$$

With this value for a, equation (4) produces

$$b = -32 \cdot \frac{5}{9} = -\frac{160}{9}$$

and equation (1) becomes

$$C = \frac{5}{9}F - \frac{160}{9} \tag{5}$$

or, upon factoring $\frac{5}{9}$ out of both terms on the right-hand side, we find the familiar (and now correct!) formula

$$C = \tfrac{5}{9}(F - 32) \tag{6}$$

Mathematics has come to the rescue! Indeed, you have just seen a demonstration of the essence and power of mathematics — taking a somewhat vague and perhaps difficult problem (finding or recalling a formula) and reducing it to a simple, clear-cut procedure (solving two linear equations).

---

[1] A *linear equation* is an equation in which each unknown appears only to the first power and no products of the unknowns appear.

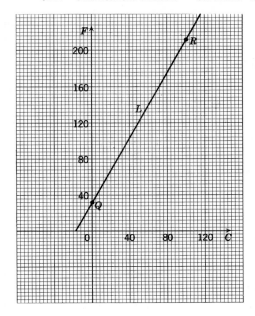

Figure 1

Geometrical model of $C = \frac{5}{9}(F - 32)$

In this book, we try to show you how to analyze problems and write a mathematical description of them. This process is often called "constructing a model" or, more precisely, a **mathematical model.** In the example the model was expressed by equations (2) and (3).

We also show you how to find solutions to these mathematical models. In the example above, we solved equation (2) for b and substituted our answer in equation (3). We then solved the resulting equation for a and used that number in equation (2) to find b. Such a procedure is called an **algorithm.** But more about that later.

1.2 Geometrical Models — Cartesian Coordinates

We can represent equation (6) geometrically. A graph of that equation is shown in Figure 1, where C is measured along the horizontal axis and F is measured along the vertical axis. The point R corresponds to the boiling point of water, and the point Q corresponds to its freezing point.

$C = 100$ and $F = 212$ are the **coordinates** of the point R. The point R can be identified by its coordinates, which can be written more conveniently as the number pair (100, 212). Similarly, the point Q has coordinates $C = 0$ and $F = 32$. This point may be identified by the number pair (0, 32). Notice that, when we write such number pairs, the value of the horizontal coordinate or **abscissa** is written first, and the value of the vertical coordinate or **ordinate** is written second. There is no ambiguity, then, if we refer to the point (100, 212). It is the point whose coordinates are $C = 100$ and $F = 212$. In Figure 1 it is the point R. We shall often refer to **the point (a, b)** and shall mean the point whose abscissa is a and whose ordinate is b.

The points which satisfy equation (6) lie on the line which passes through the points R and Q. The line L in Figure 1 is a **geometrical model** of equation (6).

Conversely, equation (6) can be thought of as a mathematical model of the line L. Equation (6) is called linear because its geometrical model is a line.

The linking of algebra and geometry is called **analytic geometry.** This subject was originated by the French mathematician and philosopher, René Descartes.[2] The use of coordinates described above was first conceived of by Descartes, and in his honor the coordinates are called **Cartesian coordinates.**

If we want to know what centigrade temperature corresponds to some Fahrenheit temperature, say 120°, we look across from 120 on the F axis to the line L and then read down to the C axis to find what the C coordinate is. In this case it appears to be 49°C. This is not quite right, as you can see by checking equation (6). *We must not rely on the geometrical model to give us great accuracy.* A geometrical model gives us a picture of the main features of a problem and allows us to discover qualitative facts. If we wish quantitative information, we must have an algebraic model.

---

[2] **René Descartes** (pronounced "day-kahrt"), 1596–1650, a famous French mathematician and philosopher, often signed his writings with a Latinized version of his name, Renatus Cartesius. For that reason his system of philosophy and of coordinate geometry are referred to as Cartesian.

According to one legend, he discovered Cartesian coordinates while lying in bed watching a fly in flight. It occurred to him that he could identify the fly's position at every moment by locating three mutually perpendicular planes that intersected at the place occupied by the fly. By connecting geometry and algebra (even then also called analysis) he gave birth to the branch of mathematics called "analytic geometry."

In philosophy Descartes was a mechanist, and he was the author of the familiar phrase *Cogito, ergo sum* ("I think, therefore I am").

We now ask the question: Is there a temperature at which centigrade and Fahrenheit thermometers have the same reading?

The points in Figure 1 for which the *C* and *F* coordinates are numerically the same ($C = F$) lie on the line at a 45-degree inclination to both axes. This is the line *M* in Figure 2.

Every point on the line *L* represents a physical temperature, and every point on the line *M* represents equal values of *C* and *F*. It follows that points on *both* lines represent physical temperatures where the centigrade and Fahrenheit thermometers have identical readings. Because these two lines, *M* and *L*, are not parallel, they must cross at some point. The answer to the question above, then, is "yes," since at the intersection of *M* and *L* we have found a physical temperature for which $C = F$. Our geometrical model has allowed us to answer a qualitative question. If we

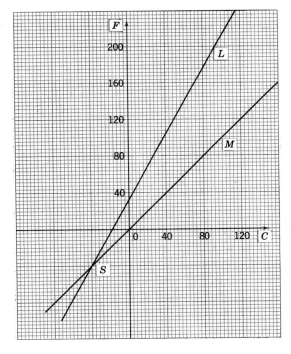

Figure 2

Geometrical solution to finding where centigrade and Fahrenheit thermometers have the same reading

ask the quantitative question: "At what temperature do the thermometers have the same reading?" we must use an algebraic model.

Let us find an algebraic model of this problem and answer the quantitative question. Line L is represented by equation (6):

$$C = \tfrac{5}{9}(F - 32) \tag{6}$$

The line M represents the equation

$$C = F \tag{7}$$

We seek a number pair (C, F), given by a value of C and a value of F, which satisfies both (6) and (7). These are two simultaneous linear equations for C and F. We can solve them just as we did equations (2) and (3). The solution is left to the reader.

We now ask: Is there a temperature at which the Fahrenheit thermometer gives a reading three times that of the centigrade thermometer? The geometrical model is given in Figure 3, which shows that there is a solution of the problem at approximately $C = 26°$. The algebraic model consists of two equations:

$$C = \tfrac{5}{9}(F - 32) \tag{8}$$

$$F = 3C \tag{9}$$

Solving them gives us the more accurate solution $C = 26.67°$.

> **Question.**   At what temperature does the Fahrenheit thermometer have a reading ⅔ that of the centigrade thermometer?

1.3   A Diet Problem

Before discussing linear equations and how to solve them we discuss one more rather simple example. Suppose you have decided to eat roast beef and a lettuce salad with French dressing for dinner. The menu may include other foods, but from these two you want to obtain half of your daily requirements for protein and ascorbic acid (vitamin C).

Here we have a somewhat vague description of a problem. We make the problem precise to be able to solve it by constructing a mathematical model. As you might expect, our model again contains two linear equations in two unknowns.

First we need some information about the protein and ascorbic acid contents of the two foods and some information about the daily requirements of these two dietary elements. Table 1 provides that information.

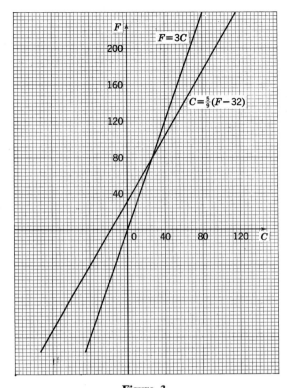

Figure 3

Geometrical model of equations (8) and (9)

The numbers vary with the food (the roast beef may have more or less fat) and the person (an athlete requires more nutrients than an office clerk), but the numbers in the table are typical.

Now let B be the amount of roast beef in the menu in units of 100 grams. That is, $B = 1$ stands for 100 grams of roast beef. Similarly, let L be the amount of lettuce salad; each unit of L stands for 100 grams. The total amount of protein in grams in a menu of B units of roast beef and L units of salad is

$$20B + L$$

As the daily requirement is 70 grams, it follows that to get half the daily requirement from this diet

$$20B + L = 35 \tag{10}$$

Table 1

	Protein (grams)	Ascorbic Acid (milligrams)
Roast beef (100 grams)	20	0
Salad with French dressing (100 grams)	1	15
Daily requirement	70	60

Similarly, the ascorbic acid requirement can be written

$$0 \cdot B + 15L = 30 \tag{11}$$

because there is no ascorbic acid in roast beef and each unit of salad contains 15 milligrams of ascorbic acid.

Equations (10) and (11) are two linear equations in two unknowns, B and L. From equation (11), we have

$$L = 2$$

Substituting this in equation (10), we obtain

$$20B + 2 = 35$$

Solving for B gives

$$20B = 35 - 2 = 33$$

$$B = 1.65$$

Thus, you should eat 200 grams of salad and 165 grams of beef.[3]

We pause now to pose a very similar question which, you will find, has an unexpected answer.

Question.   Suppose we want 165 milligrams of ascorbic acid and 10 grams of protein for a person on a special low-protein, high-vitamin-C diet. How much salad and roast beef should be in the diet?

1.4 Two Equations in Two Unknowns

The problems we have encountered so far have led to two linear equations in two unknown quantities. The two equations are popularly referred to as simultaneous equations because we wish to find values of the unknowns which "simultaneously" satisfy both equations. Mathe-

---

[3] This is equivalent to about half a head of lettuce and two small slices of beef.

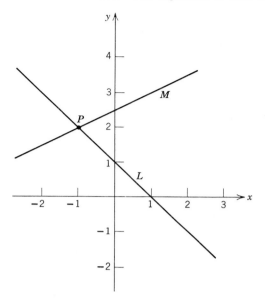

Figure 4

Geometrical model of equations (12) and (13) — unique solution

maticians, however, prefer to speak of a *system* of two linear equations in two unknowns. Mathematicians also prefer to speak of *variables* rather than unknowns. We turn now to a discussion of the mathematics of this particular kind of problem, systems of two linear equations in two variables.

Consider first the two equations

$$x + y = 1 \tag{12}$$

$$-x + 2y = 5 \tag{13}$$

We construct a geometrical model of these equations by introducing two perpendicular axes as before and labeling them x and y. The graph of equation (12) is the line L in Figure 4. The graph of the second equation, (13), is the line M.

Since all the points satisfying equation (12) lie on line L, and all the points satisfying equation (13) lie on line M, points which satisfy *both* equations (12) and (13) simultaneously must lie on *both* lines. The only point lying on both lines is the point P, where apparently $x = -1$ and

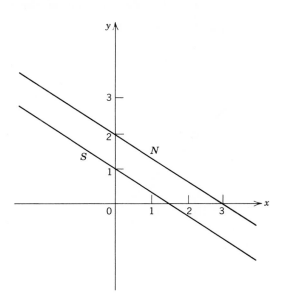

Figure 5

Geometrical model of equations (14) and (15) — no solution

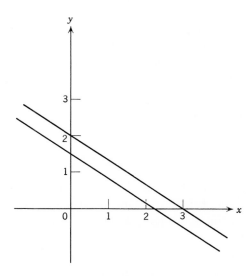

Figure 6

Geometrical model of $2x + 3y = 6$ and $4x + 6y = 9$

$y = 2$. The reader should verify that these values of the variables do indeed satisfy both equations.

Because equations (12) and (13) have one and only one solution, we call the solution **unique**. All the examples in the preceding sections also possessed unique solutions.[4] However, not all simultaneous linear equations do, as we shall now see.

Consider the simultaneous linear equations

$$2x + 3y = 6 \tag{14}$$

$$4x + 6y = 6 \tag{15}$$

Let us construct a geometrical model of this system of two equations. In Figure 5 the line N corresponds to equation (14), and the line S corresponds to equation (15). These two lines are parallel and never meet. Therefore, the system of equations (14) and (15) has *no* solution. That is, there are no values of the variables x and y which simultaneously satisfy equations (14) and (15).

We call such equations which have no solution **inconsistent** because they contradict each other.

Now, if we change the right-hand side of equation (15) from 6 to 9, the system still has no solution but the parallel lines are closer together. (See Figure 6.) As we continue to increase the right-hand side of equation (15), the lines come closer and closer to each other. When the value becomes 12, we get the system

$$2x + 3y = 6 \tag{16}$$

$$4x + 6y = 12 \tag{17}$$

and the lines become identical with one another (see the line N in Figure 7).

The values $x = 3$ and $y = 0$ now satisfy both equations. And the values $x = 0$ and $y = 2$ do too. Indeed, the coordinates of every point on the line N satisfy equations (16) and (17). This system of equations, therefore, has an infinite number of solutions and is said to be **consistent**. Notice that, if we multiply equation (16) by 2, we get equation (17).[5]

---

[4] Except for the question at the end of Section 1.2.

[5] More precisely, we mean "multiply *both sides of* equation (16) by 2." In the interests of brevity, however, we say "multiply equation (16) by 2" because no confusion exists once we understand what is meant.

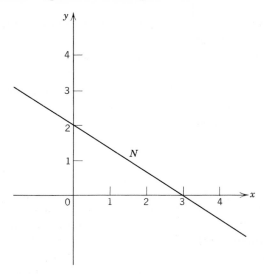

Figure 7

Geometrical model of equations (16) and (17) — infinite number of solutions

These equations are called **dependent** because they depend on one another (one is just twice the other).

We have considered three possible cases which we summarize:

1. *Unique solution.* The equations have one and only one solution (Figure 4).
2. *No solution.* The equations are inconsistent and do not possess any solution (Figure 5).
3. *Infinite number of solutions.* The equations are dependent, and an infinite number of number pairs satisfy them (Figure 7).

Since the last two cases are the exception rather than the rule, they are both designated **singular** cases and the system of equations is called a singular system. The first case is then quite naturally termed **nonsingular**. We shall develop a method for solving nonsingular equations which will also warn us if the equations happen to be singular.

Question.   Are there any possibilities other than the three cases considered above? Why?

Question.   Consider equations (12) and (13), which are nonsingular, with the right-hand sides equal to zero:

$$x + y = 0$$

$$-x + 2y = 0$$

What is the solution? Is it unique? Compare this with the case in which the right-hand sides were not zero. Now consider equations (14) and (15), which were singular and had no solution. Let the right-hand sides be zero. What is the solution? Is it unique?

1.5   Systems with n Equations and n Variables

We have discussed in detail the case of two linear equations in two unknowns. There were three possible results: a unique solution, no solution, or an infinite number of solutions.

Suppose we have more than two equations. In fact, suppose our mathematical model consists of four linear equations and four variables, or six equations and six variables. Or, indeed, suppose we are led to *n* equations and *n* variables. What can be said about the solutions? We do not discuss this question here in any detail but content ourselves with the statement:

Any system of linear equations in which the number of variables and the number of equations are the same has either: a *unique solution* (then the system is nonsingular), or *no solution* (then the system is singular and inconsistent, or an *infinite number of solutions* (then the system is said to be singular but consistent).

This is identical with the result for two equations and two variables. In the succeeding sections of this chapter we discuss a method for solving systems of linear equations which not only finds a solution when it exists but also tells us when there is no solution.

1.6   The Diet Problem Revisited

Recall that the first solution to the diet problem told how much beef and salad you should eat in order to get one-half of the daily requirement of protein and ascorbic acid. Suppose now you also want to assure yourself of consuming the proper amount of calories and calcium and have decided to add milk and spinach to your diet.

Table 2

	Protein (grams)	Ascorbic Acid (milligrams)	Calories	Calcium (grams)
Roast beef (100 grams)	20	0	325	.01
Salad with French dressing (100 grams)	1	15	80	.04
Milk (100 grams)	3.3	1.5	70	.12
Spinach (100 grams)	2.3	50	22	.07
Daily requirement	70	60	3000	1.0

Table 2 lists the nutrient content of the four foods and the daily requirements of the nutrients.[6] Suppose again that you would like to obtain one-half of the daily requirement of protein, ascorbic acid, and calcium but want to keep the calories relatively low, say 700.

If B = the amount of roast beef in the diet, L = the amount of salad, M = the amount of milk, and S = the amount of spinach, all in 100-gram units, then the number of grams of protein is

$$20B + L + 3.3M + 2.3S$$

To satisfy the requirement for protein, this should be equal to one-half of 70 or

$$20B + L + 3.3M + 2.3S = 35 \qquad (18)$$

Similarly, the ascorbic acid (vitamin C) requirement can be expressed as

$$15L + 1.5M + 50S = 30 \qquad (19)$$

the calorie requirement as

$$325B + 80L + 70M + 22S = 700 \qquad (20)$$

and the calcium requirement as

$$.01B + .04L + .12M + .07S = 0.5 \qquad (21)$$

These equations, (18)–(21), are a system of four linear equations in four variables, B, L, M, and S.

We could proceed to solve these equations as follows: We try to reduce the problem to a more simple one of solving a system of *three* equations

---

[6] Again these numbers will vary with the quality of the food and individual requirements. The numbers given in Table 2 are merely representative.

in *three* variables. If we find a way of doing this, then we should be able also to simplify our new three-variable problem to one of solving a system of two equations in two variables. Continuing in this way, we again simplify the problem to one equation in one variable. The last problem is, of course, very easy to solve.

Thus, at each step we reduce the number of equations by one and also reduce the number of variables by one. We proceed with this objective in mind.

Now we can multiply an equation by any nonzero number and obtain a valid equation. Similarly, we can add or subtract two equations and obtain a valid equation. The values of the variables which satisfy the original equations also satisfy any equation obtained as above from the original equations.

Consider the following system of four equations in four variables:

$$2x + y - z + 2t = 4 \tag{22}$$

$$4x + 3y - z + 6t = 12 \tag{23}$$

$$6x + 5y - 2z + 11t = 20 \tag{24}$$

$$-4x - 3y + 5z - 8t = -10 \tag{25}$$

Suppose we multiply the first, equation (22), by 2. Then we have

$$4x + 2y - 2z + 4t = 8 \tag{26}$$

If we subtract this from equation (23), we get an equation in which the coefficient of x is zero. In fact, the result is

$$y + z + 2t = 4 \tag{27}$$

We obtained the number 2, by which we multiplied equation (22), by dividing the coefficient of x in equation (23) by the coefficient of x in equation (22). This guarantees us that, when we subtract from equation (22), the coefficient of x will vanish. We replace equation (23) by this new equation, (27). Our system is now composed of equations (22), (27), (24), and (25).

Next we divide the coefficient of x in equation (24) by the coefficient of x in equation (22) and get $\frac{6}{2} = 3$. We multiply equation (22) by 3 and obtain

$$6x + 3y - 3z + 6t = 12$$

Subtracting this equation from equation (24), we have

$$2y + z + 5t = 8 \tag{28}$$

This replaces equation (24) in our system. Finally, we multiply equation (22) by $-\frac{4}{2} = -2$ and subtract the result from equation (25) to get

$$-y + 3z - 4t = -2 \tag{29}$$

This replaces equation (25).

Equations (22), (27), (28), (29) are again a system of four equations in four variables. This system is given by

$$2x + y - z + 2t = 4 \tag{22}$$

$$y + z + 2t = 4 \tag{27}$$

$$2y + z + 5t = 8 \tag{28}$$

$$-y + 3z - 4t = -2 \tag{29}$$

The last three equations have no x terms. These three equations constitute a system of three equations in three variables. If we can solve this system for the values of the three variables y, z, and t, then by putting these values in equation (22) we can find the value of x.

Before we do that, however, we ask ourselves an important question: Will the values of x, y, z, and t obtained by solving equations (22), (27), (28), and (29) be a solution of the original system of equations? If the answer is "no," we have done all our work for naught. Fortunately, the answer is "yes," and we now show that it is.

We must show that any values of x, y, z, and t which satisfy the second system — equations (22), (27), (28), (29) — also satisfy the original system — equations (22)–(25). Suppose we multiply equation (22) by 2 and *add* the result to equation (27). The result is

$$4x + 3y - z + 6t = 12$$

which is precisely equation (23). Similarly, multiplying equation (22) by 3 and adding the result to equation (28) produces equation (24). Finally, multiplying equation (22) by -2 and adding the result to equation (29) yields equation (25).

Thus, we can obtain again the original system of equations by multiplying equations in the second system by nonzero constants and adding the appropriate equations. Therefore, any values of x, y, z, and t which satisfy the second system — equations (22), (27), (28), (29) — must also satisfy the original system. This means that we can solve the new system of equations rather than the original one if we choose to do so. It appears that the second system will be easier to solve because x does not appear in three of the four equations.

The reader may wonder why we went through the preceding argument. Indeed, it may seem obvious that we could solve the new system of equations rather than the original system. However, suppose we took equation (26) — obtained by multiplying equation (22) by 2 — subtracted it from equation (23), and used it to replace equation (24).[7] The resulting system of equations would be

$$2x + y - z + 2t = 4 \tag{22}$$

$$4x + 3y - z + 6t = 12 \tag{23}$$

$$y + z + 2t = 4 \tag{27}$$

$$-4x - 3y + 5z - 8t = -10 \tag{25}$$

We cannot use this system of equations to replace our original system because there are solutions to this system which are not solutions of the original system of equations. For example, $x = 0$, $y = 6$, $z = 0$, and $t = -1$ is a solution to the last system. This may be verified by substituting these values into equations (22), (23), (27), and (25). However, these values do *not* satisfy the original equations. In particular, they do not satisfy equation (24). The reader should verify this fact.

The difficulty is that we replaced equation (24) by equation (27). Since equation (27) was derived from equations (22) and (23), there is no way to obtain equation (24) from the second system — equations (22), (23), (27), and (25). The information in equation (24) is no longer contained in the last system of equations above.

It is important that equation (27) replace either equation (23) or equation (22), because it was derived from those two equations. In deriving the new system — equations (22), (27), (28), (29) — each time we replaced an equation we were careful to replace it by an equation which was derived from it.

The lesson to be learned from this is that we must not assume that any system of four equations which is derived from the original system can be used as a replacement. We can use (22), (27), (28), and (29), however,

[7] Previously it replaced equation (23).

because we have shown that any solution of this system is also a solution of (22)–(25).

To summarize: It is possible to replace the system of four equations in four variables by another system. The last three equations of the new system constitute a system of three equations in three variables. Thus, if we solve a system of three equations, we can obtain the solution of the larger problem quite easily.

Now, since we have just reduced the problem of solving a system of four equations to one of solving a system of three equations, we should be able to use the same kind of procedure to reduce the problem of solving a system of three equations to one of solving a system of two equations. If we multiply equation (27) by 2 and subtract the result from equation (28), we get

$$-z + t = 0$$

Similarly, if we multiply equation (27) by -1 and subtract the result from equation (29), we obtain

$$4z - 2t = 2$$

Using these equations to replace equations (28) and (29), we arrive at the following system of equations:

$$2x + y - z + 2t = 4$$
$$y + z + 2t = 4$$
$$-z + t = 0$$
$$4z - 2t = 2$$

The last two equations may be thought of as a system of two equations in two variables, z and t. We leave the solution of this system as an exercise for the reader. Then, putting these values of z and t in equation (27), we can find y. Finally, using all these values for y, z, and t in equation (22), we find x.

Our objective has been to find a sequence of problems, all equivalent to one another, and each simpler to solve. We have accomplished this objective.

As you can see, the process outlined above is rather cumbersome. If you wanted to describe that process completely to someone who was going to do the algebra and arithmetic for you and who had never done it before, a much more detailed description would be required. Moreover, it would be difficult for the other person to follow this description, and, if he forgot some part of it, he would have trouble reconstructing the missing section. As we shall see, if our helper — the one who does the arithmetic — happens to be a computer, then the description above is entirely inadequate. The computer requires a much more orderly description. We shall develop an orderly description in the next section and then describe how a computer can be instructed to carry out this process.

Problem. Use the procedure just described to solve the system of equations (18), (19), (20), and (21) for the four-food diet problem.

1.7 Gauss's Method

We now describe a systematic method or algorithm for solving a system of four linear equations in four variables. Later we shall discuss how the algorithm can be extended to solve any number of linear equations. You may have learned how to solve two or three linear equations by using determinants (Cramer's rule). This method can be extended to solve four equations, but the evaluation of determinants with four or more rows and columns is not easy. Cramer's rule is, in fact, not very useful for more than three simultaneous equations. The method we describe is superior to Cramer's rule. It was discovered by the German mathematician Johann Karl Friedrich Gauss.[8]

We write four equations in four variables, x_1, x_2, x_3, x_4:[9]

$$a_{11}x_1 + a_{12}x_2 + a_{13}x_3 + a_{14}x_4 = b_1 \tag{30}$$

$$a_{21}x_1 + a_{22}x_2 + a_{23}x_3 + a_{24}x_4 = b_2 \tag{31}$$

$$a_{31}x_1 + a_{32}x_2 + a_{33}x_3 + a_{34}x_4 = b_3 \tag{32}$$

$$a_{41}x_1 + a_{42}x_2 + a_{43}x_3 + a_{44}x_4 = b_4 \tag{33}$$

[8] **Johann Karl Friedrich Gauss** (pronounced "gowce"), 1777–1855, was one of the greatest mathematicians in history. He performed significant work in almost every branch of mathematics including calculus, number theory, and geometry, in addition to doing fundamental work in physics (the unit of magnetic flux is named for him). Among his most famous accomplishments are the proofs of the fundamental theorem of algebra (that every algebraic equation has at least one root) and the fundamental theorem of arithmetic (that every integer can be represented as the product of prime numbers in one and only one way).

[9] We could just as well have used letters x, y, z, t rather than x_1, x_2, x_3, x_4 for the variables, but the latter system of notation allows us to have as many variables as we wish and to label them easily by the numerical subscripts 1, 2, 3, etc.

The numbers set a little below the line of print such as the 23 in a_{23} are called subscripts ("sub" for below and "script" for writing; thus, "written below the line"). The symbol x_2, for example, is read "x two" or "x sub two." The symbol a_{13} is read "a one three" or "a sub one three." The symbols $a_{11}, a_{12}, \ldots, a_{44}$ and $b_1, \ldots, b_4$ stand for the numerical coefficients in an actual problem.[10]

To gain practice with the notation, let us take a simple example of four equations:

$$
\begin{aligned}
x_2 - x_3 + x_4 &= 1 \\
3x_1 - 2x_2 + x_3 \qquad &= 2 \\
x_1 + x_2 + x_3 + x_4 &= 4 \\
2x_1 - x_2 \qquad + 2x_4 &= 3
\end{aligned}
\tag{34}
$$

The first equation is found to be a special case of equation (30) by setting

$$
\begin{aligned}
a_{11} &= 0 & a_{12} &= 1 \\
a_{13} &= -1 & a_{14} &= 1 \\
b_1 &= 1
\end{aligned}
$$

Similarly, the second equation is obtained from equation (31) by setting

$$
\begin{aligned}
a_{21} &= 3 & a_{22} &= -2 \\
a_{23} &= 1 & a_{24} &= 0 \\
b_2 &= 2
\end{aligned}
$$

The reader should determine the values of the other a's and b's, which give the third and fourth equations in (34) from (32) and (33), for example, $a_{31} = 1$, $b_4 = 3$, etc.

Notice, in equation (30), that the *first* subscripts on the a's and the only subscript on b are all 1. This identifies these coefficients as belonging

---

[10] Frequently, when a long string of symbols or numbers is to be written in a prescribed sequence, the mathematician avoids writing them all by using a comma followed by three dots and another comma to indicate that the intervening symbols have been omitted but follow the indicated sequence. Thus, $b_1, \ldots, b_4$ stands for b_1, b_2, b_3, b_4. Similarly, $1, 2, 3, \ldots,$ is often written for the sequence of all positive integers.

to the first equation in the first *row* of the system of equations. Similarly, the first subscripts on the a's and the only b subscript in the second equation, (31), are all 2. Thus, the first of the two subscripts on a letter identifies the row or equation in which that coefficient occurs.

Now notice that the *second* subscripts on the a's, which correspond to the variable x_1, are all 1. This identifies them as belonging to the first unknown or the first *column* of the system of equations. Similarly, the second subscripts on the a's in the second column are 2. Therefore, the second subscript identifies the column or variable.

Question. Without looking back at the equations, can you tell the row in which the coefficient a_{23} occurs? What variable does it multiply? In what equation does a_{34} occur? What variable does it multiply?

At least one of the numbers in the first column — a_{11}, a_{21}, a_{31}, a_{41} — must be different from zero. If all of them are zero, the variable x_1 does not appear in any equation and we have four equations in three variables. If a_{11} vanishes, we can always reorder the equations so that $a_{11} \neq 0$. For example, the first two equations of our example, (34), are

$$x_2 - x_3 + x_4 = 1$$
$$3x_1 - 2x_2 + x_3 \qquad = 2$$

That is, $a_{11} = 0$ but $a_{21} = 3$. Therefore, we interchange the two equations, and the result is

$$3x_1 - 2x_2 + x_3 \qquad = 2$$
$$x_2 - x_3 + x_4 = 1$$

Now

$$a_{11} = 3 \qquad\qquad a_{12} = -2$$
$$a_{13} = 1 \qquad\qquad a_{14} = 0$$
$$b_1 = 2$$

The second equation is now the former first equation, and

$$a_{21} = 0 \qquad\qquad a_{22} = 1$$
$$a_{23} = -1 \qquad\qquad a_{24} = 1$$
$$b_2 = 1$$

We have accomplished our purpose: to make $a_{11} \neq 0$.

Now let us return to our original equations, (30), (31), (32), and (33), representing the general case of a linear system of four equations in four variables. Suppose we want to eliminate x_1 from the second equation, (31). We can multiply both sides of the first equation, (30), by the same number m, subtract the resulting equation from equation (31), and obtain a new valid equation. If we choose the multiplier, m, properly, we can make the coefficient of x_1 in the resulting equation zero. The coefficient of x_1 in the resulting equation is

$$a_{21} - ma_{11}$$

If this is to be zero, then

$$m = \frac{a_{21}}{a_{11}}$$

You can see the reason for requiring that $a_{11} \neq 0$.

The equation which results from multiplying equation (30) by m and subtracting the result from equation (31) is

$$(a_{22} - ma_{12})x_2 + (a_{23} - ma_{13})x_3 + (a_{24} - ma_{14})x_4 = b_2 - mb_1 \quad (35)$$

Similarly, we could multiply the first equation, (30), by another multiplier and subtract the result from the third equation, (32), to obtain another equation with no x_1 term. The reader should satisfy himself that the proper multiplier in this case is

$$m = \frac{a_{31}}{a_{11}}$$

Finally, by multiplying the first equation by the multiplier $m = a_{41}/a_{11}$ and subtracting the resulting equation from the fourth equation, (33), we obtain a third equation with no x_1 term. We will then have produced three equations in the three variables, x_2, x_3, x_4. We can solve this system of linear equations in three variables. Note that our task has been reduced from solving a system of four equations to solving a system of three equations.

Before going on to the solution of three equations, we pause to introduce a simple way of describing our algorithm or procedure for solving the problem — **flow charts**. A flow chart is a diagram consisting of: boxes representing the successive steps in a calculation; and arrows

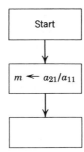

Figure 8

Flow chart for calculation of the multiplier m

connecting the boxes. Flow charts were first introduced by Goldstine[11] and von Neumann[12] in the late 1940's.

In Figure 8, we locate the first box, which is labeled Start, and follow the arrow leading from it to another box; call it box 2. We read what is in the next box (box 2) and perform whatever operation it describes. We then follow the arrow leading from box 2 to another box, and so on. This flow chart tells us to first divide a_{21} by a_{11} and call the result m. The arrow means: Compute whatever is on the right and give it the name of the symbol on the left. We then go to the blank box, which is

[11] **Herman H. Goldstine,** 1913 —, was educated at the University of Chicago. He has contributed to many branches of mathematics including the calculus of variations and numerical analysis. While an officer in the U.S. Army Ordnance Corps, he helped plan the world's first digital computer, the ENIAC, at the University of Pennsylvania. At the Institute for Advanced Study at Princeton he made many contributions to the design and use of computers. He joined IBM in 1958 and is now Director of Scientific Development for IBM.

[12] **John von Neumann** (pronounced "fon noý mahn"), 1903–1957, was without doubt one of the great scientists of the 20th century. Born in Budapest, Hungary, he was a child prodigy. He was educated in Europe, and he came to Princeton University in 1930. Three years later he moved to the Institute for Advanced Study at Princeton. He made substantial contributions to almost every branch of modern mathematics including set theory, quantum mechanics, mathematical logic, and the theory of games. von Neumann was a pioneer in the computing field and conceived of the fundamental ideas on which modern high-speed computers are based. Time and again the United States Government bestowed awards upon him for his service to his adopted country. In 1955 he was appointed a member of the U.S. Atomic Energy Commission and served brilliantly in that capacity until his untimely death from cancer in 1957.

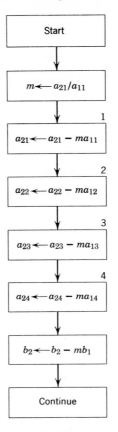

Figure 9

Flow chart for constructing equation (35)

yet to be filled in. It might seem more natural to use the $=$ sign rather than $\leftarrow$, but as we shall see the $\leftarrow$ has certain advantages.

We now change the second equation, (31), as described above. That is to say, we replace (31) with equation (35). The flow chart is shown in Figure 9.

The importance of the $\leftarrow$ becomes obvious. In the box marked 1, we take $m \times a_{11}$ and subtract it from a_{21}, calling the result a_{21} (really this is a *new* value of a_{21} but we again call it a_{21}). Had we written

$$a_{21} = a_{21} - ma_{11}$$

it would not have made sense, because this would require that $m = 0$ (recall that $a_{11} \neq 0$).

To repeat, *the arrow means: Calculate whatever is on the right and give it the name of the symbol on the left.*

It is important to notice that, if we use a_{21} later, as we shall, it is no longer the a_{21} in the original equation, (31). It has been replaced by $a_{21} - ma_{11}$.

Notice now that the contents of boxes 1, 2, 3, and 4 in Figure 9 are very similar. In fact, they all have the form

$$a_{2i} \leftarrow a_{2i} - ma_{1i}$$

where $i = 1$ in box 1, $i = 2$ in box 2, etc. Suppose, therefore, that we replace those four boxes with the boxes in Figure 10. What happens as we go through the flow chart? First, i is made equal to 1; thus, when we perform the operation in box * we perform

$$a_{21} \leftarrow a_{21} - ma_{11}$$

(see box 1 of Figure 9). We then take i (which is 1), add 1 to it, and make i equal to the result. That is to say, $i = 2$.

We now go back to box * and perform the operations in it. However, since $i = 2$, the contents of box * are

$$a_{22} \leftarrow a_{22} - ma_{12}$$

(see box 2 of Figure 9).

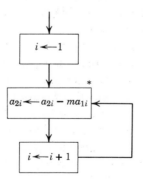

Figure 10

Condensation of portion of Figure 9

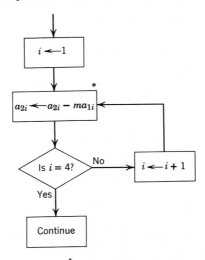

Figure 11

Condensed flow chart for calculating coefficients in equation (35)

Next we replace i by $i + 1$ and i becomes 3, and again we return to box * to perform

$$a_{23} \leftarrow a_{23} - ma_{13}$$

(see box 3 of Figure 9).

We continue in this way. Each time we do the operations in box * they are different because i is different. After doing the calculation in box * for $i = 4$, we wish to stop. However, as the flow chart now stands, we will never stop. To take care of this, we insert a **decision box** in our flow chart, as shown in Figure 11.

The decision box — diamond-shaped to distinguish it from the other rectangular boxes — asks whether i is equal to 4 or not. If it is, we go on to something else. If not, we increase i by 1 and go back to box *.

Our entire diagram now looks like Figure 12. When we have finished, equation (31) will have been replaced by equation (35).

The process of going back to a previous box in a flow chart is called **looping,** and the boxes which are used more than once are all part of a **loop.** The loop we constructed consists of the three boxes marked * in Figure 12.

Flow charts and loops are important aids in computer programming, and they are also useful concepts in themselves. For example, we are able to describe our entire algorithm for solving four simultaneous linear equations more easily by using flow charts.

Now, in place of the box containing "Continue," we want to perform calculations which will make the coefficient of x_1 in the third equation, (32), zero. Notice, however, that the third equation is basically not different from the second equation. In the second equation we used the multiplier a_{21}/a_{11}. For the third equation we quite naturally use

$$m = \frac{a_{31}}{a_{11}}$$

As we noted previously, this is the multiplier by which we multiply the first equation to make its x_1 coefficient the same as a_{31}.

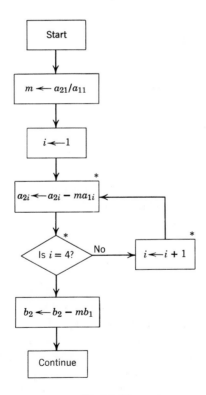

Figure 12

Flow chart for construction of equation (35)

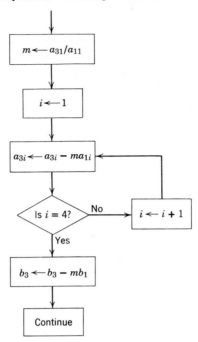

Figure 13

Flow chart for eliminating x_1 from equation (32)

The flow chart in Figure 13 arises in a completely analogous way to the first one if we simply replace all the 2's by 3's. Now, of course, we do the same thing for equation (33) and, piecing all three flow charts together, we get Figure 14.

In Figure 14, the six boxes 2, 3, 4, 5, 6, 7, the six boxes 8, 9, 10, 11, 12, 13, and the six boxes 14, 15, 16, 17, 18, 19 are very similar. In fact, the second group is obtained from the first by changing 2's to 3's, and the third from the second by changing 3's to 4's. It seems, therefore, that we can make a loop from these groups. The flow chart is shown in Figure 15, and we discuss it in detail. Notice first, however, that the six boxes marked ϕ are similar to boxes 2, 3, 4, 5, 6, 7 in Figure 14. In fact, if we let $j = 2$ in Figure 15, then the boxes marked ϕ are identical with boxes 2 through 7 in Figure 14. We now examine Figure 15 in detail.

We let $j = 2$, and then $m = a_{21}/a_{11}$. Next we let $i = 1$ and calculate

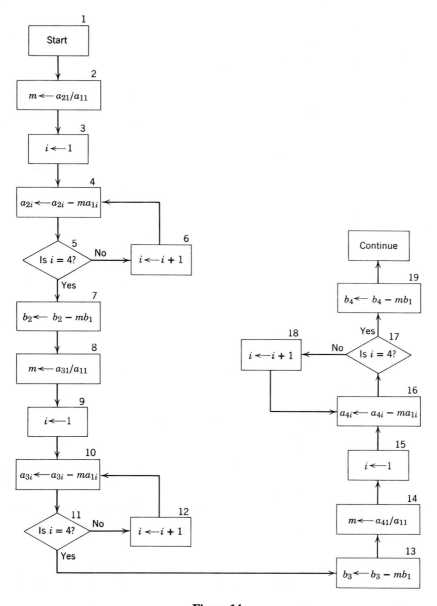

Figure 14

Flow chart for eliminating x_1 from the three equations (31), (32), (33)

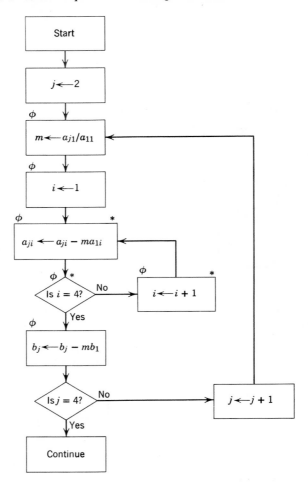

Figure 15

Flow chart using double loop for eliminating x_1 from the three equations (31), (32), (33)

$a_{21} - ma_{11}$ and call it a_{21}. Since $i \neq 4$, we let $i = 1 + 1 = 2$ and calculate $a_{22} - ma_{12}$ and call it a_{22}. In this way we calculate the left side of equation (35) as before.

When this is done, $i = 4$. We calculate the new value of b_2, and we ask the question: Is $j = 4$? Since $j = 2$, the answer is "no," and we let

$j = 2 + 1 = 3$ and return to the box for calculating the multiplier m. We compute

$$m = \frac{a_{j1}}{a_{11}} = \frac{a_{31}}{a_{11}}$$

and set $i = 1$ again. We then go through the loop of three boxes marked * four more times. Again, because $j = 3 \neq 4$, we let $j = 3 + 1 = 4$ and go back to compute $m = a_{41}/a_{11}$ and set $i = 1$, thus going through the * loop four more times. After this, of course, $j = 4$ and we go to the box containing "Continue."

We now have *two* loops: the original loop where i is changed, and another loop which "surrounds" the original one and in which j is changed. The original i loop is called the **inner loop**, and i is called the **index** of the loop; the j loop is called the **outer loop**, and j is its **index**. In the i or inner loop we compute coefficients in a new equation. The j or outer loop takes us from one equation to another.

What have we accomplished with our flow chart in Figure 15? We have described completely and accurately a method for reducing to zero the coefficients of x_1 in (31), (32), (33), the last three of equations (30)–(33), giving the new equations which involve only x_2, x_3, and x_4. We have done it concisely and in such a way that anyone who understands flow charts will be able to do the arithmetic for us with no further help. The reader should assure himself that what we have done is to systematize the algorithm we described in Section 1.6.

Actually this completes only the first part of the procedure for finding a solution to the four equations (30)–(33). If we perform all the operations in the flow chart in Figure 15, we shall end up with equations which look like

$$a_{11}x_1 + a_{12}x_2 + a_{13}x_3 + a_{14}x_4 = b_1 \tag{36}$$

$$a_{22}x_2 + a_{23}x_3 + a_{24}x_4 = b_2 \tag{37}$$

$$a_{32}x_2 + a_{33}x_3 + a_{34}x_4 = b_3 \tag{38}$$

$$a_{42}x_2 + a_{43}x_3 + a_{44}x_4 = b_4 \tag{39}$$

Equation (36) is identical with equation (30), but the coefficients a_{ij} and b_i in the last three, (37), (38), (39), are *not* the same as the a_{ij} and b_i in (31), (32), (33). To re-emphasize, a_{22} is $a_{22} - (a_{21}a_{12}/a_{11})$ in terms of the old a_{ij} and $a_{43} \leftarrow a_{43} - (a_{41}a_{13}/a_{11})$. The reader who is unsure of this should go back and study again the discussion of flow charts.

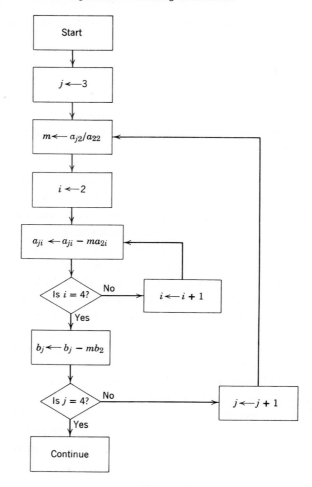

Figure 16

Flow chart for eliminating x_2 from the two equations (38) and (39)

The important point now is that, if we ignore equation (36) for the moment, the other three, (37), (38), (39), are three linear equations in three variables, x_2, x_3, x_4. Since we already know how to eliminate one variable from three equations in a system of four equations, we should be able to use a similar process to eliminate one variable from two of the equations in a system of three equations. The flow chart in Figure 16 does just that. The reader should assure himself that it does.

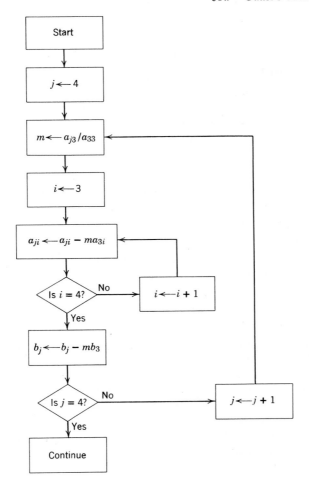

Figure 17

Flow chart for eliminating x_3 from the single equation (41)

The resulting equations will be

$$a_{22}x_2 + a_{23}x_3 + a_{24}x_4 = b_2 \qquad (37)$$

$$a_{33}x_3 + a_{34}x_4 = b_3 \qquad (40)$$

$$a_{43}x_3 + a_{44}x_4 = b_4 \qquad (41)$$

Notice that we have assumed that $a_{22} \neq 0$. If it turns out that this is not so, as indeed it may, then equations (37), (38), and (39) will have to be shuffled so that the first of them has an x_2 coefficient which is not zero. If all have zero coefficients for x_2, *then the original equations were singular.* That is, equations (30)–(33) would in this case not have a unique solution but would either have no solution or have an infinite number of solutions. This is a theorem, but we shall not prove it here.

We are now almost finished. All that remains is to solve equations (40) and (41) for x_3 and x_4. Once this is done, we can find x_2 from equation (37). When we have x_2 as well as x_3 and x_4, we can get x_1 from equation (30).

We know how to solve two linear equations, but we shall try to solve them here in a way which is consistent with what we have done in this section. We can do that quite easily by modifying the flow chart in Figure 16 slightly. The result is shown in Figure 17.

The reader should study this flow chart carefully. Notice that the very first time we go through the outer loop the answer to "Is $j = 4$?" is "yes." It would seem more reasonable, therefore, not even to ask the question. It is done to keep Figure 17 consistent with Figures 15 and 16. The clever reader has already realized that we are about to imbed all three flow charts (Figures 15, 16, and 17) in a still larger loop.

Question.   In Figure 17, how many times will we go through the inner loop (the one with an index of i)?

Each time we complete the outer or j loop we have a system with one less unknown; that is, a system of three equations in three variables, then two equations in two variables, then one equation in one variable. When we collect the first equation from each of these systems, we have replaced the original system of four linear equations in four variables by the new system:

$$a_{11}x_1 + a_{12}x_2 + a_{13}x_3 + a_{14}x_4 = b_1 \qquad (36)$$
$$a_{22}x_2 + a_{23}x_3 + a_{24}x_4 = b_2 \qquad (37)$$
$$a_{33}x_3 + a_{34}x_4 = b_3 \qquad (40)$$
$$a_{44}x_4 = b_4 \qquad (42)$$

Systems of equations in this form are called **triangular.** Note how they fit inside the triangle.

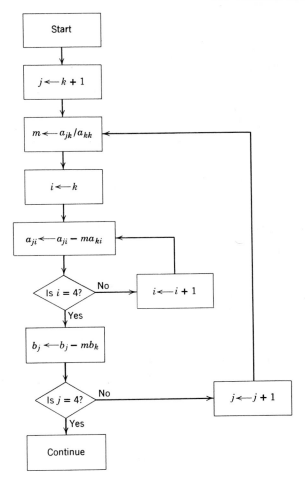

Figure 18

Condensed flow chart for Figures 15, 16, and 17

These equations are equivalent to the original equations, (30)–(33). That is, any values of x_1, x_2, x_3, and x_4 which satisfy (30)–(33) also satisfy (36), (37), (40), and (42). Conversely, any values of $x_1, \ldots, x_4$ which satisfy (36), (37), (40), and (42) also satisfy (30)–(33).

The final step in the solution is to devise an algorithm for finding the values of the variables x_1, x_2, x_3, x_4 from the triangular system (36), (37), (40), and (42), but we delay doing that for a while.

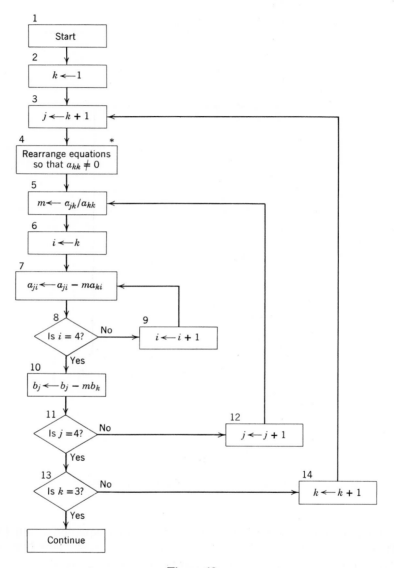

Figure 19

Flow chart for eliminating the unknowns in a system of four equations to produce a triangular system of equations

36

In Figure 18 we have drawn a single flow chart from which the three previous ones are obtainable as special cases. Indeed, we can get Figure 15 by replacing k in Figure 18 by 1. Similarly, we get Figure 16 by setting $k = 2$, and we get Figure 17 by letting $k = 3$. This immediately suggests that we can condense all three flow charts to one by introducing a loop with k as the index and letting k take on the values 1, 2, and 3. A flow chart with such a loop is given in Figure 19.

In Figure 19 we have also added a new box marked * which makes sure that we do not try to divide by zero in the next box. We have already mentioned that this is necessary and that, if it is not possible, the original equations do not have a unique solution; that is, they are singular.

The important point is that Figure 19 completely describes the algorithm for producing equations (36), (37), (40), and (42) from the original equations (30)–(33). In the next section we go through a numerical example in detail. We now go on to the problem of finding x_1, x_2, x_3, x_4 from equations (36), (37), (40), and (42). Notice that, from equation (42),

$$x_4 = \frac{1}{a_{44}} (b_4) \tag{43}$$

From equation (40),

$$x_3 = \frac{1}{a_{33}} (b_3 - a_{34} x_4) \tag{44}$$

Similarly, from equations (37) and (36),

$$x_2 = \frac{1}{a_{22}} (b_2 - a_{23} x_3 - a_{24} x_4) \tag{45}$$

$$x_1 = \frac{1}{a_{11}} (b_1 - a_{12} x_2 - a_{13} x_3 - a_{14} x_4) \tag{46}$$

We repeat once more that these are not all the same a_{ij} and b_i that appeared in the original equations. We also note that $a_{11} \neq 0$, $a_{22} \neq 0$, and $a_{33} \neq 0$, because we made sure of that in the box marked * in Figure 19. If $a_{44} = 0$, again the original equations must have been singular.

Observe now the pattern in equations (43)–(46). In each succeeding equation there is one more term in the parentheses on the right. All other terms are similar to the terms in the preceding equation except that certain of the subscripts are *reduced* by 1. For example, if we change all the 2's in equation (45) to 1's, we get

$$x_1 = \frac{1}{a_{11}} (b_1 - a_{13}x_3 - a_{14}x_4)$$

This is the same as equation (46) if we add the term $-a_{12}x_2$ inside the parentheses.

All of this leads us to believe that we can use a flow chart with a loop to describe the last stage of the solution process.

The flow chart in Figure 20 accomplishes this purpose. You should study it carefully and assure yourself that it does indeed result in equations (43), (44), (45), and (46), in that order.

> **Question.**   In Figure 20, what is the purpose of the box containing $y \leftarrow 0$? (Try calculating first x_3 and then x_2 without that box.)

The inner loop with index i calculates y which, for $k = 2$, is the sum of terms $a_{23}x_3 + a_{24}x_4$ in equation (45) and, for $k = 1$, is $a_{12}x_2 + a_{13}x_3 + a_{14}x_4$ in equation (46). The outer loop with index k computes x_3, x_2, x_1, in that order.

The two flow charts in Figures 19 and 20 will find the solution of any four linear equations in four unknowns provided the equations are nonsingular. Of course, we replace the "Continue" box in Figure 19 with all of Figure 20.

The process described in Figure 20 is usually referred to as **back substitution** because we "substitute" for the variables we have calculated at any given time "back" in the preceding equation.

If we hand these two charts to someone who understands how flow charts are used and give him the original numbers a_{11}, a_{12}, etc., and b_1, b_2, etc., he can find x_1, x_2, x_3, x_4 without further information. We follow in detail his actions in the next section.

1.8   Solution of the Diet Problem

As an example we take the diet problem described by equations (18), (19), (20), and (21), which we rewrite

$$20x_1 + \quad x_2 + 3.3x_3 + 2.3x_4 = \quad 35 \tag{47}$$

$$15x_2 + 1.5x_3 + 50x_4 = \quad 30 \tag{48}$$

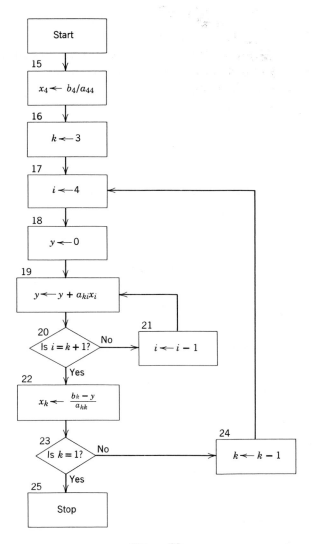

Figure 20

Flow chart for finding x_1, x_2, x_3, x_4 from results in flow chart in Figure 19

$$325x_1 + 80x_2 + 70x_3 + 22x_4 = 700 \tag{49}$$

$$.01x_1 + .04x_2 + .12x_3 + .07x_4 = 0.5 \tag{50}$$

where $x_1 = B$, $x_2 = L$, $x_3 = M$, and $x_4 = S$.

Now look at Figure 19. We shall follow the procedures outlined there. The number at the left below indicates the number of the box in the flow chart. The operation appears to the right.

1. Start

2. $k \leftarrow 1$

3. $j \leftarrow 1 + 1 = 2$

4. Do nothing since $a_{11} = 20$

5. $m \leftarrow a_{21} / a_{11} = 0 / 20 = 0$

6. $i \leftarrow 1$

7. $a_{21} \leftarrow a_{21} - ma_{11} = 0 - 0 \times 20 = 0$

8. $i = 1 \neq 4$. Go to 9

9. $i \leftarrow 1 + 1 = 2$

7. $a_{22} \leftarrow a_{22} - ma_{12} = 15 - 0 \times 1 = 15$

8. $i = 2 \neq 4$. Go to 9

9. $i \leftarrow 2 + 1 = 3$

7. $a_{23} \leftarrow a_{23} - ma_{14} = 1.5 - 0 \times 3.3 = 1.5$

8. $i = 3 \neq 4$. Go to 9

9. $i \leftarrow 3 + 1 = 4$

7. $a_{24} \leftarrow a_{23} - ma_{14} = 50 - 0 \times 2.3 = 50$

8. $i = 4$. Go to 10

10. $b_2 \leftarrow b_2 - mb_1 = 30 - 0 \times 35 = 30$

We stop now for a moment to notice that a_{21}, a_{22}, a_{23}, a_{24}, and b_2 were unchanged by all these operations. This is not surprising since equation (48) had no x_1 term and our objective was to eliminate x_1 from that equation.

Figure 21

Insertion for flow chart of Figure 19

We could have saved ourselves a lot of work by inserting between boxes 5 and 6 in Figure 19 the decision box shown in Figure 21. If the answer is "yes," an arrow is drawn to box 11. If the answer is "no," the arrow goes to box 6.

We now return to our flow chart. After computing b_2, we go on to box 11.

11. $j = 2 \neq 4$. Go to 12

12. $j = 2 + 1 = 3$

5. $m \leftarrow a_{31} / a_{11} = 325 / 20 = 16.25$

6. $i \leftarrow 1$

7. $a_{31} \leftarrow a_{31} - ma_{11} = 325 - 16.25 \times 20 = 0$

8. $i = 1 \neq 4$. Go to 9

9. $i \leftarrow 1 + 1 = 2$

7. $a_{32} \leftarrow a_{32} - ma_{12} = 80 - 16.25 \times 1 = 63.75$

8. $i = 2 \neq 4$. Go to 9

9. $i \leftarrow 2 + 1 = 3$

7. $a_{33} \leftarrow a_{33} - ma_{13} = 70 - 16.25 \times 3.3 = 16.375$

8. $i = 3 \neq 4$. Go to 9

9. $i \leftarrow 3 + 1 = 4$

7. $a_{34} \leftarrow a_{34} - ma_{14} = 22 - 16.25 \times 2.3 = -15.375$

8. $i = 4$. Go to 10

10. $b_3 \leftarrow b_3 - mb_1 = 700 - 16.25 \times 35 = 131.25$

The new third equation now looks like

$$63.75x_2 + 16.375x_3 - 15.375x_4 = 131.25 \tag{51}$$

and we go on to box 11.

11. $j = 3 \neq 4$. Go to 12

12. $j \leftarrow 3 + 1 = 4$

5. $m = a_{41} / a_{11} = .01 / 20 = .0005$

The reader should go through the inner loop again and assure himself that the results from box 7 are

$$a_{41} \leftarrow 0$$
$$a_{42} \leftarrow .0395$$
$$a_{43} \leftarrow .11835$$
$$a_{44} \leftarrow .06885$$

and the result of box 10 is

$$b_4 \leftarrow .4825$$

The fourth equation then becomes

$$.0395x_2 + .11835x_3 + .06885x_4 = .4825 \tag{52}$$

Continuing to box 11,

11. $j = 4$. Go to 13

13. $k = 1 \neq 3$. Go to 14

14. $k \leftarrow 1 + 1 = 2$

3. $j \leftarrow 2 + 1 = 3$

4. Do nothing since $a_{22} = 15$

5. $m \leftarrow a_{32} / a_{22} = 63.75 / 15 = 4.25$

6. $i \leftarrow 2$

7. $a_{32} \leftarrow a_{32} - ma_{22} = 63.75 - 4.25 \times 15 = 0$

8. $i = 2 \neq 4$. Go to 9

9. $i \leftarrow 2 + 1 = 3$

*7. $a_{33} \leftarrow a_{33} - ma_{23} = 16.375 - 4.25 \times 1.5 = 10$

  8. $i = 3 \neq 4$. Go to 9

  9. $i \leftarrow 3 + 1 = 4$

*7. $a_{34} \leftarrow a_{34} - ma_{24} = -15.375 - 4.25 \times 50 = -227.875$

  8. $i = 4$. Go to 10

*10. $b_3 \leftarrow b_3 - mb_2 = 131.25 - 4.25 \times 30 = 3.75$

 11. $j = 3 \neq 4$. Go to 12

 12. $j \leftarrow 3 + 1 = 4$

  5. $m \leftarrow a_{42} / a_{22} = .0395 / 15 = .00263$[13]

  6. $i \leftarrow 2$

  7. $a_{42} \leftarrow a_{42} - ma_{22} = .0395 - .00263 \times 15 = .00005$[14]

  8. $i = 2 \neq 4$. Go to 9

  9. $i \leftarrow 2 + 1 = 3$

  7. $a_{43} \leftarrow a_{43} - ma_{23} = .11835 - .00263 \times 1.5 = .1144$[15]

  8. $i = 3 \neq 4$. Go to 9

  9. $i \leftarrow 3 + 1 = 4$

  7. $a_{44} \leftarrow a_{44} - ma_{24} = .06885 - .00263 \times 50 = -.06265$

  8. $i = 4$. Go to 10

 10. $b_4 \leftarrow b_4 - mb_2 = .4825 - .00263 \times 30 = .4036$

 11. $j = 4$. Go to 13

 13. $k = 2 \neq 3$. Go to 14

 14. $k \leftarrow 2 + 1 = 3$

  3. $j \leftarrow 3 + 1 = 4$

---

[13] The result here is actually .0026333 . . . , with 3's continuing indefinitely. We stop with one 3. We say that we have "rounded off" the number. We return to this question in Section 1.13.

[14] This is not zero because we "rounded off" the value of m. However, we shall take it to be zero.

[15] This number is actually .114405, but again we "round off" the value to .1144.

4. No rearrangement necessary since $a_{33} = 10$

5. $m \leftarrow a_{43} / a_{33} = .1144 / 10 = .01144$

6. $i \leftarrow 3$

7. $a_{43} \leftarrow a_{43} - ma_{33} = .1144 - .01144 \times 10 = 0$

8. $i = 3 \neq 4$. Go to 9

9. $i \leftarrow 3 + 1 = 4$

*7. $a_{44} \leftarrow a_{44} - ma_{34} = -.06265 - .01144 \times (-227.875) = 2.54424$

8. $i = 4$. Go to 10

*10. $b_4 = b_4 - mb_3 = .4036 - .01144 \times 3.75 = .3607$

11. $j = 4$. Go to 13

13. $k = 3$. Go to 15

The process then continues to the back substitution described in Figure 20. First, however, notice from the lines marked * that the last two equations now read

$$10x_3 - 227.875x_4 = 3.75 \tag{53}$$

$$2.54424x_4 = .3607 \tag{54}$$

Therefore, equations (47), (48), (53), and (54) represent the triangular set of equations resulting from the calculations.

The reader should be able to follow the flow chart in Figure 20 and find in this order

$$x_4 = .1418$$

$$x_3 = 3.606$$

$$x_2 = 1.1667$$

$$x_1 = 1.0804$$

In view of the renaming of the variables at the beginning of this section and Table 2 (Section 1.6), this means that the diet consists of approximately 108 grams of roast beef (one medium slice), 117 grams of salad ($\frac{1}{4}$ head of lettuce), 361 grams of milk ($\frac{5}{8}$ of a cup), and 14 grams of spinach. This diet provides approximately 35 grams of protein, 30 milligrams of ascorbic acid (vitamin C), and 0.5 gram of calcium while providing only 700 calories.

We now digress for a moment and note that usually a dietician does not require precisely 30 milligrams of vitamin C but only that the diet have *at least* that or some other prescribed amount of vitamin C. Similarly, other nutrients are not required in precise amounts. The number of calories, for example, may be required to be *not greater than* a prescribed amount.

Moreover, the amount of each food cannot be negative. That is to say, we do not allow a solution of the equation wherein some of the variables turn out to be negative.

Returning to Section 1.3, then, a meaningful problem would be as follows: Find $L \geq 0$ and $B \geq 0$ so that at least 30 milligrams of ascorbic acid and at least 35 grams of protein will be consumed. Obviously, $L = 2$, $B = 1.65$ is a solution to this problem.

Question. Are there other solutions? What happens to the uniqueness of the solution?

Question. Can you draw a diagram of this problem using Cartesian coordinates?

We return to this kind of diet problem in Chapter 2.

1.9 Large Systems of Equations

We now have a procedure or *algorithm* which tells us to the last detail the sequence of steps needed to solve four simultaneous linear equations in four variables. It is given by Figures 19 and 20. Later we shall discuss the changes which need to be made if we have more or less than four equations. The changes will be few and simple.

Why do we need an algorithm for this problem? We certainly would be able to solve our diet problem without such a completely detailed step-by-step "recipe." Consider, however, what would happen if we were to attempt to solve a much more ambitious problem. Dieticians usually consider the levels of ten or so different nutrients. Although many more than ten are required for adequate health, it is assumed that variety in the diet automatically satisfies other requirements. If we considered only ten foods, there would be little variety. Therefore, we might wish to change foods and solve the problem several times over for different food lists.

This means that a more realistic diet problem requires solving ten or more equations several times over. An algorithm becomes not only desirable but also necessary to keep track of the work and reduce chances of error in the solution when the system becomes so large.

The problem can become even more complex. In some problems in physics, economics, and other fields, we may be faced with solving 1000 equations in 1000 unknowns. Here even an algorithm is not sufficient if we are to obtain a solution. We need a computer to do the tremendous amount of arithmetic, and we need a way of describing our algorithm to the computer. We return to this problem in the next section.

We first describe a few problems which can give rise to an extremely large number of linear equations:

Suppose we are designing a bridge. In order to be certain that the bridge is strong enough, we need to know the forces that occur in the steel beams as a result of the weight of the traffic. A mathematical model of this problem gives rise to approximately as many linear equations as there are beams in the bridge.

Suppose we want to predict the weather, and we have decided that an accurate prediction of the changes in the barometric pressure everywhere in the United States is necessary. One mathematical model of this (the simplest one) gives rise to several thousand linear equations. The more accurate we want our prediction to be, the more equations we must solve.

Suppose we want to distribute the resources (manpower, raw materials, money, etc.) of a firm or nation so that it produces specified quantities of its products. We may find ourselves confronted with several hundred equations to solve.

In *all* these problems our mathematical model may lead to *nonlinear* equations as well as linear ones. That is, quantities like x^2 or x^3 or $\log x$ or xy may occur in the equations, as well as the variables x and y themselves. We discuss such equations and their solution in Chapter 5. In general, however, if there are many equations — in the hundreds or thousands — we cannot solve nonlinear equations except in very special cases.

It is significant that for linear equations we have an algorithm, Gauss's method, which in principle will solve all sets of equations which have a unique solution. Moreover, our algorithm will tell us if our mathematical model has no solution or an infinite number of solutions. Although algorithms are known for nonlinear equations, they are not generally successful to the extent that Gauss's method is for linear equations.

1.10   Some Introductory Computer Programming — FORTRAN

We now discuss a way of describing an algorithm to a digital computer so that it can do the arithmetic for us. In particular, we want to describe Gauss's method to a computer, that is, give instructions to a computer so that it will carry out Gauss's method. Our flow charts are a complete and adequate description for people, but unfortunately computers cannot read them.

However, a computer can "read" punched cards or punched paper tape or magnetic tape. That is, punched holes in cards or paper tape or magnetized spots on magnetic tape can be used to identify and send different signals to a computer. Moreover, we can devise a simple code so that numbers, letters of the alphabet, and certain punctuation marks can be represented on cards or tape by punching the proper holes or magnetizing the proper spots.

The card in Figure 22 shows a "code" used in punched cards. There are 80 columns on the card, and one column is used for each digit, letter, or symbol. The characters printed at the top of each column indicate what the holes punched in that column represent. Notice that the digits 0 through 9 (shown in the first ten columns) are single punches in the rows 0 through 9, respectively. Similarly, the + and − signs are single

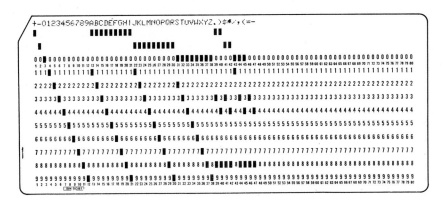

Figure 22

A punched card exhibiting symbols

punches in the top two unlabeled rows. All letters and symbols other than + and − require more than one punch in a column. For example, the letter "A" has a punch in the + row and in the 1 row. The symbol "(" requires punches in the 0, 4, and 8 rows.

> **Question.**   What letter is represented by a punch in the − row and in the 7 row in Figure 22?

Only capital letters are possible. Moreover, because all symbols are on a line (see printing at top of card), subscripts are not possible either. We have to make adjustments for these facts.

The code exhibited in Figure 22 was designed by Herman Hollerith[16] in 1890 and is still in use. Other codes which would do equally well could be invented. Recently there have been attempts to provide a standard code acceptable to all users of punched card equipment. The ASCII (American Standard Code for Information Interchange) is such a code. It contains more symbols than the Hollerith code and also uses slightly different codes for some of the punctuation marks.

Each computer has a language, just as each country does. The language which one computer uses is not necessarily the same as another computer's language. Fortunately some languages have been developed which can be understood by many different computers. One that is very widely used is called FORTRAN.[17] This is an abbreviation for FORmula TRANslator. This language was first invented in the 1950's by a small group of people. Its primary inventor, however, was John Backus.[18]

---

[16] **Herman Hollerith,** 1860–1929, was educated at Columbia University. At the age of 27, while working as a statistician for the United States Government, he designed a machine for the Census Bureau to record and sort information using punched paper tape. This technique was later extended to punched cards. As a result, the 1890 census was completed in one-fourth of the time required by the 1880 census. The code Dr. Hollerith used for alphabetic characters is still in use and bears his name. In 1896, he organized the Tabulating Machine Company which was to merge with two other companies in 1911. The merger eventually became known as IBM in 1924.

[17] Actually, most computers "translate" FORTRAN into their own language, but that is not important to our present discussion. The interested reader should see Appendix B.

[18] **John W. Backus,** 1924—, started to work for IBM upon completing his graduate studies in mathematics at Columbia University in 1950. He immediately became involved in programming digital computers and was the leading figure in the development of FORTRAN. This computer language represented a significant breakthrough in the use of computers on problems in science. No other programming development in existence can rival its impact on scientific computing.

In FORTRAN we write formulas almost exactly as we would normally. There are a few minor changes. For example, because we can use only capital letters, we write[19]

$$A = B + C$$

and the computer understands that it is to add the numbers called "B" and "C" and call the sum "A." Of course, we must have told the computer what numbers to use for B and C. We might have said, for example,

$$B = 1.326$$

and

$$C = -1.062$$

The = sign in FORTRAN is not quite the same as the usual one. It means: Compute what is on the right and call it by the name of the symbol on the left. Therefore, *there can be only one symbol on the left.* The = sign is then entirely equivalent to the ← sign we have used in our flow charts. This makes it very convenient for translating our flow charts into FORTRAN.

The usual symbols for arithmetic operations are used in FORTRAN with one exception:

Addition:	+
Subtraction:	−
Multiplication:	*
Division:	/

We do not use × for multiplication because it may be confused with the letter "x." The asterisk is used instead.

Figure 23 shows how the FORTRAN statement A = B + C looks when punched on a card. FORTRAN statements start in column 7 and continue as far as needed. They must fit on one card, and they cannot go beyond column 72. With a few exceptions, *spaces or blanks may be used anywhere.* They are ignored by FORTRAN. For example, the card in Figure 24 is equally good for representing the statement A = B + C. Spaces often can be used to make cards easier to read. The few cases for which blanks cannot be used freely will be pointed out as we go along.

We make one more note before writing the FORTRAN version of

---

[19] From now on we suppose that the FORTRAN formulas are written so that they can be read by the computer; for instance, punched on cards.

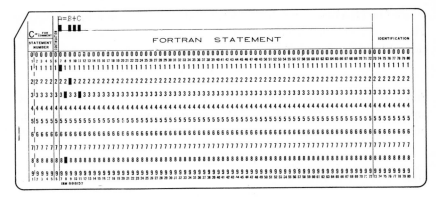

Figure 23

Punched card showing a typical FORTRAN instruction

Gauss's method. There are two kinds of arithmetic in FORTRAN. One deals only with integers (the whole numbers 0, 1, 2, . . .) and is called **fixed point.** The other uses decimals like 1.326 and −14.1 and is called **floating point.** The names are not significant now for our purposes. We discuss them in detail in Chapter 3. For now we assume that any quantity named I, J, K, L, M, or N is an integer and all others are decimals. We note also that, when we punch decimal numbers on a card, the decimal point must appear punched in a column of the card.

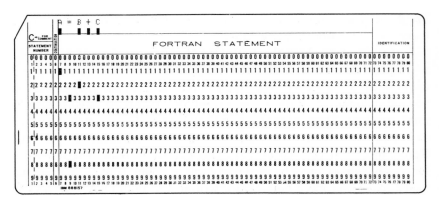

Figure 24

Punched card which is equivalent to Figure 23

Now let us look at Figure 19. The FORTRAN translation of box 2 is

$$K = 1$$

and of box 3 it is

$$J = K + 1$$

In writing a program, we do not draw arrows as we did in our flow charts; we write each instruction in successive lines down the page. Each line will then be punched on a separate card. Thus, boxes 2 and 3 together are represented by

$$K = 1$$

$$J = K + 1$$

The first line means let $K = 1$; the second line then means let $J = 1 + 1 = 2$.

We ignore box 4 and always assume that $a_{kk} \neq 0$. Box 5 becomes

$$Y = A(J, K) \, / \, A(K, K)$$

This requires some explanation. First, we did not use M on the left because M must be an integer. Since the multiplier is usually a decimal, we picked some other name, Y, arbitrarily.

Next, instead of a_{jk} we wrote A(J, K). The reason is that all symbols must be on one line; therefore, we cannot use subscripts as we usually think of them. We accomplish the same thing by enclosing the subscript letters in parentheses after the symbol and separating them by commas. When $K = 1$ and $J = 2$, the coefficient A(J, K) is A(2, 1), which is spoken "A, two, one" as before. A(2, 1) stands for the coefficient of x_1 in the second equation, that is, what we called a_{21} before.

Our FORTRAN version now can be written through box 7 as follows:

$$K = 1$$

$$J = K + 1$$

$$Y = A(J, K) / A(K, K)$$

$$I = K$$

$$A(J, I) = A(J, I) - Y * A(K, I)$$

Box 8 presents a new problem. We do not want to do arithmetic but instead want to make a decision. To be able to do this we invent a new symbol called "IF," and we number the lines of our FORTRAN program. Any numbering system is valid, but we choose one consistent with our flow chart:

2   K = 1

3   J = K + 1

5   Y = A(J, K) / A(K, K)

6   I = K

7   A(J, I) = A(J, I) − Y * A(K, I)

8

9

Now for line 8 we write

8   IF (I − 4) 9, 10, 100

which we interpret as follows: (1) if I − 4 is less than zero, go to the line marked 9 (the first number following the parentheses); (2) if I − 4 = 0, go to the line marked 10 (the second number); and (3) if I − 4 is greater than zero, go to the line marked 100. In our problem the last case should never arise; however, we shall return to this question later.

To summarize the meaning of the FORTRAN symbols in line 8: the word "IF" is followed by something in parentheses. We are to test whether that something is less than, equal to, or greater than zero and go to the line designated, by the first, second, or third number after the parentheses.

Again, in our problem, if I < 4, then I − 4 < 0 and we go to line 9. If I = 4, then I − 4 = 0 and we go to line 10. Line 9 has the following symbols:

9   I = I + 1

and is followed by

GO TO 7

Here we have our final new symbol, "GO TO." It simply states: go to line 7 and proceed from there.

Here is one case in which blanks cannot be used freely. The letters in the words "GO" and "TO" must not be separated. We cannot insert a

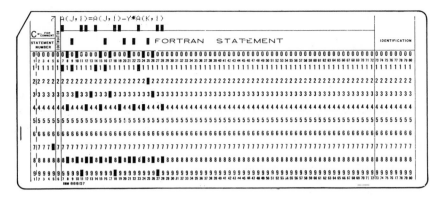

Figure 25

FORTRAN statement for box 7 of the flow chart in Figure 19

blank between G and O, nor can we insert a blank between T and O. We can write

$$GO \qquad TO \qquad 7$$

or

$$GOTO7$$

but not

$$G \quad O \quad TO \quad 7$$

The numbers attached to the statements are punched anywhere in columns 1 to 5. These five columns (1 through 5) are not used by the statement, which is punched in columns 7 through 72. The card representing the statement numbered 7 is shown in Figure 25.

The program through box 10 now becomes

2 K = 1

3 J = K + 1

5 Y = A(J, K) / A(K, K)

6 I = K

7 A(J, I) = A(J, I) − Y * A(K, I)

8 IF (I − 4) 9, 10, 100

9   I = I + 1

GO TO 7

10   B(J) = B(J) − Y * B(K)

Notice that, because *b* has only one subscript, and commas are used to separate subscripts, line 10 has no commas inside the parentheses.

The remainder of the translation follows without any new concepts. Starting at box 11 of Figure 19,

11   IF (J − 4) 12, 13, 100

12   J = J + 1

GO TO 5

13

This increases *j* by 1 if it is less than 4 and goes back to recompute *m* = Y. At box 13, then,

13   IF (K − 3) 14, 15, 100

14   K = K + 1

GO TO 3

Putting together all the pieces,

2   K = 1

3   J = K + 1

5   Y = A(J, K) / A(K, K)

6   I = K

7   A(J, I) = A(J, I) − Y * A(K, I)

8   IF (I − 4) 9, 10, 100

9   I = I + 1

GO TO 7

10   B(J) = B(J) − Y * B(K)

11   IF (J − 4) 12, 13, 100

12   J = J + 1

GO TO 5

13   IF (K − 3) 14, 15, 100

14   K = K + 1

GO TO 3

15   Continue

This describes the algorithm in the flow chart of Figure 19 *except for box 4.* The line numbers correspond to the box numbers in the flow chart. In most cases there is one line for each box, but in three cases (9, 12, 14) two lines are required for one box of the flow chart. Actually, the second line in each case corresponds to an arrow in the flow chart and therefore has no number.

We have now written a *computer program* or a FORTRAN program. The process we have gone through is called **programming,** and people who write lines of FORTRAN or other computer languages are called **programmers.**

Of course, all programs are not so simple as this one, and there is much more to the FORTRAN language than we have exhibited. However, we have discussed the basic concepts of FORTRAN programming. We consider FORTRAN in greater detail in Chapter 3.

We need to write a FORTRAN program for the flow chart in Figure 20 before we can ask the computer to solve our diet problem. We do that now. The line numbers correspond to the box numbers in Figure 20.

15   X(4) = B(4) / A(4, 4)

16   K = 3

17   I = 4

18   Y = 0.0

19   Y = Y + A(K, I) * X(I)

20   IF (I − K − 1) 100, 22, 21

21   I = I − 1

GO TO 19

22   X(K) = (B(K) − Y) / A(K, K)

23   IF (K − 1) 100, 25, 24

24   K = K − 1

     GO TO 17

25   STOP

Four things need to be pointed out. First, in line 18 we write Y = 0.0 rather than Y = 0. A constant, like zero, if written without the decimal point will be taken to be an integer. We do not want Y to be an integer, so we include the decimal point. Second, in line 22, B(K) − Y is enclosed in parentheses to make sure that

$$x_k = \frac{b_k - y}{a_{kk}}$$

and *not*

$$x_k = b_k - \frac{y}{a_{kk}}$$

Third, in line 20 the 100 is the first of the three numbers rather than the last. The reason is that, if $i > k + 1$, we want to decrease i and return in the loop. The same is true of statement 23. Finally, the line numbered 25 has a symbol "STOP." This tells the computer to stop and not to perform any more calculations.

We now have a complete description of our algorithm (Gauss's method) in terms of a FORTRAN program. It is just as complete as our flow charts. For use with a computer it is superior because the FORTRAN program can be easily recorded on cards or tape and read by a computer.

Why, then, do we bother with flow charts at all? Flow charts are valuable because they make it easy to picture the "flow" of a computation, and flaws in the logic, if any, are more easily detected than in a FOR-TRAN program. Moreover, they are universal in that they are applicable to *all* computer languages, FORTRAN and the others as well. Many programmers proceed as we did here by first drawing a flow chart and then writing out the program from it.

Suppose we wish to solve our four-food diet problem on a computer. If we have a means of getting the numerical values of a_{ij} and b_i into the computer and the values of the solutions x_i out, we can use our FOR-

TRAN program to do the arithmetic. A program to do the entire job follows.[20]

DIMENSION A(4, 4), B(4), X(4)

A(1, 1) =   20.0

A(1, 2) =   1.0

A(1, 3) =   3.3

A(1, 4) =   2.3

B(1)   =   35.0

A(2, 1) =   0.0

A(2, 2) =   15.0

A(2, 3) =   1.5

A(2, 4) =   50.0

B(2)   =   30.0

A(3, 1) = 325.0

A(3, 2) =   80.0

A(3, 3) =   70.0

A(3, 4) =   22.0

B(3)   = 700.0

A(4, 1) =   .01

A(4, 2) =   .04

A(4, 3) =   .12

A(4, 4) =   .07

B(4)   =   .5

2   K = 1

3   J = K + 1

[20] The first line is a new type of statement. It tells the computer what the maximum values of all the subscripts are. We will discuss it in detail in Chapter 3. For now we take it to be necessary on faith.

5   Y = A(J, K) / A(K, K)

6   I = K

7   A(J, I) = A(J, I) − Y * A(K, I)

8   IF (I − 4) 9, 10, 100

9   I = I + 1

    GO TO 7

10   B(J) = B(J) − Y * B(K)

11   IF (J − 4) 12, 13, 100

12   J = J + 1

    GO TO 5

13   IF (K − 3) 14, 15, 100

14   K = K + 1

    GO TO 3

15   X(4) = B(4) / A(4, 4)

16   K = 3

17   I = 4

18   Y = 0.0

19   Y = Y + A(K, I) * X(I)

20   IF (I − K − 1) 100, 22, 21

21   I = I − 1

    GO TO 19

22   X(K) = (B(K) − Y) / A(K, K)

23   IF (K − 1) 100, 25, 24

24   K = K − 1

    GO TO 17

25   PRINT 1, X(1)

PRINT 1, X(2)

PRINT 1, X(3)

PRINT 1, X(4)

100   STOP

1   FORMAT (F 10.4)

END

We have added at the beginning 20 lines specifying the coefficients in equations (47)–(50). At line 25 near the end, we have added four lines which print out on a typewriter the values of x_1, x_2, x_3, x_4. We have also renumbered the final STOP line as 100 so that any unexpected result in lines 8, 11, 13, 20, or 23 will stop the computer. The statement numbered 1 is useful to tell the typewriter just how we want the numbers typed. Finally, the END statement signifies that there are no more statements in the program. We leave a complete discussion of these to Chapter 3.

This is a complete FORTRAN program. Just as it is, it can be punched onto cards, the cards read into a computer via what is called a "card reader," and the results will be printed. This was in fact done on an actual digital computer and the printed results for x_1, x_2, x_3, x_4 or B, L, M, S are shown in Figure 26. These are not quite the same answers we obtained in Section 1.8. The reason for the discrepancy is that we previously "rounded off" our numbers in most cases with only four figures. Because the computer we used kept eight figures, the results obtained by the computer are a little more accurate. For the purpose of

```
1.0805
1.1670
3.6049
0.1417
```

Figure 26

Results printed by a computer using the FORTRAN program of this chapter

constructing a diet, however, such a high degree of accuracy is not needed. We discuss the problem of "rounding off" in more detail in Section 1.12.

Of course, if we change the daily requirements or find that the amount of calcium in a unit of milk changes, then we need to change some cards in our program. This is in fact a typical way in which a computer is used. We can, for example, raise the calcium requirement slightly and see what change that action produces in the diet. Oddly enough, we may find that by increasing the calcium (or vitamin C or some other nutrient) in the menu we can actually lower the total cost of the food in the diet. We return to this problem of a minimum *cost* diet in the next chapter.

Actually, we can write our FORTRAN program to make changes in the a_{ij} and b_i easily, and we learn how to do such things in a later chapter.

Right now, the important point is that we have written a complete computer program for a fairly complex problem and we can use it on a real computer. The basic ideas and concepts of programming have all been covered. The rest of programming consists in acquiring technique. We do not mean to imply that programming is trivial, nor that the reader is now a programmer any more than he would be a musician if he had learned the scales and how to play one tune.

1.11   Generalization to Larger Systems

So far, we have worked with systems of two and four equations in as many variables, but have had little to say about larger sets of equations.

Gauss's method is applicable to any number of equations, say n, in the same number of variables. If we wish to change our flow charts to accommodate n equations, we do the following: In Figure 19, box 8 is changed to read "Is $i = n$?"; box 11 is changed to read "Is $j = n$?"; and box 13 is changed to read "Is $k = n - 1$?". In Figure 20, box 15 is changed to read "$x_n \leftarrow b_n/a_{nn}$"; box 16 is changed to read "$k \leftarrow n - 1$"; and box 17 is changed to read "$i \leftarrow n$."

With these minor changes we can solve any number of equations. The FORTRAN program needs changes in only six statements: 8, 11, 13, 15, 16, and 17. The reader should have no trouble making these changes. We must also assign a numeric value[21] to N just as we did to A(1, 1),

[21] Remember that in FORTRAN we must use the capital letter N since lower-case letters are not permitted.

etc. We must, therefore, add a statement at the beginning of the program which reads

$$N = 4$$

Of course, we could set N equal to any other positive integer value. Then we would give the values of all the A(I, J) and B(I), as I and J take on all values from 1 to N. Finally, we would change the DIMENSION statement to read

DIMENSION A(N, N), B(N), X(N)

and we would make appropriate changes in the PRINT statements. Although much of this (especially the DIMENSION statement) may be confusing at the moment, it should be clear that with very minor alterations we can use our FORTRAN program to accommodate any number of equations. The details will become much clearer in Chapter 3.

1.12 Numerical Problems and Errors

We end this chapter with a discussion of the effects of errors. As we use the term, "error" does not mean a *mistake* or a *blunder* such as multiplying incorrectly or copying the wrong number. With modern computers, mistakes and blunders occur so infrequently that we can dismiss them as unimportant. Nevertheless, the "correctness" of a result produced by a computer may still be suspect. One reason for this is that the coefficients a_{11}, a_{12}, etc., used in a calculation may not be known exactly.

Consider, for example, our now familiar diet problem. Recall that the amount of protein, calories, and other nutrients in 100 grams of roast beef can vary with the amount of fat and other constituents of the meat. Of course, it is not practical to measure the exact amount of nutrients in each piece of meat. Instead, we take some average value for the number of calories, knowing that the actual piece of meat we eat will not have exactly the number of calories we have used in our calculations. There is, therefore, an error in the coefficients in equations (10) and (11). How accurate, then, is the answer that 200 grams of salad and 165 grams of beef will provide one-half the daily requirements of protein and ascorbic acid?

We need to see what effect an error in the coefficients will have on the solution. Usually we know something about the errors in the coefficients. Although we may not know that 100 grams of roast beef have precisely 20 grams of protein, we may know that they contain between 18 and 22 grams. From this we want to deduce the error in our answer, that 165 grams of roast beef are needed. That is, we want to be able to say that we should eat between, say, 160 and 170 grams of meat.

As we shall see, in some cases a small error in the coefficients of a system of linear equations can produce a large error in the solution of those equations. In such cases the answers must be used with great care. Suppose, for example, that we decided that the amount of roast beef to be eaten should be between 20 and 310 grams. How much should we really eat? The possible answers to that question vary so much that our solution could be useless from a practical point of view.

There is another kind of error which occurs in a computation, namely, **round-off error.** We have already encountered it in our solution of the four-food diet problem. It arises from the fact that neither a person nor a computer can handle an infinite number of digits. For example, the number π (the ratio of the circumference of a circle to its diameter) is 3.14159 . . . and on and on. If we want to calculate with the number π, we can use 3.14 or 3.1416 or some other value approximating the real value. But we cannot use π itself. The number we use is "approximately" equal to π, but there is an error in the number we use. (If we use 3.14, then the error is .00159. . . .) Such an error and the subsequent in-accuracies due to it are called round-off errors. In the solution of large systems of equations, the round-off error can become large because we have to "round off" many times.

No numerical solution of a mathematical model of a problem is complete without an analysis of the errors in the solution. The truth of this warning should be obvious. Think of the immense calculation that must go into the determination of the point of re-entry of an astronaut and the position at which his capsule will fall to earth. No one really expects the astronaut to arrive at the exact spot calculated by the banks of computers. Part of the answer to the problem consists in specifying the possible error to be expected. Thus, because of all the possible sources of error in the calculations, a maximum error in latitude and longitude is predicted and ships can be deployed over the entire area to be covered.

It is a fact, and a challenge to mathematicians, that the analysis of the errors in a computation is often more difficult than solving the original problem.

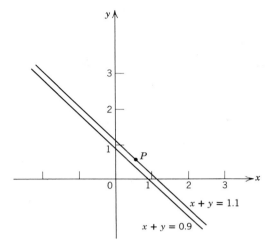

Figure 27

Strip showing allowable (x, y) for errors in right-hand side of equation (12)

Question.   Why should it be more difficult to find the errors in a solution than to find the solution itself?

In the remainder of this chapter we study the errors in the solution of systems of linear equations due both to errors in the coefficients and to round-off errors.

Suppose, for example, that we know that the right-hand sides of (12) and (13) may be in error by as much as 0.1. That is, equation (12) may actually be

$$x + y = 1.1$$

or

$$x + y = 0.9$$

or anything between them, and similarly for equation (13). Let us draw a picture of what this means. In Figure 27 the two lines represented by the last two equations are shown. They are parallel to each other.

Now consider a point on the line $x + y = 1.1$. As an example, we take the point $x = 0.5$ and $y = 0.6$ (the point P in Figure 27). Now, holding x fixed, if we increase y, then $x + y > 1.1$. Similarly, if we hold y fixed, an increase in x produces $x + y > 1.1$. This analysis holds true

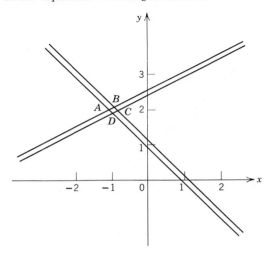

Figure 28

Parallelogram showing possible solutions to equations (12) and (13) when there are errors in the right-hand sides

for *all* points on the line $x + y = 1.1$. Since we know that $x + y$ cannot exceed 1.1, it follows that the allowable values of x and y lie on the side of the line $x + y = 1.1$ *toward the origin 0*.

On the other hand, we know that $x + y$ cannot be less than 0.9. A similar analysis leads us to the conclusion that the allowable values of x and y lie on the side of the line $x + y = 0.9$ *away from the origin 0*.

Thus, the allowable number pairs (x, y) lie in the narrow strip between the two lines in Figure 27.

Similarly, we can find a strip defined by equation (13) where the right-hand side can vary between 4.9 and 5.1. The solution then lies in the area common to both strips. This is the parallelogram $ABCD$ around the point $x = -1$, $y = 2$ in Figure 28. Any number pair lying in that parallelogram satisfies the inequalities

$$0.9 \leq x + y \leq 1.1 \tag{55}$$

$$4.9 \leq -x + 2y \leq 5.1 \tag{56}$$

The point A is the intersection of the two lines

$$x + y = 0.9$$

$$-x + 2y = 5.1$$

Hence, A is the point $(-1.1, 2.0)$. Similarly, B is the intersection of

$$x + y = 1.1$$

$$-x + 2y = 5.1$$

and B is $(-0.9667, 2.0667)$. In the same way, we find that C is $(-0.9, 2.0)$ and D is $(-1.0333, 1.9333)$. Thus it follows that x must be between -1.1 and -0.9, and y must be between 1.9333 and 2.0667, or

$$-1.1 \leq x \leq -0.9 \tag{57}$$

$$1.9333 \leq y \leq 2.0667 \tag{58}$$

The number pairs (x, y) which satisfy these inequalities lie in the rectangle $EFGH$ in Figure 29. The parallelogram $ABCD$ from Figure 28 is also shown in Figure 29. Notice that the rectangle includes all of the parallelogram. This means that, if a number pair satisfies (55) and (56) (i.e., lies inside the parallelogram $ABCD$), then it must also satisfy (57) and (58) (i.e., lie inside the rectangle $EFGH$). Thus we are "safe" if we use (57) and (58). By "safe" we mean that the actual errors will not

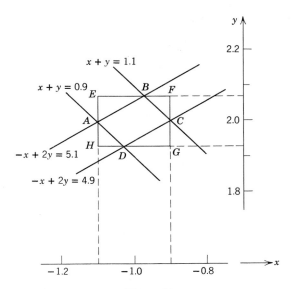

Figure 29

Error parallelogram and bounding rectangle

violate (57) and (58). Of course, (57) and (58) contain some number pairs which will never be attained. Can you find one?[22]

To treat the problem algebraically, we let

$$x = -1 + X \tag{59}$$

$$y = 2 + Y \tag{60}$$

where X and Y represent the errors in the solution to (12) and (13). If the solution $x = -1$ and $y = 2$ were exact, then the errors, X and Y, would be zero.

Next we let E_1 and E_2 be the deviations or errors in the right-hand sides. Of course, we do not know the values of E_1 and E_2. We know only that they are between $-.1$ and $+.1$.

The true equations are then

$$x + y = 1 + E_1$$

$$-x + 2y = 5 + E_2$$

where

$$-.1 \leq E_1 \leq .1 \tag{61}$$

$$-.1 \leq E_2 \leq .1 \tag{62}$$

From (59) and (60), then,

$$X + Y = E_1$$

$$-X + 2Y = E_2$$

It follows from (61) and (62) that

$$-.1 \leq X + Y \leq .1 \tag{63}$$

$$-.1 \leq -X + 2Y \leq .1 \tag{64}$$

Thus we have to find a solution to four *inequalities* to find X and Y, the errors in the solution of equations (12) and (13).

Question.   What are the *four* inequalities for the two unknowns X and Y?

---

[22] This is a "thinking question." The reader is not expected to answer simply "yes" or "no" but is supposed to think about what the answer implies. He should consider why the answer is what it is and what might change the answer. We shall encounter other "thinking questions" as we go along. Any questions that can be answered "yes" or "no" are such thinking questions.

We postpone a general discussion of inequalities until Chapter 2, but we show now how a solution to these inequalities can be obtained using Gauss's method and we compare it with our graphical solution. There are, of course, many solutions — each of the points in the parallelogram of Figure 28 leads to a value of the errors X and Y.

First we note that we cannot be so free in adding and subtracting inequalities as we were in adding and subtracting equations. We can add two inequalities *provided the inequality signs are in the same direction.* That is, if

$$a \leq b$$

and

$$c \leq d$$

then

$$a + c \leq b + d$$

Before discussing the addition of two inequalities whose inequality signs are not in the same direction, we consider the multiplication of an inequality by a constant. If we multiply both sides of an inequality by a *positive* constant, we get a valid inequality. Thus, if

$$a \leq b$$

and $p > 0$, then

$$pa \leq pb$$

If, on the other hand, we multiply both sides of an inequality by a *negative* constant, we must *reverse the direction of the inequality.* For example, if

$$a \leq b$$

and $n < 0$, then

$$na \geq nb$$

Suppose now we wish to add two inequalities whose signs are in opposite directions:

$$a \leq b$$

$$d \geq e$$

Two courses of action are open to us. We can rewrite the second inequality as

$$e \leq d$$

and add it to the first to obtain

$$a + e \leq b + d \tag{65}$$

On the other hand, we can multiply the second by -1, thus reversing the direction of the inequality so that

$$-d \leq -e$$

Adding this to $a \leq b$, we get

$$a - d \leq b - e \tag{66}$$

Actually (65) and (66) are the same inequality, because if we add $d + e$ to both sides of (66) we have (65).

To summarize the salient points: We can add two inequalities provided the inequalities are in the same direction. If we multiply an inequality by -1, we change the direction of the inequality.

Now we want a method for solving the system of inequalities (63) and (64). It would be convenient if this method were similar to Gauss's method for systems of equations. We recall that Gauss's method required us to subtract equations. We cannot subtract inequalities. We need to circumvent this difficulty, and fortunately we can do so easily.

Suppose we multiply (63) by -1. The result (remember to reverse the direction of the inequalities) is $.1 \geq -X - Y \geq -.1$ or, reading from right to left, we have just

$$-.1 \leq -X - Y \leq .1 \tag{67}$$

Notice that this is the same as (63) itself, except that the middle terms are multiplied by -1. The reason is that the left and right sides of (63) are the same except for the sign. This fact greatly facilitates our method of solution of (63) and (64).

The important rule that this demonstrates (and the one we shall use) is: In a system of inequalities such as (63) and (64), if we wish to subtract in order to eliminate one of the variables, we multiply by -1 and add. However, multiplying by -1 merely changes the signs of all terms in the middle and leaves the left side and the right side unchanged.

This rule can be simplified as follows: In a system of inequalities such as (63) and (64) we can subtract the middle terms, if we add the terms on the right side and if we add the terms on the left side.

Again returning to our example, to eliminate X we multiply (63) by -1. This produces (67). We want to subtract (67) from (64). To do this we subtract the middle terms, obtaining $3Y$, but we add the two .1 terms on both the right and the left. The result is

$$-.2 \leq 3Y \leq .2$$

Dividing by 3, we have

$$-.0667 \le Y \le .0667 \tag{68}$$

From (63), subtracting the same quantity Y from each term, we get

$$-.1 - Y \le X \le .1 - Y$$

The biggest X can be, then, is the largest value which $.1 - Y$ can take on. This occurs for $Y = -.0667$; therefore,

$$X \le .1667$$

Similarly, X takes on its smallest value when $Y = +.0667$; hence

$$-.1667 \le X$$

Combining the last two inequalities, we have

$$-.1667 \le X \le .1667 \tag{69}$$

From (59) and (69), then,

$$-1.1667 \le x \le -.8333 \tag{70}$$

and, from (60) and (68),

$$1.9333 \le y \le 2.0667 \tag{71}$$

We have found estimates of the errors in the solution $x = -1, y = 2$.

Let us now look at the geometry of these inequalities. The number pairs (x, y) which satisfy (70) and (71) lie in the rectangle *IJKL* in Figure 30, in which the parallelogram *ABCD* of Figures 28 and 29 is also reproduced.

Any number pair (x, y) which satisfies the original inequalities (55) and (56) lies inside the parallelogram *ABCD*. On the other hand, any number pair which satisfies (70) and (71) lies inside the rectangle *IJKL*. It follows that any number pair which satisfies (55) and (56) also satisfies (70) and (71).

Therefore, we know that any solution of the original equations (12) and (13) satisfies (70) and (71). The inequalities (70) and (71) are then "safe." They are actually "over-safe," because the actual solution cannot vary over as wide a range as that given by (70) and (71). The right- and left-hand sides of the inequalities (70) and (71) are called **bounds** on the solution because the solution cannot get beyond those values. That is,

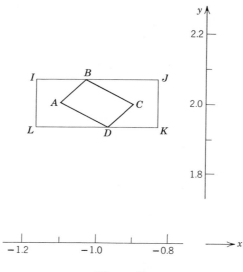

Figure 30

Error parallelogram and bounding rectangle found from Gauss's method

the actual solution can never be bigger than the right-hand side (called an **upper bound**) or smaller than the left-hand side (called a **lower bound**). In general, however, the solution will be less than the upper bound and greater than the lower bound, and perhaps by a considerable amount.

In our example, x will be considerably less than the upper bound, $-.8333$, and considerably larger than the lower bound, -1.1667. Why?

Of course, it is not a coincidence that the left sides of (68) and (69) are the same as the right sides except for the sign. In fact, this is always true. In practice, then, we need calculate only the right side. We can get the left-hand side from the right-hand side simply by changing the sign. Further reduction in the amount of calculation is achieved by observing that the coefficients in (63) and (64) are the same as those in (12) and (13). Therefore, we can perform these calculations at the same time as we are solving (12) and (13) by Gauss's method merely by: (a) carrying along an extra right-hand side equal to .1; and (b) always adding in the second right-hand side while subtracting equations.

If there are errors in the coefficients of x and y as well as in the right-hand sides, then the parallelogram in Figure 28 becomes a more general figure.

We do not discuss the algebra of finding the errors in x and y which result from errors in the coefficients a_{11}, a_{12}, a_{21}, a_{22}. Instead, we content ourselves with the note that bounds on the errors in x and y can be found in a way very similar to the one just used.

Now, besides the errors introduced in x and y by errors in the coefficients b_1, b_2, a_{11}, a_{12}, a_{21}, and a_{22}, there are errors which may arise simply because of the method of calculation. These appear even if we know the coefficients precisely. For example, suppose we try to solve

$$3x + y = 4 \tag{72}$$

$$x + y = 2 \tag{73}$$

Obviously, $x = y = 1$ is the unique solution of these equations.

Suppose, however, that we decide to solve these equations using decimals and agree to carry four decimal places. The multiplier is

$$m = \tfrac{1}{3} = 0.3333$$

Multiplying equation (72) by m and subtracting from equation (73) produces

$$0.0001x + .6667y = 0.6668$$

We expected that the coefficient of x would be zero, but it is not. Already we have an indication that something is amiss. We have little choice but to ignore this discrepancy and solve

$$.6667y = .6668$$

for y, obtaining

$$y = 1.0001$$

which is not quite correct. Going back to equation (72) to find x, we get $x = .9999$, again not quite correct. The error is in the fourth decimal place, because we took only four places in the value of $m = 0.3333$. Actually m is *not* equal to .3333 but to the infinite decimal $.3333\ldots$ which has no end. Of course, neither a human worker nor a computer can carry infinitely many decimal places. Nor does a computer carry fractions which would give an exact answer in this case. Instead, each fraction is written as a decimal and terminated at the number of digits which the computer allows. Although this number may be reasonably large, there is a limit to its size.

The fact that only a finite number of decimal places can be used gives rise to what are called *round-off errors*.

It is very difficult to analyze the effect of round-off errors on the accuracy of the solution of a system of linear equations, and we cannot give such an analysis here. Nevertheless, we can point out how round-off errors can be kept small in Gauss's method.

Recall (block 4 in Figure 19) that we must arrange the equations so that $a_{kk} \neq 0$. We can, therefore, choose for the first equation in each set any equation whose coefficient of the first unknown is not zero. The rule which tends to reduce the effect of round-off errors is: *Choose that equation which makes a_{kk} as large in absolute value[23] as possible.*

Finally, we emphasize that not all systems of linear equations are equally sensitive to errors. In the problem of equations (12) and (13), an error of .1 in the right-hand sides made only a change in the unknowns x and y of .1 at the most. However, in some systems, small errors in the coefficients can give rise to large errors in the answers. We consider now such an example given by the innocent-looking equations

$$8x + 9y = 17 \tag{74}$$

$$7x + 8y = 15 \tag{75}$$

The unique and simple solution is $x = y = 1$, which can be immediately checked by putting $x = 1$ and $y = 1$ in (74) and (75).

Consider now the pair of values $x = 0$ and $y = 1.8819$. If we substitute these values in the left-hand sides of equations (74) and (75), we get

$$8x + 9y = 16.9371$$

$$7x + 8y = 15.0552$$

and these right-hand sides are very close to the original ones. But the x and y values chosen are very far from the solution. Turning this around, we see that a change of less than $\frac{1}{2}$ of 1% in the right-hand side of the first equation (from 17 to 16.9371) and of less than $\frac{1}{2}$ of 1% in the right-hand side of the second equation (from 15 to 15.0552) has changed the solution from $x = 1$, $y = 1$ to $x = 0$, $y = 1.8819$. This is a change of 100% in x and over 88% in y!

To understand the reason for this sensitivity, we return to our geometrical model. Equations (74) and (75) are graphed in Figure 31. The point $x = 0$, $y = 1.8819$ is the point P. Although this point does not lie

[23] The absolute value of a number is found by ignoring the sign. Thus the absolute value of 12 is 12; the absolute value of -12 is also 12.

on either line, it lies very close to both of them. However, it is far from
the actual solution which lies at the intersection (1, 1) of the two lines.
The source of the difficulty lies in the fact that the two lines are almost
parallel or almost coincident.

Since parallel lines give rise to singular equations, we call these equations, (74) and (75), which represent almost coincident lines, **almost
singular.** Such systems of equations are also called **ill-conditioned.**
Moreover, because singular equations, when they have a solution at all,
have infinitely many solutions, it is not surprising that almost singular
equations might have many pairs of x and y values which are "almost
solutions."

Let us now look at what happens to our almost singular equations if
there is a small error in the right-hand sides. Suppose the right-hand
sides of equations (74) and (75) are $17 \pm .1$ and $15 \pm .1$, respectively.
The parallelogram which bounds the solution is shown in Figure 32.
Notice that all we can say is that

$$-0.7 \le x \le 2.7$$

$$-0.5 \le y \le 2.5$$

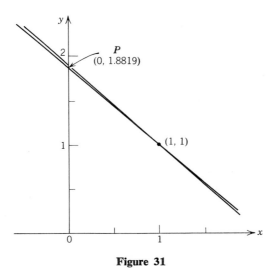

Figure 31

Geometrical model of the ill-conditioned equations (74) and (75)

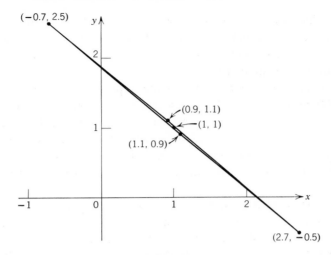

Figure 32

Error parallelogram for the ill-conditioned equations (74) and (75)

Thus both x and y can vary over a wide range. We do not even know the sign of either of them. This kind of behavior is what gives rise to the term ill-conditioned: a small change in the equations can result in a large change in the solution.

Exercises

Answers to exercises marked * are given in Appendix A.

1. Solve the following three linear equations using Gauss's method:

$$3x + 2y + \ z = 6$$
$$x + \ y - \ z = 1$$
$$2x - 3y + 3z = 2$$

Check your solution.

*2. Solve the following three linear equations using Gauss's method:

$$2y + \ z = \ 4$$
$$x - 2y - 2z = -4$$
$$3x \quad + \ z = \ 8$$

Check your solution.

3. Solve the following three linear equations using Gauss's method:

$$x + y + z = 2$$
$$x + y - z = 0$$
$$x - y - z = 0$$

Check your solution.

4. Consider three linear equations in three unknowns:

$$a_{11}x_1 + a_{12}x_2 + a_{13}x_3 = b_1$$
$$a_{21}x_1 + a_{22}x_2 + a_{23}x_3 = b_2$$
$$a_{31}x_1 + a_{32}x_2 + a_{33}x_3 = b_3$$

In Gauss's method we first find a multiplier,

$$m = \frac{a_{21}}{a_{11}}$$

and perform these replacements:

$$a_{21} \leftarrow 0$$
$$a_{22} \leftarrow a_{22} - ma_{12}$$
$$a_{23} \leftarrow a_{23} - ma_{13}$$
$$b_2 \leftarrow b_2 - mb_1$$

We then calculate

$$m = \frac{a_{31}}{a_{11}}$$

and perform the following replacements:

$$a_{31} \leftarrow 0$$
$$a_{32} \leftarrow a_{32} - ma_{12}$$
$$a_{33} \leftarrow a_{33} - ma_{13}$$
$$b_3 \leftarrow b_3 - mb_1$$

The resulting equations are

$$a_{11}x_1 + a_{12}x_2 + a_{13}x_3 = b_1 \qquad \text{(i)}$$
$$a_{22}x_2 + a_{23}x_3 = b_2 \qquad \text{(ii)}$$
$$a_{32}x_2 + a_{33}x_3 = b_3 \qquad \text{(iii)}$$

Our next step is to let

$$m = \frac{a_{32}}{a_{22}}$$

and replace

$$a_{32} \leftarrow 0$$

$$a_{33} \leftarrow a_{33} - ma_{23}$$

$$b_3 \leftarrow b_3 - mb_2$$

(a) Find a multiplier, m, such that, when you multiply equation (ii) by m and subtract the result from equation (i), the coefficient of x_2 is *zero*. The equations now look like

$$a_{11}x_1 \qquad + a_{13}x_3 = b_1 \qquad\qquad \text{(iv)}$$

$$a_{22}x_2 + a_{23}x_3 = b_2 \qquad\qquad \text{(v)}$$

$$a_{33}x_3 = b_3 \qquad\qquad \text{(vi)}$$

(b) Find two multipliers which can be used to multiply equation (vi) so that the coefficients of x_3 in both equations (iv) and (v) can be made zero. The resulting equations will be

$$a_{11}x_1 \qquad\qquad = b_1 \qquad\qquad \text{(vii)}$$

$$a_{22}x_2 \qquad = b_2 \qquad\qquad \text{(viii)}$$

$$a_{33}x_3 = b_3 \qquad\qquad \text{(ix)}$$

(c) Find the solution, x_1, x_2, x_3, from equations (vii), (viii), and (ix).

This is called the **Gauss-Jordan method.**

*5. Draw a flow chart describing the Gauss-Jordan method for three equations as described in Exercise 4.

*6. Consider the system of equations

$$-x + 2y = 5$$

$$x + \ y = 1$$

Suppose both of the right-hand sides can be in error by as much as .1. Use Gauss's method to find bounds on the errors in x and y. Use the equations in the order given above. They are identical with equations (12) and (13) except that the order of the two equations has been reversed. Why are the error bounds found here different from those in (70) and (71)?

7. (a) Solve the following system of equations:

$$x + 3y = 5$$

$$2x + y = 5$$

(b) Suppose the right-hand side of the first equation can be in error by .1 but the second equation is exact. Using Gauss's method, find bounds on the values of x and y.

(c) Reverse the order of the equations and find bounds on the values of x and y.

(d) Draw a graph similar to Figure 28 showing the set of possible values of x and y.

*8. In the equations in Exercise 7, suppose that both right-hand sides can be in error by .2.

(a) Use Gauss's method to find bounds on the values of x and y.

(b) Reverse the order of the equations and find bounds on the values of x and y.

9. Consider the system of equations

$$8x + 9y = 17$$

$$7x + 8y = 15$$

These are equations (74) and (75) in Section 1.12. Suppose the right-hand sides of both equations can be in error by 0.1.

(a) Use Gauss's method to find bounds on the values of x and y.

(b) Reverse the order of the equations and find the bounds on x and y.

(c) Compare the results of (a) and (b) with the results given for these equations at the end of Section 1.12.

10. Suppose $x = x_1$ and $y = y_1$ is the solution of the two equations

$$a_{11}x + a_{12}y = 1$$

$$a_{21}x + a_{22}y = 0$$

Let $x = x_2$ and $y = y_2$ be the solution of

$$a_{11}x + a_{12}y = 0$$

$$a_{21}x + a_{22}y = 1$$

(a) Show that

$$x = b_1x_1 + b_2x_2$$

$$y = b_1y_1 + b_2y_2$$

is the solution of

$$a_{11}x + a_{12}y = b_1 \tag{i}$$

$$a_{21}x + a_{22}y = b_2 \tag{ii}$$

(b) What does this tell you about how to solve equations (i) and (ii) if you need the answers for three or more values of the right-hand sides, b_1 and b_2?

11. Using the results of Exercise 10, solve *all* of the following systems of equations:

(a) $2x + 3y = 1$
       $x + 2y = 1$

*(b) $2x + 3y = 5$
         $x + 2y = 3$

(c) $2x + 3y = 12$
       $x + 2y = 7$

(d) $2x + 3y = 19$
       $x + 2y = 6$

(e) $2x + 3y = 4$
       $x + 2y = 0$

(f) $2x + 3y = 2$
      $x + 2y = \pi$

*12. Devise an algorithm to check to see if any four numbers x_1, x_2, x_3, and x_4 give a solution of equations (30), (31), (32), and (33). Draw a flow chart of the algorithm.

13. Draw a flow chart describing Gauss's method for the solution of three equations in three variables. Test the flow chart by trying to find a solution to equations (27), (28), and (29).

*14. Devise three problems to test the three possible types of results (no solution, unique solution, an infinite number of solutions) for a system of three equations with three variables.

15. Write a FORTRAN program to solve a system of three linear equations in three variables. As the first statement in the program, use

DIMENSION A(3, 3), B(3), X(3)

and eliminate the last PRINT statement in the program in the text. Test your program by solving

$$2x_1 + 3x_2 + 6x_3 = 11$$

$$x_1 - x_2 + 2x_3 = 2$$

$$-2x_1 + x_2 - x_3 = -2$$

which has the solution $x_1 = x_2 = x_3 = 1$.

16. In our study of the flow chart in Section 1.8, we noted that we could save considerable calculation if $m = 0$. Alter the flow chart in Figure 19 to accomplish this.

*17. Change the FORTRAN program in Section 1.10 to take advantage of the case in which the multiplier $m = 0$ as discussed in Section 1.8 and Exercise 16.

*18. Use the FORTRAN program in the text to solve the two-food diet problem given by equations (10) and (11). *Hint:* This is the same as a four-food problem except that we are requiring that $M = 0$ and $S = 0$.

19. Use the program in Section 1.10 to solve the following three equations:

$$8x_1 + 2x_2 - x_3 = -14$$
$$x_1 \qquad + x_3 = \quad 3$$
$$- x_2 + 2x_3 = \quad 7$$

Hint: You will have to change only the 20 statements following the DIMENSION and preceding the statement numbered 2.

*20. (a) In Section 1.4, the following system of equations was shown to have a unique solution:

$$x + y = 1$$
$$-x + 2y = 5$$

Consider these equations where the right-hand sides are set equal to zero.

$$x + y = 0$$
$$-x + 2y = 0$$

What is the solution of this system? Is there more than one solution?

(b) In Section 1.4, the system

$$2x + 3y = 6$$
$$4x + 6y = 6$$

was shown to have no solution, and the related system

$$2x + 3y = 6$$
$$4x + 6y = 12$$

was shown to have an infinite number of solutions. Consider these systems with their right-hand sides set equal to zero:

$$2x + 3y = 0$$
$$4x + 6y = 0$$

How many solutions does this system have?

(c) Systems of equations whose right-hand sides are all zero are called *homogeneous* equations. Homogeneous equations always have at least one solution, where all the variables are zero. This is called the *trivial solution*. Discuss the conditions under which systems of two homogeneous equations have solutions other than the trivial one. Compare these conditions with those for which non-homogeneous equations have a unique solution.

21. Use the FORTRAN program in the text to find a solution to the four-food diet problem when the calorie requirement is reduced from 700 to 650 but all other requirements remain unchanged. Discuss the changes in the menu required by this change in calories.

22. Suppose that in our four-food diet problem (Section 1.6) the requirements for protein, calcium, and calories remain unchanged. Suppose also that the ascorbic acid requirement changes.

(a) Use the FORTRAN program in Section 1.10 to find the diets for ascorbic acid requirements of 26, 28, 30, 32, and 34 milligrams.

(b) Draw a graph showing, on the vertical axis, the number of grams of spinach in the diet and, on the horizontal axis, the number of milligrams of ascorbic acid. From the graph can you guess what the number of grams of spinach would be for 31 milligrams of ascorbic acid? Check your guess by using the FORTRAN program once more.

We say that the amount of spinach is a *function* of the amount of ascorbic acid in the diet. That is, given the ascorbic acid requirement, we can find the number of grams of spinach. Can you think of other quantities of which the amount of spinach is a function? Can you think of other quantities which are functions of the ascorbic acid requirement?

*23. Which of the following systems of equations are singular and which are nonsingular?

(a) $\qquad x + 2y = 2$ $\qquad\qquad$ (b) $\qquad x + y = 0$
$\qquad\qquad -3x - 6y = 4$ $\qquad\qquad\qquad\qquad x - y = 0$

(c) x $= 5$ (d) $2x - 2y = 4$

             $y = 2$ $-2x + 2y = 4$

24. What will be the values of I and X at the end of the following FORTRAN programs?

(a)   Y = 0.0   *(b)   Y = 0.0   (c)   Y = 0.0

      J = 2   J = 2   J = 2

      J = J + 1   I = J + 2   X = 2.0 * (Y + 1.0)

      X = Y + 3.0   J = J + 1   I = J * 2

      Z = X * Y   X = Y * 3.0   I = J + 1

      I = J + 2

25. Try to use the FORTRAN program in Section 1.10 to solve the following system of equations:

$$x_1 + x_2 + x_3 + x_4 = 4$$
$$x_1 + 2x_2 + 2x_3 + x_4 = 6$$
$$-x_1 + x_2 + x_3 + x_4 = 2$$
$$x_2 - x_3 + 2x_4 = 0$$

Why does it not work? What is the solution of these equations?

26. Use the FORTRAN program in Section 1.10 to solve the following systems of equations and check the answers:

(a) $x_1 + x_2$ $= 2$

         $x_2 + x_3$ $= 2$

              $x_3 + x_4 = 2$

     $x_1 + x_2 - x_3$ $= 1$

*(b) $2x_1 + x_2$ $= 2$

     $2x_1$ $+ x_4 = 2$

     $2x_1$ $+ x_3$ $= 2$

     $2x_1$ $= 2$

(c) $x_1 - x_2 + x_3 - 2x_4 = 3$

     $x_1 + x_2 + x_3 + x_4 = 4$

     $x_1 + x_2 - x_3 + x_4 = 0$

   $2x_1 - x_2 + 2x_3 - x_4 = 8$

27. Find a two-food diet (roast beef and salad) which provides 36 grams of protein and 90 milligrams of ascorbic acid.

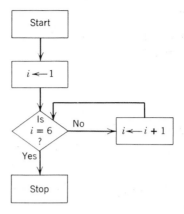

Figure 33

28. Find a two-food diet (roast beef and salad) which provides 70 grams of protein and 60 milligrams of ascorbic acid.

29. We were unable to find a two-food diet of salad and roast beef to provide 165 milligrams of ascorbic acid and 10 grams of protein. Can you find a two-food diet of milk and spinach to provide these quantities of nutrients?

*30. In Figure 33, what is the value of i when the Stop box is reached?

31. In Figure 34, what are the values of x and y when the Stop box is reached?

*32. Suppose we have two warehouses and two retail stores. We want to ship one given product from the warehouses. Let the supply at warehouse 1 be 100 units, and let the supply at warehouse 2 be 150 units. We suppose that the demand at both retail stores is 125 units. We want to know how much to ship from each warehouse to each retail store so that the warehouses will be emptied and the stores will have enough to meet the demand. We let

$$x_1 = \text{amount shipped from warehouse 1 to store 1}$$

$$x_2 = \text{amount shipped from warehouse 1 to store 2}$$

$$x_3 = \text{amount shipped from warehouse 2 to store 1}$$

$$x_4 = \text{amount shipped from warehouse 2 to store 2}$$

the total amount shipped from warehouse 1 is $x_1 + x_2$, and this must equal the supply at that warehouse; therefore,

$$x_1 + x_2 \qquad = 100$$

Similarly, by considering warehouse 2 and the two stores, we get three more equations:

$$x_3 + x_4 = 150$$

$$x_1 \qquad + x_3 \qquad = 125$$

$$x_2 \qquad + x_4 = 125$$

Solve this system of equations by hand, using Gauss's method. Why would our FORTRAN program not work in this case?

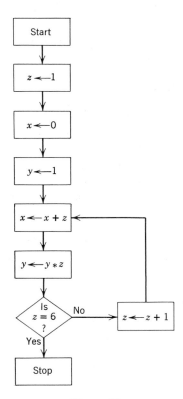

Figure 34

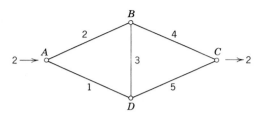

Figure 35

*33. Consider the simple electrical network pictured in Figure 35. Two amperes of current flow in at the left (A) and a like amount flows out at the right (C). We want to know the amount of current flowing in each of the five wires numbered 1, 2, 3, 4, and 5. We need to know some physics to solve this problem. The three laws of physics which we need are:

(1) The current flowing in a wire is proportional to the difference in the voltages at the two ends of the wire (*Ohm's law*). For example, the difference in the voltages at A and B ($V_A - V_B$) must be proportional to the current flowing in wire 2, x_2. Thus

$$V_A - V_B = R_2 x_2$$

The number R_2 is called the resistance of wire 2.

(2) The sum of the currents flowing into any point is zero (*Kirchhoff's first law*). Looking at the point B, we let x_1, x_2, x_3 be the currents in wires, and we assume they have directions as shown in Figure 36. Then $x_3 + x_4$ must be equal to x_2, or

$$x_2 - x_3 - x_4 = 0$$

Of course, any of the x's may turn out to be negative, in which case we have chosen the wrong direction for the current in that

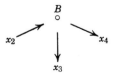

Figure 36

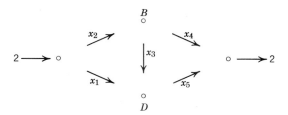

Figure 37

wire. If, for example, $x_2 = -2$, then the current in wire 2 flows from B to A.

(3) The sum of the voltage drops around any closed loop is zero (*Kirchhoff's second law*). For example, looking at the loop ABD composed of wires 1, 3, and 2 in Figure 35 we see that the voltage drop from A to B is $V_B - V_A$. The voltage drop from B to D is $V_D - V_B$. The voltage drop from D to A is $V_A - V_D$. Adding these three voltage drops together, we get zero. Now let $x_1, \ldots, x_5$ be the currents in the wires in the directions indicated by the arrows in Figure 37. Then at A, from Kirchhoff's first law,

$$2 - x_2 - x_1 = 0 \qquad\qquad \text{(i)}$$

Similarly, from B, D, and C,

$$x_2 - x_3 - x_4 = 0 \qquad\qquad \text{(ii)}$$

$$x_1 + x_3 - x_5 = 0 \qquad\qquad \text{(iii)}$$

$$x_4 + x_5 - 2 = 0 \qquad\qquad \text{(iv)}$$

(a) Suppose we add equations (i), (ii), (iii), (iv). What is the result? What does it tell us about the equations? Now let $y_1, \ldots, y_5$ be the voltage drops along the wires, again in the direction of the arrows in Figure 37; e.g., $y_1 = V_D - V_A$ and $y_3 = V_D - V_B$. From Kirchhoff's second law, using the left-hand triangle, we obtain

$$y_2 + y_3 - y_1 = 0 \qquad\qquad \text{(v)}$$

From the right-hand triangle,

$$y_4 - y_5 - y_3 = 0 \qquad\qquad \text{(vi)}$$

Finally, from the diamond, $ABCD$,

$$y_1 + y_5 - y_4 - y_2 = 0 \qquad\qquad \text{(vii)}$$

(b) If we add equations (v), (vi), (vii), what is the result? What does it tell us about those three equations? Now we use Ohm's law to write

$$y_1 = R_1 x_1$$
$$y_2 = R_2 x_2$$
$$y_3 = R_3 x_3 \qquad\qquad \text{(viii)}$$
$$y_4 = R_4 x_4$$
$$y_5 = R_5 x_5$$

where $R_1, \ldots, R_5$ are the resistances of the respective wires. Using (viii) to replace the y's in (v), (vi), and (vii), we get seven equations in the five variables, $x_1, \ldots, x_5$.

We can ignore one equation of the first four and one equation of the last three. Why? This gives us five equations and five variables.

(c) Solve this system of five equations when all the resistances in the wires are 1. What are the currents in the five wires? What are the voltage drops along each wire?

(d) What are the currents and voltage drops in the wires if

$$R_1 = 1$$
$$R_2 = 1$$
$$R_3 = \tfrac{1}{2}$$
$$R_4 = 2$$
$$R_5 = 1$$

*34. (a) Write a FORTRAN program to decide if a number is positive or not. If it is positive, execute the statements

    PRINT 100

100 FORMAT (9H POSITIVE)

    STOP

If it is not positive, execute these statements:

    PRINT 200

200 FORMAT (13H NOT POSITIVE)

    STOP

Put the statement

    END

after all other cards.

(b) Test the program by putting in various numbers.

35. (a) Write a FORTRAN program that takes three numbers X, Y, and Z and lets A be the largest, B the second largest, and C the smallest.

(b) Test the program by using the following statements at the beginning:

    X = 2.1

    Y = −6.1

    Z = 3.8

and adding the following statements at the end:

    PRINT 100, A, B, C

100   FORMAT (F5.2, F5.2, F5.2)

    STOP

    END

The numbers 3.8, 2.1, −6.1 should be printed on a line in that order.

36. (a) Write a FORTRAN program to find the largest of the five integers I(1), I(2), I(3), I(4), I(5).

(b) Test the program by prefacing it with the statements

    DIMENSION I(5)

    I(1) = 6

    I(2) = 2

    I(3) = 9

    I(4) = −2

    I(5) = −10

End the program with the following statements:

    PRINT 100, J

100   FORMAT (I5)

STOP

END

where J is the "number" of the largest integer; i.e., tells us how far from the beginning of the list we shall find the largest. In this example, J = 3. The program should print the integer 3.

(c) Put in different values for I(1), . . . , I(5) and test the program. It should always print an integer which counts how far from the beginning the largest integer is.

(d) Write a FORTRAN program to find the smallest of the integers I(1), . . . , I(5). Test the program using the statements in part (b). In this case J should be the "number" of the smallest integer and, for these particular integers, J = 5.

(e) Test the program in part (d) with other values for I(1), . . . , I(5).

*37. (a) What does the following program do?

$$I = 0$$

$$SUM = 0.0$$

1 $I = I + 1$

$$SUM = SUM + X(I)$$

IF $(I - 10)$ 1, 1, 2

2 STOP

If the fifth line is changed to

IF $(I - 10)$ 1, 2, 2

What does the program do?

(b) Test both of these programs by prefacing them with the statements

DIMENSION X(11)

X(1) = 1.0

X(2) = 3.2

X(3) = −2.1

X(4) = 1.9

X(5) = 6.2

X(6) = −3.1

X(7) = −1.9

X(8) = 9.0

X(9) = 1.1

X(10) = 3.2

X(11) = −14.2

and by adding the following statements at the end:

PRINT 100, SUM

100 FORMAT (F10.2)

STOP

END

38. (a) Write a program to add the integers from 1 to 10. Call the sum J. End the program with the statements

PRINT 100, J

100 FORMAT (I10)

STOP

END

This program should print out an integer which is the sum.

(b) Rewrite the program to find the sum of the integers from 1 to 20, from 1 to 30, from 1 to 40, and 1 to 50.

(c) Plot the results of parts (a) and (b). Can you guess at a formula for the sum of the integers from 1 to *n*?

*39. Write a FORTRAN program to find the product of the integers from 1 to 5. Call the product K. End the program with the statements

PRINT 200, K

200 FORMAT (I10)

STOP

END

This program should print out an integer which is the product.

*40. What does the following program do?

IF (X) 1, 2, 2

1 Y = −X

GO TO 3

2 Y = X

3 Continue remainder of program

*41. (a) Write a FORTRAN program that tests an integer I to see if it is the square root of another integer J. If I = $\sqrt{J}$, do the statements

PRINT   100

100 FORMAT (4H YES)

STOP

If not, execute the following:

PRINT   200

200 FORMAT (3H NO)

STOP

Use the following card as the last card in the deck:

END

(b) Test the program by running it several times with

(i)   I = 2,   J = 4

(ii)   I = 3,   J = 8

(iii)   I = −4,   J = 16

(iv)   I = 4,   J = −16

(c) Choose several sets of integers and try out your program.

CHAPTER TWO

Linear Inequalities
— The Best Solution

2.1 The Two-Food Diet Problem

We return for the last time to the diet problem. Recall that in Section 1.8 we stated the following problem: Find $L \geq 0$ and $B \geq 0$ so that at least 30 milligrams of ascorbic acid and at least 35 grams of protein will be consumed. ($L =$ the amount of lettuce in 100-gram units, and $B =$ the amount of beef in the same units.)

If we are to consume at least 30 milligrams of ascorbic acid, then

$$15L \geq 30 \tag{1}$$

for $15L$ represents the ascorbic acid in the diet. Similarly, since the grams of protein in the diet are given by $20B + L$, it follows that

$$20B + L \geq 35 \tag{2}$$

In Figure 1 we have drawn a geometrical model of the inequalities (1) and (2). The line M represents the equation

$$15L = 30$$

obtained from (1) by replacing the inequality by an equality. All points above the line M represent number pairs for which $15L$ is greater than 30. Therefore, the number pairs (B, L) which satisfy the inequality (1) must lie *on or above* the line M. On the other hand, inequality (2) says that number pairs (B, L) must lie *on or to the right of* the line N. Line N represents number pairs which satisfy

$$20B + L = 35$$

Thus, the number pairs which satisfy both inequalities must lie in the angle PQR or on the rays[1] QP and QR which form the sides of this

---

[1] A *ray* is a line segment which extends indefinitely in one direction.

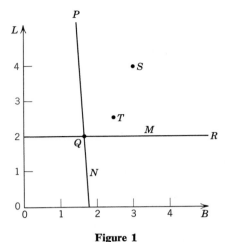

Figure 1

Geometrical model of two-food diet problem

angle. The point Q, where $B = 1.65$ and $L = 2$, is one such point. So is the point S, where $B = 3$ and $L = 4$ and the point $T(2.5, 2.5)$.

Problem.   Give two ways of checking whether points $(1, 1)$ and $(4, 2)$ satisfy the inequalities (1) and (2).

Our inequalities, therefore, have many solutions.[2] Indeed, there are infinitely many solutions. A dietician might like to choose one which has as few calories as possible. Or we might want to choose one which costs less than any of the others.

Suppose we ask for the diet which satisfies the two inequalities, (1) and (2), and which minimizes (makes as small as possible) the number of calories in the diet. The number of calories is

$$C = 325B + 80L \tag{3}$$

Since the point S which is $(3, 4)$ satisfies the inequalities, let us see how many calories it provides. From equation (3) it follows that, at S,

$$C = 1295$$

[2] Recall that two *equations* in two variables in general have only one solution. This is not true of inequalities except in unusual circumstances.

Let us now find all the diets which provide the same number of calories. They lie on the line

$$325B + 80L = 1295$$

which is the line A in Figure 2. There are, therefore, an infinite number of points which satisfy the inequalities (1) and (2) and which provide 1295 calories. They lie on that part of line A inside the angle PQR. We can see also that any diet providing less than 1295 calories satisfies the inequality

$$325B + 80L < 1295$$

The number pairs (B, L) for which this is true lie to the left of the line A.

The diet consisting of 250 grams each of lettuce and beef, the point $T = (2.5, 2.5)$, is also admissible because it satisfies both inequalities. The number of calories it provides is, from (3), 1012.5, which is less than the number of calories in the diets of line A. All the diets which provide

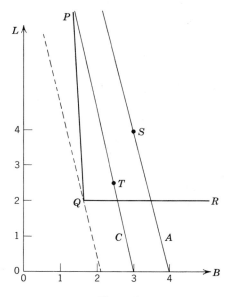

Figure 2

Geometrical model of diet problem showing lines which provide fixed number of calories

1012.5 calories lie on the line

$$325B + 80L = 1012.5$$

which is the line C in Figure 2.

Notice that lines A and C are parallel and that the one corresponding to fewer calories lies closer to the origin. This leads us to suspect (1) that the points representing diets with a given number of calories lie on a straight line parallel to A and C, and (2) the closer the line is to the origin the lower will be the number of calories. Both of these statements are indeed true. Therefore, to find the minimum number of calories possible in the diet we need only move the line as far to the left as possible without passing entirely out of the angle PQR. How far can we move the line before we pass entirely out of the angle PQR? Suppose we draw a line through the point Q and parallel to lines A and C. This is the dashed line in Figure 2. The diets corresponding to points on this dashed line will have fewer calories in them than the diets for lines A and C. Why?

Of course, only one point, the point Q, on the dashed line corresponds to a diet which satisfies the two inequalities, (1) and (2). All other points on the dashed line lie outside of the angle PQR and thus do not satisfy both inequalities. Now, if we draw any other line parallel to the dashed line but closer to the origin, it will not have any points lying inside the angle PQR. Therefore, of all the diets which satisfy the two inequalities the one with the fewest calories is given by the point Q, where $B = 1.65$ and $L = 2$. The minimum number of calories is 696.25.

Interestingly enough, there is only *one* diet which satisfies all the conditions. These conditions are that the diet provide at least 35 grams of protein and at least 30 milligrams of ascorbic acid and also the least number of calories, 696.25.

We turn now to another problem involving inequalities and finding a "best" solution. First, however, we ask the following question:

Question.   Suppose lettuce costs 10 cents per 100 grams and beef costs 25 cents per 100 grams. What diet satisfies the two original inequalities and costs the least? If the price of beef doubled, would the answer change?

2.2   A Nut Mix Problem

Suppose we can purchase four kinds of nuts — cashews, peanuts, hazels, and brazil nuts — and we want to make two mixtures of nuts for sale, a party mix and a regular mix. We want to know how much of each mix to prepare to make as much profit as possible. We need a lot more detail to construct a mathematical model of this problem. In particular, we need to know: (1) how much of each type of nut is in each mixture; (2) how much each type of nut costs and how much each mix sells for; and (3) how much of each type of nut is available to us.

This kind of problem arises in many real situations where a number of raw materials can be combined into different end products. For example, in the petroleum industry the problem arises in the blending of aviation gasoline. This blending problem is mathematically the same as our nut mix problem.

Table 1 summarizes the information we need for the nut mix problem. It tells us that one pound of mix No. 1 is made up of 6 oz of cashews, 4 oz of hazel nuts, and 6 oz of brazil nuts. It also tells us that peanuts

Table 1

	Cashews	Peanuts	Hazels	Brazils
1 lb of mix No. 1 contains	6 oz	0 oz	4 oz	6 oz
1 lb of mix No. 2 contains	0 oz	8 oz	6 oz	2 oz
Cost/lb	24¢	16¢	16¢	32¢
Supply available	75 lb	150 lb	125 lb	87.5 lb

and hazel nuts will cost us the same amount (16¢/lb), but there are more peanuts than hazel nuts available (150 lb to 125 lb). Since mix No. 1 contains more expensive nuts than mix No. 2, we should expect to receive a higher price for mix No. 1. The selling prices of the two mixes are

Mix No. 1 $1.25/lb
Mix No. 2 $0.50/lb

We first compute the profit on a pound of mix No. 1. The cost of 1 oz of cashews is 24¢ divided by 16 or $\frac{3}{2}$ cents.[3] The cost of the cashews in a pound of mix No. 1 then is $6 \times \frac{3}{2}$ or 9 cents. There are no peanuts in mix No. 1, but the cost of the hazel nuts in mix No. 1 is

$$1\,\frac{\text{cent}}{\text{oz}} \times 4\,\text{oz} = 4\,\text{cents}$$

[3] There are 16 oz in 1 lb.

Similarly, the cost of the brazil nuts in a pound of mix No. 1 is

$$2 \frac{\text{cents}}{\text{oz}} \times 6 \text{ oz} = 12 \text{ cents}$$

Thus, the total cost of the nuts in 1 lb of mix No. 1 is 9 cents + 4 cents + 12 cents = 25 cents. The net profit on a pound of mix No. 1 then is \$1.00.

The reader should be able to determine that the costs of the peanuts, hazel nuts, and brazil nuts in a pound of mix No. 2 are 8 cents, 6 cents, and 4 cents, respectively. Therefore, the profit on a pound of mix No. 2 is 32 cents.

There are other expenses involved in the business of selling the two mixes. We might rent a store, buy bags or boxes for the nuts, deliver them, advertise, etc. We shall suppose that all these other costs are unaffected by the number of pounds of nuts we prepare, and that their cost will be deducted from the total net profit. Therefore, we need not concern ourselves with these expenses.

If we make x_1 pounds of mix No. 1 and x_2 pounds of mix No. 2, then our profit in cents will be

$$100x_1 + 32x_2 \tag{4}$$

It is this sum that we want to make as large as possible.

Of course, our supply of each type of nut is limited. In x_1 pounds of mix No. 1 we shall use $6x_1$ ounces of cashews. This cannot exceed 75 lb = 1200 oz. Therefore, $6x_1$ must be less than or equal to 1200:

$$6x_1 \leq 1200 \tag{5}$$

Similarly, since $8x_2$ oz of peanuts are used in x_2 pounds of mix No. 2 and we have 150 lb = 2400 oz of peanuts available,

$$8x_2 \leq 2400 \tag{6}$$

The limit on hazel nuts is slightly more complicated. In x_1 pounds of mix No. 1 we use $4x_1$ oz of hazel nuts, and in x_2 pounds of mix No. 2 we use $6x_2$ oz of hazel nuts. Therefore, the total number of ounces of hazel nuts used in x_1 pounds of mix No. 1 *and* x_2 pounds of mix No. 2 is $4x_1 + 6x_2$; therefore,

$$4x_1 + 6x_2 \leq 2000 \tag{7}$$

Finally, the supply of brazil nuts ($87\frac{1}{2}$ lb = 1400 oz) requires that

$$6x_1 + 2x_2 \leq 1400 \tag{8}$$

Of course, we cannot make a negative amount of either mix, so we must require that

$$x_1 \geq 0 \tag{9}$$

$$x_2 \geq 0 \tag{10}$$

Our mathematical model is now complete. We wish to maximize (make as large as possible) (4), where x_1 and x_2 must satisfy the six inequalities, (5) through (10).

We shall solve this problem by constructing a geometrical model. We shall see that we need to be careful in using a geometrical model and that such a solution is not particularly straightforward. Later we shall devise an algorithm which will solve this problem using algebra. This will be easier and more accurate than using a geometrical model. *Geometry is used here to give us a picture of what is happening and to suggest how an algorithm might be constructed.* Just as with linear equations, we can use a geometrical model to give us qualitative results. If we want quantitative results, however, we must use an algebraic model.

The number pairs (x_1, x_2) which satisfy the inequality (5) lie on or to the left of the line C (for cashews) in Figure 3. Similarly, the number pairs which satisfy the inequality (6) lie on or below the line P (for

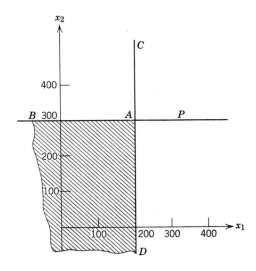

Figure 3

Geometrical model of inequalities (5) and (6)

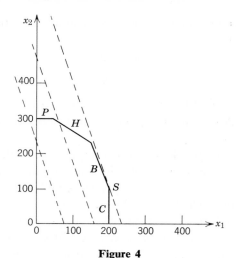

Figure 4

Geometrical model of nut mix problem

peanuts) in Figure 3. It follows, therefore, that the number pairs (or points) which satisfy both (5) and (6) lie in the *shaded* area in Figure 3 or on the rays *AB* and *AD*. (Note that the rays and the shaded area extend indefinitely.)

Not all number pairs in the shaded area in Figure 3 satisfy all the conditions of the problem. For example, the number pair (150, 250) which lies in the shaded area does not satisfy (7).

Question.   Does the number pair (150, 250) satisfy the inequalities (8), (9), and (10)?

The reader should be able to construct lines arising from (7) through (10) when the inequalities are replaced by equalities. He should also be able to decide on which side of these lines the number pairs which satisfy the inequalities lie.

The final result is that number pairs (x_1, x_2) which satisfy all six inequalities simultaneously must lie in or on the boundary of the polygon bounded by the two axes and the four line segments *P*, *H*, *B*, and *C* in Figure 4.

Of all the number pairs lying in the polygon, we wish to find the number pair which maximizes (makes as large as possible) the profit given by (4). For any given value of the profit, say $80.00, the number pairs which produce that profit lie on a line. For an \$80.00 profit, (4) becomes

$$100x_1 + 32x_2 = 8000$$

(Remember that we have measured profit in cents.) This is represented by the dashed line farthest to the left in Figure 4. The other dashed lines represent other values for the profit. As the lines move *away* from the origin, the profit increases. Therefore, we want to find a line as far to the right as possible and parallel to the dashed lines. Of course, at least one point on the line must be in the polygon or on the line segments bounding the polygon. Why?

The line we seek is the dashed line farthest to the right in Figure 4. It passes through one point in the polygon, the point S, where $x_1 = 200$ and $x_2 = 100$. This is the solution to our problem. Therefore, we should make 200 lb of mix No. 1 and 100 lb of mix No. 2. If we do so, our profit will be \$232.00.

Let us pause a moment to analyze our geometrical model in more detail and see what other insights we can get into our problem. Notice that number pairs on the line segment C (for cashews) represent values of x_1 and x_2 which use the entire supply of cashew nuts. This is so because the line segment C is part of the line given by

$$6x_1 = 1200$$

Similarly, number pairs on the line segment B correspond to x_1 and x_2 values which use the supply of brazil nuts completely. The same is true for the line segments H and P and the supplies of hazel nuts and peanuts, respectively.

At the corners where these line segments meet, then, the entire supplies of two of the types of nuts are used. For example, at the point S, which represents the solution, all the brazil nuts and cashew nuts are used. The reader should verify this by checking that the number pair (200, 100) satisfies (5) and (8) when the inequalities are replaced by equalities.

> **Question.** Find the point where all the peanuts and all the hazel nuts are used and check your answer. What is the profit in that case? Is it greater or less than the profit when all the cashews and brazil nuts are used?

Now notice that the dashed lines are almost parallel to the line segment B. If we are not extremely careful in drawing our graph, we may have trouble deciding exactly how far to the right we can move the dashed line. If the dashed line were accidentally tilted just a little to the left, we would stop at the point where the line segments *H* and *B* meet. Then we would use all the hazel nuts and all the brazil nuts and have some cashews left over.

We shall find that we can devise an algorithm for the solution of this type of problem. The algorithm will allow us to obtain a more accurate solution than we can by using a graph, and to obtain it more easily.

We first discuss the mathematics of linear inequalities. Before doing that, however, we close this section with another question.

Question.   If the supply of cashew nuts is reduced to 40 lb., what happens to the solution of the problem?

2.3   Mathematics of Linear Inequalities — Introduction to Linear Programming

Optimization problems are concerned with finding the minimum (smallest) or maximum (largest) of some combination of the unknown quantities (variables). We are going to consider only *linear* combinations of the variables. A linear combination is a sum or difference of terms in which each variable appears only to the first power and no products of the variables appear.[4] Moreover, we shall be concerned with problems where the requirements placed on the unknowns are also linear. We have already encountered such problems in the preceding section. In Section 2.1, we wanted to

$$\text{Minimize}\quad 325B + 80L$$

where *B* and *L* were required to satisfy

$$15L \geq 30 \tag{1}$$

$$20B + L \geq 35 \tag{2}$$

$$B \geq 0 \tag{3}$$

$$L \geq 0$$

In Section 2.2, we wanted to

$$\text{Maximize}\quad 100x_1 + 32x_2 \tag{4}$$

---

[4] Recall the definition of **linear equation** from Chapter 1 (page 2).

where x_1 and x_2 satisfied

$$6x_1 \leq 1200 \tag{5}$$

$$8x_2 \leq 2400 \tag{6}$$

$$4x_1 + 6x_2 \leq 2000 \tag{7}$$

$$6x_1 + 2x_2 \leq 1400 \tag{8}$$

$$x_1 \geq 0 \tag{9}$$

$$x_2 \geq 0 \tag{10}$$

Notice that the quantities to be minimized or maximized and the requirements on the variables are all linear. Such problems are called **linear programming** problems. The word "programming" as used here is *not* the same as the word "programming" used in connection with writing instructions for a computer. It is unfortunate that the same word is used in two different senses. This, however, is a perversity often found in the English language. Programming in the *mathematical* sense is finding a solution to certain kinds of optimization problems. Programming in the *computing* sense is producing instructions for a computer. Later in this chapter we shall write a program (computer) to solve a programming (mathematical) problem.

The quantity which we wish to maximize (or minimize) is called the **objective** or sometimes the **objective function**. In the diet problem, $325B + 80L$ is the objective. In the nut mix problem, (4) is the objective.

The inequalities which must be satisfied are called the **constraints**.[5] The constraints in the nut mix problem are the inequalities (5) through (10). What are the *four* constraints in the diet problem?

Before discussing solutions of linear programming problems, we discuss in some detail the character of all possible *solutions to the constraints*.[6]

Recall, from Figure 1, that the number pairs which satisfied all the constraints were in the angle PQR bounded by the rays QP and QR. This region extended indefinitely to the right and up. On the other hand, the number pairs satisfying the constraints (5) through (10) in the nut

---

[5] They constrain the values which the variables may have.

[6] The solutions of the linear programming problem will be among the solutions to the constraints. However, not all solutions to the constraints are solutions of the linear programming problem. We return to this point in the next section.

mix problem were in the polygon bounded by the two axes and the line segments *P*, *H*, *B*, and *C* in Figure 4.

In general, the number pairs which satisfy linear constraints on two variables correspond to points lying in a region bounded by line segments, rays, or both. In any case, the set of points consisting of the number pairs which satisfy the constraints is called the **constraint set**. The line segments and/or rays which delineate the constraint set are called the **boundary** of the constraint set.

Finally, the "corners" where the line segments and rays that make up the boundary meet are called the **vertices** or **extreme points** of the constraint set. These extreme points are important because the solutions of all linear programming problems will occur at extreme points. We elaborate on the last statement later.

Starting from any point in the constraint set for the nut mix problem (Figure 4), no matter in which direction we try to go we meet the boundary of the constraint set. In such cases the region is said to be **bounded**. Not all constraint sets are bounded. The constraint set for the diet problem (Figure 1) is **unbounded**. Starting from any point in this constraint set, if we move to the left we meet the boundary, but if we move to the right we never meet the boundary. This gives rise to the term unbounded.

Suppose now we change our nut mix problem slightly. We suppose that, in addition to all the requirements already imposed, we are asked to deliver 250 lb of mix No. 1 to a customer. This means that

$$x_1 \geq 250 \tag{11}$$

There are no number pairs (x_1, x_2) which simultaneously satisfy (5) through (10) and (11), because the polygon in Figure 4 lies to the left of the line $x_1 = 250$ and (11) requires that the solution lie on or to the right of $x_1 = 250$. The system of inequalities (5) through (10) and (11) is called *inconsistent* because it has no solution at all.

We consider now a second variation of our nut mix problem. Suppose that, instead of being asked for 250 lb of mix No. 1, we are asked for only 50 lb but also are asked for 300 lb of mix No. 2. Thus we require that

$$x_1 \geq 50 \tag{12}$$

$$x_2 \geq 300 \tag{13}$$

There is only one number pair which satisfies (5) through (10) and (12) and (13) simultaneously. That is the point $x_1 = 50$ and $x_2 = 300$.

In summary then, given a system of linear inequalities, four possibilities exist:

1. There are an infinite number of solutions but the solutions are bounded; i.e., no unknown can become indefinitely large or small. Example: (5) to (10).
2. There are an infinite number of solutions and they are unbounded. Example: (1) and (2).
3. There are no solutions. Examples: (5) to (10) and (11).
4. There is one and only one solution. Example: (5) to (10) and (12) and (13).

In possibilities 1, 2, and 4, the inequalities are said to be **consistent;** i.e., they have at least one solution. In the third one, they are said to be **inconsistent.**

Question. Which case covers the following inequalities?

$$x + y \geq 1$$
$$-x - y \geq -1$$
$$x \geq 0$$
$$y \geq 0$$

What is the boundary of the constraint set?

We have demonstrated the alternatives only for the case of two variables. However, they are the only alternatives possible even when more variables are present. The geometrical interpretation of a system of linear inequalities carries over as well, but it becomes impractical to attempt actually to graph the constraints when three variables are being considered. Beyond three variables it is, of course, impossible actually to construct the regions.

2.4 Solutions of Linear Programming Problems

We turn now to the solution of linear programming problems. A **solution** of a linear programming problem is a set of values of the variables which (a) satisfies the constraints and (b) maximizes or minimizes the objective. It is not to be confused with a "solution of the constraints" which needs to satisfy (a) only.

As our primary example we return to the nut mix problem. Recall that the solution to that problem occurred at the extreme point where the line segments *B* and *C* met (Figure 4). It is a fact that, when a linear programming problem has a solution, it occurs at an extreme point of the constraint set. We do not prove this, but we present an argument to indicate that it is so.

Suppose we wish to maximize any linear objective with a constraint set given by the inequalities (5) through (10). Then the constraint set is the polygon in Figure 4. For any given value of the objective the number pairs which produce that value of the objective lie on a line. We want to move this line parallel to itself as far to the right (or left) as we can and still have it contain some number pairs in common with the constraint set.

What is to stop us from continuing indefinitely to move the line? Because the constraint set is bounded, it is clear that eventually we shall have to stop moving the line. Since the moving line must have at least one number pair in common with the constraint set, it must cross at least one line segment of the boundary. We can continue to move the line until it reaches one of the extreme points at the end of the line segments it crosses. For this reason, the maximum (or minimum) of an objective must occur at an extreme point of the constraint set.

In the nut mix problem the solution occurred at one and only one point (200, 100). The solution is then called **unique**. Unfortunately, not all linear programming problems have unique solutions.

Suppose that in our nut mix problem the selling price of mix No. 1 is reduced from $1.25 to $1.21. All other requirements of the problem remain unchanged. The profit in the changed problem is given by

$$96x_1 + 32x_2 \tag{14}$$

The constraints are still given by (5) through (10). The maximum of the profit (14) is $224.00, and we can achieve this profit by letting $x_1 = 200$ and $x_2 = 100$ *or* by letting $x_1 = 180$ and $x_2 = 160$ *or* by letting $x_1 = 170$ and $x_2 = 190$. In fact, there are an infinite number of number pairs which satisfy all the constraints, (5) through (10), and give a profit of $224.00. The reader should assure himself that any point on the line segment *B* in Figure 4 produces this maximum value of the profit. This nonuniqueness arises because the lines representing a given profit are now parallel to the line segment *B* in Figure 4.

There are, therefore, points which are not extreme points but which do maximize the objective. But previously we said that the maximum of the objective must occur at an extreme point. Have we reached a contradiction? The answer to this question is "no." We said that the maximum does occur at an extreme point. We did not say that it did not occur elsewhere as well. In other words, the solution may not be unique.

Why worry about extreme points at all, then? First, there are always only a finite number of them. (There are six in our nut mix example. Can you find them?) If we know that the maximum occurs at an extreme point, then there are only a finite number of points in the constraint set which we must examine in looking for the maximum. If we did not know this, we would have to look at an infinite number of points — the entire constraint set (in our example, the boundary and the entire inside of the polygon). Of course, if the solution is not unique, there will be an infinite number of solutions. By considering only extreme points we may not find *all* solutions, but we shall surely find one.

Before summarizing, we need to look at one more example. Suppose we wish to

$$\text{Maximize} \quad 4x + y \tag{15}$$

subject to

$$x + y \geq 1 \tag{16}$$

$$x \geq 0 \tag{17}$$

$$y \geq 0 \tag{18}$$

The constraint set is the shaded region in Figure 5. The boundary is composed of the line segment QR and the rays QP and RS. The constraint set is unbounded because, starting from any point in the constraint set, we can move either to the right or up indefinitely.

The dashed lines represent different values of the objective, (15). The values of the objective become larger as the lines move to the right. Therefore, the objective can be as large as we please, since as we move to the right we shall never strike an extreme point of the constraint set. In this case we say that the solution is **unbounded.**[7]

For all linear programming problems there are these four possibilities:

1. No solution exists. The constraints are inconsistent. Example: Any objective and constraints (5) through (10) and (11).
2. A unique, bounded solution exists and occurs at an extreme point. Example: Objective (4) and constraints (5) through (10).

---

[7] Recall that the constraint set is also called unbounded. However, an unbounded constraint set does not mean an unbounded solution. Recall the diet problem of Section 1.3.

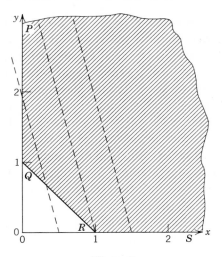

Figure 5

Unbounded region defined by (16), (17), (18)

3. An infinite number of bounded solutions exists and at least one of them occurs at an extreme point. Example: Objective (14) and constraints (5) through (10).
4. The solution exists but is unbounded. Example: Objective (15) and constraints (16) through (18).

We have demonstrated these alternatives only for the case of two variables, but again they are the only alternatives in all cases.

In the algorithm we develop in the next section to solve linear programming problems, we shall be able to detect the three possibilities 2, 3, and 4. We shall always assume that the constraints are consistent so that possibility 1 never arises. However, the algorithm can be extended to determine when the constraints are inconsistent.

Before leaving this discussion of linear inequalities, we point out once more that all the statements made here regarding inequalities with two unknowns apply to inequalities with three or more unknowns as well.

2.5   A Method for Solving Linear Programming Problems

We now describe a method for solving linear programming problems with two variables. We consider first a simple example with four inequalities. Later we generalize our argument to include six inequalities so that we can solve our nut mix problem.

Consider the following linear programming problem:

$$\text{Maximize} \quad x_1 + x_2 \tag{19}$$

where

$$2x_1 + x_2 \leq 2 \tag{20}$$

$$x_1 + 3x_2 \leq 3 \tag{21}$$

$$x_1 \geq 0 \tag{22}$$

$$x_2 \geq 0 \tag{23}$$

Let us for clarity and emphasis restate this problem in more verbal fashion. The problem is to find the number pair (x_1, x_2) which satisfies the constraints (20), (21), (22), (23) and which makes the objective (19) as large as possible.

Of course, we could solve this problem geometrically, but we need an algebraic method for two reasons: (1) we must not rely on a geometrical solution to give us an accurate answer, and (2) if we want to solve problems with three or more variables, we shall not be able to find a geometrical solution.

Our algorithm starts by adding two new variables, x_3 and x_4, as follows: We replace the inequalities (20) and (21) by the equations

$$2x_1 + x_2 + x_3 \quad = 2$$

$$x_1 + 3x_2 \quad + x_4 = 3$$

For example, if $x_1 = \frac{1}{2}$ and $x_2 = \frac{1}{2}$, then $x_3 = \frac{1}{2}$ also and $x_4 = 1$. Actually, x_3 tells by how much $2x_1 + x_2$ is less than 2. Now, since $2x_1 + x_2$ is at most equal to 2, it follows that x_3 can never be negative. Similarly, since $x_1 + 3x_2$ cannot exceed 3, it follows that x_4 is never negative either.

We can replace our original linear programming problem by the following problem:

$$\text{Maximize} \quad x_1 + x_2 \tag{19}$$

where

$$2x_1 + x_2 + x_3 \quad = 2 \tag{24}$$

$$x_1 + 3x_2 \quad + x_4 = 3 \tag{25}$$

$$x_1 \geq 0 \tag{26}$$

$$x_2 \geq 0 \qquad\qquad (27)$$

$$x_3 \geq 0 \qquad\qquad (28)$$

$$x_4 \geq 0 \qquad\qquad (29)$$

The variables x_3 and x_4 are called **slack variables** because they take up the slack between the left-hand and right-hand sides of (20) and (21).

Let us look now at a geometrical model of this problem and see how we can tell when we have a solution that produces an extreme point. Remember that the maximum occurs at an extreme point. A geometrical model of the constraint set (20)–(23) is shown in Figure 6. The constraint set is the interior and boundary of the quadrilateral $OABC$. There are four extreme points: O, A, B, and C. At O the values of x_1 and x_2 are zero. From (24) and (25) then, $x_3 = 2$ and $x_4 = 3$. Similarly, at A, $x_1 = 1$ and $x_2 = 0$. From (24) and (25), again we find that $x_3 = 0$ and $x_4 = 2$. We can find the values of x_1, x_2, x_3, and x_4 at B and C in the same way. The results are summarized in Table 2.

Table 2

Extreme Point $\rightarrow$	O	A	B	C
$x_1 =$	0	1	$\frac{3}{5}$	0
$x_2 =$	0	0	$\frac{4}{5}$	1
$x_3 =$	2	0	0	1
$x_4 =$	3	2	0	0

When x_3 is zero, it follows from (24) that $2x_1 + x_2 = 2$, and the number pair (x_1, x_2) lies on the line segment AB. To verify this, we look at Table 2 and see that $x_3 = 0$ at points A and B. Similarly, we find that, when $x_4 = 0$, the number pair (x_1, x_2) must lie on the line segment BC. Finally, we find that, if $x_1 = 0$, the number pair lies on OC, and, if $x_2 = 0$, the number pair lies on OA.

Since an extreme point lies on two line segments, it follows that if *at least two* of the variables are zero the corresponding values of x_1 and x_2 lie at an extreme point. This means that at *most two* of the variables are nonzero at an extreme point. Looking at the columns of Table 2, we see that at each extreme point two of the variables are zero and two are not. However, it is not necessary that precisely two variables be zero and that precisely two variables be nonzero at an extreme point.

We shall find it helpful to distinguish between the variables which *must* be zero at an extreme point and those which *may* be zero. Those which must be zero are called the **nonbasic variables.** For example, at the point O the variables x_1 and x_2 are nonbasic variables. They must be zero because the lines $x_1 = 0$ and $x_2 = 0$ pass through O and, in fact, define O. Of course, other lines could pass through O as well, and then other variables would be zero. However, we do not require these other variables to be zero and therefore we do not call them nonbasic variables. As another example, at the point A the nonbasic variables are x_2 and x_3 because the lines $x_2 = 0$ and $x_3 = 0$ ($2x_1 + x_2 = 2$) pass through A. There are always precisely two nonbasic variables.

The other variables which may be zero or nonzero are called the **basic variables.** There are always precisely two basic variables also. In our example the basic variables are nonzero, but this is not always the case if, for example, three lines intersect at a point.

In everything that follows in this text, (a) the basic variables will be nonzero, and (b) the nonbasic variables will be zero. The reader is warned, however, that (a) is not true in all linear programming problems. On the other hand, (b) is always true. To repeat, then: For our purposes, basic variables are synonymous with nonzero variables, and nonbasic variables are synonymous with zero variables.

We look for solutions of equations (24) and (25) which have non-negative values for all four variables and for which two of the variables are nonzero. The latter two variables we call the basic variables. In this way, we find the extreme points of the constraint set and, hence, the solution of our linear programming problem. We start by letting all the variables in the original constraints, (20) and (21), be zero (nonbasic). That is to say, we set $x_1 = 0$ and $x_2 = 0$. Then each of the slack variables, x_3 and x_4, will be equal to one of the right-hand sides of the inequality constraints. In this case $x_3 = 2$ and $x_4 = 3$. Since the right-hand sides of the constraints were positive, we have the correct number of nonzero (basic) variables. Hence we have an extreme point which is the point O.[8] The value of the objective (19) at this extreme point is zero.

Now we devise an algorithm to find a new extreme point which will have a larger value of the objective than does the current extreme point. Since each step of the algorithm will lead us from one extreme point to another and there are only a finite number of extreme points, we might try to conclude that, after a finite number of steps, we shall find an

[8] If one or more of the right-hand sides of the inequalities were negative, we could not have found an extreme point so easily. Methods for finding extreme points for this case exist, but we do not discuss them here.

extreme point which will yield the maximum value of the objective. But, suppose that after some number of steps we come back to some extreme point which we had already encountered. For example, suppose we start at O and go to A, then to C, and back to O. Since O took us to A before, it will take us to A again, and we shall then once again go to C and back to O. We shall never arrive at the point B which is the one we are seeking. We are caught in a never-ending "loop." However, we shall now prove that, if each succeeding extreme point has a higher value of the objective than its predecessor, this looping cannot occur.

The proof is quite simple. Suppose we start at the extreme point O. Once we leave O, our algorithm guarantees that the value of the objective becomes larger. From then on, the objective remains larger than the value at the extreme point O because each succeeding step increases the objective even more. If we were to return to O, we would have to decrease the objective. But our algorithm does not allow this. This argument could be applied to any other extreme point as well as to O. Therefore, if, in our algorithm, we arrive at and then leave any extreme point, we shall never return to that extreme point again. This prevents any "looping" and thus completes the proof.

Let us now try to find a solution to our example starting at the extreme point O where $x_1 = x_2 = 0$ and $x_3 = 2$, $x_4 = 3$. We "solve" (24) and (25) for x_3 and x_4, the two basic (nonzero) variables:

$$x_3 = 2 - 2x_1 - x_2 \qquad (30)$$

$$x_4 = 3 - x_1 - 3x_2 \qquad (31)$$

Since x_1 and x_2 are zero, the objective $(x_1 + x_2)$ is zero at this extreme point.

We always express an extreme point in this way: The basic variables will be on the left and the nonbasic variables on the right. As another example, for the point C in Figure 6,

$$x_3 = 1 - \tfrac{5}{3}x_1 + \tfrac{1}{3}x_4$$

$$x_2 = 1 - \tfrac{1}{3}x_1 - \tfrac{1}{3}x_4$$

These can be obtained by solving (24) and (25) by Gauss's method (see Chapter 1). It may seem to the reader that all we need is $x_3 = 1$ and $x_2 = 1$, and that all the other information on the right is unnecessary. However, we do need all that information about the extreme points for our algorithm.

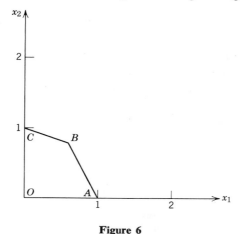

Figure 6

Constraint set for (20) to (23)

We return now to the extreme point O and equations (30) and (31). The unknowns on the right of (30) and (31) are all zero. We cannot decrease either of them because they cannot be negative; see (26) and (27). We can increase them, however, and, since the objective is $x_1 + x_2$, it would make the objective larger if we did make x_1 or x_2 larger than zero. In our algorithm we will change only one variable at a time, so let us arbitrarily choose x_1 to become larger and keep $x_2 = 0$.[9]

Suppose we try to make x_1 positive and x_4 zero. (Remember that, at most, two unknowns can be positive at an extreme point; then, if we make x_1 positive, either x_3 or x_4 must become zero.)

We could go back to (24) and (25) and solve them for x_1 and x_3. However, (30) and (31) are just as satisfactory because they are (24) and (25) in a slightly altered form. Thus we solve the equation with x_4 on the left for x_1. That is, we find the equation in which the variable we want to make zero (nonbasic) appears on the left. Since we want to make the variable x_4 zero, we rearrange that equation to place x_4 on the right with the zero (nonbasic) variables. At the same time we place

---

[9] We could choose x_2 to become larger and keep $x_1 = 0$. We arrive at the correct final solution no matter which choice we make. However, one choice may involve more work (arithmetic) than the other in the long run. Unfortunately, there is no way to know ahead of time which choice will cause us the least amount of labor, and we have chosen x_1 to become larger in an arbitrary way.

the variable x_1 (the one selected to change from zero to some positive value) on the left where the basic (nonzero) variables are to be.

Repeating again, because we want x_4 to become zero, we look for the equation with x_4 on the left. That is equation (31). We rearrange it so that x_4 is on the right and x_1 is on the left as follows:

$$x_1 = 3 - x_4 - 3x_2 \tag{32}$$

Now x_4 is on the right where nonbasic variables appear, and x_1 is on the left where basic variables should be. We want to remove x_1 from the right side of (30) also, because basic variables should not appear on the right according to our rules. Using (32) to replace x_1 in (30), we get

$$x_3 = 2 - 2(3 - x_4 - 3x_2) - x_2$$

or

$$x_3 = -4 + 2x_4 + 5x_2 \tag{33}$$

Equations (32) and (33) *appear* to represent a new extreme point because there are two basic variables on the left and two nonbasic variables on the right. The nonbasic variables, x_2 and x_4, on the right are zero; therefore, this represents the solutions $x_1 = 3$ and $x_2 = 0$ and $x_3 = -4$ and $x_4 = 0$. But we cannot allow x_3 to be -4 because all the variables must be greater than or equal to zero. This tells us we made an error in choosing x_4 to be zero. Therefore, we must choose x_3 to become zero rather than x_4, since it is our only other choice. To do this we go back to (30) and (31) and this time we solve (30) for x_1:

$$x_1 = 1 - \tfrac{1}{2}x_3 - \tfrac{1}{2}x_2 \tag{34}$$

thus placing x_3 on the right with the nonbasic (zero) variables and x_1 on the left with the basic (nonzero) variables. Replacing x_1 in (31) by (34), we obtain

$$x_4 = 3 - (1 - \tfrac{1}{2}x_3 - \tfrac{1}{2}x_2) - 3x_2$$

or

$$x_4 = 2 + \tfrac{1}{2}x_3 - \tfrac{5}{2}x_2 \tag{35}$$

Equations (34) and (35) now do represent a new extreme point. The variables on the right are zero, and equations (34) and (35) do correspond to the extreme point A where

$$x_1 = 1, \qquad x_2 = 0$$
$$x_3 = 0, \qquad x_4 = 2$$

It should now be clear why we express extreme points as we do: with the basic (nonzero) variables on the left and the nonbasic (zero) variables on the right. If we did not have all this information available, then for each extreme point we would have to go back to the original equations, (24) and (25), and solve them again using Gauss's method. Instead, we get a new extreme point much more easily by solving one equation (in extreme point form) for one variable and substituting the result in all the other equations (in extreme point form). The reader should note that this amounts to eliminating one variable from all the original equations. This is just one step in Gauss's method, and it is a lot less work than the entire algorithm for Gauss's method. Thus, it is to our advantage to keep the information about extreme points the way we do for it means less work for us.

The objective is $x_1 + x_2$ and x_1 is given by equation (34); therefore,

$$x_1 + x_2 = 1 - \tfrac{1}{2}x_3 + \tfrac{1}{2}x_2$$

The variables x_2 and x_3 are zero, and the objective's value is 1. We have increased the objective from 0 to 1.

We can let x_2 and x_3 become positive if we wish. Making x_3 positive will decrease the objective because x_3 is multiplied by $-\frac{1}{2}$. However, x_2 is multiplied by $+\frac{1}{2}$, so by making x_2 positive we can increase the objective. Thus, we choose to let x_2 become a basic variable.

We try to make x_4 zero (the only other choice is x_1, which we just made nonzero). We solve (35), the equation with x_4 on the left, for x_2:

$$x_2 = \tfrac{4}{5} + \tfrac{1}{5}x_3 - \tfrac{2}{5}x_4 \tag{36}$$

thus placing x_4 on the right, where nonbasic variables appear, and x_2 on the left, where basic variables appear. Using this value for x_2 in (34), we get

$$x_1 = \tfrac{3}{5} - \tfrac{3}{5}x_3 + \tfrac{1}{5}x_4 \tag{37}$$

Equations (36) and (37) represent a third extreme point.

Question. Which extreme point in Figure 6 is represented by equations (36) and (37)?

Now from (36) and (37) the objective is

$$x_1 + x_2 = \tfrac{7}{5} - \tfrac{2}{5}x_3 - \tfrac{1}{5}x_4$$

With $x_3 = x_4 = 0$ we have, from (36) and (37), $x_1 = \frac{3}{5}$ and $x_2 = \frac{4}{5}$. The objective is $\frac{7}{5}$, an increase above its previous value of 1. Can we do better?

The two variables which are zero, x_3 and x_4, are both multiplied by negative numbers in the objective above. Increasing either of them would only decrease the objective. Thus we can no longer increase the objective, and we have arrived at its maximum value. The solution given by (36) and (37) corresponds to the point B in Figure 6.

Question.   Why can't we decrease x_3 or x_4?

We now describe, through the crude flow chart shown in Figure 7, the algorithm we have just used. There are a few difficulties with this flow chart. Notice that the only way out of the loop composed of boxes 7, 8, and 9 is to have all the constants on the right sides of the equations become positive. How can we know that this will ever happen since in box 9 we pick a different equation with no guiding rule?

There is another difficulty too: the process described in boxes 9 and 7 is not a particularly precise one. We certainly would have trouble writing a FORTRAN program to accomplish this process.

It would be helpful if we had to perform boxes 6 and 7 only once and never had to use box 9. That is, we would like a rule which would guarantee us that the answer to the question in box 8 would always be "yes" the first time it is asked. As it happens, we can do precisely that when a bounded solution exists. On the other hand, if the solution is unbounded, our new rule also will tell us this fact.

2.6   The Simplex Method

We proceed to this refinement of our algorithm now. Consider a more general linear programming problem, but one which still has two variables and four inequalities:

$$\text{Maximize} \quad c_1 x_1 + c_2 x_2 \qquad (38)$$

where

$$a_{11} x_1 + a_{12} x_2 \leq b_1 \qquad (39)$$

$$a_{21} x_1 + a_{22} x_2 \leq b_2 \qquad (40)$$

$$x_1 \geq 0 \qquad (41)$$

$$x_2 \geq 0 \qquad (42)$$

The numbers c_1, c_2, a_{11}, a_{12}, a_{21}, a_{22}, b_1, and b_2 are given to us, and we are to find x_1 and x_2. Again we introduce slack variables and consider the equivalent problem.

$$\text{Maximize} \quad c_1 x_1 + c_2 x_2 \qquad (38)$$

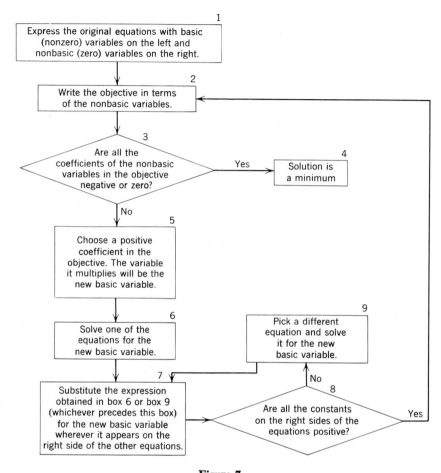

Figure 7

Rough flow chart for solving a linear programming problem

where

$$a_{11}x_1 + a_{12}x_2 + x_3 \qquad = b_1 \tag{43}$$

$$a_{21}x_1 + a_{22}x_2 \qquad + x_4 = b_2 \tag{44}$$

$$x_1 \geq 0 \tag{45}$$

$$x_2 \geq 0 \tag{46}$$

$$x_3 \geq 0 \tag{47}$$

$$x_4 \geq 0 \tag{48}$$

We look for values of the variables where two of the variables are not zero. If the nonzero variables are also non-negative, we call such a set of values for x_1, x_2, x_3, and x_4 a **basic feasible solution.**[10] This solution corresponds to an extreme point of the constraint set defined by the inequalities (39)–(42). The reader who is unsure of the last statement should reread the beginning of Section 2.5.

Now recall that in our numerical example we obtained a basic feasible solution easily by letting $x_1 = 0$ and $x_2 = 0$ and then letting $x_3 = 2$ and $x_4 = 3$. This worked well because the right-hand sides of the inequalities (20) and (21) were positive. From now on, *we shall assume that $b_1 > 0$ and $b_2 > 0$*. This assumption always allows us to find one basic feasible solution easily. It also assures us that the original system of inequalities, (39) through (42), are consistent.

As our first basic feasible solution, then, we take $x_1 = 0$, $x_2 = 0$, $x_3 = b_1$, and $x_4 = b_2$. We rewrite the equations so that the basic (non-zero) variables are on the left and the nonbasic (zero) variables are on the right, as follows:

$$x_3 = b_1 - a_{11}x_1 - a_{12}x_2 \tag{49}$$

$$x_4 = b_2 - a_{21}x_1 - a_{22}x_2 \tag{50}$$

Now we must consider different cases that can arise depending on the numbers c_1 and c_2 appearing in the objective (38). If both $c_1 \leq 0$ *and* $c_2 \leq 0$, then the objective $c_1x_1 + c_2x_2$ can be made larger only by decreasing either x_1 or x_2. Since x_1 and x_2 are zero, we cannot decrease either of them without violating (45) or (46). The solution we have in this case is the maximum one.

Suppose, however, that $c_1 > 0$. Then, by increasing x_1 from zero to some positive value, we can increase the objective. To obtain another basic feasible solution, however, either x_3 or x_4 will have to become zero while the other remains non-negative. We make x_1 positive so that it becomes a basic variable. We try to keep x_4 basic also. This means that x_2 will remain equal to zero, and x_3 will be reduced to zero. That is, we seek a basic feasible solution where x_1 and x_4 are the basic variables.

---

[10] Here the word "solution" does not refer to a solution of the entire linear programming problem but only to a solution of the linear system (43) through (48).

To do this we "solve" equations (49) and (50) so that x_1 and x_4 appear on the left. If, when we have done so, the constants on the right are non-negative, then we will have accomplished our goal. We proceed now to find the conditions which b_1, b_2, a_{11}, a_{12}, a_{21}, and a_{22} must satisfy if these constants are to be non-negative.

Keeping x_2 zero, let us try to make x_3 zero. We solve equation (49) (with x_3 on the left) for x_1 (assuming $a_{11} \neq 0$) in order to place x_3 on the right where zero variables appear:

$$x_1 = \frac{b_1}{a_{11}} - \frac{1}{a_{11}} x_3 - \frac{a_{12}}{a_{11}} x_2 \tag{51}$$

Substituting this into (50) for x_1, we get

$$x_4 = \left(b_2 - b_1 \frac{a_{21}}{a_{11}} \right) - \left(-\frac{a_{21}}{a_{11}} \right) x_3 - \left(a_{22} - a_{12} \frac{a_{21}}{a_{11}} \right) x_2 \tag{52}$$

Since this is supposed to be a basic feasible solution (corresponding to an extreme point), the variables on the right of (51) and (52) must be zero, producing

$$x_1 = \frac{b_1}{a_{11}} \tag{53}$$

$$x_4 = b_2 - b_1 \frac{a_{21}}{a_{11}} \tag{54}$$

Both of these must be greater than or equal to zero.

We examine (53) first. Since $b_1 > 0$, the only way that x_1 can be non-negative is for a_{11} to be positive; that is,

$$a_{11} > 0 \tag{55}$$

If this is true, then $x_1 > 0$. If not, then x_1 is not non-negative and (51) and (52) do not represent a basic feasible solution (extreme point). In this case we made the wrong choice in letting x_3 become nonbasic (zero). We should have chosen x_4 to be the new nonbasic variable.

This is summarized in the block labeled 1 in Figure 8, where we ask "Is $a_{11} > 0$?" If the answer is "no," we go to box 4 where we try another possible solution which will have x_1 and x_3 as basic variables. If, on the other hand, the answer is "yes," we go on to check (54) to see if x_4 is non-negative. We do that now.

Recall that $b_2 > 0$. We have assumed for the moment that $b_1/a_{11} > 0$. Therefore, if

$$a_{21} \leq 0 \tag{56}$$

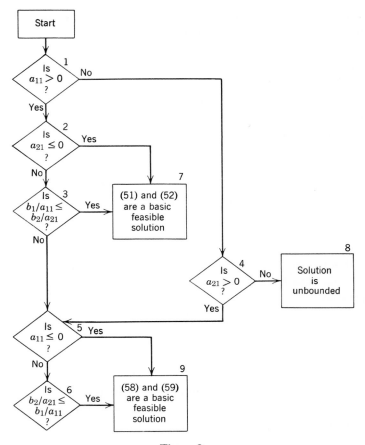

Figure 8

Flow chart for finding which solution is a basic feasible one

then from (54) it follows that $x_4 > 0$. Again in Figure 8, block 2 asks the appropriate question. If blocks 1 and 2 *both* result in "yes" answers, then (53) and (54) indicate that x_1 and x_4 are non-negative and hence (51) and (52) represent a basic feasible solution (extreme point). Figure 8 indicates that we go to block 7, where this fact is noted.

On the other hand, suppose (56) is not true. Then, if x_4 is to be non-negative, (54) tells us that

$$b_2 - b_1 \frac{a_{21}}{a_{11}} \geq 0$$

or

$$\frac{b_1}{a_{11}} a_{21} \leq b_2$$

Since (56) is not true (we left block 2 with a "no"), $a_{21} > 0$ and we can multiply both sides of this last inequality by $1/a_{21}$ without changing the direction of the inequality. The inequality becomes then

$$\frac{b_1}{a_{11}} \leq \frac{b_2}{a_{21}} \tag{57}$$

This means that, if the answer to the question in box 2 of Figure 8 is "no," then, if x_4 is to be non-negative, we must require that (57) be true. The appropriate question is asked in box 3 of Figure 8.

If (57) is not true, then the answer to the question in box 3 is "no," and we must seek a different solution (one where x_1 and x_3 are basic variables).

Summarizing: If x_3 is to become nonbasic and x_1 is to become basic in its place, then *first*

$$a_{11} > 0 \tag{55}$$

and *second* either

$$a_{21} \leq 0 \tag{56}$$

or

$$\frac{b_1}{a_{11}} \leq \frac{b_2}{a_{21}} \tag{57}$$

These requirements are also summarized in boxes 1, 2, and 3 of Figure 8. If (55) is not true, we get a "no" reply from box 1 and go to box 4. Even if we get a "yes" from box 1, either (56) or (57) must be true. If both are not true, we get "no" replies in both boxes 2 and 3, and we go on to box 5.

Once we reach either box 4 or box 5, we know that (51) and (52) do not represent a basic feasible solution; that is, either x_1 or x_4 is negative. We have already decided that x_1 is to become basic (nonzero), and, now that we have reached either box 4 or box 5, we know that x_1 and x_4 cannot be basic together. Our only choice is to try to keep x_3 basic (nonzero) rather than x_4. To do this we solve (50) for x_1 [before we solved (49) for x_1]:

$$x_1 = \frac{b_2}{a_{21}} - \frac{1}{a_{21}} x_4 - \frac{a_{22}}{a_{21}} x_2 \tag{58}$$

Using this in (49), we have

$$x_3 = \left(b_1 - b_2 \frac{a_{11}}{a_{21}}\right) - \left(-\frac{a_{11}}{a_{21}}\right)x_4 - \left(a_{12} - a_{22}\frac{a_{11}}{a_{21}}\right)x_2 \quad (59)$$

If (58) and (59) are to offer a basic feasible solution, the constants on the right-hand sides of both of these equations must be non-negative. We reason as before, and x_1 will be non-negative if and only if $a_{21} > 0$. Therefore in box 4 we ask the question "Is $a_{21} > 0$?" For the moment we postpone the case when the answer is "no." If we left box 3 with a "no," we need not ask the question in box 4 because the only way we could have arrived at box 3 was by leaving box 2 with a "no." This means that the answer to "Is $a_{21} > 0$?" must be "yes," and hence $x_1 > 0$. Therefore, if we leave box 3 with a "no," we can skip box 4 and go directly to box 5.

We turn next to the question "Is $x_3 \geq 0$?" Again, since $a_{21} > 0$ and both $b_1 > 0$ and $b_2 > 0$, if $a_{11} \leq 0$ then $x_3 > 0$. We ask the appropriate question in box 5 of Figure 8. A "yes" leads us to box 9, where we note a basic feasible solution is indeed given by (58) and (59).

However, if $a_{11} > 0$, then for x_3 to be non-negative requires that

$$\frac{b_2}{a_{21}} \leq \frac{b_1}{a_{11}}$$

In box 6 we ask if this is true. Notice, however, that the only way we could leave box 5 with a "no" would be to have left box 1 with a "yes." Leaving box 1 with a "yes" means that to get to box 5 we must have passed through boxes 1, 2, and 3, in that order. Moreover, we must have left box 3 with a "no." Therefore, the answer to the question in box 6 must be "yes."

Summarizing: If x_4 is to become nonbasic and x_1 is to become basic in its place, then *first*

$$a_{21} > 0 \quad (60)$$

and *second* either

$$a_{11} \leq 0 \quad (61)$$

or

$$\frac{b_2}{a_{21}} \leq \frac{b_1}{a_{11}} \quad (62)$$

Notice that (62) is (57) with the inequality sign reversed.

We have one more case to examine, the one which results if we leave box 4 with a "no." Suppose both $a_{11} \leq 0$ and $a_{21} \leq 0$. Then we leave box 1 with a "no"; this tells us that x_4 cannot be basic with x_1. We also leave box 4 with a "no"; and this tells us x_3 cannot be basic with x_1 either. What does this mean? Are there no other basic feasible solutions? To answer these questions we look back at two of the original inequalities, (39) and (40). If $a_{11} \leq 0$ and $a_{21} \leq 0$, then the coefficients of x_1 in both inequalities are less than or equal to zero. Thus, the larger we make x_1, the smaller the left-hand sides of (39) and (40) become. We can make x_1 as large as we wish, and we never violate either inequality. Since $c_1 > 0$ by assumption — see argument following equations (49) and (50) — making x_1 indefinitely large will make the objective, $c_1 x_1 + c_2 x_2$, indefinitely large. The solution, therefore, is *unbounded*, as noted in box 8 of Figure 8.

We now simplify the flow chart in Figure 8. We should have an intuitive feeling that it is possible to do so because of these facts: (a) box 6 always results in a "yes"; (b) boxes 1 and 5 ask the same question in slightly altered form; (c) boxes 2 and 4 ask the same question in slightly altered form. The simplified flow chart is shown in Figure 9. There are four distinct and different possibilities: (A) a_{11} and a_{21} are both nonpositive; or (B) a_{11} is nonpositive but a_{21} is positive; or (C) a_{11} is positive but $a_{21} \leq 0$; or (D) both $a_{11} > 0$ and $a_{21} > 0$. We consider them in that order.

(A) If both a_{11} and a_{21} are nonpositive, then the solution is unbounded. We leave boxes 10 and 11 in Figure 9 with "no" and go to box 16.

(B) If $a_{11} \leq 0$ and $a_{21} > 0$, then in Figure 8 we would have gone from box 1 to box 4 to box 5. However, the answer to box 5 must be "yes," because the answer to box 1 was "no." This then would lead to box 9. Therefore, if in Figure 9 we leave box 10 with a "no," then we go to box 11. We leave box 11 with a "yes" and are led to box 15, where we find that x_1 and x_3 are the new basic variables.

(C) Now, if $a_{11} > 0$ and $a_{21} \leq 0$, then in Figure 8 we go from box 1 to box 2 to box 7. In our simplified chart in Figure 9 we go from box 10 to box 12 to box 14, obtaining the same result.

(D) Finally, we consider the case where $a_{11} > 0$ and $a_{21} > 0$. In Figure 8 we went from box 1 to box 2 to box 3. If we left box 3 with a "yes," we went to box 7. If, however, we left box 3 with a "no," we

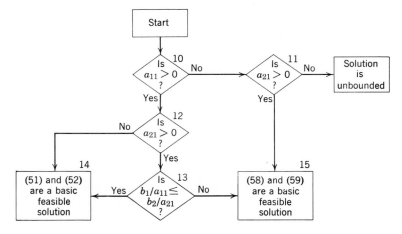

Figure 9

Refined flow chart for finding basic feasible solution

went to box 5 (where we would have had a "no" because $a_{11} > 0$) and then went to box 6. Since we left box 3 with a "no," we must leave box 6 with a "yes" as we noted previously. The critical question then is:

$$\text{Is } \frac{b_1}{a_{11}} \leq \frac{b_2}{a_{21}} \text{ ?}$$

If the answer is "yes," we go to box 7 in Figure 8, and, if the answer is "no," we must end up at box 9. Therefore in Figure 9, if both $a_{11} > 0$ and $a_{21} > 0$, we go from box 10 to box 12 to box 13, where we ask the critical question referred to above. If the answer is "yes," we go to box 14. If the answer is "no," we go to box 15.

We have exhausted all the possibilities.

We now summarize the results which we have derived. Once we have decided upon the variable to change from a zero value to a nonzero value, we examine the coefficients[11] of that variable on the right side of equations (49) and (50). Three possibilities exist:

---

[11] The coefficients referred to are assumed to be multiplied by a minus sign as indicated in equations (49) and (50). For example, the coefficient of x_3 in

$$x_4 = 2 + 1/2x_3 - 5/2x_2$$

is negative. The coefficient of x_2 is positive.

(i) The coefficients are both less than or equal to zero. In this case the maximum is unbounded.

(ii) Only one coefficient is greater than zero. In this case the equation with that positive coefficient is solved for the new nonzero variable.

(iii) Both coefficients are greater than zero. In this case the constants in each equation are divided by the value of the coefficient in the same equation. The equation for which this ratio is the smaller is solved for the new basic variable.

We have not yet discussed whether either of these basic feasible solutions, (51) and (52) or (58) and (59), produces a larger value of the objective. Recall that the original basic feasible solution given by (49) and (50) produced an objective of zero. Since $c_1 > 0$ — we made this assumption immediately following equations (49) and (50) — we deduced that we could increase the objective to some positive value by letting x_1 become basic. We verify this deduction now. Consider first the basic feasible solution given by (51) and (52). The objective is

$$c_1 x_1 + c_2 x_2 = c_1 \left(\frac{b_1}{a_{11}} - \frac{1}{a_{11}} x_3 - \frac{a_{12}}{a_{11}} x_2 \right) + c_2 x_2$$

$$= \frac{b_1}{a_{11}} c_1 - \frac{c_1}{a_{11}} x_3 + \left(c_2 - \frac{a_{12}}{a_{11}} c_1 \right) x_2$$

Since x_2 and x_3 are nonbasic variables they are zero, and the objective is $b_1 c_1 / a_{11}$. The only way we could have arrived at this basic feasible solution (box 14 in Figure 9) was by leaving box 10 in Figure 9 with a "yes." Therefore, $a_{11} > 0$. Since we have assumed $b_1 > 0$ and $c_1 > 0$, it follows that the objective is positive and has increased from zero.

Next we consider the basic feasible solution given by (58) and (59). The objective in this case is

$$c_1 x_1 + c_2 x_2 = c_1 \left(\frac{b_2}{a_{21}} - \frac{1}{a_{21}} x_4 - \frac{a_{22}}{a_{21}} x_2 \right) + c_2 x_2$$

$$= \frac{b_2}{a_{21}} c_1 - \frac{c_1}{a_{21}} x_4 + \left(c_2 - \frac{a_{22}}{a_{21}} c_1 \right) x_2$$

Because x_2 and x_4 are now nonbasic (zero), the value of the objective is $b_2 c_1 / a_{21}$. There are two paths in the chart in Figure 9 which could lead to this solution. One is box 10, box 11, and box 15. The other is box 10, box 12, box 13, and box 15. Along both paths we pass through a box which asks "Is $a_{21} > 0$?" In both cases the answer to that question must be "yes." Therefore, $a_{21} > 0$ and, since again by assumption $b_2 > 0$ and $c_1 > 0$, it follows that the objective is also positive. Thus, the objective has increased from zero to some positive value.

Our procedure, therefore, leads us to a basic feasible solution of the form

$$x_1 = b_1' - a_{11}'x_k - a_{12}'x_2$$

$$x_p = b_2' - a_{21}'x_k - a_{22}'x_2$$

where k and p are either 3 or 4 but are not the same. The numbers b_1', b_2', a_{11}', a_{12}', a_{21}', a_{22}', have been calculated from the numbers b_1, b_2, a_{11}, a_{12}, a_{21}, a_{22}. The objective is

$$c_1x_1 + c_2x_2 = z + c_p'x_p + c_2'x_2$$

where z is the numerical value of the objective at the new basic feasible solution. As we have shown above, z is greater than zero.

If $c_2' \leq 0$, then the solution is the maximum one. The reader should assure himself that $c_p' \leq 0$. If, however, $c_2' > 0$, then we can increase the objective by making x_2 positive. We decide whether x_1 or x_p is to become zero or not in the same way we decided that x_k was to become zero before. In fact, the equations for x_1 and x_p are very similar to the basic feasible solution, (49) and (50), and we can proceed by replacing the b_1, b_2, a_{11}, a_{12}, a_{21}, a_{22} by b_1', b_2', a_{11}', a_{12}', a_{21}', a_{22}'.

We are now ready to write our algorithm for selecting the new nonbasic variable in a form which can be inserted in Figure 7. We have already described the algorithm in Figures 8 and 9, but we rewrite it once more in terms consistent with Figure 7. We do that in Figure 10, which follows box 5 in the flow chart in Figure 7 and replaces boxes 6 through 9.

The flow chart of boxes 1 through 5 in Figure 7 and boxes 10 through 14 in Figure 10 is now a complete description of an algorithm for the solution of a linear programming problem of the form given by (38)–(42).

The algorithm we have described was discovered in the 1940's by George B. Dantzig[12] and is called the *simplex method*. Just as with

[12] **George B. Dantzig,** 1914 —, the son of a famous mathematician, Tobias Dantzig, has become equally famous in his own right. George Dantzig was a statistician for the U. S. Air Force during World War II when he discovered the simplex method. This method is still the most widely used mathematical technique in the new field of operations research. Although from a theoretical point of view it may require an exorbitant amount of calculation to find a solution, in practical cases it has proved to be extremely efficient. George Dantzig joined the RAND

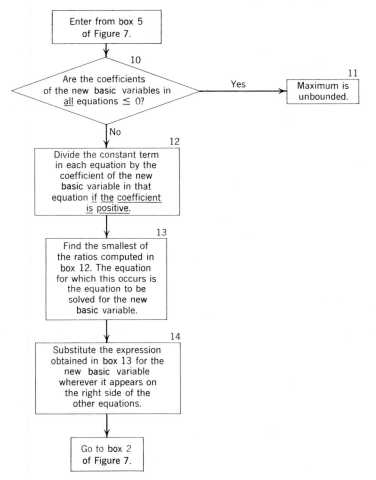

Figure 10

Flow chart for finding the equation to be solved for the nonzero variable

Gauss's method we need to systematize it more before we can use it to write a FORTRAN program.

In the next section we present a much more detailed description of the algorithm.

Corporation in 1952 and is now on the faculty of Stanford University; he continues to carry out research in linear programming and other related fields of mathematics. He is the author of the already classical textbook, *Linear Programming and Extensions,* Princeton University Press.

2.7   Flow Chart for the Simplex Method

We consider a slightly more general problem and construct a detailed flow chart for its solution. We wish to maximize

$$c_1 x_1 + c_2 x_2 \tag{63}$$

where x_1 and x_2 satisfy

$$a_{11} x_1 + a_{12} x_2 \leq b_1$$
$$a_{21} x_1 + a_{22} x_2 \leq b_2$$
$$a_{31} x_1 + a_{32} x_2 \leq b_3 \tag{64}$$
$$a_{41} x_1 + a_{42} x_2 \leq b_4$$

$$x_1 \geq 0$$
$$x_2 \leq 0 \tag{65}$$

We have made a change: we have allowed for six inequalities instead of four. We assume again that $b_1 > 0$, $b_2 > 0$, $b_3 > 0$, $b_4 > 0$.

Once more we introduce slack variables; this time there are four, x_3, x_4, x_5, x_6, making four of the inequalities into the equalities

$$a_{11} x_1 + a_{12} x_2 + x_3 \qquad\qquad = b_1$$
$$a_{21} x_1 + a_{22} x_2 \qquad + x_4 \qquad\qquad = b_2$$
$$a_{31} x_1 + a_{32} x_2 \qquad\qquad + x_5 \qquad = b_3$$
$$a_{41} x_1 + a_{42} x_2 \qquad\qquad\qquad + x_6 = b_4$$

and where

$$x_1 \geq 0, \qquad x_2 \geq 0$$
$$x_3 \geq 0, \qquad x_4 \geq 0$$
$$x_5 \geq 0, \qquad x_6 \geq 0$$

We take the initial basic feasible solution to be $x_1 = x_2 = 0$ and

$$x_3 = b_1 - a_{11} x_1 - a_{12} x_2$$
$$x_4 = b_2 - a_{21} x_1 - a_{22} x_2$$
$$x_5 = b_3 - a_{31} x_1 - a_{32} x_2$$
$$x_6 = b_4 - a_{41} x_1 - a_{42} x_2$$

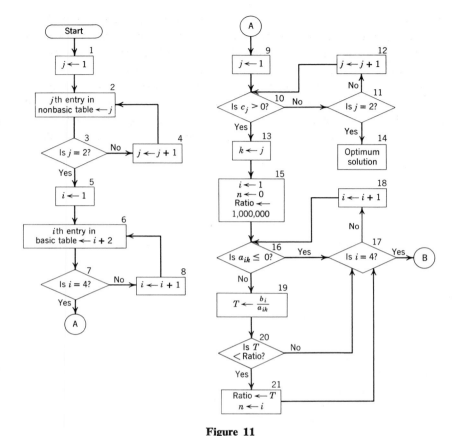

Figure 11

Part 1 of flow chart for simplex method

Notice that now, at most, four variables are positive in a basic feasible solution. In this case *precisely* four are positive. These four variables are again called basic variables. The objective function is, of course,

$$c_1 x_1 + c_2 x_2$$

The flow chart for proceeding from this basic feasible solution to the maximum solution is shown in Figures 11 through 14. We need to analyze the flow chart carefully. First we point out that we have introduced a new type of box in our flow chart. It is called a **connector,** and it is a small circle enclosing a letter. An arrow leading to a connector tells us to find another connector with the same symbol and with an arrow leading from it. We then proceed as before. The purpose of connectors is to simplify drawing the lines in flow charts so that confusion does not arise from lines which cross each other.

Because, at a later stage, we will not know just what the names of the basic variables are, we establish two tables telling us the names of the basic and nonbasic variables. Initially, x_1 and x_2 are nonbasic and x_3, x_4, x_5, and x_6 are basic. Blocks 1 through 4 put 1, 2 in the table of

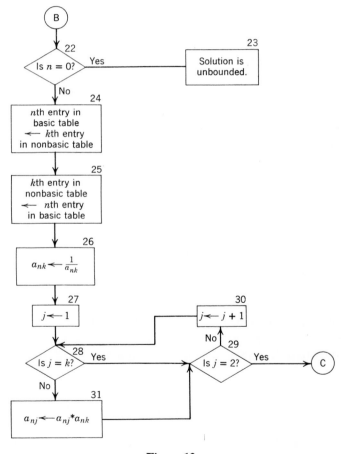

Figure 12

Part 2 of flow chart for simplex method

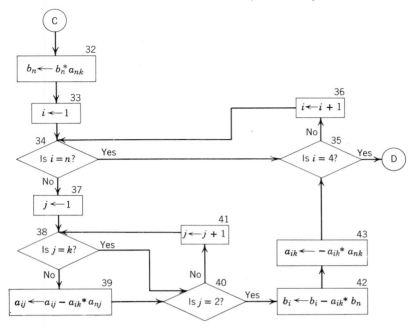

Figure 13

Part 3 of flow chart for simplex method

variables which are nonbasic; blocks 5 to 8 put the numbers 3, 4, 5, 6 in the table of basic variables.

Blocks 9 to 12 check to see if all the coefficients in the objective are less than or equal to zero.[13] If they are, we go to block 14. If not, we find the first positive one and call it k, so that the kth entry in the nonbasic table will be placed in the basic table. (Look ahead to block 24 in Figure 12.)

The next step is to see if all the a_{ij} coefficients in the column with $c_j > 0$ are negative. If they are, then the solution is unbounded. Blocks 15, 16, 17, 18 of Figure 11 and blocks 22, 23 of Figure 12 do that.[14] If any positive coefficients are found, the b_i in that row is divided by the positive a_{ij}. The smallest of all these ratios is called RATIO, and the row which produces the smallest ratio is labeled n (blocks 16 through 21

---

[13] This corresponds to block 3 of Figure 7.
[14] See blocks 10 and 11 of Figure 10.

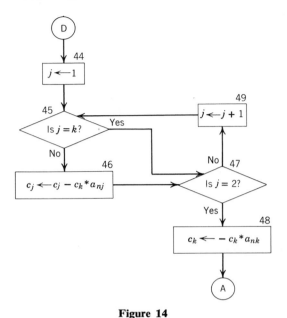

Figure 14

Part 4 of flow chart for simplex method

in Figure 11).[15] Notice that, the first time we get to block 20, the value of T will be less than RATIO, since RATIO is initially chosen to be very large (1,000,000 here — usually the largest number the computer can accept). Thus, the answer to the question is "yes" at least once, and n will be different from zero. Therefore, the test in block 22 will result in a "yes" only if we have never gone through blocks 19, 20, and 21. That is, $n = 0$ if and only if the answer to the question in block 16 is always "yes."

Blocks 24 and 25 in Figure 12 exchange the entries in our two tables telling us the names of the basic and nonbasic variables.

Blocks 26 through 32 calculate the new nth equation.[16] Notice that block 31 should be

$$a_{nj} \leftarrow \frac{a_{nj}}{a_{nk}}$$

in terms of the original a_{ij}; see equation (51) or (58). However, in block

---

[15] See block 13 of Figure 10.
[16] See last part of box 13 in Figure 10.

26, the value assigned to a_{nk} has been changed. Therefore, block 31 reads the way it does in terms of the "new" value of a_{nk}.

The next step (blocks 33 through 43 of Figure 13)[17] computes the new equations starting with the first and skipping the nth (which was just computed). The question in block 34 is used to skip the nth equation. The actual computations are done in blocks 39, 42, and 43. Recall that the numbers a_{nj} and b_n used in those blocks were previously changed in blocks 31 and 32. The reader should refer to equations (52) and (59) to verify the calculations.

Finally, in blocks 44 through 49 of Figure 14 the new coefficients of the nonbasic variables in the objective are computed. We then return to block 9 to check the signs of these coefficients.

The flow chart may seem rather complicated, but it should be remembered that it handles any problem given in the form of (63), (64), and (65) including problems with unbounded solutions.[18] In addition, the changes necessary to handle more inequalities and more variables are small indeed. We catalog them here for reference. If there are M inequalities and L variables, then:

1. The 2's in blocks 3, 11, 29, 40, and 47 are changed to L.
2. The 4's in blocks 7, 17, and 35 are changed to M.
3. The $i + 2$ in block 6 is changed to $i + L$.

No other changes are required.

2.8 A FORTRAN Program To Solve a Linear Programming Problem

As we promised at the beginning of Section 2.3, we now write a computer program to solve a linear programming problem. We use FORTRAN and follow the flow charts of the previous section very closely. No new FORTRAN concepts are involved, although a few steps require some explanation. The reader will be asked to supply some of the program from what he has learned about FORTRAN in Chapter 1.

We return to our nut mix problem in order to have a specific problem in mind. The mathematical model of that problem as we derived it in Section 2.2 is given by (4) through (10), which we reproduce here.

$$\text{Maximize} \quad 100x_1 + 32x_2 \tag{4}$$

---

[17] See block 7 in Figure 7.
[18] Of course, the right-hand sides in (64) must be positive for our flow charts to work.

where

$$6x_1 \leq 1200 \tag{5}$$

$$8x_2 \leq 2400 \tag{6}$$

$$4x_1 + 6x_2 \leq 2000 \tag{7}$$

$$6x_1 + 2x_2 \leq 1400 \tag{8}$$

$$x_1 \geq 0 \tag{9}$$

$$x_2 \geq 0 \tag{10}$$

This is a problem in two unknowns and with six inequalities for which the flow chart in the previous section was written. A FORTRAN program for the flow chart blocks from 1 through 25 follows:

```
      DIMENSION A(4, 2), B(4), ITAB(4), JTAB(2), C(2)
      A(1, 1) =     6.0
      A(1, 2) =     0.0
      A(2, 1) =     0.0
      A(2, 2) =     8.0
      A(3, 1) =     4.0
      A(3, 2) =     6.0
      A(4, 1) =     6.0
      A(4, 2) =     2.0
      B(1)    = 1200.0
      B(2)    = 2400.0
      B(3)    = 2000.0
      B(4)    = 1400.0
      C(1)    =  100.0
      C(2)    =   32.0
   1  J = 1
   2  JTAB(J) = J
*  3  IF(J − 2) 4, 5, 100
```

```
      4   J = J + 1
          GO TO 2
      5   I = 1
*     6   ITAB(I) = I + 2
**    7   IF(I − 4) 8, 9, 100
      8   I = I + 1
          GO TO 6
      9   J = 1
     10   IF(C(J)) 11, 11, 13
*    11   IF(J − 2) 12, 14, 100.
     12   J = J + 1
          GO TO 10
     13   K = J
     15   I = 1
          N = 0
          RATIO = 1 000 000.
     16   IF(A(I, K)) 17, 17, 19
**   17   IF(I − 4) 18, 22, 100
     18   I = I + 1
          GO TO 16
     19   T = B(I) / A(I, K)
     20   IF (T − RATIO) 21, 17, 17
     21   RATIO = T
          N = I
          GO TO 17
     22   IF (N) 100, 23, 24
```

24   ISAV = ITAB(N)

ITAB(N) = JTAB(K)

25   JTAB(K) = ISAV

GO TO 26

The numbers at the left correspond to the box numbers in the flow chart. Following the DIMENSION statement, the data a_{ij}, b_i, and c_j are given. Again we go to 100 if an error occurs and stop (see e.g., lines numbered 3, 7, . . .). If we find the optimal solution, we go to 14 and print the results (see line 11). If the solution is unbounded (see line 22), we go to 23 where the word "unbounded" will be printed.

There are two items which need to be explained: the dimension statement and the three lines from 24 to 25. Before explaining them, however, we discuss a portion of the FORTRAN notation in more detail.

In Chapter 1 we said that variables in FORTRAN are integers if they are named I, J, K, L, M or N (see Section 1.10). Otherwise, FORTRAN variables are floating-point. Because this allows us only six possible different integer variables and we need more than six integer variables in our program, we expand our notation now. We allow a variable to have more than one letter in its name. In fact, we allow it to have as many as *five* letters in its name. If the *first* letter in the name is I, J, K, L, M, or N, the variable is an integer. If the first letter is any other letter, the variable is a floating-point variable.

Question.   Which of the following variables are floating-point variables and which are integer variables:

AND   NOT

ILL   THEN

SICK   XTRA

Let us look now at the dimension statement and lines 2 and 6 where we have used ITAB and JTAB. These are the names we have given to our tables of the basic and nonbasic variables.

ITAB = table of basic variables

JTAB = table of nonbasic variables

That is, ITAB is a list of integers which are the subscripts of the basic variables. If x_3, x_4, x_5, and x_6 are basic variables, then ITAB contains the integers 3, 4, 5, and 6. The last three letters, "TAB," help us to remember that these are tables. The first letters, "I" and "J," tell us that the entries in the tables are integers. ITAB(K) is the Kth entry in table ITAB.

Next we look at the three lines from 24 to 25. They are used to alter the tables so that they contain the subscripts of the correct variables. Suppose that, instead of these three lines, we wrote the simpler instructions

24 ITAB(N) = JTAB(K)

25 JTAB(K) = ITAB(N)

After we perform these two steps, the Kth entry of the table JTAB is unchanged; and this is certainly not what we intended. For example, at the start the four entries in ITAB are 3, 4, 5, 6 (indicating that x_3, x_4, x_5, and x_6 are basic). The two entries in JTAB are 1 and 2. Suppose x_1 is to become basic, and x_5 is to become nonbasic. Then ITAB(N) = 5 so N = 3,[19] and JTAB(K) = 1 so K = 1. Now line 24 will change ITAB to read 3, 4, 1, 6, which is correct. However, line 25 tells us to take the 3rd entry in ITAB, which is now 1, and place it in the 1st entry in JTAB. So JTAB reads 1, 2, which is not correct.

Question.   What should JTAB read?

Let us look at the correct **FORTRAN** code, which reads

24 ISAV = ITAB(N)

ITAB(N) = JTAB(K)

25 JTAB(K) = ISAV

In our example, the first line takes the 3rd entry in ITAB and calls it ISAV. Thus ISAV = 5. The next line takes the 1st entry in JTAB(I) and places it in the 3rd entry of ITAB, so ITAB reads 3, 4, 1, 6. The third line places ISAV in the 1st entry of JTAB, so JTAB reads 5, 2. These two tables tell us that x_3, x_4, x_1, and x_6 are nonbasic and x_5 and x_2 are basic, which is precisely what we wish.

The remainder of the program is straightforward and contains nothing new. Therefore, the reader is asked to provide the program to perform the operations described in boxes 26 through 31 in the flow chart. There

---

[19] The 3rd entry in ITAB is 5.

is no one correct program. The most straightforward one will require eight lines of FORTRAN. Six of them will be numbered with the numbers 26 through 31 in the flow chart. There will be unnumbered lines following lines 30 and 31.

The reader actually should be able to write all the remaining FOR-TRAN program except perhaps the PRINT statements. However, for convenience the remainder of the program is produced here.

<pre>
       32   B(N) = B(N) * A(N, K)

       33   I = 1

       34   IF(I − N) 37, 35, 37

  **   35   IF(I − 4) 36, 44, 100

       36   I = I + 1

            GO TO 34

       37   J = 1

       38   IF(J − K) 39, 40, 39

       39   A(I, J) = A(I, J) − A(I, K) * A(N, J)

   *   40   IF(J − 2) 41, 42, 100

       41   J = J + 1

            GO TO 38

       42   B(I) = B(I) − A(I, K) * B(N)

       43   A(I, K) = −A(I, K) * A(N, K)

            GO TO 35

       44   J = 1

       45   IF(J − K) 46, 47, 46

       46   C(J) = C(J) − C(K) * A(N, J)

   *   47   IF(J − 2) 49, 48, 100

       48   C(K) = −C(K) * A(N, K)

            GO TO 9
</pre>

```
X(1) =   200.0000
X(4) = 1599.9999
X(5) =   600.0000
X(2) =   100.0000
```

Figure 15

49 J = J + 1

GO TO 45

100 STOP

14 PRINT 200, ITAB (1), B(1)

PRINT 200, ITAB (2), B(2)

PRINT 200, ITAB (3), B(3)

PRINT 200, ITAB (4), B(4)

STOP

23 PRINT 201

STOP

200 FORMAT (3H① X(, 11, 3H)① = , F10.4)

201 FORMAT (10H① UNBOUNDED)

END

The symbol ⓧ means: leave ⓧ blank spaces on the card. Thus, ① means leave one blank.

If we wish to change the number of variables, only the lines marked * need to be changed. (The line 29 in the part of the program the reader has written should be marked *.) If we wish to change the number of inequalities, only the lines marked ** need be changed. In either case, the dimension, print, and data statements would also have to be altered.

This program with the missing portion filled in was actually run on a computer, and results were printed as shown in Figure 15. They can be read

$$x_1 = 200$$

$$x_4 = 1600$$

$$x_5 = 600$$

$$x_2 = 100$$

Notice that x_4 was not computed to be precisely 1600. The discrepancy is due to "round-off error."

> **Question.**   How would you change this FORTRAN program if the selling price of mix No. 1 were reduced to $1.21?

2.9   Cautions and Difficulties

We have assumed throughout that the right-hand sides of the inequalities are positive. Our flow chart and FORTRAN program will work only for that case. Needless to say, problems arise in which the right-hand side of an inequality is not positive. An extension of the simplex method can be made to handle this kind of problem. Basically, the extension amounts to finding a basic feasible solution from which to start. We do not discuss it here.

We also assumed that, as we moved from one basic feasible solution to another, the objective actually increased. However, in choosing RATIO to be the smallest of the b_i/a_{ik} for all positive a_{ik} (see blocks 16 through 21 in the flow chart), there may be a tie for the smallest b_i/a_{ik}. If this occurs, then at some succeeding point in the calculation the value of the objective may not increase. (We can be sure the objective will never decrease, but it may remain the same.) Thus, we may find ourselves going in a never-ending loop in which a sequence of basic feasible solutions corresponding to the *same* value of the objective is repeated over and over without ever reaching the final solution. Such behavior is referred to as **degeneracy.** Examples exhibiting degeneracy can be and have been constructed. Again, an extension of the simplex method to prevent this kind of difficulty is available. Practical problems are not degenerate, however, and it is usual to assume that we need not worry about it.

Finally, we mention that you may want to *minimize* the objective rather than maximize it (recall the diet problem in Section 2.1). Then we merely multiply the objective by -1 and maximize the new objective. For example, suppose we wish to minimize $2x_1 - x_2$. Instead we maximize $-2x_1 + x_2$.

> **Question.**   Why can we change a maximizing problem into a minimizing one by multiplying the objective by -1?

2.10   Applications of Linear Programming

The problems which can be solved by linear programming are legion. A few simple ones are discussed in the exercises at the end of this chapter. In closing, we point out a few of the more important ones.

Suppose you have a number of warehouses where material is stored, and you also have a number of stores where material is sold. You wish to transport the material from the warehouses to the stores in such a way that it costs as little as possible. If the cost of shipping one unit of material is the same no matter how much is shipped, then this is a linear programming problem. It is usually referred to as the *transportation problem.*

Consider now a different problem: to find the greatest number of telephone calls which can be made between New York and Los Angeles at the same time. There is a trunk line between these two cities which can handle a large number of calls. When this trunk line is being fully used, calls can be sent over another trunk line to Chicago and then over still another trunk line to Los Angeles. Thus, the total number of calls which can be placed between New York and Los Angeles is increased.

We could also route a call through San Francisco. If we wanted to be more complicated, we could send calls from New York to Chicago to San Francisco and finally to Los Angeles.

The last route involves four cities, and two of the trunk lines used by it are also used in some of the other routes. Therefore, the different routes are not independent of one another.

The problem of finding the maximum number of calls which can be handled simultaneously over all possible routes can be expressed as a linear programming problem. Of course, in general many cities will be involved and each possible route will be related to many other routes.

These kinds of problems are called *network problems* because they involve a network of communication lines. We can also study electrical networks, networks of streets and highways, and other kinds of networks using linear programming.

Another interesting and important application is the cutting stock or *trim problem.* Suppose you are building a garage. You draw plans and determine how many pieces of 2 x 4 wood you will need and what lengths they must be. However, the lumber yard only sells 8-ft and 12-ft lengths. You want to know how many of each standard length (8 ft and 12 ft) to buy so that you waste as little wood as possible. An interesting feature of this problem is that the answer must be in integers. That is, you cannot buy 8.6 pieces of lumber. The problem is called, therefore, a *linear integer programming problem.* (See Exercises 27 and 28.)

There are applications of linear programming outside the field of economics as well. The problem of finding the largest load which a steel bridge can withstand is a linear programming problem. An even more interesting problem which can be solved by linear programming is to decide where the beams in a bridge should be placed and how big they should be so that the bridge weighs as little as possible.

Finally, the problem of finding the amount of various gases present in a chemical mixture can be approximated by a linear programming problem.

There are many other important applications of this technique. More are being discovered every day, and considerable mathematical research continues to be done in linear programming and its extensions.

Exercises

Answers to exercises marked * are given in Appendix A.

*1. Construct a geometrical model of the following linear programming problem:

$$\text{Maximize} \quad x_1 + x_2$$

where

$$x_1 - 10x_2 \leq 0$$
$$x_1 - 5x_2 \leq 5$$
$$x_1 - x_2 \leq 13$$
$$x_1 \leq 20$$
$$x_1 \geq 0$$
$$x_2 \geq 0$$

What are the extreme points? What is the solution?

2. Construct a geometrical model of the following linear programming problem:

$$\text{Maximize} \quad 3x - y$$

where

$$x - y \leq 1$$
$$-x + y \leq 1$$
$$x \leq 2$$
$$2x + 2y \leq 7$$
$$x \geq 0$$
$$y \geq 0$$

What are the extreme points? What is the solution?

3. (a) Construct a geometrical model of the following linear programming problem:

$$\text{Maximize} \quad 2x_1 + x_2$$

where

$$x_1 + x_2 \leq 3$$

$$x_1 + 5x_2 \leq 10$$

$$2x_1 \qquad \leq 3$$

$$16x_1 + 5x_2 \leq 40$$

$$x_1 \geq 0$$

$$x_2 \geq 0$$

What are the extreme points? What is the solution?

(b) If the constraint

$$16x_1 + 5x_2 \leq 40$$

were not present, what would happen to the constraint set? What would happen to the solution?

(c) If the constraint

$$2x_1 \leq 3$$

were not present and the constraint in part (b) were present, what would happen to the constraint set? What would happen to the solution?

*4. (a) Find an initial basic feasible solution as shown at the beginning of Section 2.7 for the linear programming problem in Exercise 3.

(b) Attempt to increase the objective by making x_2 basic. Which equation would you "solve" for x_2? Why?

(c) Find a new basic feasible solution in which x_2 is basic.

(d) What is the value of the objective at this new basic feasible solution?

(e) Which nonbasic variable would you try to make basic next?

(f) Which basic variable would become nonbasic?

(g) Find the basic feasible solution corresponding to the choices in (e) and (f).

(h) Which nonbasic variable would you try to make basic next?

(i) Which basic variable should it replace?

(j) Find the new basic feasible solution making the replacement described in parts (h) and (i).

(k) Show that this is the basic feasible solution which maximizes the objective.

5. Redo steps (b), (c), etc., in Exercise 4, but let x_1 become basic first. [See step (b).]

*6. Alter the FORTRAN program in the text to solve the linear programming problem in Exercise 1.

7. Alter the FORTRAN program in the text to solve the linear programming problem in Exercise 2.

8. Alter the FORTRAN program in the text to solve the linear programming problem in Exercise 3.

*9. (a) Using the method described at the beginning of Section 2.7, find a basic feasible solution of

$$\text{Maximize} \quad 2x_1 + x_2$$

where

$$x_1 - x_2 \leq 0$$
$$x_1 \qquad \leq 2$$
$$x_2 \leq 2$$
$$x_1 + x_2 \leq 3$$
$$x_1 \geq 0$$
$$x_2 \geq 0$$

(b) What do you notice about the number of nonzero variables? Compare this with the number of basic variables.

(c) Let x_1 become basic. By how much does the objective increase?

(d) Starting from the solution obtained in (c), let x_2 now become basic. By how much does the objective increase?

(e) Show that this is the basic feasible solution which maximizes the objective.

(f) Construct a geometrical model of the linear programming problem and use it to explain the behavior of the algebraic solution.

(g) What constraints could you eliminate from the problem without changing either the constraint set or the final solution?

10. (a) Using the method described at the beginning of Section 2.7, find a basic feasible solution of

$$\text{Maximize} \quad 2x_1 + x_2$$

where

$$x_1 - x_2 \leq 3$$
$$x_1 + x_2 \leq 4$$
$$x_1 \qquad \leq 3$$
$$x_1 \geq 0$$
$$x_2 \geq 0$$

(b) Let x_1 become basic and find a new basic feasible solution. How many nonzero variables are there? How many basic variables are there?

(c) Construct a geometrical model of the problem and use it to explain the answers to part (b).

(d) Complete the algebraic solution of the problem.

(e) What constraints could you eliminate from the problem without changing either the constraint set or the final solution?

11. (a) Suppose you are a manufacturer producing two products. The first requires 2 hr of labor and $2.00 worth of raw materials. The second only requires 1 hr of labor but requires $3.00 worth of raw materials. Both products sell for the same price, $10.00. If the labor supply is 100 hr, and there is a supply of $180 of raw materials, how much of each product should you make in order to maximize your income?

(b) If you keep the price of the first product fixed at $10.00, how much would the price of the second product have to be before you would not use all of the labor supply of 100 hours?

(c) If you keep the price of the first product fixed at $10.00, how much would the price of the second product have to be before you would not use all of the $180 worth of raw materials?

*12. According to the well-known nursery rhyme, "Jack Spratt could eat no fat, his wife could eat no lean." Suppose Jack needs at least 4 lb of lean meat per week, and his wife needs at least 3 lb of fat per week. Their diet consists of beef and pork. The beef that they buy is 20% fat, and the pork is 60% fat.

(a) If beef and pork sell for the same price, how much of each should the Spratts buy?

(b) If the price of beef rises to 2½ times that of pork, how much of each meat should they buy?

13. Another way to solve a linear programming problem is to eliminate one variable at a time until only one remains and then to use back substitution as in Gauss's method for linear equations. Consider the problem given by (19) through (23); that is,

$$\text{Maximize} \quad x_1 + x_2 \tag{19}$$

where

$$2x_1 + x_2 \le 2 \tag{20}$$

$$x_1 + 3x_2 \le 3 \tag{21}$$

$$x_1 \ge 0 \tag{22}$$

$$x_2 \ge 0 \tag{23}$$

We let

$$y \le x_1 + x_2$$

and try to maximize y. The last inequality means that

$$y - x_1 \le x_2 \tag{i}$$

Inequality (20) implies that

$$x_2 \le 2 - 2x_1 \tag{ii}$$

and (21) implies that

$$x_2 \le 1 - \frac{x_1}{3} \tag{iii}$$

Finally, (23) says

$$0 \le x_2 \tag{iv}$$

Now (i) and (ii) tell us that x_2 must be greater than or equal to $y - x_1$ and at the same time less than or equal to $2 - 2x_1$. If both of these are to be so, then $y - x_1$ must be less than or equal to $2 - 2x_1$ or

$$y - x_1 \le 2 - 2x_1 \tag{a}$$

Similarly, from (i) and (iii),

$$y - x_1 \le 1 - \frac{x_1}{3} \tag{b}$$

From (ii) and (iv),

$$0 \le 2 - 2x_1 \tag{c}$$

and, from (iii) and (iv),

$$0 \le 1 - \frac{x_1}{3} \tag{d}$$

If we can find values of x_1 and y which satisfy (a), (b), (c), and (d), then we can find a value of x_2 satisfying (i), (ii), (iii), and (iv). We now try to solve (a), (b), (c), and (d) along with (22). These five inequalities involve only two variables, y and x_1. The inequality (a) tells us

$$x_1 \le 2 - y \tag{A}$$

and (b) says

$$\tfrac{3}{2}y - \tfrac{3}{2} \le x_1 \tag{B}$$

The inequalities (c) and (d) then tell us

$$x_1 \le 1 \tag{C}$$

$$x_1 \le 3$$

and (22) is

$$0 \le x_1 \tag{D}$$

We may eliminate $x_1 \le 3$ because, if (C) is satisfied, then $x_1 \le 3$.

We now require that all the quantities which restrict x_1 from getting large, (A) and (C), be $\ge$ all the quantities which restrict x_1 from getting small, (B) and (D). This leads to four inequalities on y.

(I) What are they? What is the biggest value y may have?

(II) Substitute this largest value of y in (A), (B), (C), and (D). What is the only value x_1 can have? This is the first step in the back substitution.

(III) Substitute the maximum y found in (I) and the value of x_1 found in (II) into the inequalities (i), (ii), (iii), and (iv). What is the only value x_2 can have?

This method of solving linear inequalities was first discovered in 1826 by Jean Baptiste Joseph Fourier. It was rediscovered in 1936 by Theodore S. Motzkin. It is usually referred to as the *Fourier-Motzkin method*.

14. Use the Fourier-Motzkin elimination method described in Exercise 13 to solve the two-food diet problem:

$$\text{Minimize} \quad C$$

where

$$C \ge 325B + 80L$$

$$20B + \quad L \ge 35$$

$$15 \ L \geq 30$$

$$B \geq \ 0$$

$$L \geq \ 0$$

Here C is the number of calories, B is the amount of beef to be eaten, and L is the amount of salad to be eaten.

15. Use the FORTRAN program in the text to solve the following linear programming problem:

$$\text{Minimize} \quad -x_1 + x_2$$

where

$$x_1 + x_2 \leq 2$$

$$2x_1 + x_2 \leq 3$$

$$x_1 \geq 0$$

$$x_2 \geq 0$$

(*Hint:* Add two constraints which do not affect the solution.)

16. Suppose you have two warehouses, one in Dallas and one in Atlanta. The Dallas warehouse contains 100 units and the Atlanta warehouse contains 150 units. You want to ship the material in the warehouses to stores in New York and Chicago. Both cities need 125 units. The shipping costs per unit are

Dallas to Chicago	$2.00
Dallas to New York	$4.00
Atlanta to Chicago	$3.00
Atlanta to New York	$2.00

Let

$x_1 = $ amount shipped from Dallas to Chicago

$x_2 = $ amount shipped from Dallas to New York

$x_3 = $ amount shipped from Atlanta to Chicago

$x_4 = $ amount shipped from Atlanta to New York

The total shipped to Chicago is $x_1 + x_3$ and, since Chicago needs 125 units, then

$$x_1 + x_3 = 125$$

(a) Write down three other equations which x_1, x_2, x_3, x_4 must satisfy. Do these four equations in four variables have a solution? Is it unique?

(b) If you want to minimize the shipping cost, write down the objective to be minimized.

(c) By adding the requirements that all x's be greater than or equal to zero, we have a linear programming problem. Our FORTRAN program cannot handle it because it is not in our standard form. However, we can neglect one of the four equations since they are not independent of one another. We choose to neglect $x_1 + x_3 = 125$. A basic feasible solution to the other three is given by

$$x_2 = 100 - x_1$$
$$x_3 = 125 - x_1$$
$$x_4 = 25 + x_1$$

where x_1 is taken to be zero. What is the objective in terms of the zero variable, x_1? Can the objective be lowered?

(d) Take one step in the simplex method. This yields the minimum cost solution.

This is a simple example of the classical *transportation problem*. It is a sufficiently important problem that special algorithms have been developed to solve it.

*17. Suppose an estate wishes to invest its capital in bonds and stocks. The terms of the estate require that no more than 50% of the investments can be in stocks and that at least 40% of the investments must be in bonds. In addition, the investment in stocks must be no more than two-thirds the investment in bonds.

(a) Construct a geometrical model of the constraint set.

(b) Assuming that the income from both stocks and bonds is positive, under what conditions will it be profitable to invest less than 50% in stocks?

(c) Tell why the FORTRAN program in the text cannot be used to solve this problem.

*18. Suppose we have two tables called T and S. Each has ten entries. Write a FORTRAN program which takes the 3rd entry in table T and exchanges it with the 6th entry in table S.

19. Using table T in Exercise 18, write a FORTRAN program to exchange the 1st entry in table T with the 10th entry in the same table.

*20. Given a table T with 10 entries, write a FORTRAN program to reverse the order of the entries in the table. That is, the entry in T(1) should be transferred to T(10), the entry in T(2) should be transferred to T(9), and so on until the entry in T(10) is transferred to T(1).

21. Given a table T with 10 entries, write a FORTRAN program to move the 10th entry into T(1) and to move all other entries down one; i.e., the 1st entry goes into T(2), the second entry into T(3), etc.

22. Write a FORTRAN program which checks to see if all B(I) are positive for I = 1, 2, 3, 4. Insert it in the program in Section 2.8 before the statement labeled 1. If all B(I) > 0, then go on to statement 1. If not, go to the following set of statements:

> PRINT 300
>
> 300   FORMAT (25H ① NON ① POSITIVE ① RIGHT ① SIDES)
>
> STOP

which should be placed between statement 201 and the END statement.

*23. Write a FORTRAN program to calculate the absolute value of a number X. Let $Y = |X|$.

24. Write a FORTRAN program to perform the task described in the flow chart in Figure 16. The following program should appear at statement 100:

> 100   PRINT 200, A, Y
>
> 200   FORMAT (6H ① SQRT (, F9.4, 4H) ① = ①, F9.4)
>
> STOP
>
> END

Place the following statement at the beginning of the program:

> A = 2.0

This program should calculate the square root of 2 to two decimal figures. You can use it to calculate other square roots by changing the statement defining A. Try it on a computer. We return to this problem in Chapter 5.

*25. Write a FORTRAN program which calculates X under the following conditions. If an integer K is 0, then

$$X = AY^2 + BY + C$$

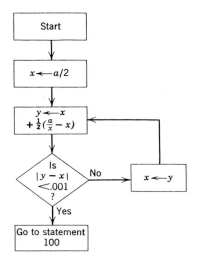

Figure 16

If K = 1, then

$$X = CY^2 + AY + B$$

If K = 2, then

$$X = BY^2 + CY + A$$

Place statements at the beginning of the program which define K, A, B, C, and Y. End the program with

PRINT 100, K, X

100   FORMAT (5H ① K ① = ①, I2, 5H ① X ① = ①, F9.4)

STOP

END

Run the program several times with different values of K. Try K = 0, K = 1, K = 2, and K = 6.

26. Write a FORTRAN program which calculates K under the following conditions:

If a variable X is negative,

$$K = -1$$

If X is zero,
$$K = 0$$
If X is positive,
$$K = +1$$

Place a statement at the beginning of the program defining X. End the program with

PRINT 200, X, K

200   FORMAT (5H ① X ① = ①, F9.4, 5H ① K ① = ①, I2)

STOP

END

Run the program with several values of X. Test all three possibilities.

27. Consider the following linear programming problem

$$\text{Minimize} \quad x + 2y$$

where

$$x + y \leq 7$$
$$2x \leq 11$$
$$2y \leq 7$$
$$x \geq 0$$
$$y \geq 0$$

(a) Draw a geometrical model. What is the solution?

(b) Suppose the variables x and y must be integers. What is the solution?

(c) The problem in part (b) is called a linear *integer* programming problem. Could its solution be obtained by "rounding off" the non-integer solution in part (a) to the nearest integers?

28. Consider the following linear programming problem:

$$\text{Maximize} \quad x$$

where

$$2x + 7y \leq 17$$
$$6x - 7y \leq 9$$
$$x \geq 0$$
$$y \geq 0$$

(a) Draw a geometrical model. What is the solution?

(b) Suppose the variables x and y must be integers. What is the solution?

(c) The problem in part (b) is called a linear *integer* programming problem. Could its solution be obtained by "rounding off" the non-integer solution in part (a) to the nearest integers?

CHAPTER THREE

Computer Arithmetic and FORTRAN Programming

3.1 An Introduction to Digital Computers

We have already seen how digital computers can be used to help us understand and describe mathematical processes. There is much more we can learn by using the computer as a mathematical tool — an extension of our reasoning power. First, however, we must learn a little more about computers and about programming. In Appendix B you can find out even more about these subjects if you wish.

Computers can perform arithmetic very quickly and very accurately. That in itself is a big help. But, if this were all they could do, they would not be very different from an extremely large desk calculator that adds, subtracts, multiplies, and divides. The fact is that computers are very different from a desk calculator of any size.

First recall that a computer — given the proper FORTRAN program — can decide whether a number is negative, zero, or positive and can take different courses of action depending on which of these cases arise.[1] This is a very elementary type of decision, but, when a number of such decisions are followed by one another in the proper order, a rather sophisticated process can be constructed. With just such simple decisions and a bit of arithmetic we have already done such tasks as: finding solutions to systems of linear equations and finding solutions of linear programming problems. Later we carry out even more complicated processes using a computer. This *decision-making power* is an essential part of a digital computer and makes it much more powerful than a desk calculator.

A second distinguishing property of computers is that they possess a *memory*. It usually is fairly large and extremely reliable. The memory of

[1] Recall the IF statement we used earlier.

152

a computer allows it to "remember" numbers such as: all the coefficients of the variables in a system of equations. A computer also "remembers" programs. For example, it can keep in its memory all the FORTRAN statements of the programs we wrote earlier.

We now investigate how we can exploit these two fundamental and powerful properties: the decision-making ability and the memory. We use FORTRAN to converse with the computer, because most computers "understand" FORTRAN.

FORTRAN is a language, and as such it has several dialects. The two most important ones are called FORTRAN II and FORTRAN IV. Everything we have said so far and everything in this chapter applies to *both* dialects. Readers interested in the details of the differences in the dialects are referred to *A Guide to FORTRAN Programming* and *A Guide to FORTRAN IV Programming*, both by D. D. McCracken and published by John Wiley and Sons in 1961 and 1965, respectively. To repeat, then, everything in this text applies equally well to FORTRAN II *and* FORTRAN IV.[2]

We should note that the FORTRAN used on many computers will permit you much more freedom than we are allowing you in this text. For example, we are going to tell you that the names of variables cannot have more than five letters, when indeed many computers will allow you to use six letters. We also are going to tell you that there are certain words which cannot be used as names for variables. For instance, we do not allow you to use "GO" as a variable name. Most computers will, in fact, accept "GO" as a perfectly legitimate variable name in FORTRAN. The list of restrictions that we place on you, but which are not restrictions required by all computers, goes on and on. You will find that, whatever computer you are using, you will be able to violate many of the rules we give you, yet your FORTRAN program will run and give correct results.

Why, then, do we make you follow all these rules, many of which you need not follow? The answer is that we want all our FORTRAN programs to run and give correct results on *all* computers. The rules which you can break without any penalty may be precisely the rules which the student at a neighboring school, using a different computer, finds will

---

[2] Actually the material covered in this text is basic FORTRAN and all programs can be run on a computer with only FORTRAN I available. A list of computers which can accommodate any of the FORTRAN programs in this text is given in Appendix E.

stop his program without any results or with incorrect results. The converse may also be true. Your neighbor may be able to violate some rules which your computer requires you to follow.

All the rules set forth in this chapter and all the programs in this text will run on any of the computing systems listed in Appendix E. It is in the interest of this universality that we have restricted ourselves to the rules set forth in this chapter.

The reader is warned that, although he may be able to violate many of our rules without suffering a penalty, he does so at his own risk. If he tries to take a FORTRAN program in which he has violated these rules to another computer, he may find that the program no longer is correct.

It is not our intention that the reader should be an accomplished programmer even when he has mastered this chapter. We discuss only enough programming to allow us to describe better the mathematical processes in later chapters. Fortunately, we also learn to write a good many types of useful computer programs in the process.

3.2   Computer Arithmetic

We have already discussed the fact that in FORTRAN we distinguish between integers and numbers with fractional parts. The latter kind of number is called a *floating-point number* in FORTRAN. Until now we have written such numbers in a form such as 165.2 or 21.0 or -0.012. For use with a computer it is more convenient to write numbers in a different form. For example, we rewrite 165.2 by multiplying and dividing by 1000 so that

$$165.2 = \frac{165.2}{1000} \times 1000 = .1652 \times 10^3$$

The representation at the right has the decimal point in front of the first nonzero digit. We shall usually write numbers with the decimal point in front of the first nonzero digit. The only exception will be the number "zero."

Numbers with their first digit nonzero are called **normalized** numbers. Again, as an example we take 21.0 and multiply and divide by 100 so that

$$21.0 = \frac{21.0}{100} \times 100 = .21 \times 10^2$$

Of course, in both of these examples we did not actually perform any divisions. Division by 10 can be accomplished by shifting the decimal point one place to the left while the digits remain in a fixed position (17.6 ÷ 10 = 1.76). We could equally well think of the decimal point remaining in a fixed position on the paper and all of the digits shifting one place to the right. For example,

$$17.6$$

divided by 10 is

$$1.76$$

It happens that, in a computer, decimal points are not physically present. They are always imagined to be at a fixed place, in front of the first digit. Therefore, to divide by 10 we shift all the digits in a number 1 place to the right.

Numbers in our computer then have a decimal or fractional part usually called the **mantissa** and are multiplied by 10 raised to some power. The power of 10 is called the **exponent**. For example, in the number $165.2 = .1652 \times 10^3$, the mantissa is .1652 and the exponent is 3.

Numbers written with a mantissa and exponent, as we have just done, are called **floating-point numbers**. When we speak of floating-point numbers we always think of them in that form: a mantissa with the decimal point at the extreme left multiplied by a power of 10, the exponent.[3]

One more example before we proceed to addition of two floating-point numbers: If we have a number less than .1, say .0261, we shift all the digits to the *left* until the decimal point is just in front of the first non-zero digit. This is equivalent to multiplying by some power of 10; therefore, we must also divide by the same power of 10. For example,

$$.0261 = (.0261 \times 10) \div 10$$
$$= .261 \times 10^{-1}$$

Suppose now we want to add 165.2 and 21.0. We write these as floating-point numbers, $.1652 \times 10^3$ and $.21 \times 10^2$. We cannot add the mantissas directly. However, suppose we shift the second mantissa one more place to the right and increase the exponent by 1 so that it looks like $.021 \times 10^3$. We no longer have the decimal point in front of the first nonzero digit. However, it is immediately in front of the first digit.

---

[3] Many computers use an exponent which is a power of 2, and some newer computers use an exponent which is a power of 16. This need not concern us here.

Notice, though, that we have not changed the value of the number. Now we can write the sum as

$$.1652 \times 10^3 + .021 \times 10^3 = (.1652 + .021) \times 10^3$$

where we have factored 10^3 from each number. We add the two mantissas in the parentheses to get $.1862 \times 10^3$. Thus, when we add two numbers, we must adjust one of them so that the exponents of both numbers are equal. We can then add the mantissas and give the result the same exponent as both addends.

A more precise rule for addition of floating-point numbers is as follows: **(1)** Arrange the numbers so that the exponent of the first is at least as large as the exponent of the second. **(2)** Subtract the second exponent from the first. **(3)** Shift the second mantissa to the right a number of places given by the result found in **(2)**. **(4)** Add the mantissas. **(5)** Attach the exponent of the first number to the result.

Problem. Draw a flow chart to describe this process.

As another example, consider adding

$$.0329 = .329 \times 10^{-1} \quad \text{and} \quad 1.246 = .1246 \times 10^1$$

Since the second exponent is larger, we rearrange the numbers to be $(.1246 \times 10^1) + (.329 \times 10^{-1})$. We subtract the exponents, $1 - (-1) = 2$, and we rewrite the second number to be $.00329 \times 10^1$. The result of the addition is $.12789 \times 10^1 = 1.2789$. The reader should verify that this is the correct result.

The two examples which we have discussed resulted in a sum which was a normalized number; that is, the first nonzero digit immediately followed the decimal point. Because this does not always happen, we now consider two examples which exhibit the two other possible types of results.

First, suppose we add 9.961 and 9.803. That is,

$$\begin{array}{r} .9961 \times 10^1 \\ + \ .9803 \times 10^1 \\ \hline 1.9764 \times 10^1 \end{array}$$

Here the first nonzero digit is to the left of the decimal point. We say that there was **overflow** in the sum. In this case we shift the decimal point to the left one place (or think of the decimal point as fixed in place and shift all the digits right one place) and increase the exponent by 1. Thus,

$$1.9764 \times 10^1 = .19764 \times 10^2$$

Finally, suppose we subtract 19.76 from 26.31. We get

$$\begin{array}{r} .2631 \times 10^2 \\ -.1976 \times 10^2 \\ \hline .0655 \times 10^2 \end{array}$$

Here the first nonzero digit is too far to the right, so we shift all the digits one place to the left and decrease the exponent by 1:

$$.0655 \times 10^2 = .655 \times 10^1$$

We shall return to both of these examples shortly.

The floating-point numbers kept in a computer's memory usually have a fixed number of digits in the mantissa and a fixed number of digits in the exponent. Both the mantissa and the exponent also have a sign, $+$ or $-$. Suppose we have a computer with four digits in the mantissa and one digit in the exponent:

$$165.2 = .1652 \times 10^3$$

$$.0329 = .3290 \times 10^{-1}$$

$$1.246 = .1246 \times 10^1$$

The largest number our computer can have is $.9999 \times 10^9$, because there is only one digit in the exponent. This is equal to 999,900,000 (nearly 1 billion).

We say the **precision** of our computer is four digits since any four-digit mantissa can be represented. The **range** of the numbers is 10^9. In Appendix E the precision and range of most computers which use FORTRAN are given.

Now, if we add the last two of the three numbers listed above, we get $.12789 \times 10^1$ as we exhibited earlier. But the mantissa in this result has five digits and our computer only allows four. What are we to do? Several alternatives are available to us. One is simply to ignore the last digit and write

$$.1278 \times 10^1$$

This is only approximately equal to the sum. That is, it is in error. We define the **error** to be the true result minus the approximate result. The error, e, then is

$$e = .12789 \times 10^1 - .1278 \times 10^1 = .00009 \times 10^1$$

This process, dropping the fifth and any succeeding digits, is called **chopping** because we "chop" off the excess digits.

Another way of handling our five-digit number is to look at the fifth digit. If it is less than 5, we chop the number as we did above. However, if the fifth digit is 5 or greater, we add 1 to the fourth digit and chop the result. This is often called **symmetric rounding.**

Again we return to our example of adding $.3290 \times 10^{-1} + .1246 \times 10^1$ and obtaining a sum of $.12789 \times 10^1$. Since the fifth digit, 9, is greater than 5, we add 1 to the fourth digit and chop to get

$$.1279 \times 10^1$$

The error in this result is

$$e = .12789 \times 10^1 - .1279 \times 10^1 = -.00001 \times 10^1$$

which is nine times smaller in absolute value than the error from chopping.

The absolute value of the error caused by symmetric rounding is never greater than the absolute value of the error caused by chopping. About half of the time the symmetric rounding error is less than the chopping error in absolute value. Why, then, would anyone ever chop? Chopping is considerably easier to accomplish in a computer than is symmetric rounding. Chopping also can be done faster than symmetric rounding. A great many computers when using **FORTRAN** do, in fact, chop. If the number of digits in the mantissa is large enough, the effect of chopping is relatively small. Whether we use chopping or symmetric rounding the error caused is called a **round-off error.** We have already encountered round-off errors in Chapter 1. This is the same type of round-off error we considered there.

We return now to the two examples which led to unnormalized results. Recall that

$$
\begin{array}{r}
.9961 \times 10^1 \\
+ \ .9803 \times 10^1 \\
\hline
1.9764 \times 10^1
\end{array}
$$

In a computer with four digits in its mantissas, this becomes

$$.1976 \times 10^2$$

whether we chop or round symmetrically. Next recall that

$$.2631 \times 10^2$$
$$-.1976 \times 10^2$$
$$\overline{.0655 \times 10^2}$$

When we normalize this result we get

$$.6550 \times 10^1$$

However, the final zero in the mantissa is not a significant digit. In fact, suppose the $.1976 \times 10^2$ subtracted above was really the result of the previous addition ($.9961 \times 10^1 + .9803 \times 10^1$). Then this number is really $.19764 \times 10^2$. If we had had a five-digit computer we would have computed

$$.26310 \times 10^2$$
$$-.19764 \times 10^2$$
$$\overline{.06546 \times 10^2}$$

The "correct" four-digit result then is

$$.6546 \times 10^1$$

The point is that, in the result obtained in our four-digit computer ($.6550 \times 10^1$), there is no way for us to know what the fourth digit should be. It could be 0 or 1 or 2 or . . . or 9. Usually computers automatically place a zero in the unknown digit. The user of a computer must be aware of this fact and must not assume that, because a computer contains or prints out four, five, or more digits in a number, all of them are meaningful. In this case only three digits are meaningful although four are present.

Similar round-off errors arise in multiplication and division. We discuss multiplication but do not consider the details of division.

Suppose we wish to multiply $.7219 \times 10^1$ by $.6200 \times 10^2$. We can write this as

$$(.7219 \times .6200) \times 10^1 \times 10^2$$

Multiplying the two mantissas, we get $.447578$. Moreover, $10^1 \times 10^2 = 10^3$ and the result is

$$.447578 \times 10^3$$

This mantissa has six digits. If we chop, the approximate result is

$$.4475 \times 10^3$$

which is in error by $.000078 \times 10^3$. If we use symmetric rounding, we get

$$.4476 \times 10^3$$

in which the error is $-.000022 \times 10^3$.

The rules for multiplying two floating-point numbers are: **(1)** Multiply the two mantissas. **(2)** Chop or round symmetrically.[4] **(3)** Add the two exponents.

We close this section by exhibiting a peculiar and unexpected property of computer arithmetic with floating-point numbers. Suppose we wish to add 7219. and 32.51 and .4942. Writing these as floating-point numbers, we have

$$.7219 \times 10^4 + (.3251 \times 10^2 + .4942 \times 10^0)$$

or, equally well,

$$(.7219 \times 10^4 + .3251 \times 10^2) + .4942 \times 10^0$$

In the first case we add the last two numbers first and then add the first to the sum. In the second case we add the first two numbers together and then add the third to that sum. That we can do either is a result of the fact that ordinary addition is *associative*.

Let us consider the first case. We add

$$
\begin{array}{r}
.3251 \times 10^2 \\
+.004942 \times 10^2 \\
\hline
.330042 \times 10^2
\end{array}
$$

If we chop, the result is $.3300 \times 10^2$. Now we add the first number to get

$$
\begin{array}{r}
.7219 \times 10^4 \\
+.003300 \times 10^4 \\
\hline
.725200 \times 10^4
\end{array}
$$

and, by chopping again, $.7252 \times 10^4$.

Now we take the second case. The first addition is

$$
\begin{array}{r}
.7219 \times 10^4 \\
+.003251 \times 10^4 \\
\hline
.725151 \times 10^4
\end{array}
$$

[4] In general, two four-digit mantissas produce an eight-digit product.

After chopping the result, the next addition is

$$
\begin{array}{r}
.7251 \quad\ \times 10^4 \\
+.00004942 \times 10^4 \\
\hline
.72514942 \times 10^4
\end{array}
$$

Again we chop, and the final result is $.7251 \times 10^4$. But this is not the same as the result obtained in the first case!

Our conclusion is that, in a computer with floating-point numbers, *addition is not associative*. This surprising result comes about because each mantissa must have the same number of digits. It is a warning that we must not take all the usual laws of arithmetic for granted when we use a computer.

Question. Is addition commutative if we use floating-point arithmetic in a computer?

The observant reader has noticed that, if we used symmetric rounding instead of chopping in the example above, we would have avoided difficulty. However, examples involving more than three numbers can be constructed wherein symmetric rounding produces different results depending on the order in which the numbers are added.

Questions. Which of the two results above is more accurate? When we have three numbers should we add the two smallest numbers first and then add the largest to that sum? Would it be better to add the two largest numbers first and then add the smallest to that sum? Do you think your answer will always be true? (*Hint:* Try Exercise 11.)

3.3 FORTRAN Constants and Variables (Review)

We now review and summarize the parts of the FORTRAN language which we used in earlier chapters. Actually, some new information regarding FORTRAN appears in these sections to clarify some of the concepts.

There are two kinds of numbers in FORTRAN: integers[5] and floating-point numbers.[6] When we write a number with a decimal point, it is

---

[5] Integers are also referred to as *fixed-point* numbers in FORTRAN.
[6] Many FORTRAN manuals refer to floating-point numbers as *real* numbers. They are not to be confused with real numbers as defined and used in mathematics. FORTRAN real numbers are floating-point numbers as described in Section 3.2.

assumed to be a floating-point number. If no decimal point is present, the number is assumed to be an integer. For example, 14.2, 10.0, −1. and .0 are all floating-point numbers. On the other hand, 12, −1, 0, and 32567 are integers. Because *commas are never used* in numbers, 32,567 is an illegal number. Explicit numbers, whether integer or floating-point, are referred to as **constants** in FORTRAN. This is to distinguish them from variables, which are represented by letters or combinations of letters and numbers.

Variables may also be either integers or floating-point numbers. If a variable is an integer, its *name* must begin with one of the six letters I, J, K, L, M, or N. The name of a variable can be a combination of five or less letters or integers with no intervening spaces. The first symbol in the name must not be an integer. However, the second or succeeding symbols may be integers. For example, K, IXYZ, M3, NUM are all integer variables. There are some restrictions on the allowable combinations of letters. They are noted at the end of this section.

If a variable is a floating-point number, its name must *not* begin with one of the six letters listed in the previous paragraph. Thus, Y, AZJ, VAR, and TIN are all floating-point variables.

In any case the name of a variable has five or fewer letters or integers with no blank spaces. Whether it is an integer or a floating-point number is determined solely by the first letter.

Question.   Which of the following names represent integer variables? Which are not legitimate variable names?

(a) ABC	(b) JUMP
(c) MOVE	(d) TRY
(e) X	(f) SPEED
(g) DISTANCE	(h) ITAB
(i) LZ	(j) NEXTONE

We must emphasize that I and II are different variables. They are both integer variables but bear no relation to each other unless some FORTRAN statements connect them.

Some computers reserve certain words for their own use; therefore, not all five-letter combinations are legitimate variable names.[7] For

---

[7] In particular, FORTRAN for the minimum IBM System/360 machines, the IBM 7010, and GE-200 series, and the CDC-160 reserve certain five-letter names for their own use.

example, a variable named **IF** might cause some confusion with the statement **IF** which is concerned with whether something is negative, zero, or positive. A list of 56 names which should *not* be used as variable names is given here.

ABS	EXIT	MAX1
AINT	EXP	MIN0
ALOG	FIND	MIN1
AMAX0	FILE	MOD
AMAX1	FLOAT	NE
AMIN0	GE	PAUSE
AMIN1	GO	PUNCH
AMOD	GOTO	READ
ATAN	GT	REAL
CALL	IABS	SIGN
COS	IDIM	SIN
DABS	IF	SLITE
DBLE	IFIX	SNGL
DIM	INPUT	SQRT
DO	INT	STOP
DSIGN	ISIGN	TANH
DVCHK	LE	TO
END	LT	WRITE
EQ	MAX0	

Many computers (in fact, most) accept these names as legitimate variable names. However, in the interest of writing all our programs so that they can be run on any computer, we avoid using as variable names the entries in this list.

Finally, we note that *the last letter of any variable having four or more letters in its name should not be an* F. The reason is that in some computers a terminal F signals that the name is not a variable but a function (like square root). We do not discuss FORTRAN functions in this text, but we do avoid use of a terminal F in any variable name so that our programs will be valid for any computer.

3.4   Expressions (Review)

The four[8] basic symbols which can be used to combine variables and numbers are

$+$	Addition
$-$	Subtraction
$*$	Multiplication
$/$	Division

For example, we can write

$$A + 16.0 \quad \text{(floating-point)}$$

or

$$I - 1 \quad \text{(integer)}$$

We cannot, however, combine integers and floating-point numbers. For example,

$$A + 2$$

and

$$I - 16.0$$

are not allowed. However, integers may be used as subscripts for floating-point variables. Indeed, *subscripts must always be integers*. Thus

$$A(I, J)$$

and

$$INT(K)$$

and

$$BVAR(3, 2)$$

are legitimate expressions. Moreover,

$$A(I - 1, J + 4)$$

is a legitimate expression. The first subscript of A is $I - 1$. Since I and 1 are integers, so is $I - 1$.

---

[8] Of course, there is also the $=$ sign, and there is another symbol $**$ which we study later.

Question. What are the subscripts in the last expression when I = 2 and J = 3?

The restrictions on the form of subscripts are given in Section 3.7.

Blank spaces may be used freely in a FORTRAN expression because they are ignored.[9] For example,

$$A + 16.0$$

and

$$A + \quad 16.0$$

are identical as far as FORTRAN is concerned.

When there is doubt about the order in which operations are to be performed, parentheses are used to group terms. As examples,

$$(A + B) * C$$

means first add A and B and multiply the sum by C, and

$$VAR + (X * Y)$$

means multiply X by Y and add VAR to the product. The operation in parentheses is performed first.

Question. What is the difference between

$$(I - J) + K$$

and

$$I - (J + K)?$$

What is the value of these two expressions when I = 4, J = 1, K = 2?

When several terms are found in an expression and parentheses are not present, multiplications and divisions are performed first. The additions and subtractions are performed after the multiplications and divisions. Thus,

$$A + B * C$$

is equivalent to

$$A + (B * C)$$

Both are different from

$$(A + B) * C$$

[9] Except, of course, in the name of a variable.

As another example,

$$X * Y - B / C$$

is the same as

$$(X * Y) - (B / C)$$

There may be several sets of parentheses in one statement. The operation in the innermost parentheses is performed first, and we proceed outward. Again, by way of example,

$$C * (B + (A * (X + Y)))$$

means add X and Y. We then multiply that sum by A and add B to the product. Finally we multiply by C.

> **Question.**   If $A = 2.0$, $B = -1.0$, $C = 3.0$, $X = 9.0$, and $Y = -4.0$, what is the value of the expression above? For the same values of the variables, what is the value of
>
> $$C * (B + (A * X + Y))?$$
>
> What would be the difference if the innermost parentheses in the last expression were removed?

Parentheses, therefore, have two uses in FORTRAN: (1) to group terms in an expression, and (2) to enclose subscripts.

3.5   Arithmetic Statements (Review)

Another symbol used in FORTRAN is the equality sign. *One* variable must appear *alone* on the left of the = sign. On the right there may be any legitimate expression. Of course, if the variable on the left is a floating-point variable, the expression on the right usually[10] is composed of floating-point variables and numbers. Similarly, if the left-hand variable is an integer, the variables and numbers on the right will also be integers in most cases. Thus, we might have

$$J = J + 1$$

or

$$VAR = X * Y - 4.0$$

The first says: increase J by 1. The second says: multiply X by Y, subtract 4, and call the result VAR. A combination of variables, numbers,

---

[10] There are exceptions, and we study them later in this chapter.

and symbols starting with a variable followed by an = sign is a FOR-TRAN **arithmetic statement**. Statements may be numbered at the left. The statement numbers need not be in any given order. Statement numbers should not exceed 9999.

FORTRAN statements are punched on cards, one statement to a card. The statement is punched in columns 7 to 72 of the card. The statement number, if any, is punched in columns 1 to 5. The cards are read in sequence into a computer, and the statements are performed in the order read. For example, suppose we punch I = 1 on the first card, J = 2 on the second, I = I + J on the third, and J = I + 2 on the fourth. If we read them in the order given, at the end I = 3 and J = 5. If we read them in the following order,

$$I = 1$$

$$J = 2$$

$$J = I + 2$$

$$I = I + J$$

then at the end I = 4 and J = 3. *The order of the statements is important.*

Question. If we reverse the order of the first two statements in the example above, what is the effect?

3.6 Control Statements GO TO and IF (Review)

Sometimes we want to perform a certain set of statements over again some number of times. Rather than write the statements down many times and punch many cards, we use the two statements IF and GO TO. They have the following meanings: IF (X) i, j, k, where X is any expression and i, j, and k are integer constants, means: (1) if X is less than zero, the next statement to be performed is the one numbered i; (2) if X equals zero, the next statement is numbered j; and, (3) if X is greater than zero, the next statement is k. For example,

$$IF (A - B * C) 10, 30, 20$$

means: if A − B * C < 0, then the next statement performed is numbered 10; if A − B * C = 0, then 30 is the next statement; while if A − B * C > 0, then 20 is the next statement. Notice that i, j, and k must be integer *constants* and they are statement numbers. Variables are not allowed.

There must be no space between the I and the F of the word IF.

GO TO n, where n is any integer constant, means: the next statement to be performed is numbered n. There must be at least one space or blank after the word GO and after the word TO. There must not be a space between G and O, nor can there be a space between T and O.

The IF and GO TO statements are called **control statements** because they control the processing of information.

Problem.   Write a program to add ten floating-point numbers named O, P, Q, . . . , X. Call the result Y.

3.7   Subscripted Variables (Review)

Variables may have one or two subscripts. Subscripts are enclosed in parentheses following the name of the variable. If there are two subscripts, they are separated by a comma. Examples are $B(1)$ = the first element of B, $A(I, 2)$ = the element of A in the Ith row and 2nd column, $VAR(2, 1)$ = the element of VAR in the 2nd row and 1st column. *A subscript is never zero or negative.* Thus the smallest value a subscript may have is 1. For example,

$$A(I - 2)$$

is illegal if I is 2 or less. It is legal if I is 3 or greater.

Subscripts may be (i) an integer variable, (ii) an integer constant, or (iii) the sum or difference of an integer variable and an integer constant. Thus,

$$MAX \qquad N + 6$$

$$I3 \qquad ITAB - 2$$

are all legitimate subscripts. However,

$$J + K \qquad MAX - 3.0$$

$$2 * J \qquad ITAB - 3 * 2$$

are *not* legitimate subscripts.

Question.   Which of the following are legitimate subscripts?

(a)	I+2	(b)	X−1
(c)	3 * K	(d)	JMAX
(e)	L+3	(f)	L+M

We have now reviewed the FORTRAN concepts used in previous chapters. These concepts are: integer and floating-point constants, integer and floating-point variables and their proper names, the operation symbols (+, −, *, /) and = sign, statement numbers, parentheses, subscripts, arithmetic statements, and the two control statements, GO TO and IF.

The reader who is not sure of these points would do well to review Section 1.9 in Chapter 1, and Sections 3.3 through 3.7 of this present chapter as well, before going on.

3.8   Input and Output — READ, PRINT, FORMAT

Now that we know how to write a program using arithmetic and control statements, we must learn how to get data (like the coefficients in an equation) into a computer and how to get answers (like the values of the variables) out of the computer. This is generally referred to as input and output.

We use two *input-output statements:* READ and PRINT.[11] The READ statement causes *one* card to be read. The word READ is followed by a list of variables. The numbers read from the card are given the names of the variables in the list. For example, suppose we use the statement

READ A, X, I

Suppose also that we punch a card with the three numbers − 16.7, 1.0, and 6 on it in that order and place it in the card reader following our program. When the READ statement is encountered, the computer reads the three numbers on the card and effectively performs the following arithmetic statements:

$$A = -16.7$$

$$X = 1.0$$

$$I = 6$$

Thus the first variable is assigned the first number as its value, the second variable is assigned the second number, and so on.

Similarly, the PRINT statement causes *one line* to be printed. The word PRINT is also followed by a list which gives the names of the variables to be printed on that line.

---

[11] In Section 3.8* we discuss slight variations of these statements which are required by some computers.

For every card to be read a READ statement must be executed. For every line printed a PRINT statement must be executed.

Two questions which arise are: Where on the card should the numbers be punched? Where on the line will the numbers be printed? These questions are answered by use of the FORMAT statement. There is a FORMAT statement associated with each READ or PRINT statement. Every FORMAT statement is numbered at the left, and the READ and PRINT statements refer to the number of the FORMAT statement with which they are associated. Thus

READ 5, A, X, I

means: read three numbers from one card, the first is the value of A, the second is the value of X, the third is the value of I, and statement number 5 tells us where the numbers will be on the card.

In the FORMAT statement there is a *field specification* for each variable in the list of the READ or PRINT statement. We discuss three types of field specification: one for integer variables, one for floating-point variables, and one for printing text. We take them in that order.

An **integer field specification** consists of the letter I followed by an integer. The integer specifies how many columns of the card or spaces on the printed line are allotted to that variable. For example, if we are allowing 5 columns for an integer on a card, we write I5 as the field specification in the FORMAT statement.

Before going on we take a specific example. Suppose we want to read the values of the integer variables K, L, M, and N from one card. Suppose K and N can be as large as 9999 but L and M will never be larger than 999. Then we need 4 columns for the first and last and only 3 columns for the middle two. We could use the following FORMAT statement:

5   FORMAT (I4, I3, I3, I4)

and the READ statement

READ 5, K, L, M, N

The card with the numbers on it should have the value of K punched in the first 4 columns, the value of L in columns 5 to 7, the value of M in columns 8 to 10, and the value of N in columns 11 to 14.

The card might look like the one shown in Figure 1, where K will be 261, L will be 23, M will be 249, and N will be −91.

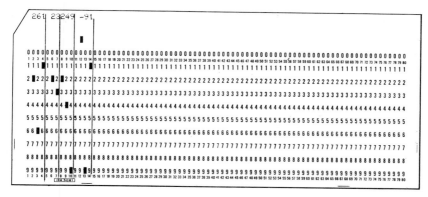

Figure 1

Card used for reading for integers in FORTRAN

For positive integers the $+$ sign may be punched or it may be left out when punching a card. When using a PRINT statement, the $+$ is never printed. For negative integers the $-$ sign must be punched, and it is printed. The number of columns or spaces used in the FORMAT statement must include room for the $-$ sign if it is likely to occur. Thus, if an integer can vary between -99 and $+99$, a specification of I3 should be used (one for the sign and two for the digits).

A **floating-point field specification** consists of a letter F followed by an integer, a decimal point, and another integer. The first integer following F specifies the number of columns or spaces allowed for the number, including the sign and decimal point. The second number specifies the number of digits *after* the decimal point. For example, F 8.4 means that we will read (or print) a floating-point number using 8 columns (or spaces) with 4 digits following the decimal point. There can be at most 2 digits in front of the decimal point, because 6 columns are accounted for by the 4 digits after the decimal point, the sign, and the decimal point itself.

The previous discussion means that we must know how big the numbers can get. If, for example, we used an F 8.4 field specification for a PRINT statement and the result turned out to be -321.6782, then we would not have room because this uses 9 spaces. In this case, the minus sign would be lost, and we would print the erroneous result 321.6782. There are other field specifications which avoid this difficulty, but we do not discuss them here.

We return now to the FORTRAN program written in Section 1.9 of Chapter 1. Toward the end the following statements appear:

25   PRINT 1, X(1)

     PRINT 1, X(2)

     PRINT 1, X(3)

     PRINT 1, X(4)

100 STOP

  1 FORMAT (F 10.4)

It should now be clear what these statements do. Statement 25 says: "print the value of $X(1) = x_1$ on the first line using 10 spaces and having 4 digits after the decimal point." As we can assume that x_1 is never bigger than 9, this will leave at least 3 blanks in front of the number (7 spaces will be used: 1 for the sign, 1 for the digit in front of the decimal, 1 for the decimal point itself, and 4 for the digits after the decimal point). When several numbers are printed on a line, blanks are often purposely left to make the numbers easier to read.

Question.   What do the three PRINT statements following statement 25 do?

With either I or F field specifications, if the actual number is larger than that allowed in the specification, the *left-most* digits are lost in printing. In reading cards, if the number does not require all the columns allotted to it, it should be punched in the *right-most* columns. See, for example, the punched card in Figure 1, where the blanks, if any, are in front (to the left) of the number.

Suppose we wanted to print the four answers from the linear equations problem in Chapter 1 on one line. Suppose again that we know that each variable cannot be greater than 9. Now we also suppose that we know that all variables will be positive, so we do not have to allow room for the − sign (+ signs are not printed). We decide to print only three digits after the decimal point, and we would like at least four blank spaces between numbers to make them easier to read. The following three statements can be substituted for the six statements used in Chapter 1.

25   PRINT 1, X(1), X(2), X(3), X(4)

100 STOP

  1 FORMAT (F 9.3, F 9.3, F 9.3, F 9.3)

Notice that the specification fields in a FORMAT statement are separated by commas and enclosed in parentheses. In PRINT and READ statements the FORMAT statement number follows the word PRINT or READ with a space but no comma separating the statement number and the word PRINT (READ). The FORMAT statement number is followed by a comma and a list of the variables to be printed or read, all separated by commas. The punctuation described in this paragraph is important. If it is not adhered to strictly the FORTRAN program will not run correctly.

Question. What is wrong with the following FORTRAN statements?

    (a)   6   FORMAT, F 6.4, I2, F 7.3

    (b)   FORMAT (I1, I2, F 6.4)

    (c)   PRINT 5 (A, X, B)

    (d)   7   FORMAT (F 4.6, I3)

    (e)   READ, 5, X(1)

So far we have only learned how to read and print numbers. For reading this is usually adequate. For printing, however, we usually like to print some letters or words which describe the results. For example, in Chapter 2 we printed "X(1) =" followed by the value of x_1, and so forth. To print text we need one more type of field specification.

A **Hollerith**[12] **field specification** starts with an integer specifying the number of characters (letters, numbers, or symbols) to be printed, followed by the letter H, followed by the characters to be printed. For example, suppose we use the two statements

   102   PRINT 201

   201   FORMAT (10H UNBOUNDED)

When we encounter the PRINT statement numbered 102, we refer to the FORMAT statement numbered 201. This FORMAT statement says: print the 10 characters following the letter H. The 10 characters are one blank followed by UNBOUNDED, so our typewriter or printer will print the word "unbounded" and nothing else. These two instructions were used in the program in Chapter 2.

---

[12] Named for Herman Hollerith who invented the punched card code for representing letters and symbols (see footnote 16 in Chapter 1).

For convenience when punching cards the number of blanks is often written as a number with a circle around it. Thus in Chapter 2 we wrote

201   FORMAT (10H ① UNBOUNDED)

The ① is not actually punched. It merely tells the person punching the card to leave one blank space. The symbol ⑬ would mean leave 13 consecutive blank spaces.

In H-type FORMAT statements, blanks are important. Suppose, for example, we wrote

201   FORMAT (10H ④ UNBOUNDED)

When we perform the PRINT statement numbered 102, we will print the 10 characters following the H, which are 4 blanks and UNBOUN. The last three letters, DED, are lost. Some computers may not even accept such a statement.

Question. What would the statement

201   FORMAT (13H ④ UNBOUNDED)

cause to be printed?

Before summarizing, we make one final point. When printing a line, the symbol in the first column governs the spacing of the lines and is not actually printed. That is, depending on what is entered in the first column by the FORMAT statement, the printing may be single-spaced or double-spaced or a new page may be started. In any case, whatever is entered in that first column is not printed. We shall always arrange to have a "blank" in the first column, which will single-space the printed lines. That is the reason for the ① in statement 201 above.

We now summarize the input-output statements discussed in this section. There are three types of statements: READ, PRINT, and FORMAT.

The READ statement reads one card. The word READ is followed by a space and then a number which refers to a FORMAT statement. Following the FORMAT number is a comma and a list of the names of the variables whose values are to be read from the card. The variable names are separated by commas.

The PRINT statement prints one line. The word PRINT is followed by a space then a FORMAT statement number, a comma, and a list of the names of the variables whose values are to be printed. The variable names are separated by commas.

   The FORMAT statement describes how the numbers or letters to be read from cards or printed on paper are to be arranged. There are three types of field specifications: I for integers, F for floating-point numbers, and H for Hollerith. The I format uses the letter I followed by an integer which specifies the number of columns or spaces (plus blanks if any) used by the integer plus sign. The F format uses the letter F followed by two integers separated by a decimal point. The first number specifies the number of columns or spaces (plus blanks if any) used by the number plus sign and decimal point. The second number specifies the number of digits after the decimal point. The H format uses an integer followed by the letter H followed by text. The integer specifies how many characters of text are used. That number of characters immediately following the letter H are used for the text. The FORMAT statement should always arrange for a blank in column 1 when printing.

   A FORMAT statement does not actually do anything itself. It merely tells READ and PRINT statements how to perform their functions. Thus FORMAT statements are called *nonexecutable*. Since they are not executed, they may be placed anywhere in the program. Their order is immaterial. This is not true of the other types of statements we have studied. Arithmetic, control, and read-print statements must be in the proper order. It is customary to try to place FORMAT statements near the READ or PRINT statement that uses them, but it is not necessary.

   Finally we return to the FORMAT statement 200 in Chapter 2 which reads

   200   FORMAT (3H ① X(, I1, 3H) ① =, F 10.4)

This uses all three types of field specifications. One of the PRINT statements that refers to it is

   101   PRINT 200, ITAB (1), B(1)

When this is encountered, the following takes place. The Hollerith characters: "blank X (" are printed. Then a one-digit integer which is the first entry in ITAB is printed. This is followed by three more Hollerith characters, ") blank =," and then a floating-point number which is the value of b_1. The result looks like

   X(1) = 200.0000

   There are other types of FORMAT statements and other types of input-output statements that read magnetic tapes, magnetic disk files, etc. We do not discuss them here but refer the interested reader to *A Guide to FORTRAN Programming* or *A Guide to FORTRAN IV Programming*, both by Daniel D. McCracken (published by John Wiley and Sons, Inc., in 1961 and 1965, respectively).

3.8* Alternate Input-Output Statements — READ and WRITE

Most computers which use FORTRAN will accept the READ and PRINT statements described in Section 3.8. A few, however, will not accept them, and we describe here slight modifications to these statements which will make them acceptable to these other computers.

Computers which will not accept the READ and PRINT statements described in Section 3.8 include the *minimal* IBM System/360, the IBM 1130, the IBM 1800, the IBM 1440, the IBM 1460, the PDP-7, the DATA 620, the CDC 1700, the CDC 160, the SEL 810/840, the Hewlett-Packard HP-2116A, the Honeywell 200, and the Honeywell 1200/2200/4200. The READ and WRITE statements described in this section should be used for these computing systems. For all other computers listed in Appendix E, the statements

$$\text{READ } n, \text{ list}$$

and

$$\text{PRINT } n, \text{ list}$$

should be used as described in Section 3.8.

For the computers named above (which also are marked with an asterisk in Appendix E), the following READ and WRITE statements should be used. To read one card the statement

$$\text{READ } (m, n) \text{ list}$$

is used. Here m is an integer constant which designates the *card reader*. Just what integer it is depends upon the particular computer. The number of the FORMAT statement is the integer constant n. The "list" is a list of variables to be read according to the FORMAT statement labeled n. Entries in the list are separated by commas.

By contrast the equivalent READ statement described in Section 3.8 is

$$\text{READ } n, \text{ list}$$

Some computers accept either form.

To print one line the statement

WRITE (m, n) list

is used. Here m is an integer constant which designates the *printer* or *typewriter*. The value of m depends on the particular computer. Once again, n is the number of the appropriate FORMAT statement, and "list" is the list of variables to be printed.

For contrast the equivalent PRINT statement from Section 3.8 is

PRINT n, list

Some computers will accept either READ n, list or READ (m, n) list. Those computers will also accept either PRINT n, list or WRITE (m, n) list. In any case the form of *the FORMAT statement is unchanged.*

There are three special cases which need to be discussed. They are FORTRAN for the PDP-7, the CDC 160, and the IBM 1620 when FORGO is used instead of FORTRAN. For the PDP-7 the proper statements are

READ m, n, list

and

WRITE m, n, list

where m, n and list have the same meanings as they do above. The point to note is that the left parenthesis is missing, and the right parenthesis has been replaced by a comma.

There is one more possibility. When the CDC 160 is used, or when FORGO (a special version of FORTRAN) is used on the IBM 1620, all PRINT statements should be replaced by PUNCH statements. That is, instead of

PRINT n, list

one should use

PUNCH n, list

The READ statements used by FORGO and the CDC 160 are those described in Section 3.8:

READ n, list

In all that follows, we shall always use READ n, list and PRINT n, list. The reader using any of the computing systems listed in the beginning of this section should change these statements in accordance with the rules above.

3.9 DIMENSION Statements

There are three other FORTRAN statements which we used in earlier chapters but which have not yet been explained. They are the DIMENSION, STOP, and END statements.

The DIMENSION statement is used with subscripted variables. It specifies: (1) which variables are subscripted, (2) how many subscripts there are for each variable, and (3) the *largest possible value* for each subscript. For example, if we write

DIMENSION A(10, 8)

we know that the variable A has two subscripts. The first subscript may be any positive integer up to and including 10. The second subscript can be 8 or less. The reason for specifying this information is to enable the computer to set aside enough of its memory for the subscripted variables. In the example above it must set aside 80 memory cells: one for A(1, 1), one for A(1, 2), and so forth up to A(10, 8). For a nonsubscripted variable only one memory cell is needed to retain the current value of that variable.

A DIMENSION statement is nonexecutable. That is, it does not perform any action itself. In that respect it is similar to the FORMAT statement. However, *the DIMENSION statement for any subscripted variable must appear before any other statement using the variable.* Therefore, it is customary to put all DIMENSION statements at the beginning of the program.

One DIMENSION statement may refer to any number of subscripted variables. For example, in Chapter 1 we wrote

DIMENSION A(4, 4), B(4), X(4)

which tells the computer it will need $4 \times 4 = 16$ memory cells for the 16 coefficients in the four equations, it will need 4 memory cells for the four right-hand sides of the equations, and 4 memory cells for the values of x_1, x_2, x_3, and x_4.

At least one blank or space must follow the last letter of the word DIMENSION.

Question. How many memory cells are set aside by the following DIMENSION statement taken from Chapter 2?

DIMENSION A(4, 2), B(4), ITAB(4), JTAB(2), C(2)

We remind the reader that subscripts must never be less than 1; zero and negative subscripts are not permitted.

3.10 STOP and END Statements

The STOP statement stops the computer. It signals that the present problem is finished or has encountered an error beyond which we do not wish to go or cannot go. In many computing centers several programs are performed on the computer one after another. In these cases it may be inconvenient for the person operating the computer to have programs with STOP statements. When a STOP statement is encountered, the computer operator will have to take some action — push buttons, load in cards, etc. This is wasteful because the computer is not doing any useful work while the operator is doing these things. For this reason many computing centers do not allow programmers to use the STOP statement. The procedures vary, but one common way is to substitute a statement CALL EXIT where STOP would normally be. This allows the computer to go on immediately to the next person's program. We do not discuss the details of how this is accomplished.

The STOP or CALL EXIT statement stops the *execution* of a program. It may appear anywhere in a program and may in fact appear in many places. In addition the computer needs to know which is the last physical card in a program. The END statement does that.

An END *statement is always the last card in a program.* This means that it is physically the last card, in contrast to the last card executed which is a STOP (or CALL EXIT). In fact, the END statement, like the FORMAT and DIMENSION statements, is nonexecutable.

Finally, we wish to discuss a new symbol, ******, arithmetic with integers, the use of integers and floating-point variables in the same statement, and DO and CONTINUE statements.

3.11 Raising to a Power

We often wish to raise a number (integer or floating-point) to a power. If we wish to write $y = x^4$ we can write

$$Y = X * X * X * X$$

A simpler way is to write

$$Y = X**4$$

The double asterisk is considered to be one symbol and indicates that the expression preceding it is to be raised to the power following it.

We can raise floating-point numbers to either integer or floating-point powers. Thus,

$$Z = X**5$$

and

$$R = Z**3.4$$

and

$$S = Y**X$$

are all legitimate. However, integers can be raised only to integer powers; thus,

$$I = J**2$$

is valid but

$$I = K**3.1$$

is *not* valid.

In an expression involving $+$, $-$, $*$, $/$ and $**$, the $**$ are performed first followed by $*$ and $/$, and finally $+$ and $-$. Of course, parentheses can be used to alter this ordering.

3.12 Arithmetic with Integers

When we add, subtract, or multiply integers, the result is always an integer. Thus

$$I = 4 + 2$$

$$I = 7 - 1$$

$$I = 2 * 3$$

do not present any difficulties. In each case $I = 6$.

Suppose, however, we write the FORTRAN statement

$$I = 7 / 2$$

The result of the division is certainly not an integer. What value is given to I? The rule which FORTRAN uses is: I will be the largest integer less than or equal to $7 / 2$. Thus, $I = 3$.

Let us take a more general case. Let

$$I = J / K$$

Then I will be the whole number part of the ratio J / K. *The remainder is thrown away.* In other words, J is divided by K and the result is "rounded" or "chopped" to the nearest integer toward zero. For example, if J = 13 and K = 6, then I = 2. If, however, J = −13 and K = 6 then I = −2.

If J and K have the same sign, then I is less than or equal to the ratio J / K. If, on the other hand, J and K have opposite signs, then I is greater than or equal to the ratio J / K.

Table 1 summarizes some of the possibilities.

Table 1

J	K	I	J	K	I
0	anything not zero	0	12	6	2
4	6	0	−12	6	−2
−4	6	0	21	7	3
6	6	1	−21	−7	3
8	6	1	27	7	3
8	−6	−1	143	12	11
			−143	12	−11

Suppose now we wish to know what the remainder is upon dividing the two *positive* integers, J and K. If we let

$$I = J / K$$

then I is the quotient. If we multiply this by K we do not in general get J. We get J *less the remainder* from the division. Therefore, the remainder L is given by

$$L = J − K * I$$

Rather than use the two statements

$$I = J / K$$

$$L = J − K * I$$

we could use the one statement

$$L = J − K * (J / K)$$

Problem. Using Table 1, verify that L as defined above is the remainder for the numerical examples in the table for which both J and K are positive.

We shall find these concepts and rules useful in Chapter 9.

3.13   Converting Integers to Floating-Point Numbers

Another frequently encountered problem appears when we want to use an integer in a floating-point calculation. This is not possible from what we have said thus far, but we can write

$$X = I$$

in which case the integer I is transformed to a floating-point number numerically equal to I and is called X. Thus the sequence

$$I = 4$$

$$X = I$$

$$Y = 3.5 * (X - 1.5)$$

produces Y = 8.75.

It is also possible to transform floating-point numbers to integers. Since floating-point numbers in general will have a fractional part, there are some difficulties in making such a transformation, and we will not use such operations in this text.

3.14   DO Statements

Finally we come to one of the most powerful FORTRAN statements, the DO statement. It simplifies the writing of loops and is more convenient and less subject to clerical errors than the IF and GO TO combination which we have used so far.

The DO statement is written as follows:

$$DO \ n \ i = \ell, m$$

where n is a statement number, i is a nonsubscripted integer variable, and ℓ and m are unsigned integers or nonsubscripted integer variables. For example,

$$DO \ 57 \ I = 1, 10$$

might be used. Here n = 57, i = I, ℓ = 1, and m = 10.

The statements following the DO, up to and including the statement numbered n, are executed repeatedly. They are first executed with i = ℓ. The second time they are executed they are done with i = $\ell + 1$. The third time i = $\ell + 2$, and so on. After these statements are executed with i = m, they are no longer executed.

Another example is

$$DO\ 30\ J = I,\ K$$

Here n = 30, i = J, ℓ = I, and m = K.

However, i, ℓ, *and* m *must not be expressions*. They must be constants or single variable names. In particular, expressions such as

$$DO\ 20\ I = 1,\ N + 1$$

are not allowed. Here m = N + 1, and this is not permissible.

We illustrate the use of the DO statement with an example. Suppose we wish to add 10 numbers X(1), X(2), . . . , X(10) and call the result, SUM. We can write

    SUM = 0.0

    DO 6 I = 1, 10

6   SUM = SUM + X(I)

We shall analyze this in detail. We first set SUM equal to zero. The DO statement says set I = 1 and perform all the succeeding statements up to and including the one numbered 6. There is only one such statement, the one numbered 6 itself. We do this as follows: Take SUM (now equal to 0) and add X(1) to it (I = 1), calling the result SUM. We now increase I by 1, making it 2, and perform statement 6 again. Since SUM = X(1), we add X(2) to it so SUM will be equal to X(1) + X(2). We continue to add successive X's until X(10) is added. We then go on to whatever follows.

If we used the GO TO and IF statements on this problem we would write

    SUM = 0.0

    I = 1

6   SUM = SUM + X(I)

    IF (I − 10) 3, 4, 4

3   I = I + 1

    GO TO 6

4   Whatever follows

or something equivalent to it. Clearly, this is more complicated and more susceptible to mistakes on the part of the programmer than the program using the DO statement.

The set of repeatedly executed statements (statement 6 in our example) is called the **range** of the DO statement. The integer variable which increases by 1 each time the statements in the range are executed is called the **index** of the DO statement. The DO statement together with the statements in its range often are referred to as a **DO loop.**

There may be DO loops within DO loops. They correspond to inner and outer loops in a flow chart. For example, consider the flow chart for Gauss's method given in Figure 19 of Chapter 1. The inner loop given by boxes 6, 7, 8, and 9 in the flow chart can be programmed as follows.

DO 7 I = K, 4

7   A(J, I) = A(J, I) − Y * A(K, I)

Here I is set equal to K and the statement numbered 7 is performed; that is, we compute A(J, K) − Y * A(K, K). (Recall that we use Y in place of M because it is a floating-point variable.) K and J will have been given values earlier in the program. I is then increased by 1 to K + 1 and statement 7 is repeated. This continues until I = 4.

Now this loop is within another loop given by boxes 3, 5, 6, 7, 8, 10, 11, and 12 in Figure 19 of Chapter 1. If we again ignore box 4 we may write the outer loop with index *j* as follows

KA = K + 1

DO 10 J = KA, 4

Y = A(J, K) / A(K, K)

DO 7 I = K, 4

7   A(J, I) = A(J, I) − Y * A(K, I)

10   B(J) = B(J) − Y * B(K)

The first statement defines a new variable, KA, which is 1 greater than K. We need to do this because the index of the DO statement following should vary from K + 1 to 4 but the statement

DO 10 J = K + 1, 4

is not allowed. In particular, we cannot use an expression with the operations $+$, $-$, $*$, $/$ as either the lower or the upper limit. Thus, we circumvent this difficulty by defining a new variable, KA.

The fourth and fifth lines of the program above accomplish the same thing as the two FORTRAN statements written earlier and represent the inner loop or the inner DO. Again K will have been assigned a value previously. The first DO statement says: do all the succeeding statements up to and including statement 10 first with $J = KA = K + 1$, then with $J = K + 2$, and so on until $J = 4$. Thus we first compute $Y = A(K + 1, K) / A(K, K)$. The next statement is another DO. We perform that DO, which means performing statement 7 for $I = K$, $I = K + 1$, ..., $I = 4$. After completing that DO loop, we compute $B(K + 1) = B(K + 1) - Y * B(K)$. After that, J is set equal to $KA + 1 = K + 2$ and we go back to the third statement of the six statements above.

Of course, there is another loop in Figure 19 which surrounds the two already described. We can include it by adding one more statement. The result is

        DO 10 K = 1, 3

        KA = K + 1

        DO 10 J = KA, 4

        Y = A(J, K) / A(K, K)

        DO 7 I = K, 4

    7   A(J, I) = A(J, I) − Y * A(K, I)

    10 B(J) = B(J) − Y * B(K)

These seven lines represent boxes 1 through 14 (excluding box 4) of Figure 19. Using GO TO and IF statements, this required fifteen FORTRAN statements — more than twice as many.

We now summarize and present all the details regarding the DO statement. The word DO is followed by a space, a statement number, another space, a nonsubscripted integer variable, an $=$ sign, an unsigned integer or nonsubscripted integer variable, a comma, and another unsigned integer or nonsubscripted integer variable. There may be other spaces besides the two required anywhere in the statement except between the letters D and O. *Notice that only one comma and at least two blanks appear in the statement.*

The following rules apply to the use of the DO statement.

(i) The first statement after the DO statement must be executable. Thus, DO cannot be followed immediately by DIMENSION or FORMAT.

(ii) All statements in the range of an inner DO must also be in the range of an outer DO.

(iii) No instructions in the range of a DO may alter the index of that DO.

(iv) It is not permissible to transfer control from outside of the range of a DO into the range of a DO. Specifically, the following is *illegal:*

> DO 1 I = 1, 10
>
> A(I) = B(I) + C(I)
>
> 2   X(I) = A(I) * B(I)
>
> 1   Y(I) = X(I)**I
>
> . . .
>
> . . .
>
> . . .
>
> GO TO 2

(v) The last statement in the range of a DO must not transfer control. That is, the last statement cannot be an IF or a GO TO or another DO. To avoid this a special instruction, CONTINUE, is provided.

(vi) The last statement in the range of a DO must not be a STOP or a READ or a PRINT statement. The CONTINUE statement is also used to circumvent this problem.

As an example of the use of CONTINUE, consider the problem of adding the *absolute values* of the floating-point numbers $X(1), \ldots, X(10)$. We call the result SUM:

$$SUM = |X(1)| + |X(2)| + \cdots + |X(10)|$$

A partial program to perform this is as follows:

> SUM = 0.0
>
> DO 3 I = 1, 10

IF (X(I)) 1, 3, 2

1   SUM = SUM − X(I)

GO TO 3

2   SUM = SUM + X(I)

3   ?

We first set SUM to zero and then proceed to a DO loop which adds |X(I)| each time it is performed. To do this we first see if X(I) is positive or negative. If it is positive we want to add X(I), so we go to statement 2 and then to statement 3, which we have yet to complete. If X(I) is negative we want to subtract X(I), so we go to statement 1, then to statement 3. If X(I) = 0 we simply go to statement 3.

The question which arises is: What are we to put in statement 3? If we try to use a GO TO where should it go? If we transfer to the DO statement we will start the DO loop all over again with I = 1. We really want to increase I by 1 and return to the IF statement. On the other hand, a GO TO the IF statement at 3 would indicate that we wish to transfer to the IF statement every time we reach 3. This is not so, because when we reach statement 3 we want to go back only so long as I < 10.

To solve this problem and others like it the CONTINUE statement was invented. We write the word CONTINUE in statement 3. This serves only to complete the DO loop. When CONTINUE is reached, I is increased by 1 if it is less than 10 and control returns to the statement following the DO. In this case it is the IF statement.

There is no logical reason why READ or PRINT cannot be the last statement in the range of a DO loop. In fact, most computers allow READ and PRINT anywhere in a DO loop. Some IBM 1620 computers, however, do not. This is a quirk of that particular FORTRAN.

By way of example, suppose we wish to read five two-digit integers punched one to a card. The integers are punched in the first two columns and are to be called $x_1, \ldots, x_5$. On most computers the following program would be correct:

DO 1 I = 1, 5

1   READ 100, X(I)

100   FORMAT (I2)

However, some IBM 1620 computers require the following:

    DO 1 I = 1, 5

    READ 100, X(I)

  1   CONTINUE

100   FORMAT (I2)

Of course, in either case the FORMAT statement can be placed any-where except immediately after the DO statement itself.

To avoid difficulties arising from the requirements of different com-puters we shall use the latter form. It is acceptable to all computers.

We now have completed all of the FORTRAN which we shall use in the remainder of the text. We turn now to an example which uses most of the FORTRAN we have learned.

3.15   Gauss's Method for Any Number of Equations

We now write a FORTRAN program to solve a system of any number[13] of linear equations in the same number of variables. We shall use the flow charts in Figures 19 and 20 of Chapter 1 except that the 4's in boxes 8, 11, 15, 17 are changed to N (the number of equations) and the 3's in boxes 13 and 16 are changed to N − 1. The reader should assure himself of the meanings of these changes. The program is shown below. We shall analyze it in detail.

    DIMENSION A(10, 10), B(10), X(10)

  1   READ 100, N

100   FORMAT (I2)

    DO 2 I = 1, N

    DO 2 J = 1, N

    READ 200, A(I, J)

  2   CONTINUE

200   FORMAT (F 10.4)

    DO 3 I = 1, N

---

[13] Of course, the number will be limited by the size of the computer memory. We assume that the number of equations never exceeds 10.

```
        READ 200, B(I)
  3   CONTINUE
        NS = N − 1
        DO 10 K = 1, NS
        KA = K + 1
        DO 10 J = KA, N
        Y = A(J, K) / A(K, K)
        DO 7 I = K, N
  7   A(J, I) = A(J, I) − Y * A(K, I)
 10   B(J) = B(J) − Y * B(K)
        X(N) = B(N) / A(N, N)
        DO 22 L = 1, NS
        K = N − L
        Y = 0.0
        NSK = N − K
        DO 20 M = 1, NSK
        I = N − M + 1
 20   Y = Y + A(K, I) * X(I)
 22   X(K) = (B(K) − Y) / A(K, K)
        DO 30 I = 1, N
        PRINT 300, I, X(I)
 30   CONTINUE
300   FORMAT (3H ① X(, I2, 4H) ① = ①, F10.4)
        STOP
        END
```

We give the maximum size of A, B, and X in the DIMENSION statement. In any given problem none of these may be this maximum size, but our computer will always save enough of its memory to accommodate ten equations and ten variables. If we have a system of four equations, some of the memory which has been set aside will be unused.

We then read a card which tells us how many equations we are going to solve. Next we use two DO statements to read the A(I, J) and another DO statement to read the B(I). Notice that the integer N must be read *before* A(I, J) and B(I) are read. Otherwise the computer will not know the upper limit on the DO statements.

Notice also that we do not allow a READ statement to be the last statement in a DO loop. This is to accommodate IBM 1620 computers.

The next eight statements (down to and including 10) are those previously described in this chapter. They reduce the original equations to triangular form. We then proceed to back substitution as shown in Figure 20 of Chapter 1.

In Figure 20 the indices K and I in the loops decrease as we go through the loops. DO loops, however, always increase the index. In order to use DO statements then, we define a new index, $L = N - K$. Thus, as K decreases, L increases. If we start with $K = N - 1$ then $L = 1$. As K decreases by 1, L increases by 1. When K is reduced to 1, then $L = N - 1$. Therefore, we write our DO loop with L going from 1 up to $N - 1$, and $K = N - L$. If we do this, K will decrease from $N - 1$ to 1. The outer DO starting with DO 22 $L = 1$, NS and ending with statement 22 does just that.

We have a similar problem with the inner loop. The index I decreases from N to $K + 1$ in steps of 1. Thus, we replace I by $M = N - I + 1$ so that M increases from 1 to $N - K$ in steps of 1. The four statements

$$NSK = N - K$$

$$DO\ 20\ M = 1,\ NSK$$

$$I = N - M + 1$$

$$20\quad Y = Y + A(K, I) * X(I)$$

do that for us.

Finally, we use another DO loop to print the results. Once again, we use the CONTINUE statement to end the loop.

When we perform substitutions as we have done above, we must be careful that *no subscript ever becomes zero or negative*. This is not allowed in FORTRAN.

A deck of punched cards containing the FORTRAN statements

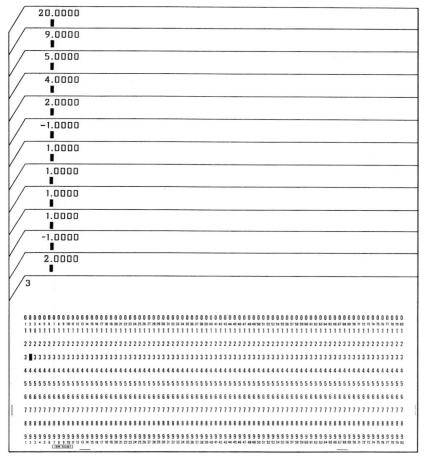

Figure 2

Input cards for solving system of three linear equations

above should be followed by a set of cards containing values of N, A(I, J), and B(I). For example, suppose we wished to solve the three equations

$$2x_1 - x_2 + x_3 = 5$$

$$x_1 + x_2 + x_3 = 9$$

$$-x_1 + 2x_2 + 4x_3 = 20$$

The cards containing the data would look like those in Figure 2.

```
X( 1 ) =      2.0000
X( 2 ) =      3.0000
X( 3 ) =      4.0000
```

Figure 3

Computer results from solving system of three linear equations

The first card contains the number of equations, 3. The next three cards contain the coefficients of x_1, x_2, and x_3 in the *first* equation. The three coefficients in the second equation follow and so on. We must be careful not to try to read the three coefficients of x_1 first followed by the coefficients of x_2. That is, the coefficients are to be read row by row *not* column by column. To understand this we must examine the READ loops.

Since the index of the inner DO in the READ loop is J (the second subscript), J goes from 1 to 3 while I is held fixed at 1. Then I increases to 2 and we perform the inner loop again. Thus we read A(1, 1), A(1, 2), A(1, 3), A(2, 1), A(2, 2), A(2, 3), A(3, 1), A(3, 2), A(3, 3), in that order.

This program with the data was run on a computer with the results shown in Figure 3.

Now a typical way of using a computer is not to solve just one system of equations but to solve many systems of equations. We might wish to change a few of the coefficients and note the resulting change in the solution. For example, if we were solving the diet problem we might like to know if a change in the protein content of the meat would seriously affect the diet.

To make our program do this we merely replace the STOP statement with the statement GO TO 1. This causes a new N to be read, and the program starts all over reading coefficients, solving the equations, and printing results. Thus, the cards containing the FORTRAN program must be followed by the data (N, A(I, J), B(I)) for several systems of linear equations.

The observant reader has already realized that by replacing STOP by GO TO 1 we have formed a large outer loop from which there is no exit. In fact, there is no STOP anywhere in the program. The program will read cards indefinitely or at least try to do so. One way out of this unhappy situation is to notice that N, the number of equations, always must be a positive integer. Thus, if the program reads a value of N which is zero, it should stop. Our present program does not do this.

Problem.   Alter the preceding program to stop if it ever reads a value of zero for N.

Our procedure is as follows. We have our computer read our program followed by the data for as many systems of linear equations as we wish. The data for each system contains, in order, the number of equations, the coefficients row by row, and the right-hand sides row by row. Following the data for the last system to be solved is a card with a zero punched in column 2.

The reader should try this process for solving several systems of equations. The data in Exercise 1 can be used.

3.16 Summary of FORTRAN Language

We close this chapter with a summary of the FORTRAN that we have learned, and which we shall use throughout the remainder of the text. We emphasize that the rules we set forth are overly restrictive in order that all programs will run on all the computers listed in Appendix E.

In the following, blanks which are indicated by an integer in a circle must be placed in punched cards. For example, ① means place one blank where the ① is placed. *Underlined words must not have any blanks interspersed in them.*

Constants are integers if no decimal point is present. They are floating-point numbers if a decimal point is present.

Variables have names which have one to five letters and/or digits. The first symbol in the name must be a letter. If the first letter is I, J, K, L, M, or N, the variable is an integer variable. Otherwise, it is a floating-point variable. If the name contains four or five symbols, the last symbol cannot be the letter F. There are 56 names which are not legal variable names. They are listed in Section 3.3.

Subscripts must be either an integer constant, an integer variable, or the sum or difference of an integer constant and an integer variable. Subscripts must always be positive. Every subscripted variable must be used in a DIMENSION statement before it appears elsewhere. The form of the DIMENSION statement is:

$$\underline{\text{DIMENSION}} \ ① \ A(m, n), B(i)$$

where m, n, and i are integer constants and are the maximum values of the subscripts.

Statement numbers should not exceed 9999.

Arithmetic statements have one variable followed by an = sign, followed by an expression. All variables in any one statement must be of the same type (integer or floating-point) except when the expression on the right of the = sign is an integer variable and nothing else. In the latter case, the variable on the left may be a floating-point variable. This is used to convert integers to floating-point numbers.

Control statements have one of the following forms:

$$\underline{GO} \enspace ① \enspace \underline{TO} \enspace ① \enspace i$$

$$\underline{IF} \enspace (X) \enspace i, \enspace j, \enspace k$$

$$\underline{DO} \enspace ① \enspace i \enspace ① \enspace n = \ell, \enspace m$$

$$\underline{CONTINUE}$$

$$\underline{STOP}$$

where i, j, and k are statement numbers; n is a nonsubscripted integer variable; and ℓ and m are unsigned integer constants or nonsubscripted integer variables. Finally, X is any expression.

Input-Output statements have one of the following forms:

$$\underline{READ} \enspace ① \enspace i, \enspace list \qquad or \qquad \underline{READ} \enspace (m, \enspace i) \enspace list$$

$$\underline{PRINT} \enspace ① \enspace i, \enspace list \qquad or \qquad \underline{WRITE} \enspace (m, \enspace i) \enspace list$$

$$i \enspace \underline{FORMAT} \enspace (A, \enspace B, \enspace \dots, \enspace C)$$

where i is a statement number; m is an integer constant which designates the card reader or printer; and A, B, and C are field specifications. Computers in Appendix E which are *not* marked with an asterisk use the READ and PRINT statements on the left. Those which are marked with an asterisk in Appendix E use the READ and WRITE statements on the right. There are three exceptions: the PDP-7, the CDC 160 and the IBM 1620 when using FORGO. Section 3.8* should be consulted when using any of these systems.

Field specifications take one of the three forms:

$$In$$

for integer constants (n is the number of columns used by the integer plus its sign);

$$Fn.d$$

for floating-point constants (n is the number of columns used by the number including the decimal point and the sign, and d is the number of digits after the decimal point);

$$nHtext$$

for printed text where n is the number of characters (letters, numbers, or symbols) to be printed, and "text" lists the actual symbols to be printed. In printed results always arrange to have a blank in the first column.

In all programs in the remainder of this text we use the READ n, list *and* PRINT n, list statements on the left above. Users of computers marked with an asterisk in Appendix E should change all these statements. The FORTRAN manual for the particular computer should be consulted to determine the proper value for m.

The **last card** should always be

$$\underline{\text{END}}$$

Exercises

Answers to exercises marked * are given in Appendix A.

*1. Solve the following systems of linear equations.

(a) $x - 2y = 1$
        $2x - 2y = 0$

(b) $x + .y + z = 4$
        $2x + 2y - z = 2$
        $x \qquad + z = 3$

(c) $a - b \qquad\qquad = 3$
        $\qquad b + c + d = 6$
        $a \qquad\qquad + d = 5$
        $-a - b + c + d = 6$

2. Alter the program in Section 3.15 to

   (a) Check to see that $N \geq 2$ (The DO statement two lines below statement 3 requires this.) Print N LESS THAN 2 if the check fails and then stop.

   (b) Check to see that we never try to divide by zero. Print DIVISION BY ZERO if the check fails and then stop.

*3. Write a FORTRAN program which (1) reads a floating-point number from a card; (2) using this number as the radius, computes the area and the circumference of a circle; (3) prints the results; and (4) reads another card. Make the program stop when it reads a radius larger than 100.0.

4. Write a FORTRAN program which (1) reads two floating-point numbers from a card; (2) using the first number as the base and the second

number as the altitude, computes the area of the triangle with that base and altitude and the rhombus with that base and altitude; (3) prints the results; and (4) reads another card. Make the program stop if the altitude exceeds the base.

*5. Write the following numbers as floating-point numbers:

    (a) 17623.15   (b) -326.592 (c) $-.00023$

    (d) 869.288   (e) 1.000035   (f) -100.265

*6. Write the numbers in Exercise 5 as they would appear in a computer with 5 digits in the mantissa and 1 digit in the exponent. Use chopping to perform any round-offs necessary.

*7. What is wrong with the following FORTRAN statements?

    (a) X + Y = A   (b) GOTO13   (c) J = I**3.0

    (d) DO   5, I = 1, 3   (e) X = 3,212.16

8. What is wrong with the following FORTRAN statements?

    (a) IF = IF + 1   (b) GOTO13   (c) 5 FORMAT (F4.7)

    (d) X = H + I   (e) X = 3,212.16

*9. Write a FORTRAN program that prints three blank lines.

10. Write a FORTRAN program that prints four lines which are blank except that an integer which represents the number of that line appears ten spaces in from the left edge of the paper.

*11. Let A = $.3652 \times 10^4$, B = $.9000 \times 10^0$, and C = $.1000 \times 10^0$. Assume that you have a computer with 4 digits in the mantissa and which "chops" after additions.

    (a) Find the following sums, doing operations in parentheses first:

$$S = (A + B) + C$$

$$R = A + (B + C)$$

    Explain why $R \neq S$.

    (b) Would S change if B were $.3000 \times 10^0$? Would R change?

    (c) Suppose B and C have *any* mantissa but still an exponent of zero. Will this change S? Why?

12. Draw a flow chart to describe what must be done to the mantissas and exponents when we multiply two floating-point numbers. Assume 4 digits in the mantissa and 1 digit in the exponent.

13. (a) Write a FORTRAN program which will solve a linear programming problem of the form

Maximize $\qquad c_1x_1 + c_2x_2 + \cdots + c_nx_n$

$$a_{11}x_1 + a_{12}x_2 + \cdots + a_{1n}x_n \leq b_1$$

$$a_{21}x_1 + a_{22}x_2 + \cdots + a_{2n}x_n \leq b_2$$

$$\cdot \qquad\qquad\qquad\qquad \cdot$$
$$\cdot \qquad\qquad\qquad\qquad \cdot$$
$$\cdot \qquad\qquad\qquad\qquad \cdot$$

$$a_{m1}x_1 + a_{m2}x_2 + \cdots + a_{mn}x_n \leq b_m$$

Assume all $b_i > 0$ and that m never exceeds 15 and n never exceeds 12.

(b) Arrange to solve several programs in succession.

*14. Write a FORTRAN program to check whether $X(1)$, $X(2)$, . . . , $X(N)$ is a solution of N linear equations. Read the $X(J)$, $A(I, J)$, $B(I)$ from cards and print some indication of the accuracy of the solution.

15. (a) Suppose the protein content of 100 grams of roast beef is between 18 and 22 grams. Solve the four-food diet problem nine times with the protein in roast beef 18 grams, then 18.5 grams, and 19, 19.5, 20, 20.5, 21, 21.5, and 22 grams.

(b) Draw a graph showing how the amount of roast beef in the diet depends on the amount of protein in the beef. We say that the beef in the diet is a *function of* (depends upon) the protein in the beef.

(c) Draw a graph showing how the salad in the diet depends on the protein in the roast beef. The amount of salad is also a *function* of the protein in the roast beef.

(d) The roast beef in the diet depends on many things. List the quantities of which the beef in the diet is a *function. Hint:* There are 20 quantities.

16. The symbol $[x]$ is often used in mathematics to refer to the *integral part of x,* i.e., $[x]$ is the largest integer less than or equal to x. For example, if $x = 3.9$ then $[x] = 3$, and if $x = 4$ then $[x] = 4$ as well. Suppose, on the other hand, that $x = -3.9$, then $[x] = -4$ since -4 is the largest integer not exceeding -3.9. Thus $[x] \leq x$ for all x.

Write a FORTRAN program to compute $y = [x]$ for positive, zero, and negative x.

17. Suppose X(1), X(2), . . . , X(N) have been computed and are all greater than or equal to zero. Assume that N is never larger than 20.

*(a) Write a FORTRAN program which finds which of these is the largest.

(b) Write a FORTRAN program which reorders the numbers so that X(1) ≥ X(2) ≥ ··· ≥ X(N). This process is called *sorting* because we sort numbers into a given order.

18. What is I equal to in the following programs?

*(a) J = 2	(b) I = 3	(c) K = 4
K = 3	J = 2	J = 8
I = J + K	J = J/I	I = K + J
I = (I/J) + (I/K)	I = I + J	I = I/K

19. A prime number is an integer greater than one which, upon division by another positive integer other than itself and 1, results in a quotient which is not an integer. Write a FORTRAN program which tests any one- or two-digit integer and determines if it is a prime number. Print the integer followed by two spaces and either the word PRIME or the words NOT PRIME. Test the program on the two integers, 39 and 53.

*20. Write a FORTRAN program which prints out all the prime numbers less than or equal to 99.

21. Suppose we wish to find all the prime numbers $\leq n^2$. We first find all the prime numbers, $p_1, p_2, . . . , p_k$ such that $p_i \leq n$. We then strike out all numbers of the form rp_i, where $r = 1, 2, . . . ,$ as long as $rp_i \leq n^2$. The numbers remaining are all the prime numbers $\leq n^2$.

Use the results of Exercise 20 and the rule above to write a FORTRAN program to find all the prime numbers less than or equal to 1000. How many are there?

This method is due to the Greek mathematician Eratosthenes (276–194 B.C.). Since it sorts out the nonprimes, leaving the primes behind, it is often called the *sieve of Eratosthenes.*

22. Write a FORTRAN program to find all the prime factors of any two-digit integer. The program should read the integer which is punched in columns 4 and 5 of a card. It should print out the integer on one line and all its prime factors on succeeding lines, one per line. It should then read another two-digit integer from a card and continue. If it reads a "zero," the program should stop.

*23. To find the greatest common divisor (g.c.d.) of two positive integers a and b we can use *Euclid's algorithm*. We arrange first that $a > b$. We then divide a by b, getting a quotient q_1 and a remainder r_1. If $r_1 = 0$, then b is the g.c.d. If not, we divide b by r_1, getting a quotient q_2 and a remainder r_2. If $r_2 = 0$, then r_1 is the g.c.d. If not, we divide r_1 by r_2, getting a quotient q_3 and a remainder r_3. We continue this way, dividing r_i by r_{i+1} and getting a quotient q_{i+2} and a remainder r_{i+2} as follows:

$$a = bq_1 + r_1$$

$$b = r_1 q_2 + r_2$$

$$r_1 = r_2 q_3 + r_3$$

$$\cdot$$
$$\cdot$$
$$\cdot$$

$$r_i = r_{i+1} q_{i+2} + r_{i+2} \qquad i = 1, 2, \ldots$$

Eventually $r_{i+2} = 0$ and r_{i+1} is the g.c.d.

(a) Draw a flow chart describing Euclid's algorithm for finding the g.c.d. of two integers.

(b) Write a FORTRAN program to find the g.c.d. of two five-digit integers. You may make use of Lamé's theorem which says that the number of divisions will not exceed five times the number of digits in the smaller number. The program should read the integers from one card and print out the integers and the g.c.d.

24. The least common multiple (l.c.m.) of two integers is the product of the two numbers divided by their greatest common divisor. Using Exercise 23, write a FORTRAN program to find the l.c.m. of two three-digit integers.

*25. In the English currency system there are 20 pence in a shilling and 12 shillings in a pound. Write a FORTRAN program that computes the change in pounds, shillings, and pence from a purchase of 2 pounds, 3 shillings, and 17 pence which is paid for by a 5-pound note.

26. Referring to Exercise 25, write a FORTRAN program which reads a card with four integers. The first three are the pounds, shillings, and pence in a purchase. The fourth is the number of pounds with which the bill is paid. Compute the change and print out the result as:

_____POUNDS, _____SHILLINGS, _____PENCE

*27. The Reverend Zeller has given a formula for computing the day of the week upon which any given date of the Gregorian calendar fell or will fall (see, e.g., *Elementary Number Theory*, J. V. Uspensky and M. A. Heaslet, McGraw-Hill, 1939, pp. 206–211, or *Problems for Computer Solution*, Fred Gruenberger and George Jaffrey, John Wiley and Sons, Inc., 1965, p. 255). Let m be the month of the year, starting with March as $m = 1$. January and February are months 11 and 12 of the *previous* year. Let d be the day of the month. Let y be the year of the century. Let c be the century.

Thus January 22, 1954 has $m = 11$, $d = 22$, $y = 53$ (the previous year), and $c = 19$.

To compute the day of the week on which any date falls we:

   (i) Take the integer part of the ratio $(13m - 1)/5$. Call this A.
  (ii) Take the integer part of the ratio $y/4$. Call this B.
 (iii) Take the integer part of the ratio $c/4$. Call this C.
 (iv) Compute $A + B + C + d + y - 2c$.
  (v) Divide the result of step (iv) by 7 and keep the remainder.

The remainder from step (v) is either 0 or 1 or . . . or 6. Sunday corresponds to 0, Monday to 1, . . . , Saturday to 6.

(a) To check that you understand the process determine that January 22, 1954 fell on Friday.

(b) Write a FORTRAN program which reads three integers with a FORMAT:

FORMAT (I2, I2, I4)

The first is the month of the year with January as the first month, the second is the day of the month, and the third is the year. Compute the day of the week on which the date falls. Print out the result. Check the program using the result in (a) above.

(c) Test the program by using it to find on what day of the week you were born.

(d) Use the program to find on what day of the week July 4, 1776 fell.

28. Alter the program in Exercise 27 to find when the next time Washington's Birthday will produce a three-day weekend.

CHAPTER FOUR

Never-Ending Algorithms

4.1 Never-Ending or Infinite Algorithms

In Chapter 1 we studied Gauss's method, which is an algorithm or procedure for solving systems of linear equations. This algorithm could be described as *finite* in length; that is, after a definite number of instructions (such as adding two numbers or testing whether a number is zero or not) have been carried out, the algorithm is ended. When the algorithm ends, either the problem is solved or, if there is no solution, this fact is discovered. The number of steps required to carry out these instructions can be exactly determined from the flow chart by seeing how many times each loop must be repeated and counting the number of multiplications, additions, etc., that must be performed. However, there are problems which cannot be solved by means of a finite algorithm. For these problems one requires a different kind of algorithm, one which would have to be repeated indefinitely in order to obtain an exact answer. Such a never-ending algorithm is called an **infinite algorithm.** Of course, in practice one would have to be content with some finite number of repetitions. Therefore, the best answer we can obtain is one "close" to the solution of the problem. If the algorithm is a good one, however, it is possible to get as close to the solution as one wishes simply by repeating the process long enough. This kind of process is often called an **iterative process,** for the word "iterate" which means to repeat. The term **successive approximations** is also used to describe this kind of method because after each successive stage (or iteration) we have a better approximation to the precise answer.

The idea of a never-ending algorithm may seem strange to you at first, but you have already used such algorithms in arithmetic. Multiplication of two numbers (such as 17 and 13) is a finite process, while division, if it does not come out exactly (as, for example, $17 \div 13$), leads to decimals which never end.

An algorithm for dividing 17 by 13 can be described as follows: (1) Since $17 = 1 \times 13 + 4$, the integer part of the quotient is 1; the remainder is 4. (2) The remainder is multiplied by 10, yielding 40. (3) Since $40 = 3 \times 13 + 1$, the first decimal of the quotient is 3; the remainder is 1.

We then return to step 2 and multiply the remainder by 10. This time we get 10. Since $10 = 0 \times 13 + 10$, step 3 tells us that the second decimal of the quotient is zero. The remainder is 10. Our quotient so far is 1.30. We can continue going back through steps 2 and 3. Each time we do so we will get another decimal in the quotient. This describes an algorithm for dividing 17 by 13. *Only if at some point the remainder is zero will we get the exact quotient.* In the case of $17 \div 13$ the remainders obtained in step 3 will never be zero. Therefore, the algorithm never ends.

Notice, however, that we can get as close to the exact quotient as we wish. For example, we can calculate

$$17 \div 13 = 1.307\ 692\ 307\ 692\ldots$$

Question. What is the effect on the subsequent quotient in the division algorithm if the remainder found at some stage is equal to the remainder at some previous stage? Note that this situation occurs in the quotient of 17 by 13 after the sixth decimal place has been calculated.

A more complicated infinite algorithm is the one you may have been taught for calculating the square root of a number, in which successive digits in the square root are determined. Later in this book we find an algorithm for calculating the square root which is much better than that one, although the new algorithm is also infinite.

One further word before we begin our study of never-ending algorithms. A great mathematician[1] once said that infinity is the soul of mathematics. In this chapter and the three following ones, you will indeed be learning to answer questions dealing with infinite processes that have been the soul of mathematics for over 300 years.

---

[1] **David Hilbert,** 1862–1943, a German mathematician, made many contributions to the logical foundations of mathematics. The axioms of geometry which to the ancient Greeks were simply "self-evident truths" were to Hilbert themselves only mathematical statements subject to logical laws from which valid mathematical consequences could be derived. Hilbert looked for and found a small number of precisely formulated mathematical axioms from which all of Euclidean geometry could be deduced.

4.2 The Falling-Object Problem

Did you ever try to estimate the distance to the bottom of a well or canyon by dropping a stone and counting off the number of seconds before it hit the bottom? In the study of mechanics (a branch of the science of physics that has to do with the motion of masses under forces such as gravity) one finds that there is an equation which connects time with the distance fallen under the action of gravity. This equation states that the distance an object falls from rest is equal to one-half the acceleration[2] of gravity times the square of the elapsed time. If, as is customary, we let s = distance, g = acceleration due to gravity, and t = time, we have the formula

$$s = \tfrac{1}{2}gt^2$$

If we measure t in seconds and distance s in feet, then, rounded off to the nearest whole number, g = 32 ft/sec²,[3] and we have

$$s = 16t^2 \tag{1}$$

Now equation (1) supposes that no other force but gravity acts on the object. Hence it holds only in a vacuum. A falling object on which gravity is the only force that acts is called a **freely falling object.** Near the surface of the earth we would have to make a correction due to the resistance of air.

Question. Would the correction due to air resistance increase or decrease the distance s an object falls during a certain time?

Question. What other corrections would have to be made if we wanted to make use of the formula to estimate the depth of a deep canyon by simply dropping a stone and listening for the sound of impact?

A graph of equation (1) appears in Figure 1 where we have measured t in seconds on the horizontal axis and s in feet on the vertical axis. Each number pair (t, s) satisfying equation (1) locates a point on the graph. The curve obtained is part of a parabola. From the graph we can

---

[2] Acceleration is the rate at which an object is changing its speed. When an automobile's speed changes from 20 mph to 30 mph it has accelerated.

[3] This unit is read feet per second per second. Acceleration has the dimensions of length divided by time squared. The value of g correct to three decimal places is 32.172 ft/sec².

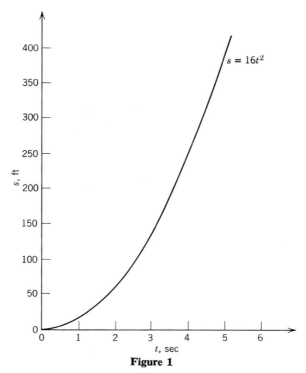

Figure 1

Distance versus time for free fall in a vacuum $(s = 16t^2)$

read off the distance traveled by a freely falling object after any time up to 5 sec. This graph was drawn from a table of values obtained by substituting $t = 1, 2, 3, 4, 5$ in equation (1) and calculating the corresponding values of s. Some of these values are given in Table 1. The remainder of the values are left for you to determine.

Table 1

t	0	1	2	3	4	5
s	0	16		144		400

We now ask this question: Knowing the distance-time relation for a falling object, can we find the *speed* of the object at any desired time? From this natural and seemingly simple question came the invention of the calculus by Newton[4] and Leibnitz[5] in the eighteenth century and the main developments of mathematical analysis of the eighteenth and nineteenth centuries.

> **Question.** Why is it more natural to suppose that the relation between distance and time is known to begin with, rather than to suppose that the relation between speed and time is known?

To help us determine how fast the object actually falls, we perform an imaginary experiment. Suppose we had at our disposal two adjacent elevator shafts so that we could stage a race between a stone allowed to fall down one shaft and an elevator whose speed we could accurately control moving down the other shaft. We shall neglect air resistance (which would not affect the motion of a small stone appreciably over relatively small distances) so that the stone will fall "freely," and equation (1) can be supposed to hold. Suppose next that we start the elevator off a few floors above the floor from which we drop the stone, so that by the time the elevator reaches the "starting line" it is already going at some desired speed. When the race begins, the stop watch begins to tick off the seconds from $t = 0$. We suppose that the car passes the starting line at a speed of 40 ft/sec and maintains this speed throughout the race.[6] At the same instant the stone is simply released and allowed to fall freely down the adjacent shaft.

To see what happens, it is most helpful and instructive to work with

---

[4] **Sir Isaac Newton,** 1642–1727, the English mathematician and scientist, was probably the greatest intellect that ever lived. According to legend and his own writings, he was led to the discovery of a universal force of attraction between all objects by observing a falling apple from a tree in his mother's garden. In addition to the calculus and the law of gravitation, Newton made fundamental discoveries concerning the nature of light and formulated the three laws of motion that bear his name. His treatise, *Mathematical Principles of Natural Philosophy,* often called by the Latin title, *Principia Mathematica,* set forth his discoveries and is considered the greatest scientific work ever written.

[5] **Gottfried Wilhelm Leibnitz** (pronounced "lipé nits"), 1646–1716, was a German mathematician, philosopher, and diplomat. He discovered the calculus at about the same time as Newton, and a long scientific dispute (England versus the continent of Europe) over the credit for this discovery resulted. Today it is acknowledged that both Newton and Leibnitz independently created the calculus. The symbols and terms employed by Leibnitz, however, proved more convenient and are the ones commonly used.

[6] This is rather a high speed even for elevators in modern skyscrapers, but we are safe to "imagine" it, and we can see if at this speed the elevator can win the race.

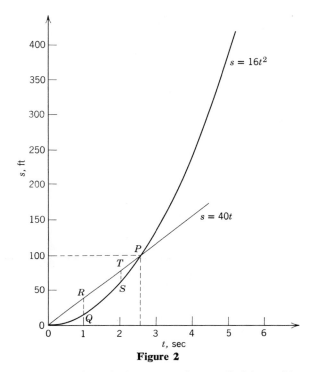

Figure 2

Comparison of motion of elevator moving at 40 ft/sec with motion of freely falling object

a geometric model of the motion. Since the elevator car moves at 40 ft/sec, we can calculate how far it has gone at a number of successive times such as $t = 1, 2, 3, 4, 5$ sec, and this will enable us to draw a graph for the motion of the car. A table of values for distance s versus time t for the car is given in Table 2. Plotting the number pairs (t, s) from the table and joining the points gives the straight line through 0 and P shown in Figure 2. The graph of $s = 16t^2$, which is a record of the motion of the falling stone, is also plotted in Figure 2 for comparison.

The line for the elevator's motion appears to cross the parabola at the point $t = 5/2$, $s = 100$. Indeed, when $t = 5/2$ sec, we find from equation (1) that $s = 16(5/2)^2 = 16(25/4) = 100$, so that the stone has traveled 100 ft. The point $t = 5/2$, $s = 100$ is therefore on the parabola. Similarly, at $t = 5/2$ the elevator has traveled $40 \times 5/2 = 100$ ft, so that the point

Table 2

t	0	1	2	3	4	5
s	0	40	80	120	160	200

($\frac{5}{2}$, 100) also lies on the line representing the motion of the elevator car. Therefore the point P with coordinates ($\frac{5}{2}$, 100) is the precise point at which the line and curve intersect. This means that $2\frac{1}{2}$ sec after the race started the stone and the elevator are even.

The point of intersection can also be found algebraically. To do this we need the equation of the line. Since at each point on the line the s coordinate is 40 times the t coordinate, the equation of the line is simply

$$s = 40t \qquad (2)$$

To find the number pairs (t, s) which simultaneously satisfy equations (1) and (2) we subtract equation (2) from equation (1). This gives

$$0 = 16t^2 - 40t$$

Simplifying, we get

$$t(t - \tfrac{5}{2}) = 0$$

Two solutions are possible, one for which $t = 0$, the other for which $t = \frac{5}{2}$. Corresponding to $t = 0$, from either (1) or (2) we get $s = 0$. Thus one solution to equations (1) and (2) is the number pair $(0, 0)$ corresponding to $s = 0$, $t = 0$. This simply means that the car and the stone were together at the starting position at the time $t = 0$. However, the value $t = \frac{5}{2}$, substituted into either (1) or (2) gives $s = 100$, which is the second solution. It corresponds to the point P found graphically where, again, the stone and the elevator are even.

> **Question.**   Given a system of two simultaneous equations, which correspond geometrically to a parabola and a line, how many solutions can there be?

After starting at $t = 0$, the elevator jumps to an early lead, as we see graphically in Figure 2 because the line (the graph of the elevator's motion) lies above the parabola (the graph of the stone's motion). Therefore, the distance traveled by the elevator is greater. At $t = 1$ sec, for example, the lead is measured by the segment QR in Figure 2. (Estimate this distance given that 1 unit along the vertical axis = 50 ft). At $t = 2$ sec, the lead has been cut to the distance represented by the line segment *ST*. At $t = \frac{5}{2}$ sec, the lead is cut to zero as the stone over-takes the car. After $t = \frac{5}{2}$ sec, the stone is ahead of the car, and its lead is constantly increasing.

Question. What is the exact lead of the car at $t = 1$ sec? At $t = 2$ sec? At $t = \frac{3}{2}$ sec?

4.3 Estimating Speed

So far we have talked about the distance each object has traveled. We now ask: What can we say about the speed of the car compared to the speed of the stone during the race? At the beginning the car's speed is greater than the stone's because the car pulls away from the stone; that is, the distance between the stone and the car increases throughout the first second or so of the motion. At or near $t = 1$, however, the distance between the curve and the line begins to decrease; this means that the stone has been picking up speed, and its *speed* has reached and then passed the speed of the car. By going faster than the car the stone eventually catches up with the car at $t = 2\frac{1}{2}$. Further on the curve gets increasingly steep, showing that the stone continually picks up speed or accelerates. To verify that the stone is accelerating or gaining in speed let us refer to Table 1 from which we find that in the first second the stone moves 16 ft; in the second second the stone moves from $s = 16$ to $s = 64$, a distance of 48 ft; in the third second the stone moves a distance of 80 ft; in the fourth second the stone moves a distance of 112 ft; etc. Since in each successive second the stone moves further than in the preceding second, we see that the stone indeed is constantly speeding up. This is in contrast to the car, which moves 40 ft each and every second, neither speeding up nor slowing down and, therefore, having no acceleration.

Geometrically the speed of the object is associated with the "steepness" of its graph when distance is plotted versus time. As we see in Figure 2, as the stone speeds up, the curve becomes steeper and steeper as the stone moves further each second than the previous second. The straight line, however, has a constant "steepness," and this indicates a constant speed.

Question. If the car moved at 20 ft/sec, would the line representing its motion be more or less steep than the line *OP* in Figure 2?

Now that we have a general picture of the motion, can we give a quantitative or precise answer to our question concerning the speed of

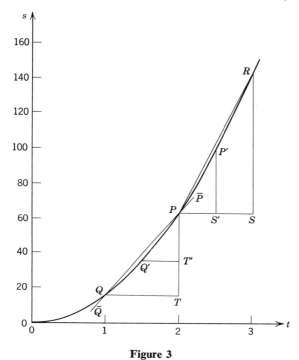

Figure 3

Estimating the speed at $t = 2$ sec

the stone at any desired time? Suppose we pick a particular time, say $t = 2$ sec, and try to determine the speed of the stone at that time. We shall use the letter v to denote the speed of the stone.

At $t = 2$ the stone is at $s = 64$. At $t = 1$ the stone was at $s = 16$. Therefore, in the second just preceding $t = 2$ the stone moved a distance of 48 ft. This corresponds to an average speed of 48 ft/sec. (The average speed is found by dividing the distance traveled by the time elapsed.)

In Figure 3 we again draw the curve for the motion of the stone. This time we use a larger scale in order to avoid crowding the lines, and we concentrate on the motion which takes place just before and after $t = 2$. Point P with coordinates $t = 2$ and $s = 64$ represents the position of the stone at $t = 2$. Point Q represents the position 1 sec earlier. The average speed of the stone in going from Q to P is 48 ft/sec. Suppose that a second elevator has been at Q at $t = 1$. That is, suppose the second elevator was the same distance, $s = 16$, from the starting line as the stone at $t = 1$. Suppose also that this elevator proceeded at the constant speed 48 ft/sec. Then at $t = 2$ it would be at $s = 16 + 48 = 64$ and so would be tied with the stone at P. The graph of the motion of the second elevator during this second of time would be given by the straight line segment QP. Extending QP beyond P to $\bar{P}$ (pronounced "P bar") shows that the curve rises more steeply and passes the line at this point so that the stone at P is traveling more rapidly than the second elevator. Thus the stone's speed is greater than 48 ft/sec. We express this fact by writing the inequality

$$48 < v$$

Another way of looking at this fact is that, since the stone is constantly speeding up, its speed at $t = 2$ will be greater than its average speed in the second just preceding $t = 2$.

Let us now draw a line from the point P perpendicular to the t-axis and also draw a line from Q perpendicular to the s-axis. These two lines intersect at the point T in Figure 3. The segment[7] QT measures the time elapsed (1 sec) during which the second elevator and the stone moved from Q to P. On the other hand, the segment[7] TP measures the distance (48 ft) both the elevator and the stone traveled in that time. Thus,

$$\frac{TP}{QT} = 48 \text{ ft/sec}$$

is the average speed of both objects during the time from $t = 1$ to $t = 2$.

The ratio TP/QT is called the **slope** of the line through Q and P. The "steepness" of a line is measured by its slope. The steeper the line is, the greater the vertical change (TP) for a given horizontal change (QT) and, consequently, the greater the slope.[8]

---

[7] The notation QT refers not to the length of the segment in inches or centimeters but to the number of units of time contained in the segment QT. Similarly, TP is not an actual length but the number of units of distance contained in the segment TP. The actual length on the graph used for the unit of distance (1 ft) in the s-direction and the length used for the unit of time (1 sec) in the t-direction are arbitrary and may be chosen for convenience. The unit lengths chosen will not affect the values of QT, TP, or any other time or distance measurements taken from the graph.

[8] Slope as defined here is also not affected by the actual lengths chosen for the units. Taking different unit lengths in the s- or t-direction will, of course, affect the appearance of the graph and make lines appear more or less steep. The value of the slope, however, is unaltered.

Question. What is the slope of a line through two points Q and P if P lies exactly above Q?

If P lies below T (as it would if the graph were falling instead of rising), then TP is taken to be a negative quantity and the slope is negative.

It is very important to understand that slope is a property of a line and not of the two points on the line that you happen to select to find the value of the slope. For instance, if some other points on the line through Q and P such as $\bar{Q}$ and $\bar{P}$ were used to find the slope of this line, we would find that the slope has precisely the same value as before, namely 48.

In a graph of distance versus time, slope is a measure of speed. The faster an object travels, the greater is the slope. The slower it travels, the smaller is the slope. We summarize our discussion of slope and speed in the following statement. *Any straight-line graph of distance versus time represents a motion at constant speed. This speed is equal to the numerical value of the slope of this line.*

We return now to the determination of the stone's speed v at $t = 2$. Recall that we have found that $48 < v$. Let us now consider the stone's motion in the second just following $t = 2$. It moved from $s = 64$ to $s = 144$. This corresponds to an average velocity of 80 ft/sec, since the distance moved is 80 ft and the time elapsed is 1 sec. On the graph in Figure 3, at $t = 3$ the stone is at $s = 144$. This is the point R. If a third elevator starting at the point P began to move with the constant speed 80 ft/sec, it, too, would just reach the point R at $t = 3$. Its motion would be given by the line segment PR. The graph verifies the fact that the speed of the stone at P is less than 80 ft/sec, since the line segment PR is steeper than the curve at P. We can express this by the inequality

$$v < 80$$

Question. What is the slope of the line through P and R?

We have found two estimates of the stone's speed at $t = 2$. One, which is too small, namely 48 ft/sec, we found by considering the stone's average speed in the second *prior* to $t = 2$. The second estimate of the stone's speed, namely 80 ft/sec, which is too large, was found by considering its average speed in the second just following $t = 2$. Therefore, we are able to say with certainty that $48 < v$ and that $v < 80$. These two statements can be written in the one expression

$$48 < v < 80 \qquad (3)$$

The number 48 which is *less* than v is called a **lower bound** for v; the number 80 which is *greater* than v is called an **upper bound**.

To improve our estimate for v we can consider smaller time intervals than 1 sec and repeat what we have done. Take the $\frac{1}{2}$ sec preceding $t = 2$. At $t = \frac{3}{2}$, the stone's position, from equation (1), is $s = 36$. In the $\frac{1}{2}$ sec from $t = \frac{3}{2}$ to $t = 2$ it moves to $s = 64$, a distance of 28 ft. This corresponds to an average speed of $28/(\frac{1}{2}) = 56$ ft/sec.

Geometrically the stone in the half second moves along the curve from the point Q' (pronounced "Q prime") in Figure 3 with coordinates $t = \frac{3}{2}, s = 36$ to the point P. If we join Q' to P by a straight-line segment, this would represent motion at constant speed from Q' to P equal in value to the average speed of 56 ft/sec. Because the segment $Q'P$, when extended past P, drops below the curve, the slope of $Q'P$ is less than the slope of the curve at P. The speed of the falling stone at P $(t = 2)$ is therefore greater than 56 ft/sec. This is expressed by the inequality

$$56 < v$$

Question.   Does increasing a lower bound for a quantity improve the estimate?

Similarly, we may take a $\frac{1}{2}$-sec time interval just following $t = 2$ to get an improved upper bound for v. By considering a 1-sec interval we found that $v < 80$. In the $\frac{1}{2}$ sec just following $t = 2$, the stone moves from $s = 64$ (at $t = 2$) to $s = 100$ (at $t = 2\frac{1}{2}$). This is a distance of 36 ft, and it corresponds to an average speed of $36/(\frac{1}{2}) = 72$ ft/sec.

Returning to Figure 3, the position of the stone at $t = 2\frac{1}{2}$ is P'. The line segment PP' represents motion at the constant speed $S'P'/PS' = 72$ ft/sec. This is also the slope of the line through PP'. The segment PP' rises above the curve just after P, indicating that the speed or slope of this segment is greater than the speed of the stone (slope of the curve) at P. This tells us that 72 ft/sec is an upper bound for the speed at P, so that

$$v < 72$$

Combining our estimates found by taking $\frac{1}{2}$-sec intervals, we have

$$56 < v < 72 \qquad (4)$$

Comparing (4) with (3) we see that taking $\frac{1}{2}$-sec time intervals in place of 1-sec time intervals has improved our estimate of v.

Question.   Why does our estimate of v improve when we take smaller time intervals?

We do not intend to stop here, of course. Choosing a still smaller time interval will give still better estimates because the speed during the shorter time interval will vary less from the speed at $t = 2$. So let us take an interval of $\frac{1}{4}$ sec. One-quarter second prior to $t = 2$, at $t = \frac{7}{4}$, the stone was at $s = 16(\frac{7}{4})^2 = 49$ ft. It therefore traveled $64 - 49 = 15$ ft in this quarter-second in going to $s = 64$. A distance of 15 ft in $\frac{1}{4}$ sec gives an average speed of $15/(\frac{1}{4}) = 60$ ft/sec. Reasoning as before, since the stone constantly speeds up, its speed at $t = 2$ is greater than its average speed in the $\frac{1}{4}$ sec just prior to $t = 2$, and so

$$60 < v$$

Similarly, we take the $\frac{1}{4}$ sec just following $t = 2$ and find that

$$v < 68$$

Combining our last two estimates, we have

$$60 < v < 68 \qquad\qquad (5)$$

Comparing this to (4), we see that the range of possible values of v has been narrowed down again.

Problem.   Carry through the graphical construction which leads to the estimates of (5).

4.4   Algorithms for Finding Speed

Now we are ready to describe an algorithm or procedure for getting better and better estimates for the speed of the stone at $t = 2$. Indeed, it looks as if there are two procedures: one that gives upper bounds and comes from taking smaller and smaller time intervals just following $t = 2$, and one that gives lower bounds and comes from taking smaller and smaller time intervals just prior to $t = 2$. These procedures are so similar, however, that once we have described one we will not need to change much to describe the other.

Let us now try to work out a flow chart for an algorithm designed to give us successively improved estimates for the speed at $t = 2$ using intervals just following $t = 2$. To begin, we must decide on the successive time interval sizes we shall use. Rather than continuing by cutting the time interval in half at each stage, let us go to the decimal system and

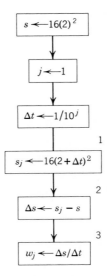

Figure 4

Flow chart to estimate speed of stone

use successive time intervals of $1/10$, $1/100$, $1/1000$, ... measured in seconds. These are powers of $1/10$; hence, if we use the letter j to denote the successive positive integers $j = 1, 2, 3, ...$, we may write that the jth time interval taken is just $1/10^j$.

Having decided on the time interval, the first step in the computation is to find where the stone is at the end of the time interval. (We have already found the position s at the beginning $t = 2$ of the time interval.) This means that we must find s at $t = 2 + 1/10^j$. The second step is to find the distance traveled by the stone during the time interval. This distance is usually denoted by Δs (the symbol Δ is the capital Greek letter "delta" and the term Δs is read "delta-s") which stands for a single quantity, the change in distance s. The letter Δ is frequently used to indicate that it is the *change* in the symbol following the Δ that is being considered. Similarly, the time interval between $t = 2$ and $t = 2 + (1/10^j)$ will be denoted by Δt (change in the time t), so that $\Delta t = 1/10^j$. The third and last step is to find the average speed in the time interval by dividing distance by time, that is $\Delta s \div \Delta t$. The flow chart for the algorithm thus far is shown in Figure 4.

The preliminary calculation of s at the initial time $t = 2$ is shown in the top box. The next box sets the index $j = 1$. The next box corresponds to selecting the time interval, which for $j = 1$ would be $\Delta t = 1/10$ sec. The box labeled 1 corresponds to the first step, which is to locate the stone at the end of the elapsed time interval. This position is labeled s_j. The second step (box 2) is to find the distance Δs covered in the elapsed time. Finally, the third step (box 3) is to divide the distance by the time to find the average speed. This quantity has been labeled w_j and is the estimate of v furnished by the application of the algorithm.

The algorithm must then be repeated using the next interval of time which would be 1/100 sec according to our intention. To incorporate the reapplication of the algorithm into the flow chart we need to introduce a loop based on the index j. To do this we add the box $\boxed{j \leftarrow j + 1}$ and then return to the box which calculates Δt as shown in Figure 5.

The algorithm of Figure 5 if carried through would first furnish the value w_1 of the average speed of the stone over the 1/10 of a second following $t = 2$. Then j would be replaced by 2, and w_2, the average speed during the 1/100 of a second following $t = 2$ would be found. Then successively $w_3, w_4, w_5, \ldots$, would be calculated corresponding to the average speeds over the shorter and shorter time intervals 1/1000, 1/10,000, 1/100,000, $\ldots$, of a second. Since there is no provision for stopping, in theory, an infinite sequence of estimates would be generated.

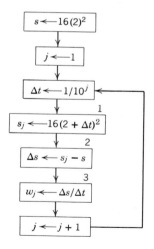

Figure 5

Flow chart to improve estimates of speed of stone

Of course, we expect that for all practical purposes we may decide how accurately we need to know the speed at $t = 2$ and then stop this process when we are convinced that our answer is correct to the desired accuracy. Accuracy is usually specified by requiring a certain number of decimal places to be correct in the answer. What we need therefore is a way of deciding when the current w_j estimate is correct to the required number of decimal places. Since we do not know what the answer is, it would seem that it is impossible to make this decision. However, our intuition tells us, and more advanced mathematics enables us to prove, that the algorithm we have constructed will give estimates which more and more closely approximate the exact speed v at $t = 2$, and will ultimately give any desired degree of accuracy. That is, no matter how small a number we may choose, the error in our estimate will eventually be smaller than this number for some w_j and for all succeeding ones. In mathematical terminology, the sequence $w_1, w_2, w_3, \ldots$, is said to **converge** to v. The number v is called the **limit** of the sequence.

The question remains: how to tell when an estimate w_j has the desired number of correct digits? We cannot look at all succeeding estimates to make sure that these digits do not change, because there are an infinite number of them. However, one possible way to proceed is simply to compare successive estimates and terminate the algorithm when we find that in going from w_j to w_{j+1} the required digits do not change. This, of course, does not guarantee that the estimates following w_{j+1} will also not change in these digits, but this is a convenient criterion to use and one which will furnish us correct results in many problems. One must always check insofar as possible to see whether the use of this condition is justified.

In particular, then, suppose we want the answer correctly rounded off to four decimal places. We assume that eventually our algorithm will give an estimate w_j in which the first five decimal places have the same digits as the real speed v and that all succeeding estimates $w_{j+1}, w_{j+2}, \ldots$, will also have the same digits in these first five places. That is the same as saying that after some point in the computation the estimate w_j and all succeeding ones will be in error by less than .00001. The criterion for terminating the algorithm which we use is the change in successive estimates. If $|w_j - w_{j-1}| < .00001$, we assume that w_j and the exact answer have the same digits in the first five decimal places.

Having the same numbers in the first five decimal places as v we can then correctly round off to four decimal places. We shall use symmetric rounding; thus, our round-off rule is to take the first four places as they stand if the fifth digit is under 5 and to increase the fourth-place digit by one if the fifth digit is 5 or larger. This is done most conveniently by adding 5 to the fifth place and then "chopping" the resulting number after the fourth place.

The procedure to be used to terminate the algorithm and, we hope, obtain the answer correctly rounded to 4 decimal places is then the following:

1. Check in the sequence of estimates w_j to find when successive estimates differ in absolute value by less than .00001; that is, see when the condition

$$|w_j - w_{j-1}| < .00001$$

   is satisfied.
2. When this condition is satisfied, add .00005 to w_j. Call this new number w_j'.
3. Chop w_j' after four decimal places and take this number as v to four decimal places. To get v correctly rounded to r decimal places (where r now can be any of the integers 1, 2, 3, 4, 5, . . . ,) we may replace $.00001 = 10^{-5}$ in the above by 10^{-r-1} and .00005 by $5 \times 10^{-r-1}$.

Before continuing with the flow chart, we emphasize again that this terminating criterion rests on the assumption that, if two successive estimates, w_{j-1} and w_j, are the same to a certain number of decimal places, then all succeeding estimates and the exact answer (the number to which the estimates tend) are the same in value to that number of places. This assumption seems reasonable enough in the present problem on the basis of two things. One is our intuition, and the second is our calculation of estimates of the speed of the falling stone at $t = 2$, using shorter and shorter time intervals. However, as we pointed out before, one must always look carefully at the problem in hand and check the results against known data before adopting this criterion or any other one for terminating an infinite algorithm when a certain accuracy is desired.

Questions. Suppose an infinite algorithm generated the sequence of estimates 1, 1, ½, ½, ⅓, ⅓, ¼, ¼, . . . , tending toward zero. Could the terminating criterion given above be used to stop the algorithm with a given accuracy, say to four decimal places? What criterion could be used instead to end the process with a given accuracy?

We continue now with the construction of the flow chart for the problem of finding the speed of the falling stone. If we added to the flow chart set down in Figure 5 the terminating criterion presented above, we would have a flow chart to describe completely the algorithm for determining the speed of the falling stone at $t = 2$ sec correct to r decimal places.

To do this in a way that facilitates writing a computer program, however, requires a few modifications. First we change the name of the value of the distance at $t = 2$ from s to p in order to avoid later confusion with the subscripted variables $s_1, s_2, \ldots,$. We also name the initial time t_0. Secondly, we calculate s_1 and w_1 before entering the loop, because the loop will ask us to compare w_j and w_{j-1}. We need two values of w the first time through the loop. Since only one w is calculated in the loop, we need to have calculated another one prior to entering the loop the first time. We also let t_j be the time corresponding to the distance s_j. The flow chart in Figure 6 describes the entire process.

Let us now use the flow chart of Figure 6 to find the speed of the stone at $t = 2$ sec correct to two decimal places. This requires that $r = 2$ in the chart. Beginning with $j = 1$, we find from the successive boxes that

$$p = 64.00$$

$$\Delta t = 0.1$$

$$t_1 = 2.1$$

$$s_1 = 70.56$$

$$\Delta s = 6.56$$

$$w_1 = 65.6$$

We then set $j = 2$ and enter the loop to calculate

$$\Delta t = .01$$

$$s_2 = 64.6416$$

$$\Delta s = .6416$$

$$w_2 = 64.16$$

Now

$$|w_2 - w_1| = 1.44$$

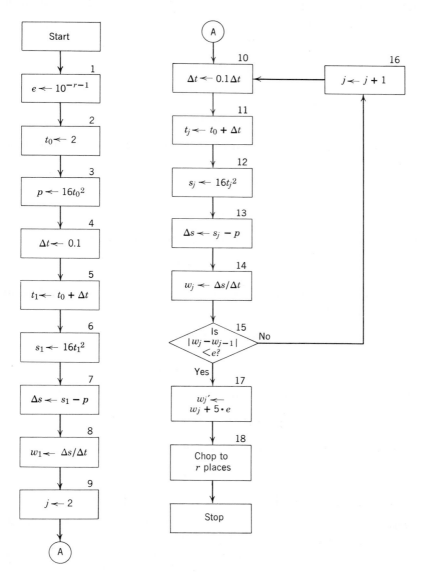

Figure 6

Flow chart for computing speed at $t = 2$ to r decimal places

219

Because this result is not less than $e = .001$, we return to box 10 with $j = 3$. This leads to

$$\Delta t = .001$$

$$s_3 = 64.064016$$

$$\Delta s = .064016$$

$$w_3 = 64.016$$

Again the test fails and we return to perform the loop again. This time we find

$$w_4 = 64.0016$$

and since

$$|w_4 - w_3| = .0144$$

we must again return to the calculation. The next value is

$$w_5{}' = 64.00016$$

Since this number differs from w_4 by 1 in the third place, we once again return to box 10. Now we find

$$w_6 = 64.000016$$

so that

$$|w_6 - w_5| = .000144$$

This is indeed less than .001, and we proceed to box 17 to find

$$w_j{}' = 64.000016 + .005 = 64.005016$$

which we chop after two places to obtain

$$v = 64.00$$

as our value of the speed v correct to two decimal places.

Questions. Comparing w_2, w_3, w_4, w_5, w_6 reveals a pattern. Without calculation give the values of the next three estimates, w_7, w_8, w_9. Is w_1 consistent with the pattern? Based on the pattern, what is v correct to 4 decimal places? To 10 decimal places?

In this problem we see that a pattern emerges in which the jth estimate (where j stands for any integer $1, 2, 3, \ldots,$) is given by

$$w_j = 64 + 16 \times 10^{-j}$$

The reader should check this formula for $j = 1, 2, 3, 4, 5, 6$ against the calculated values.

The result of this trial calculation has been to demonstrate a number of things. First, the flow chart contains no errors. Second, the algorithm does indeed furnish a sequence of estimates which approach ever more closely to some fixed number. Third, the termination criterion is valid; that is, when two successive estimates agree to a specified number of decimal places, all succeeding estimates will remain unchanged in those places.

However, we can go beyond our original goal which was to estimate v to a predetermined number of places. From the pattern, we see that w_j differs from 64 by 16×10^{-j}, an amount which can be made as small as we please just by taking j large enough (since $\Delta t = 10^{-j}$, this is the same as taking the time interval small enough). We conclude therefore that the exact value of v is precisely 64, no more and no less.

The reader should realize that, although we have made this conclusion seem very reasonable, we have not *proved* that the speed at $t = 2$ is 64 ft/sec. Our conclusion is based on the assumption that the algorithm we use will give the answer to any desired degree of accuracy. This assumption, in turn, was suggested by:

1. Our physical intuition, which tells us that the average speed w_j over the time interval of 10^{-j} sec will approximate the actual speed v as closely as we please.

2. The geometrical model relating speed to the slope of the line segments approximating the curved graph of the motion of the stone. (We shall come back to this model shortly.)

Nevertheless, our conclusion is correct and our reasoning, though partly intuitive, can be made mathematically precise so as to furnish a complete proof of the validity of our algorithm.

Before continuing with the main discussion, we pause to see what changes are needed to describe the related algorithm for estimating speed based on taking time intervals just *preceding* the time $t = 2$. The algorithm of the flow chart of Figure 6 gives estimates using time intervals just following $t = 2$, but, as we promised earlier, only slight changes are needed. Before we state what these are, see if you can do the following problem yourself.

Problem. Work out the complete flow chart for estimating the speed v at $t = 2$, correct to r decimal places, based on time intervals just preceding $t = 2$. Follow the form of the chart in Figure 6. Let s_j be the position of the stone at $1/10^j$ seconds before $t = 2$; let u_j be the average speed in the time interval between $2 - \Delta t$ and 2; let u_j' be $u_j + 5 \times 10^{-r-1}$, and finally chop u_j' after r places.

The only change necessary in the flow chart of Figure 6, is in box 4 which should be changed to read $\Delta t \leftarrow -0.1$. Of course, all the w_j in boxes 8, 14, 15, and 17 should be changed to u_j, but this is only for our later convenience. The reader is warned, however, that the **FORTRAN** programs will require more extensive changes due to numerical problems which will be discussed in Section 4.6.

Let us now use the flow chart of Figure 6, with box 4 changed as indicated above, to find the speed of the stone at $t = 2$ correct to two decimal places. Beginning with $j = 1$, we find the successive approximations

$$u_1 = 62.4 \qquad\qquad u_4 = 63.9984$$

$$u_2 = 63.84 \qquad\qquad u_5 = 63.99984$$

$$u_3 = 63.984$$

At this point the difference $|u_j - u_{j-1}|$ is

$$|u_5 - u_4| = 63.99984 - 63.9984 = .00144$$

This is *not* less than $10^{-3} = .001$. Hence, we repeat the loop once more to find

$$u_6 = 63.999984$$

and now we find the termination criterion to be satisfied. Adding 5 in the third decimal place gives $u_6' = 64.004984$ and chopping after two places gives the estimate

$$v = 64.00$$

for the speed at $t = 2$, again correct to two decimal places.

Knowing as we do that this algorithm based on average speeds before $t = 2$ gives estimates too small (remember that the stone is always speeding up) and the previous algorithm gives estimates too large, we can combine the two algorithms to give both lower and upper bounds for v as we did before. Indeed, the actual v must be larger than every estimate u_j generated in the last calculation no matter how big we take j, that is, no matter how many times we repeat the loop. At the same time, v must be smaller than every estimate w_j generated by the previous calculation no matter how large j becomes. If we use the first six values generated in both calculations we have the successively improved bounds

$$62.4 \qquad < v < 65.6$$
$$63.84 \qquad < v < 64.16$$
$$63.984 \qquad < v < 64.016$$
$$63.9984 \quad < v < 64.0016$$
$$63.99984 \; < v < 64.00016$$
$$63.999984 < v < 64.000016$$

Note the pattern for the lower bounds as well as the previously observed pattern for the upper bounds. This leads us to conclude that v must be a number larger than

$$63.9999 \ldots 984$$

(where the dots represent any finite number of 9's) and at the same time smaller than

$$64.0000 \ldots 016$$

(where the dots represent any finite number of 0's). There is, however, only one number that satisfies these requirements and that number is precisely 64.

Using both algorithms and physical plus geometrical intuition enabled us to write inequalities for v and to precisely determine v. Either algorithm by itself, however, as we have seen, can be followed to give v accurately only to a prescribed number of decimal places. The student should reflect on the difference between these results. To get v precisely means to apply the algorithm without end — to infinitely many decimal places. Of course, we cannot do this, but using *mathematical reasoning plus some intuition* we were able to deduce in the previous example what the precise value of v had to be. In the study of differential calculus, a purely mathematical algorithm very similar to the ones just presented enables one to find precisely the speed v with no need for repeated approximations or arguments based on intuition.

However, we do not discuss the calculus here, and we content ourselves with the algorithms we have developed in this chapter when we wish to calculate the speed of a falling object. We use a computer to help us with the numerical work.

So far we have done our calculations "by hand," retaining all digits and implying that all digits would continue to be retained in each number. In a computer we have only a finite number of digits in each floating-point number, and this will require that we make some changes in our algorithm. We turn now to a discussion of these numerical problems.

4.5   Numerical Problems

We have already seen in Chapter 3 that we must be very careful when we use a computer to do our arithmetic because some unexpected things may happen. For example, we found that addition in a computer is not associative. There the problem was that each number in a computer had a fixed number of digits. The same thing is going to cause us difficulties in computing speeds on a computer. We should expect some trouble of this kind since in our hand calculations in the previous section s_3 required eight digits and s_4, although it is not shown, required ten digits. Succeeding values of s_j will require even more digits. Modern computers seldom have more than ten digits in the mantissa of a floating-point number. Appendix E lists the precision (number of digits in the mantissa) of several computers.

We can analyze the problems we shall encounter by considering a computer with four digits in the mantissa and one digit in the exponent. Thus, 246.748 would be represented as $.2467 \times 10^3$. We shall "chop" numbers because many computers using FORTRAN do just that.

We return to the problem of calculating the speed of the stone at $t = 2$ sec, using the flow chart in Figure 6. We choose $r = 0$, which means that we want only the integer part of the result. That is, we expect to get 64 as the result. Thus $e = .1000 \times 10^0$ and

$$p = .6400 \times 10^2$$
$$\Delta t = .1000 \times 10^0$$
$$t_1 = .2100 \times 10^1$$
$$s_1 = .7056 \times 10^2$$
$$\Delta s = .6560 \times 10^1$$
$$w_1 = .6560 \times 10^2$$

This is precisely what we obtained before. However, s_2 will require six digits and therefore results in the succeeding calculations will differ from the exact ones. In the next step with $j = 2$,

$$\Delta t = \quad .1000 \times 10^{-1}$$
$$t_2 = \quad .2010 \times 10^1$$

$$s_2 = \quad .6464 \times 10^2$$

$$\Delta s = \quad .6400 \times 10^0$$

$$w_2 = \quad .6400 \times 10^2$$

$$w_2 - w_1 = -.1600 \times 10^1$$

Now notice that w_2 is the exact value of the speed to four digits, but since $|w_2 - w_1|$ is greater than e we do not stop (see box 15 of Figure 6). The results for $j = 3, 4,$ and 5 are

$$j = 3$$

$$\Delta t = \quad .1000 \times 10^{-2}$$

$$t_3 = \quad .2001 \times 10^1$$

$$s_3 = \quad .6406 \times 10^2$$

$$\Delta s = \quad .6000 \times 10^{-1}$$

$$w_3 = \quad .6000 \times 10^2$$

$$w_3 - w_2 = -.4000 \times 10^1$$

$j = 4$		$j = 5$	
$\Delta t =$	$.1000 \times 10^{-3}$	$\Delta t =$	$.1000 \times 10^{-4}$
$t_4 =$	$.2000 \times 10^1$	$t_5 =$	$.2000 \times 10^1$
$s_4 =$	$.6400 \times 10^2$	$s_5 =$	$.6400 \times 10^2$
$\Delta s =$	0	$\Delta s =$	0
$w_4 =$	0	$w_5 =$	0
$w_4 - w_3 =$	$-.6000 \times 10^2$	$w_5 - w_4 =$	0

Box 15 in Figure 6 tells us to stop since $|w_5 - w_4| < e$, and we errone-ously conclude that the speed is zero!

Before trying to find our way out of this dilemma we point out two things. First, in these calculations we cannot even conclude that $v < w_j$ as we did before. Second, even if we let $r = -1$ so that all we want is the very first digit of the result, our process would produce the same result because $|w_j - w_{j-1}| > 1$ for $j = 2, 3,$ and 4.

If we had a computer with five digits in the mantissa, we could do a little better. In this case the successive values of w_j would be

$$w_1 = .65600 \times 10^2$$

$$w_2 = .64100 \times 10^2$$

$$w_3 = .64000 \times 10^2$$

$$w_4 = .60000 \times 10^2$$

$$w_5 = 0$$

$$w_6 = 0$$

Here $|w_3 - w_2| = .1000 \times 10^0$. The more digits we have in the mantissa, the more accurately we can compute. Notice, however, that with four digits we could not get even one digit of accuracy, and with five digits we barely got two digits of accuracy.

What is happening should be clear. The digits that we need have been lost at the right end of the numbers and they disappear in the computer. When we form Δs, we subtract two four- (or five-) digit numbers which are nearly equal. The leading digits in the result of the subtraction are zeros. For example, in the four-digit computer, when $j = 3$, $s_3 = .6406 \times 10^2$ and

$$\Delta s = s_3 - p = .6406 \times 10^2 - .6400 \times 10^2$$

$$= .0006 \times 10^2$$

There is only *one digit* in the result which contains any real information. The leading zeros serve only to change the exponent so that $\Delta s = .6000 \times 10^{-1}$. Actually, the precise result from the previous section is $\Delta s = .6401 \times 10^{-1}$ to four figures. The digits 401, which are vital to the success of the method, have been lost in our four-digit computer.

Whenever two positive numbers of approximately the same magnitude are subtracted in a computer, there is a great loss of accuracy. This is often referred to as "subtractive cancellation." It appears in many circumstances, and the user of a computer must beware of it at all times.

All we can ask for is the most accurate result the computer we are using can produce. We cannot specify the accuracy we want but must be content with the best our computer can give us. Fortunately, in this case there is a way of determining this. Recall from our discussion in the previous section that the values of w_j decreased as j increased. That is,

$$w_0 > w_1 > \cdots > w_{j-1} > w_j > \cdots$$

Thus the values of $w_j - w_{j-1}$ are always negative. This means that the test in box 15 of Figure 6 can be simplified. Since $w_j - w_{j-1} < 0$, we need only check to see if

$$w_j - w_{j-1} > -e$$

or, equivalently, if

$$w_{j-1} - w_j < e$$

Notice, moreover, that

$$w_1 - w_2 > w_2 - w_3$$
$$w_2 - w_3 > w_3 - w_4$$

$$\cdot \qquad \cdot$$
$$\cdot \qquad \cdot$$
$$\cdot \qquad \cdot$$

$$w_{j-2} - w_{j-1} > w_{j-1} - w_j$$

in the exact calculations of the previous section. In the four-digit computer calculations in this section, however,

$$w_1 - w_2 < w_2 - w_3$$

This is an indication that numerical errors have crept into our calculations. It is this test that we use to tell us when our computer has done as well as it can with its limited number of digits.

Thus, if

$$w_{j-2} - w_{j-1} \leq w_{j-1} - w_j$$

we stop the calculation. It would appear from our examples that w_{j-1} is closer to the precise solution v than any other of our estimates. For example, in our four-digit computer

$$w_1 - w_2 < w_2 - w_3$$

and indeed w_2 is the best estimate. Similarly, in our five-digit computer

$$w_2 - w_3 < w_3 - w_4$$

and w_3 is the best result. Unfortunately, matters are not quite that simple. Consider once more our four-digit computer where, instead of multiplying each interval by $\frac{1}{10}$ in the succeeding calculation, we multiply by $\frac{1}{2}$. That is, we take time intervals of $\frac{1}{2}$, $\frac{1}{4}$, $\frac{1}{8}$, $\frac{1}{16}$, ..., of a second. The results are

$$w_1 = .7200 \times 10^2$$

$$w_2 = .6796 \times 10^2$$

$$w_1 - w_2 = .4040 \times 10^1$$

$$w_3 = .6592 \times 10^2$$

$$w_2 - w_3 = .2040 \times 10^1$$

$$w_4 = .6416 \times 10^2$$

$$w_3 - w_4 = .1760 \times 10^1$$

$$w_5 = .6336 \times 10^2$$

$$w_4 - w_5 = .8000 \times 10^0$$

$$w_6 = .5762 \times 10^2$$

$$w_5 - w_6 = .5740 \times 10^1$$

Here

$$w_4 - w_5 < w_5 - w_6$$

but w_5 is *not* the best result. The best estimate of v is w_4. The magnitude of the error in w_4 is 0.16, while the magnitude of the error in w_5 is 0.64.

Nevertheless, we take w_{j-1} as an estimate of the speed v, even though a prior estimate may be better.

Figure 7 shows a flow chart which incorporates the preceding stopping criterion into the calculations along with the previous stopping criterion. This replaces boxes 15, 17, and 18 in Figure 6.

Thus, we stop if either (a) we get the accuracy we ask for or (b) we obtain the "best" estimate our computer permits. Here the "best" estimate is not necessarily the estimate which differs from the precise result by less than any other estimate, although in many cases it will be.

We need to explain one point in the flow chart. Box 19 is necessary because, if $j = 2$, then one of the subscripts in box 20 will be zero, and this is not allowed in FORTRAN.

Finally, we make a few remarks about choosing time intervals Δt. Suppose that, instead of steps decreasing by one-tenth we chose steps decreasing by one-third. We would introduce an additional error into our results because $\frac{1}{3}$ is a nonterminating decimal, .333 ... 333 .... In our four-digit computer it would be .3333 $\times$ 10^0, which is only approximately correct. It is better to choose an interval which is a terminating

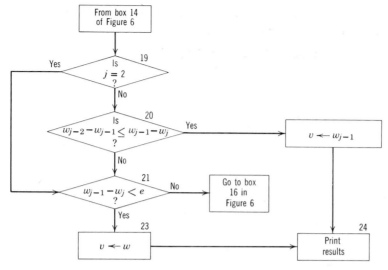

Figure 7

Part of flow chart for computing speed; replaces boxes 15, 17, 18 of Figure 6

decimal such as $\frac{1}{10} = .1000 \times 10^0$ or $\frac{1}{2} = .5000 \times 10^0$. Actually $\frac{1}{10}$ is preferable to $\frac{1}{2}$ because we will arrive at a solution in fewer steps.

If our computer is a *binary* computer rather than a decimal one, the $\frac{1}{10}$ is a poor choice since in binary $\frac{1}{10}$ is a never-ending string of digits. In fact, it is .0001100110011 . . . 0011 . . . . It is better to choose $\frac{1}{2}$ when using a binary computer even though more steps are needed since in binary $\frac{1}{2}$ is .1.

If the computer you use is binary, then use $\Delta t = 2^{-j}$. If the computer is a decimal computer, use $\Delta t = 10^{-j}$. If it is hexadecimal (base 16), use $\Delta t = 16^{-j}$.

4.6 A FORTRAN Program to Calculate v

We now describe a FORTRAN program to estimate the velocity of the stone at a time 2 sec after it starts to fall. We follow the flow charts in Figures 6 and 7. Once again the statement numbers correspond to the box numbers in the flow charts.

The value of $r = 3$, hence $e = 10^{-4}$. Since zero subscripts are not allowed in FORTRAN, we rename t_0 as TZ. The names TZ and T

represent two different variables in FORTRAN. In this case T is a
subscripted variable and TZ is not.

DIMENSION S(50), W(50), T(50)

1 E = 0.0001

2 TZ = 2.0

3 P = 16.0 * TZ**2

4 DELT = 0.1

5 T(1) = TZ + DELT

6 S(1) = 16.0 * T(1)**2

7 DELS = S(1) − P

8 W(1) = DELS / DELT

9 DO 16 J = 2, 50

10 DELT = 0.1 * DELT

11 T(J) = TZ + DELT

12 S(J) = 16.0 * T(J)**2

13 DELS = S(J) − P

14 W(J) = DELS / DELT

19 IF (J − 2) 20, 21, 20

20 A = W(J − 1) − W(J)

    B = W(J − 2) − W(J − 1)

    IF (A − B) 21, 22, 22

21 IF (W(J − 1) − W(J) − E) 23, 16, 16

16 CONTINUE

22 V = W(J − 1)

    GO TO 24

23 V = W(J)

24 PRINT 100, V

    STOP

100   FORMAT (5H ① V ① = ①, F7.4)

ⓐ   END

The preceding program was run on three different computers. The first was a decimal computer with 8 digits in the mantissa of floating-point numbers (the IBM 1620). The second was a binary computer with 8+ decimal digits in the mantissa (the IBM 7094). The third was a hexadecimal computer with 6+ decimal digits in the mantissa (the IBM System/360). The results are shown in Table 3 in the columns labeled $\Delta t = 10^{-j}$. The values of V and the value of the index J for which $V = W(J)$ are shown.

The program was then rerun using $\Delta t = \frac{1}{2}, \frac{1}{4}, \frac{1}{8}, \ldots,$. This required changing the 0.1 in lines 4 and 10 to 0.5. The results are shown in the columns of Table 3 labeled $\Delta t = 2^{-j}$.

Table 3

	$\Delta t = 10^{-j}$		$\Delta t = 2^{-j}$	
	V	J	V	J
Decimal (IBM 1620)	64.0000	5	63.9877	12
Binary (IBM 7094)	63.9915	4	64.0039	12
Hexadecimal (IBM System/360)	63.9802	3	64.0156	10

Notice that the second case, where $\Delta t = 2^{-j}$, required more calculation but produced more accurate results than $\Delta t = 10^{-j}$ except with the decimal computer.

In only one case, the decimal computer, with $\Delta t = 10^{-j}$, did we achieve the accuracy we desired: an error less than 10^{-4}.

In one case, the decimal computer with $\Delta t = 2^{-j}$, we did not get the estimate which differed by the least amount from the precise result. In that case $w_{11} = 64.9959$ was a better estimate than w_{12}.

There is one more point to make about such a program. Although we have attempted to guard against all eventualities through the tests in boxes 20 and 21, it is not always possible to foresee all the difficulties which may arise in a computer. It is wise, therefore, to make sure that an infinite algorithm does indeed end sometime even if the unforeseen occurs. One way to do this is to place an upper limit on the number of times every loop in a program is used.

In the program in the text we placed an upper limit of 50 on the loop. That is, we do not allow the computing loop to be used if J exceeds 50. When a DO loop is used, such a limit is automatically imposed by the upper limit on the DO statement. If GO TO and IF statements are used, then the programmer must allow for such a check on the computation.

Exercises 21 and 22 ask the reader to draw a flow chart and write a FORTRAN program to calculate v using time intervals *prior* to $t = 2$. The reader should have no trouble with these exercises at this point. However, care must be exercised in modifying the four statements starting with 20 and ending with 21.

4.7 Speed and the Slope of the Tangent to the Curve

We leave numerical problems and programming now and return to the geometrical model to interpret the significance of the successive approximations w_1, w_2, w_3, . . . , furnished by the first algorithm, and the successive approximations u_1, u_2, u_3, . . . , furnished by the second algorithm. We also want to interpret the meaning of v geometrically and see why these two sequences of approximations both must eventually agree with v to any required number of decimal places when we compute by hand. Mathematically speaking, we say that in both cases the sequences *converge* to the limit v.

We do not attempt to locate the precise points on the curve $s = 16t^2$ corresponding to the times $2 + 10^{-j}$ and $2 - 10^{-j}$ because their exact location is not important. What is important is that the times approach 2. In Figure 8 we draw a section of curve intended to represent the graph near $t = 2$. We locate a sequence of points t_j, t_{j+1}, t_{j+2} to the right of $t = 2$ intended to suggest three successive times getting closer to $t = 2$ (distances are not to scale). The corresponding points P_j, P_{j+1}, P_{j+2} on the curve represent positions of the stone successively closer to P.

The value of Δs at time t_j is equal to the distance between the points P_j and P measured along the s-axis. This is the number of units in the line segment R_jP_j. The value of Δt at time t_j is just the number of units of time between 2 and t_j measured along the t-axis or, what is the same thing, the number of units in the line segment PR_j. Now the average speed during the time interval is $w_j = \Delta s/\Delta t$ or just

$$w_j = \frac{R_jP_j}{PR_j}$$

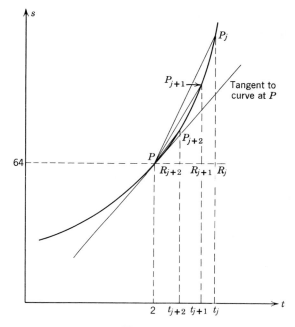

Figure 8

Tangent at P and chords which approximate it from the right

This, however, is just the slope of the line segment PP_j joining the two points on the curve.

Similarly, when we take the closer point P_{j+1} corresponding to the closer time t_{j+1} at the next step in the iteration, we find the speed estimate to be

$$w_{j+1} = \frac{\Delta s}{\Delta t} = \frac{R_{j+1}P_{j+1}}{PR_{j+1}}$$

and this is just the slope of the line segment PP_{j+1}.

The next closer point to P in the sequence is P_{j+2}. The average speed in the time interval between $t = 2$ (when the stone is at P on the curve) and $t = t_{j+2}$ (when the stone is at P_{j+2}) is

$$w_{j+2} = \frac{\Delta s}{\Delta t} = \frac{R_{j+2}P_{j+2}}{PR_{j+2}}$$

which is just the slope of the line segment PP_{j+2}.

The question we now wish to answer is: What is the geometric significance of v, the speed at P? Let us seek the answer by consideration of what we already know to be true. Two facts stand out:

1. The estimates $w_1, w_2, w_3, \ldots, w_j, w_{j+1}, w_{j+2}, \ldots$, converge to v in value; that is, the difference between v and w_j becomes and remains as small as we please if we take j large enough.
2. The estimates w_j each can be identified as the slope of the line segment joining P to the corresponding point on the curve.

It is natural to interpret v also as a slope. It is the slope of a particular line through P, since all the lines $P_j P$, $P_{j+1} P$, $\ldots$, pass through P. The line passing through P, with slope equal to v (the number to which the sequence $w_1, w_2, w_3, \ldots$, converges) is called the **tangent** to the curve at P. This is a precise way of defining the tangent to a curve, a notion which is familiar to you in an intuitive way from elementary geometry.

Returning to Figure 8 on which the tangent line has been indicated, we see that, as the points $P_j, P_{j+1}, \ldots$, approach P, the slopes of the line segments get closer and closer to the slope of the tangent line, and the line segments come closer and closer to the tangent line itself.

Thus, we have come to the following geometric interpretation of our problem: The speed of the stone at a given instant is equal to the slope of the tangent to the distance-time curve at the corresponding point P on the curve.

As often happens in mathematics, when we find the solution of one problem we may also find that we have uncovered the key to a great many other problems as well. This is the case here. Starting with the problem of determining the exact speed of a falling object at a given time, we find that we have been led to an exact definition for the tangent line to a curve and to an algorithm for finding the slope of the tangent.

Let us think about this problem of finding the tangent at a given point of a curve. Of course, we could try to draw the tangent line graphically. Then, to get the equation of the tangent line we would take two points on the line to find the slope. Knowing the slope and the coordinates of P, we can find the equation of the line. But would this be anything more than an estimate? And how could one get a better estimate? Suppose we wanted the slope of the tangent very exactly, say rounded correctly to six decimal places. How would one solve this mathematical problem?

Our algorithm described in Figure 6 gives a sequence of slopes which converge in value to the slope of the tangent. This algorithm, to repeat,

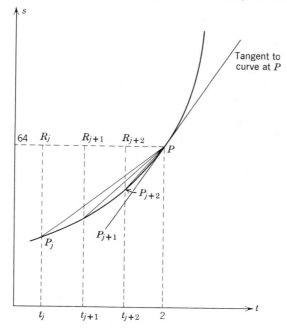

Figure 9

Tangent at P and chords which approximate it from the left

chooses a sequence of points on the curve. This sequence of points approaches the point where we wish to find the slope. We then find the slopes of the line segments joining this sequence of points to the point in question.

Question.   Does this process work for every point on the curve $s = 16t^2$?

Question.   Does this process find the slope of the tangent to other curves as well?

Next let us find the geometric interpretation of the second algorithm, which furnished the successive approximations $u_1, u_2, u_3, \ldots ,$. This was based on a sequence of times just prior to $t = 2$ and getting closer to $t = 2$. On the graph of Figure 9 we have again exaggerated a portion of the curve $s = 16t^2$ near $t = 2$. Three successive points in the sequence just prior to $t = 2$ are represented again as $t_j, t_{j+1}, t_{j+2}.$[9] The corre-

[9] Note that these are not the same t_j, t_{j+1} and t_{j+2} as before. They merely have the same names as the previous points in Figure 8, but they are different from them.

sponding points on the curve are P_j, P_{j+1}, P_{j+2}. Joining the points to P gives the segments P_jP, $P_{j+1}P$, $P_{j+2}P$. As before, these segments are successive approximations to the tangent to the curve at P. The slopes are successive approximations to the slope of the tangent. In terms of our falling stone problem, we are approximating the instantaneous speed of the falling stone at $t = 2$ sec by taking shorter and shorter time intervals just prior to $t = 2$. Since the tangent to the curve at P is a *uniquely* determined line, it makes no difference whether we approximate it by a sequence of line segments to the right of P (as in Figure 8) or by a sequence of line segments to the left of P (as in Figure 9). The slopes of both sequences of line segments converge to the slope of the tangent.

> **Question.**   Can you draw a curve such that at some point on it the sequence of slopes in Figure 8 and Figure 9 would converge to different values? Does the curve possess a tangent at this point?

We can summarize the geometric significance of the instantaneous speed v and the algorithms we have derived for determining v as follows. *The speed of the falling body at any time is equal to the slope of the tangent to the distance-time curve at that time. Calculating the average speed in smaller and smaller time intervals following or preceding that time gives a sequence of values which correspond to the slopes of chords. The slopes of these chords converge to the slope of the tangent to the curve at the given instant of time.*

> **Question.**   What changes must be made in the algorithm of Figures 6 and 7 to calculate the speed of the falling stone correct to r decimal places at time $t = 3$ sec? At time $t = 1$ sec?

4.8   Speed or Slope at Any Time

We may use the algorithm in Figures 6 and 7 to calculate the speed of the falling stone at any desired time t by making very minor changes in the flow chart. Let t now signify the time in seconds at which we wish to determine the speed v correct to r decimal places. To each value of t there corresponds a value of v. For this reason we say that v is a **function** of t. The fact that the value of v depends on the time t is frequently indicated by writing $v(t)$ (read this "v of t") instead of merely v. The set of all number pairs $\{(t, v)\}$ where t may take on any positive value and v for each t is the corresponding value of the speed completely specifies (or defines) the function v. At the moment, we know the value of v at one time, $t = 2$, to be $v = 64$. In the function notation we would write $v(2) = 64$. In the notation of ordered pairs we would express the same information by writing (2, 64).

Question. What is the value of v at $t = 0$? Give a physical reason for your answer.

If possible, we would like to find not only the value of v at several values of t but also the law or functional relation between v and t as a formula so that we can find v for any desired t from an equation. We already have written down one such functional relation, not between v and t, but between s and t. Recall that the position of the stone at any t is given by the equation

$$s = 16t^2$$

This determines s as a function of t since to each t there corresponds a value $s(t) = 16t^2$. The set of ordered pairs $\{(t, s)\}$ or $\{(t, 16t^2)\}$, where t is permitted to be any positive number or zero, completely specifies the function s.

Let us now alter the flow chart of Figures 6 and 7 to permit the calculation of $v(t)$ for any t. The change required is simple indeed. Only box 2 needs to be changed. Instead of setting t equal to 2, we set it equal to any desired value.

We now use the flow chart in Figure 6 to calculate the speed of the stone at $t = 1$ sec, using hand calculations.[10] In the notation of functions we want the value of $v(1)$. If we again select $r = 2$ so that our result will be correct to two decimal places, we get for the w's the values

$$w_2 = 31.16$$

$$w_3 = 32.016$$

$$w_4 = 32.0016$$

$$w_5 = 32.00016$$

Each time, the test of box 15 fails and we repeat the loop once again to find

$$w_6 = 32.000016$$

[10] Figure 6 is quite adequate for hand calculations. If we are going to use a computer, Figure 7 must be used as well.

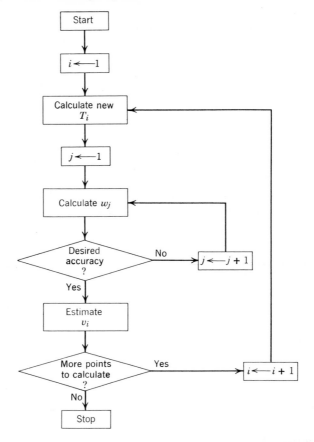

Figure 10

Rough flow chart for calculating speed at several times

so that $|w_6 - w_5| < .001$ and we proceed to box 17. This gives

$$w_j + 5e = 32.005016$$

and thus

$$v = 32.00$$

as the value of $v(1)$ correct to two decimal places. As before, by observing the pattern in w_j, we can deduce that the value of $v(1)$ correct to any number of decimal places is 32.

Before continuing, repeat the above calculation using the flow chart in Figure 6 to find the speed at $t = 3$ sec. You will again have to change box 2.

The need for repetition of the entire process each time we select a new point t suggests that we make an addition to our flow chart to include this aspect of the calculation. What is required is a second (outer) loop, in which a new point t is selected and after which there is a return to the inner loop where the speed $v(t)$ is calculated to the desired accuracy.

Figure 10 shows the main structure of the resulting flow chart. Let the successive times at which the speed is to be found be denoted as $T_1, T_2, T_3, \ldots,$. For brevity and for later convenience in programming, we write v_i to stand for $v(T_i)$, the value of the speed at T_i. The outer loop selects a different time on each occasion that it is traversed. We start with $i = 1$ and increase it by 1 as we finish the loop. Once a time has been selected, the inner loop is used to calculate the corresponding speed v_i. Each time j is increased we get a better estimate of v_i. When we have v_i to the desired accuracy, we leave the inner loop and return to the outer loop.

For definiteness, suppose that the variable t can have any value lying in an interval of the time axis from $t = a$ to $t = b$. To aid us in graphing v as a function of t we want to find $v(t)$ at a number of equally spaced points in the interval. We divide the interval from a to b into N equal subintervals, each having a length $h = (b - a)/N$. Here N stands for any one of the positive integers $1, 2, 3, \ldots,$. Labeling the first point a as T_1, the second point $a + h$ as T_2, etc., we have in Figure 11 the subdivision of the axis. The point T_{N+1}, reached after N steps of length h, takes us to the end point b of the whole interval. In our flow chart, then, we can calculate T_i from the relation

$$T_i = a + (i - 1)h$$

where i successively takes on the values $1, 2, \ldots, N + 1$. When $i = N + 1$ there are no more points at which to find the speed, and the process ends.

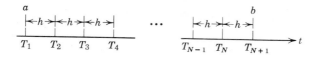

Figure 11

Time interval from a to b divided into n parts

```
        DIMENSION S(50),W(50),T(50)
        DO 25 I=1,6
   1    E=0.0001
   2    TZ=I-1
   3    P=16.0*TZ**2
   4    DELT=0.1
   5    T(1)=TZ+DELT
   6    S(1)=16.0*T(1)**2
   7    DELS=S(1)-P
   8    W(1)=DELS/DELT
   9    DO 16 J=2,50
  10    DELT=0.1*DELT
  11    T(J)=TZ+DELT
  12    S(J)=16.0*T(J)**2
  13    DELS=S(J)-P
  14    W(J)=DELS/DELT
  19    IF (J-2) 20,21,20
  20    A=W(J-1)-W(J)
        B=W(J-2)-W(J-1)
        IF (A-B) 21,22,22
  21    IF (W(J-1)-W(J)-E) 23,16,16
  16    CONTINUE
  22    V=W(J-1)
        GO TO 24
  23    V=W(J)
  24    PRINT 100,TZ,V
  25    CONTINUE
 100    FORMAT (4H  V(,F3.1,4H) = ,F6.2)
        STOP
        END
```

Figure 12

FORTRAN program to find the speed of falling stone at several times

For the falling stone suppose we want to find the speed at subintervals of $h = 1$ sec between $t = 0$ and $t = 5$. The end points of the time interval are then $a = 0$ and $b = 5$. The number of subintervals is $N = (b - a)/h = 5$. We would then calculate the speed at the times $T_1 = 0$, $T_2 = 1$, $T_3 = 2$, $T_4 = 3$, $T_5 = 4$, and $T_6 = 5$.

Problem. Write out the detailed flow chart for calculating the speed of the falling stone at the times 0, 1, . . . , 5 based on the charts of Figures 6, 7, and 10.

Question. Instead of the distance-time relation $s = 16t^2$, suppose s were some other function of t, say $s(t)$. In addition, suppose the speeds were required at the equally spaced points T_1, . . . , T_{N+1}, where $a = T_1$ and $b = T_{N+1}$. What changes are required in the flow chart of the problem above to handle this more general situation?

With very minor changes the FORTRAN program in Section 4.6 can be used to calculate the speed at the six times 0, 1, 2, . . . , 5. Indeed, all we need do is add the statement DO 25 I = 1, 6 following the DIMEN-SION statement and change the statement numbered 2 to read TZ = − 1 and add 25 CONTINUE immediately after statement number 24. A complete listing of the program is given in Figure 12. The FORMAT statement was also changed to make the printed results easier to read.

This program was run on a computer (the IBM 7094), and the printed results are shown in Figure 13.

Problem.   Change the FORTRAN program above to calculate the speed at the times ½, ³⁄₂, ⁵⁄₂, ⁷⁄₂, and ⁹⁄₂ sec.

4.9   More About Speed and Acceleration

Having calculated the speed $v(t)$ of the falling stone at a number of times, we are ready to reach some general conclusions. It is evident from the computer print out in Figure 13 that

$$V(1) = 32 \times 1$$
$$V(2) = 32 \times 2$$
$$V(3) = 32 \times 3$$
$$V(4) = 32 \times 4$$
$$V(5) = 32 \times 5$$

or

$$V(i) = 32i$$

where i = 1, 2, 3, 4 or 5. We can assume, therefore, that for any time t the speed is just 32 times the time or

$$v = 32t \qquad\qquad (6)$$

```
V(0. ) =     0.00
V(1.0) =    32.00
V(2.0) =    63.99
V(3.0) =    95.98
V(4.0) =   127.94
V(5.0) =   159.91
```

Figure 13

Results of FORTRAN program in Figure 12

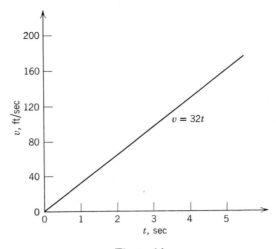

Figure 14

Speed versus time for falling stone ($v = 32t$)

which specifies v as a function of t. In Figure 14 we have plotted the number pairs (t, v) from the results computed earlier and have joined the points to form the line which is the graph of equation (6).

Question.   What would the speed v be as a function of time if, instead of using 32 ft/sec² for the acceleration of gravity, we had used the more accurate value 32.172 ft/sec²? Justify your answer.

Although we have calculated the speed at only a few points, we have been led to a conclusion which enables us to deduce very simply the speed of a freely falling object at any time. We now have two ways to find the speed of the object t seconds after it begins falling:

1. Find the slope of the tangent to the curve $s = 16t^2$ at the time t using our numerical algorithm or, more simply,
2. Find the value of v from the equation $v = 32t$.

Speed is usually defined as the rate of change of distance with time. This is simply another way of saying that the speed is the slope of the tangent to the curve of distance versus time. In the terminology of calculus, v is called the **derivative** of the distance with respect to time. The derivative with respect to t of the function $16t^2$ is $32t$.

We emphasize that to find the derivative of a function requires an infinite process or, as it is customarily called in mathematics, a **limiting process**. The derivative $v = 32t$ of the function $s = 16t^2$ was found by studying the limit of a convergent infinite sequence of numbers w_1, w_2, $w_3, \ldots$, or equivalently u_1, u_2, $u_3, \ldots$, for a number of values of t.

To complete the discussion of the motion of the falling stone we look at the way the speed itself is changing. Acceleration is the term used for the rate at which the speed changes. Suppose we take some particular time, say $t = 2$ sec, and ask how fast the speed is changing at that instant. (Remember that previously we asked for the speed at $t = 2$, which is the same as asking how fast s is changing at that instant). Of course, we know the answer to the question: How fast is the speed of the stone changing? A falling body has constant acceleration equal to the acceleration of gravity, which we have taken to be 32 ft/sec². Can we check this from the graph in Figure 14?

Let us estimate the acceleration g of the stone at $t = 2$ by taking the 1-sec interval from $t = 2$ to $t = 3$. The speed changes from 64 ft/sec to 96 ft/sec, that is, by 32 ft/sec. Dividing by the elapsed time of 1 sec gives 32 ft/sec² as the average acceleration during that time and serves as our estimate of g. This is also the estimate of the slope of the graph at $t = 2$. Since the graph is a line, the slope is constant and our estimate is exactly equal to the slope of the line. Thus, we have checked our original assumption that the acceleration is constant and equal to 32 ft/sec². No matter what time t we choose on the graph in Figure 14, the slope (acceleration) has the value 32 ft/sec².

Before going on to a final problem which is closely related to our falling stone problem, we pause to emphasize some of the points of this chapter. We have learned how to calculate the speed of a falling object and the slope of the tangent to a curve. We have also seen that not only can we calculate the speed, but also we can write an equation to give the speed for any given time. See equation (6).

All of this serves as an introduction to *differential calculus*. When you study the calculus, you will learn more about speed and slope and the general concept of the derivative of a function. In particular, you will learn convenient techniques for finding the derivative of a function directly from the formula defining the function, without numerical computation. For now, we must be content with numerically calculating such quantities as slope. However, the analytical methods of the calculus are direct extensions of the procedures and ideas we have used here.

4.10 A Problem in Ballistics

The subject of ballistics has to do with the motion under gravity of objects that are shot from the surface of the earth. The scientific study of this kind of motion began with Galileo.[11] Not until Newton, however, had the laws of motion and the mathematical tools been worked out to permit the complete solution of these problems. During World War I extensive ballistic tables were calculated for the first time for all kinds of guns up to very large cannons with ranges of many miles. These tables gave the elevation for each gun necessary to achieve a certain range. Since the projectiles of that day, once fired, moved only under the influence of gravity (plus corrections due to air resistance and wind), these were true ballistic problems. Nowadays, missiles or rockets are propelled by engines, at least for part of their flight, so that the motion is not purely ballistic. However, once the engines have cut out, the problem becomes a ballistic one (only gravity acts) until such time as the engines may be reignited.

Question. Does the use of jets on a space craft to change its orientation in space through rotation affect its trajectory?

Question. Is the term intercontinental ballistic missile an appropriate name?

We can learn a good deal from the simple problem of finding the motion of an object which is fired vertically upward from the ground with some initial speed v_0 at the initial time $t = 0$ sec. This situation could be approximately realized by having the object propelled by an explosive charge that is consumed almost instantly. The reader may think, for example, of a bullet being fired from a gun pointing straight up and leaving the muzzle with the speed v_0 feet per second. Less violently, the same effect would be obtained mechanically by placing the object on a

---

[11] **Galileo Galilei,** 1564–1642, is usually referred to by his first name only, Galileo (pronounced "gahl-ih-láy-oh"). He was a noted astronomer as well as a mathematician. He invented one of the first practical telescopes and used it to verify the Copernican theory of the universe (the earth rotates about the sun). Because of his writings on this subject, Galileo was convicted of heresy in 1632. He was forced to renounce his views publicly and accept the theory of Ptolemy that the earth was the center of the universe. Legend has it, however, that as he rose from his knees after completing his renunciation he said, "And yet it (the earth) moves."

compressed spring and suddenly releasing the spring, or by using a sling shot to propel the object.

If there were no gravitational force acting on the object, Newton's first law of motion asserts that it would move straight upward at the constant speed of v_0 feet per second. At the end of t seconds, the object would have moved a distance found by multiplying speed by time or

$$v_0 t$$

However, gravity *is* acting and the distance just calculated must be decreased by the distance an object would fall in t seconds as the result of gravity. We have seen in the falling stone problem that this distance is $\frac{1}{2} g t^2$, where g is the acceleration of gravity. Therefore, the height of the object above the earth, which we shall call y (the letter y is often used to denote a vertical coordinate), is given by subtracting the distance $\frac{1}{2} g t^2$ from the distance $v_0 t$ or

$$y = v_0 t - \tfrac{1}{2} g t^2 \tag{7}$$

The actual motion of the object is therefore the result of combining the effect of the initial speed v_0 and the effect of gravity. (Notice that increasing y corresponds to the *rising* of the object. In the falling stone problem we used s to denote distance fallen; there increasing s corresponded to the *falling* of the object.)

Let us suppose that the initial upward speed is 480 ft/sec. This is about the speed of a bullet upon firing. Again suppose we take the value 32 ft/sec² for g. This gives us the equation

$$y = 480t - 16t^2 \tag{8}$$

from which the height y can be calculated for each time t. To emphasize that y is a function of t, we may write $y(t)$ in place of simply y.

We can answer all questions concerning the motion of the object by calculations based on equation (8), just as in the case of the falling stone where we used equation (1). Now, however, the motion is more complicated. Physically, we know that the object will first rise and then fall to earth. While it rises its speed will be decreasing, while it falls its speed will be increasing. Among the questions that may be asked are: (i) How far does it rise? (ii) How fast is it going when it hits the ground? (iii) How much time elapses before it comes back to earth? (iv) What is the exact speed at different times during the flight?

Since equation (8) is a distance versus time relation, we can apply our general algorithm which enables us to calculate speed or slope at any point of the graph. Before doing this, however, let us look at the graph of equation (8) (Figure 15). By calculating y at 1-sec intervals we find the successive entries of Table 4. Continue filling out the table past $t = 30$ sec. A FORTRAN program for this calculation is easily written. Again, however, we must be careful that "subtractive cancellation" does not cause errors in our results.

Table 4

t	0	1	2	3	4	5
y	0	464	896	1296	1664	2000

The graph of the function y in Figure 15 gives us a geometrical picture of the motion from which we can answer, at least approximately, some of the questions asked. The object rises to a height of 3600 feet 15 sec after it leaves the ground. The curve itself is a parabola and has an **axis of symmetry** shown by the dashed vertical line MN in the figure. (The axis of symmetry has the property that the portion of the curve on one side is the "mirror image" of the portion on the other side.) The height of the curve at symmetrical points such as Q and Q', P and P', O and O' is the same.

Problem. Show that the height y is the same at $t = 15 + \Delta t$ and $t = 15 - \Delta t$, where Δt may be any interval of time. Can Δt be greater than 15 sec?

Question. From the symmetry, what can you deduce about the slopes of the tangents to the curve at corresponding points such as P and P', Q and Q', O and O'? What about the speeds at the times corresponding to these symmetrically placed points?

The tangent to the graph at the topmost point is horizontal (parallel to the t-axis). This gives zero slope and, therefore, zero speed to the object at the highest point. At $t = 15$ sec, then, the object is at its highest point and has zero speed. It then falls freely under gravity. Its subsequent motion should just duplicate the distance versus time graph of the falling stone. Indeed, the portion of the curve from M to Q' to P', and so on, is very similar to the rising graph of Figure 1. The apparent differences are due to the different lengths chosen to represent 1 sec

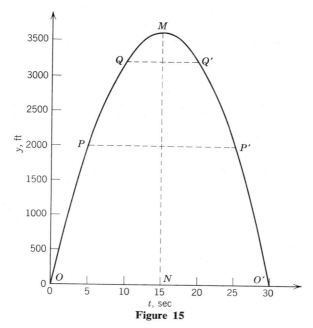

Figure 15

Graph of $y = 480t - 16t^2$

and 1 ft in the two graphs and to the fact that in Figure 1 we are plotting s (distance *fallen*) versus time, while in Figure 15 we are plotting y (distance *risen*). Next let us find the speed at various times.

Question. What is the slope of the curve in Figure 15 at $t = 0$?

Finding the speed at a time such as $t = 5$ sec, for example, means finding the slope of the tangent to the curve at P. This is done, as we know, by taking a sequence of times approaching $t = 5$ and computing the average speeds in these intervals. This corresponds to a sequence of points on the curve approaching P and the slopes of the chords joining P to these points. These sequences converge to the slope of the tangent to P or, what is the same thing, to the speed of the object at P.

Let us now apply the flow charts of Figures 6, 7, and 10 and the corresponding **FORTRAN** program written in Section 4.6 to calculate the speed at a number of times. The distance-time function to be used is now $y = 480t - 16t^2$ in place of $s = 16t^2$. As the interval of time, we take $t = 0$ to $t = 30$ sec and subintervals of length $h = 1$ sec. This means that $N = 30$. Carrying out the computations gives the values shown in Table 5 for the speeds at 1-sec intervals during the rising part of the motion. We let v stand for speed.

Table 5

t	0	1	2	3	4	5	6	7	8	9	10	11	12	13	14	15
v	480	448	416	384	352	320	288	256	224	192	160	128	96	64	32	0

Question.   Before continuing to the rest of the motion, what regular pattern do you observe in this table of numbers?

Clearly, each succeeding value of v in Table 5 is found by subtracting 32 from the number to its left. If we let $v(t)$ denote the value of v at time t, we have

$$v(1) = 480 - 32 \cdot 1$$

$$v(2) = 480 - 32 \cdot 2$$

$$v(3) = 480 - 32 \cdot 3$$

We can write this as

$$v(i) = 480 - 32i$$

where i stands for any integer $= 1, 2, 3, \ldots ,$. We can write the single algebraic equation for $v(t)$ for any number t (integer or not) as follows:

$$v(t) = 480 - 32t \tag{9}$$

Let us justify in another way this simple formula for the speed as the object rises. The number 480 is the initial upward speed. From this we subtract the *downward* speed due to the acceleration of gravity on a freely "falling" body after t seconds. From the falling stone problem we know this to be just $32t$. So we can arrive at equation (9) through our intuition and through our previous discussions in this chapter.

What happens to the speed after $t = 15$ sec as the object falls? The FORTRAN program will also yield the subsequent speeds. The values turn out to be those of Table 6. Entries for $t = 15, 16, \ldots ,$ are displayed

Table 6

t	30	29	28	27	26	25	24	23	22	21	20	19	18	17	16	15
v	−480	−448	−416	−384	−352	−320	−288	−256	−224	−192	−160	−128	−96	−64	−32	0

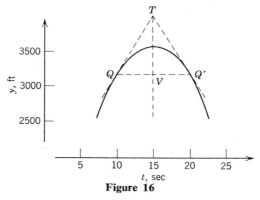

Figure 16

Section of graph of $y = 480t - 16t^2$ showing tangents at Q and Q'

from right to left for comparison with the entries of Table 5. Note the pattern!

As we expected from the symmetry of the problem, the speed i seconds after $t = 15$ is the same numerically (this means the same number except for sign) as it was i seconds before $t = 15$. For example, one second before $t = 15$ the speed is 32 ft/sec. One second after $t = 15$ the speed is -32 ft/sec. Again, seven seconds before $t = 15$ the speed is 224 ft/sec, while seven seconds after $t = 15$ the speed is -224 ft/sec.

Question.   How does the minus sign get there, and what does it mean?

To see these relationships geometrically let us take a section of the curve of Figure 15 containing two corresponding points such as Q and Q'. In Figure 16 we have drawn the tangents to these points. Extended, these tangents meet at the point T, and we have the triangle QTQ' which is an isosceles triangle because the base angles are equal (by symmetry). Now the slope of line QT is the speed of the object at Q (the speed at $t = 10$ sec). This slope can be found by taking the two points Q and T and calculating the change in y divided by the change in t in going from Q to T. This is just the ratio VT/QV [In our algorithm, $y(t + \Delta t)$ is greater than $y(t)$ as long as the object rises. Therefore, Δy is positive, and $\Delta y/\Delta t$ is positive. This means that all our estimates and the speed itself are positive.] On the other hand, the slope of the tangent $Q'T$ can be found by calculating the change in y divided by the change in t in going from T to Q'. Because the change in y is negative (the curve is falling), the slope is now $-VT/VQ'$. Since $QV = VQ'$, the slope may also be expressed as $-VT/QV$. Therefore, the slope at Q' is just the negative of the slope at Q.

Geometrically, the negative slope indicates that the curve is falling as we move to the right. In our problem, negative speed[12] means that the object is falling rather than rising, that is, its height above ground is decreasing, not increasing.

> **Questions.** What happens to our conclusion about the negative slope and speed at Q' if we use the algorithm based on points on the curve to the *right* of Q'? What happens to our conclusion about the positive slope and speed at Q if we use the algorithm based on points on the curve to the *left* of Q? Should slope and speed depend on the algorithm we apply or on the points on the tangent we use to calculate slope?

Returning to Table 6, the pattern is the same as that of Table 5. Increasing t by 1 sec corresponds to decreasing v by 32 ft/sec. Indeed, the formula of equation (9) holds for the entries of Table 6 as well as Table 5, and it will give all of the entries of Table 6 if we substitute in the values of t from 15 to 30.

What we have found is that the slope of the tangent to the curve described by the function $y(t) = 480t - 16t^2$ is given by the function $v(t) = 480 - 32t$. Once again, to use the language of the calculus we say that the *derivative* of the function $y(t) = 480t - 16t^2$ is $v(t) = 480 - 32t$.

> **Question.** If the initial speed is the number v_0 and the acceleration of gravity is the number g so that the distance is given by $y = v_0 t - \frac{1}{2} gt^2$ as in equation (7), what is the speed v as a function of t, that is, what is the derivative?

The graph of $v(t)$ given by equation (9) is shown in Figure 17. It is a straight line. What is its slope? That is easily determined. Select two points on the line such as the points $(0, 480)$ and $(15, 0)$. The slope is the ratio of the change in the y-coordinate to the change in the t-coordinate or

$$\frac{0 - 480}{15 - 0} = -\frac{480}{15} = -32$$

---

[12] It is customary to reserve the word speed for the numerical (unsigned) value of the time rate of change of position of an object. When direction as well as numerical value is to be referred to by a single term, the word velocity is used.

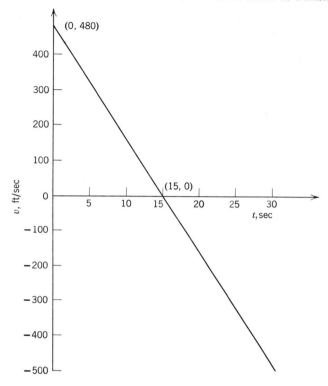

Figure 17

Graph of $v = 480 - 32t$

The slope is -32, a negative number, corresponding to the fact that the line is falling as we move to the right in the graph. What is the physical meaning of a negative slope for the graph of speed?

The slope is the rate of change of the speed with respect to time. This is precisely what we mean by acceleration. We are led once again to the acceleration of the object, and this is precisely the acceleration of gravity except for the minus sign. The significance of the minus sign for the acceleration is that the effect of the acceleration is to decrease the upward speed of the object. In popular terminology, the object is *decelerating* as it rises to its maximum height.

In the present problem it would be said that the velocity in the y-direction is positive between $t = 0$ and $t = 15$ and negative thereafter.

4.11 Graphing Curves

You have learned here and elsewhere to identify and describe the graphs of certain curves given by equations such as

$$y = x^2 \tag{10}$$

$$y = 5x - 3 \tag{11}$$

$$x^2 + y^2 = 25 \tag{12}$$

You have also been taught a procedure for finding the graph corresponding to an equation. Roughly speaking, if the variables in the equation are x and y (any other pair of letters would do as well), you first solve the equation to get y in terms of x. Then, by assigning various values to x, you find the corresponding y values. This gives a table of values. Interpreting each pair of values (x, y) as a point in a rectangular x, y-coordinate system, the graph is obtained by locating the points given in the table and joining these points by a smooth curve.

This procedure must always be carried through if one wants a carefully drawn graph. However, when drawing the graph it is helpful to have a pretty good idea of what the final curve will look like even before you plot any points. This also helps in deciding what points should go into your table and how to join them to each other.

For example, knowing that (10) is the equation of a parabola with vertex at the origin and opening upward with the y-axis as an axis of symmetry, we need calculate only two or three values, say at $x = 1, 2, 3$, to draw quite a good graph.

Knowing that (11) is the equation of a line, it is only necessary to find two points on this line to draw it. In fact, we know by inspection that the line has slope 5 and intersects the y-axis at $y = -3$, so no calculation is actually necessary to draw this graph.

The same is true of equation (12). We know that it represents a circle of radius 5 with center at the origin. If we did not know this we would soon discover, in trying to make a table of points, that for some x's there are two values of y and for some other x's there are no values of y. There would then be the problem of connecting these points properly to give a smooth curve. After some effort we would discover that the points could be joined to form a circle.

Thus, the usual procedure of graphing is of little help in visualizing what the graph looks like until it is all over. You will recall the kind of children's puzzle often found in newspapers or magazines where a seemingly meaningless array of numbered black dots is displayed. When the dots are joined, a figure suddenly emerges and can be identified.

What we seek now is information which will help us to visualize the shape of a graph *before* plotting it. For example, what does the graph of

$$y = x^3 - 12x \tag{13}$$

look like? Or the graph of

$$y = 2x^3 + 6x^2 - 18x - 5 \tag{14}$$

Problem. Write a FORTRAN program to tabulate the points you need to adequately graph equation (14). Sketch the curve.

The information needed to tell what the graph of an equation $y = f(x)$ (read this "y equals f of x") looks like, where $f(x)$ is a given function of x [e.g., one of those appearing on the right-hand sides of equations (10), (11), (13), (14)] is found by examining the *derivative* of the function $f(x)$. The necessary information is obtained by examining the slope of $f(x)$ as a function of x. This can be done numerically, using an algorithm for calculating the slope at a number of points. Such an algorithm is given in Figures 6, 7, and 10. Or it can be done analytically from a formula for the derivative or slope if this formula is known.

In particular, there are two pieces of information which are needed to visualize the appearance of the graph of $y = f(x)$ in a certain interval of the x-axis. The first is whether the function $f(x)$ is increasing or decreasing. This corresponds to checking whether the slope or derivative of $y = f(x)$ [usually denoted by y' or $f'(x)$ and read "y prime" or "f prime of x"] is positive in sign or negative. The second is whether the slope *itself* is increasing or decreasing. This corresponds to checking whether the graph of $y' = f'(x)$ has positive or negative slope. The slope of this curve is denoted by y'' or $f''(x)$ and is the derivative of $y' = f'(x)$. This slope is also termed the **second derivative** of $y = f(x)$, being the derivative of the derivative (or the derivative of the first derivative) of $y = f(x)$.

Four cases arise out of the possibilities for y' and y''. These cases and the appearance of the corresponding segments of the curve are given in Table 7. Case 1 corresponds to the function increasing and the slope increasing. In symbols, the fact that the function is increasing is expressed by $y' > 0$; the fact that the slope is increasing is expressed by $y'' > 0$. The segment of curve drawn shows the function rising to the right and

Table 7   Summary of Cases. Information for Graphing y = f(x)

Case	Function	Slope	Appearance of Curve
1	Increasing ($y' > 0$)	Increasing ($y'' > 0$)	
2	Decreasing ($y' < 0$)	Increasing ($y'' > 0$)	
3	Increasing ($y' > 0$)	Decreasing ($y'' < 0$)	
4	Decreasing ($y' < 0$)	Decreasing ($y'' < 0$)	

becoming steeper, that is, increasing slope. Similarly, the other cases should be checked through by the reader.

> **Questions.** What does the corresponding segment of curve look like if $y'' = 0$ at each point of the segment? What does it look like if $y' = 0$ at each point? What does the curve look like if $y' = 0$ at only one point? What does the curve look like if $y'' = 0$ at only one point?

To use Table 7 to visualize and sketch the graph of an equation $y = f(x)$, it is necessary to divide the x-axis into intervals in each of which the function $f(x)$ either increases or decreases (not both in the same interval) and the slope either increases or decreases. This can be done either from a table of values of the function and its slope, that is, numerically, or directly from equations giving y' and y'', that is, analytically.

To illustrate, we return to Section 4.10 to the problem of the bullet fired vertically upward. The independent variable was time t and the equation giving height y as a function of t was

$$y = 480t - 16t^2 \qquad (8)$$

A table of values of y was begun in Table 4 and filled out to $t = 30$ sec. From this table, two intervals of values of t pertinent to our discussion appear. In the first interval, $0 \le t < 15$, the function y is increasing. In the second interval, $15 < t \le 30$, the function y is decreasing. Thus, for $0 \le t < 15$ we have $y' > 0$, while for $15 < t \le 30$ we have $y' < 0$.

To determine from Table 7 the cases to which these intervals correspond, we need to check whether the slope is increasing or decreasing.

From Tables 5 and 6 we see that the slope, denoted by v, decreases throughout $0 \leq t < 15$ and continues to decrease in $15 < t \leq 30$. We conclude, therefore, that in the interval $0 \leq t < 15$ we have case 3, while in the interval $15 < t \leq 30$ we have case 4. The appearance of the curve is shown by joining the two segments of curves from Table 7 as in Figure 18. At the topmost point the slope is zero; therefore, the tangent to this point is horizontal. An accurate graph of equation (8), shown in Figure 15, confirms the appearance of the curve predicted by the sketch.

The appearance of the graph of equation (8) can be more easily deduced if we have, in addition to the equation for y as a function of t, the equations for y' and y'', the first and second derivatives. In Section 4.10 we established that the slope was given by equation (9), so that

$$y' = 480 - 32t \tag{15}$$

We also found the slope of the graph of this equation, that is, the derivative of the function $480 - 32t$, to be constant and equal to -32. Hence,

$$y'' = -32 \tag{16}$$

Equation (15) tells us that when $t < 15$ we have $y' > 0$, and that when $t > 15$ we have $y' < 0$. This identifies two intervals, $0 \leq t < 15$ and $15 < t \leq 30$ and tells us the sign of y' in each. From equation (16) we know that y'' is negative, that is, the slope y' is decreasing, for all t. Combining this information and using Table 7, we conclude at once that we have case 3 for $0 \leq t < 15$ and case 4 for $15 < t \leq 30$.

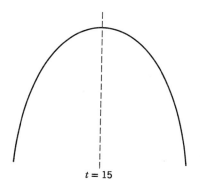

$t = 15$

Figure 18

As a second example, let us take the problem of finding what the graph of equation (14) looks like and making a rough sketch of it. In a previous problem you were asked to write a FORTRAN program to tabulate the values of *y* for a number of values of *x*. We assume that you have already completed a table such as the one given in Table 8.

Table 8   Values of y = 2x³ + 6x² − 18x − 5

x ···	−6	−5	−4	−3	−2	−1	0	1	2	3	4	5	···
y ···	−113	−15	35	49	39	17	−5	−15	−1	49	147	305	···

Inspection of this table indicates that *y* is increasing as we move to the right along the negative *x*-axis, up to some *x* between *x* = −4 and *x* = −2. We cannot be very precise about where the function *y* ceases to increase and begins to decrease without tabulating some additional values between *x* = −4 and *x* = −2, in addition to that at *x* = −3. However, since we are interested only in the appearance of the curve, we may as well describe *y* tentatively as increasing all along the negative *x*-axis up to *x* = −3. (A check of values of *y* to the left of *x* = −6 indicates that *y* becomes more and more negative because of the term $2x^3$, which dominates the others.)

Proceeding to larger values of *x* in Table 8, we see that from *x* = −3 (or thereabouts) to somewhere near *x* = +1, the function *y* decreases. Following *x* = 1 (or thereabouts), the function *y* increases. On the number line we therefore have distinguished the three intervals shown in Figure 19.

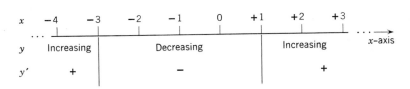

Figure 19

Intervals of increase and decrease of $y = 2x^3 + 6x^2 - 18x - 5$

To proceed further, we need a table of values of the slope *y′* in order to distinguish the intervals of increase and decrease of *y′*. That is, we need the intervals in which the slope of *y′* is positive (*y″* > 0) and the intervals in which the slope of *y′* is negative (*y″* < 0). These intervals and those shown in Figure 19 will enable us to apply Table 7 to determine the shape of the graph in successive intervals.

To obtain the values of y' we may, with minor alterations, make use of the flow charts of Figures 6, 7, and 10 and the corresponding FORTRAN program written in Section 4.6. The distance-time function $s = 16t^2$ is replaced by the equation $y = 2x^3 + 6x^2 - 18x - 5$. The FORTRAN program already written for calculating this function will be needed and should be inserted at the appropriate place in the program. As the interval for x, we may take $x = -6$ to $x = +5$ and sub-intervals of length $h = \Delta x = 1$. Carrying out the computations gives Table 9.

Table 9   Slope y' computed for $y = 2x^3 + 6x^2 - 18x - 5$

x $\cdots$	−6	−5	−4	−3	−2	−1	0	1	2	3	4	5 $\cdots$
y' $\cdots$	126	72	30	0	−18	−24	−18	0	30	72	126	192 $\cdots$

Examination of this table indicates that y' is decreasing for values of x up to $x = -1$ (or thereabouts), and that thereafter y' is increasing. We therefore are led to believe that there are two intervals of constant sign for the slope of the y' curve. That is, for $x < -1$ we have $y'' < 0$, while for $x > -1$ we have $y'' > 0$. These intervals are identified in Figure 20. Again, without further computation we cannot accurately locate the boundary between the two intervals which in Figure 20 we have placed at $x = -1$.

Combining this information with that in Figure 19 reveals the intervals in which both y' and y'' have constant sign. In Figure 21 we locate these intervals along the axis and indicate the shape of the curve in each of these intervals, using the results of Table 7. Linking the arcs

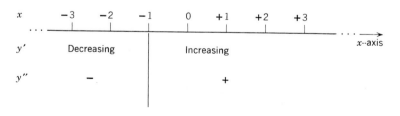

Figure 20

Intervals of increase and decrease of slope y' of $y = 2x^3 + 6x^2 - 18x - 5$

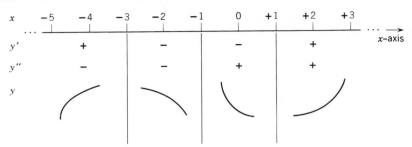

Figure 21

Intervals of constant sign of y' and y'' for $y = 2x^3 + 6x^2 - 18x - 5$ and shape of curve in these intervals

in successive intervals produces a curve shaped like that in Figure 22. For comparison, the points of Table 8 have been plotted and joined by the smooth curve shown in Figure 23.

The determination of the shape of the curve corresponding to equation (14) is more readily accomplished if one has the first and second derivatives given by equations. In the sequence of problems in Exercises 13 through 19, you will discover how to find the equation for the derivative of a function consisting of a sum of terms each of which is a number times an integer power of x, such as $2x^3$, $6x^2$, $-18x$, and -5 in equation (14). Such functions are called **polynomials.** For the present, however,

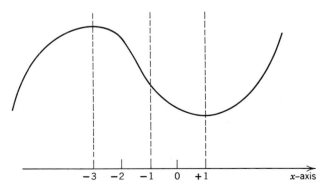

Figure 22

Rough sketch of curve $y = 2x^3 + 6x^2 - 18x - 5$

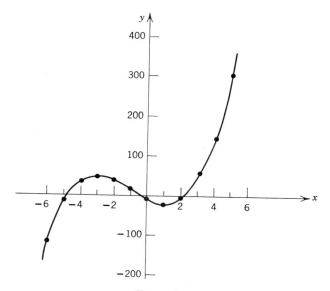

Figure 23

Graph of $y = 2x^3 + 6x^2 - 18x - 5$

we may simply take it as given that the derivative of the function in equation (14) is

$$y' = 6x^2 + 12x - 18 \tag{17}$$

and the derivative of this function is

$$y'' = 12x + 12 \tag{18}$$

To check where y' changes sign is particularly easy because the function can be factored as follows:

$$y' = 6(x^2 + 2x - 3) = 6(x + 3)(x - 1) \tag{19}$$

We see that, for $x < -3$, the factor $(x + 3)$ is negative and the factor $(x - 1)$ is negative. Therefore, the slope y' is positive. Between $x = -3$ and $x = 1$, the factor $(x + 3)$ in equation (19) is positive, but $(x - 1)$ is negative, so that here y' is negative. For $x > 1$ both factors are positive, therefore y' is positive. This establishes the intervals of constant sign for y'. From equation (18) we have that

$$y'' = 12(x + 1) \tag{20}$$

from which it follows that $y'' < 0$ for $x < -1$ and $y'' > 0$ for $x > -1$. This gives us all the information we need to determine the intervals in which y' and y'' are constant in sign and to construct the same table as in Figure 21 from which the shape of the graph of y is determined as shown in Figure 22.

From equations (17) and (18) or (19) and (20) we are able to state exactly the values of x that separate the intervals of constant sign of y' and y''. We recall that, in our determination via numerical calculation of y and y', we could not be sure that we had exactly found the end points of these intervals. Equation (19) verifies that y' is exactly zero at $x = -3$ and that y' changes from $+$ to $-$ at this point. This corresponds to the first boundary between intervals in Figure 21. Similarly, at $x = 1$, we again have, from equation (19), $y' = 0$, which marks the boundary between the last two intervals, where $y' < 0$ and $y' > 0$ as shown in Figure 21. To locate exactly the intermediate boundary, we note that y'' must change from negative to positive. Examining equation (20), we find that this takes place at $x = -1$, verifying the location shown in Figure 21.

Values of x for which the slope y' vanishes are of particular importance in the calculus. Geometrically, this corresponds to a point on the graph where the curve has a horizontal tangent. Such a point may correspond to a *maximum* value of the function, as at $x = -3$ (see Figure 23), where the curve reaches a "peak," or to a *minimum* value of the function, where the curve reaches a low point as at $x = +1$. In many problems in the calculus one is attempting to find where a function reaches a maximum or minimum value. This corresponds generally to finding the points at which $y' = 0$. Finding these points in advance is obviously an additional aid in curve sketching.

It is also important to locate points at which the second derivative y'' vanishes. When the sign of y'' changes at such a point, it is called an *inflection point*. In the problem just considered there is an inflection point at $x = -1$. Notice from Figure 23 how the shape of the curve changes at this point as the slope stops decreasing and begins to increase; that is, y'' changes from negative to positive.

We end with a word of caution about graphing which is most important. As usual, if one is working numerically there are certain inherent dangers. For example, suppose we wish the graph of an equation $y = f(x)$ from $x = a$ to $x = b$. After tabulating a number of values of y corresponding to x values which are spaced h units apart, we may draw the sketch of a

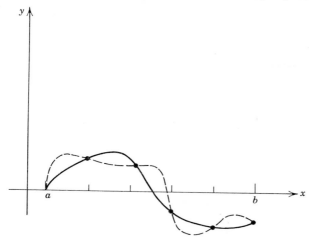

Figure 24

Two curves with the same values of y at a number of points

curve as in the solid curve joining the points shown as dots in Figure 24. However, it is conceivable that a calculation of more points between the original ones would reveal more oscillations in the graph. Then the actual curve might appear like the dashed line in Figure 24, which also goes through the original points.

If y' as well as y were tabulated at the original points and if the slope of the solid curve at each of the original points were correct, we would gain more confidence in the solid curve sketched in Figure 24. The dashed curve could not be correct as drawn because it does not have the correct slope at these points. However, it is still possible that further calculation would reveal oscillations not present in the solid curve. The actual curve could go through the original points and have the same slope as the solid curve at these points but could oscillate between those points.

Problem.   Sketch a curve which does this.

Thus, if one is seeking to determine what the graph of an equation looks like and to produce a rough sketch by using the criteria of Table 7, one may be misled if one only has numerical values of y and y' at a number of points to go on. Further tabulation might reveal new intervals of increase and decrease for y and y'. However, in the case of polynomial functions such as $y = 2x^3 + 6x^2 - 18x - 5$, general theorems are known about the number of intervals of increase and decrease which the graph of the function can display.

One such theorem is the following: The number of points where the slope of a polynomial can change sign is *at most* one less than the highest power appearing in the polynomial. The points referred to in the theorem are points at which $y' = 0$. These include the relative[13] maximum and relative minimum points of a polynomial. Therefore, the number of maximum and minimum points in the graph of a polynomial is also *at most* one less than the highest power appearing in the polynomial.

This theorem restricts the number of oscillations which can appear in the graph of a polynomial and so furnishes us with useful information about the correctness of a sketch made from a table of values.

For example, in Figure 23 we have two points where the slope of the curve changes sign: at $x = -3$ the slope is zero and the change in sign is from $+$ to $-$. At $x = 1$ the slope is again zero and the change in sign is from $-$ to $+$. The number of such points is 2, one less than the highest power, 3, appearing in the polynomial $2x^3 + 6x^2 - 18x - 5$. Hence, further tabulation of this function at intermediate points will not reveal any further oscillations.

Another example is furnished by Figure 15, which shows the graph of the polynomial $y = 480t - 16t^2$. At $t = 15$ the slope is zero and the sign of the slope changes from $+$ to $-$. There is one such point on the curve, one less than the highest power of t, 2, appearing in the polynomial $480t - 16t^2$.

On the other hand, the polynomial $y = x^3$ has positive slope at every x except at $x = 0$, where the slope vanishes. Hence there is *no* point at which the slope of this polynomial changes sign.

Question. Does this contradict the theorem? Why?

Exercises

Answers to the exercises marked * are given in Appendix A.

1. Construct a flow chart for the long division algorithm providing for the quotient of two integers to r decimal places. The algorithm should

---

[13] If a polynomial has a relative maximum at x_0, then we can find an interval from a to b on the x-axis such that $a < x_0 < b$, and such that the value of the polynomial at all points in the interval does not exceed its value at x_0. The interval from a to b may, in some cases, be very small.

terminate if the quotient is found to be exact or to result in a repeating decimal.

*2. If we drop a rock into a deep well or canyon, we must take into account the length of time required for the sound of impact to reach our ears in addition to the time required for the rock to reach the bottom if we wish to estimate the depth s accurately. The speed of sound in air at sea level is approximately 1,088 ft/sec. If it takes x seconds for the sound to travel the distance s, in feet, then

$$s = 1088x$$

Let T stand for the total time elapsed from the instant the rock is dropped until the sound reaches our ears. Equation (1) may be used for the relation between s and t, the time of fall of the rock to the bottom.

(a) Find an equation for T in terms of s.

(b) Using an accurate stop watch it is found that $T = 4.7$ sec. What is the distance fallen by the rock? What percent error in distance would be made if the time required for the sound to travel is not taken into account?

(c) The Grand Canyon is 1 mile deep at one place. If you could hear the sound of a rock striking bottom, how many seconds would elapse after dropping the rock until the sound reached you?

3. An elevator moves downward at 35 ft/sec. As it passes a floor, a stone is dropped down the adjacent shaft from the same height. How far ahead is the elevator after 1 sec? After 2 sec? After how many seconds does the stone pass the elevator? Draw a graph showing the stone's motion and the elevator's motion. At what time do you estimate the stone will be moving as fast as the elevator?

4. Show that the slope of the line through P and Q in Figure 3 as found from any other points $\bar{P}$ and $\bar{Q}$ on the line is the same as the slope found using the points P and Q. (*Hint:* Make use of similar triangles.)

5. Two distinct points P_1 and P_2 with coordinates (x_1, y_1) and (x_2, y_2), respectively, determine a line. The line has slope

$$m = \frac{y_2 - y_1}{x_2 - x_1} \qquad \text{(providing } x_1 \neq x_2\text{)}$$

and all points (x, y) lying on this line satisfy the equation

$$y = y_1 + m(x - x_1)$$

Find the slope and the equation of the line determined by each of the following pairs of points:

*(a)   (1, 1) and (4, 4)   (b) (1, 2) and (2, 1)
*(c)   (−4, 3) and (0, 7)   (d) (2, 6) and (4, 6)
(e)   (3, 1) and (3, −4)

Draw all these lines on a single graph.

6. What is the equation of a line through the point (0, 4) with slope 2? Draw this line. Draw a line through the same point with slope −2; with slope $\frac{1}{3}$; with slope −$\frac{1}{2}$.

7. (a) A train travels at a constant speed of 60 mph for 4 hr. Graph the motion, plotting time t in hours along the horizontal axis and distance s in miles along the vertical axis. Let 1 in. in the s-direction represent 60 miles. What is the slope of the line representing the motion?

   (b) Plot the motion of a jet plane traveling at a constant 600 mph for 4 hr and the train's motion on a single graph. To do this you will need to change the scale in the s-direction. Let 1 in. equal 600 miles. Which line in this graph has the same slope as the line in the graph in part (a)?

8. Find upper and lower bounds for the speed of a freely falling object at $t = 3$ sec following the beginning of its fall. Use intervals of .1 sec, .01 sec, and .001 sec just prior to and just following $t = 3$ to find your estimates. With no further calculation, predict what the estimates will be using intervals of .0001 and .00001 sec. What is the exact value of the speed at $t = 3$?

9. What is the slope of the tangent to the curve $s = 16t^2$ at $t = 2$? What is the equation of the tangent at $t = 2$? Give the slope and equation of the tangent at $t = 3$.

10. An object is fired straight up with an initial speed of 960 ft/sec. Using a FORTRAN program for calculating slopes, find its speed v at 5-sec intervals until it returns to earth. Take $g = 32$ ft/sec². What is v as a function of time? Graph speed versus time, and find the slope of the resulting curve. Be careful to change the stopping criterion used in Figure 7.

11. Lunar gravity is approximately one-sixth as strong as earth gravity; therefore, g on the moon is approximately 5.4 ft/sec². If an object is fired straight up on the moon with an initial speed of 480 ft/sec, how

far will it rise? How long will it take to return to the surface? Compare your answers with the corresponding answers for earth given in the text.

12. An object is dropped from the top of a 1000-ft building. Find the speed with which it hits the ground. If it is projected downward with an initial speed of 100 ft/sec, with what speed will it hit the ground?

*13. Consider the equation $y = x^2$.

(a) Make a table of values of y at the points $x = 0, 1, 2, \ldots , 10$.

(b) Graph the curve $y = x^2$ from the table in part (a).

(c) Use a computer and modify the FORTRAN program in Section 4.6 to make a table of values of the slope of the curve at the points $x = 0, 1, 2, \ldots , 5$.

(d) Plot the slope on the vertical axis and x on the horizontal axis from the table of values in part (c).

(e) What is the equation relating slope and x for the equation $y = x^2$?

14. Consider the equation $y = x^3$.

(a) Draw a graph of this equation with y measured along the vertical axis and x measured along the horizontal axis.

(b) Construct a flow chart to describe an algorithm for estimating the slope of the curve graphed in part (a) at $x = 2$.

(c) Write a FORTRAN program to carry out the calculations described by the flow chart in part (b).

(d) Alter the flow chart and FORTRAN program to estimate the slope of $y = x^3$ for a number of values of x.

(e) Use the program written in part (d) to find the slope at $x = 0$, $\frac{1}{2}, 1, \ldots , 5$. Can you find a formula that gives the slope as a function of x?

15. Change the flow chart in Figure 6 to start with $\Delta t = \frac{1}{5}$ and decrease it to $\frac{1}{5}$ of its previous value at each step. Does this change the results? Test the program by computing the speed at $t = 2$ to two decimal places. Will this require more or less calculation than starting with $\Delta t = 0.1$ and decreasing to $\frac{1}{10}$ of its previous value at each step? Why?

16. Notice that in the flow charts in Figures 6 and 7 only three values of w_j are needed. Once we have calculated w_j we no longer need w_{j-3}, $w_{j-4}, \ldots$. Therefore, we do not need to save all the w_j nor the s_j and t_j. Draw a flow chart to find the slope of $s = 16t^2$ at $t = 2$ which does not use subscripted variables.

17. Write a FORTRAN program to carry out the steps in the flow chart in Exercise 16. This program has the advantage that it requires less of the computer's memory than the FORTRAN program in the text.

18. Carry out all the parts of Exercise 14 for the equation $y = x^4$.

*19. Compare the equation giving the slope of the curve $y = x^2$ (Exercise 13) with the equation giving the slope of the curve $y = x^3$ (Exercise 14), and the equation giving the slope of the curve $y = x^4$ (Exercise 18). Put your results in Table 10. Can you discover from this a

Table 10

Function $y =$	x^2	x^3	x^4
Slope y' $=$			

pattern which tells you what the slope of the curve $y = x^5$ will be? What formula do you predict from this pattern for the slope of the function $y = x^m$, where m is any integer? Is this formula correct when $m = 1$? Is the formula correct when $m = 0$?

20. What is the slope of the curve given by the equation $y = x^{100}$ at $x = 1$?

21. Draw a flow chart similar to those in Figures 6 and 7 to calculate v, using time intervals of $t = 10^{-j}$ for $j = 1, 2, \ldots$, *preceding* $t = 2$.

22. Write a FORTRAN program to calculate v at $t = 2$ correct to three decimal places or the accuracy of the computer using time intervals of 10^{-j} *prior* to $t = 2$.

23. Write a FORTRAN program to perform the calculations in the flow chart of Figure 5. Go through the loop ten times and print all ten values of the speed — $w_1, \ldots, w_{10}$ — with four digits after the decimal place. What would you say the speed is at $t = 2$?

24. The following two theorems aid us in the calculation of the derivative or slope of more complicated functions.

I. The derivative of $c \cdot f(x)$, where c is a constant and $f(x)$ a given function, is equal to c times the derivative of $f(x)$, i.e., $cf'(x)$.

II. The derivative of the sum of two functions $f(x) + g(x)$ is equal to the sum of the derivatives, i.e. $f'(x) + g'(x)$.

It is also a theorem that the derivative of x^m, where m is any positive integer, is mx^{m-1} (see Exercise 19). Make use of these facts to find the derivatives of each of the following functions:

*(a) $y = x^2 + x^3$ (b) $y = 2x^2$

(c) $y = 3x^3 + x^2$ (d) $y = x^2 - 5x + 1$

*(e) $y = x^4 + x^3 + x^2 + x + 1$ (f) $y = 5x^4 - 7x^3 + 2x^2 - 4x + 7$

*25. Check the validity of theorem II of Exercise 24 for the function $x^2 + x^3$, actually computing the slope of $x^2 + x^3$ by the algorithm of this chapter at $x = 0, 1, 2, 3, 4, 5$ and comparing these results with the sum of the previously calculated slopes of the individual functions x^2 and x^3 in Exercises 13 and 14. Use a FORTRAN program and a computer to carry out the calculations.

26. Prepare a table of values of y and y' for each of the following equations. Calculate y' by means of the algorithm of Figures 6, 7, and 10. Use these tables together with the criteria of Table 7 to predict the appearance of the graph in each case and draw a sketch. Compare with an accurate graph found by plotting points.

(a) $y = x^3 - 12x$ (b) $y = x^4 - 4x^3$

(c) $y = 2x^3 - 24x$ (d) $y = -2x^4 + 8x^3$

Use a FORTRAN program and a computer to carry out the calculations.

27. Figure 25, showing intervals of constant sign of y' and y'' along the x-axis, was prepared from a table of values of y and y' for the equation $y = x^5 - 30x^3 + 160x - 10$. Draw a sketch showing the shape of the curve. From values of y calculated only at the end points of these intervals and a pair of additional points such as $x = \pm 5$ prepare a rough graph of the equation.

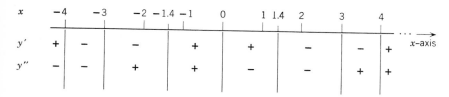

Figure 25

28. At a certain point x, the slope y' corresponding to the curve $y = f(x)$, is zero. What does the curve look like in a small interval containing this point? Show all possibilities.

29. At a certain point x, the second derivative y'' of an equation $y = f(x)$ is zero. What does the graph of $y = f(x)$ look like in a small interval containing this point? Show all possibilities.

*30. What is the sign of y'' at a maximum point of a curve such as occurs at $x = -3$ in Figure 23? (*Hint:* Is the slope increasing or decreasing? Check Table 7.)

31. What is the sign of y'' at a minimum point of a curve (such as occurs at $x = 1$ in Figure 23)?

*32. The slope of a certain function $f(x)$ is given by the equation

$$y' = x^2 - 1$$

What does the graph of $y = f(x)$ look like? Make a rough sketch. (*Hint:* Graph y' to determine the intervals needed to apply Table 7.) Where is $y = f(x)$ a maximum? A minimum?

33. Answer the questions of the preceding problem for the function $y(x)$ given that its derivative is:

(a) $y' = x^3$ (b) $y' = x^4$ (c) $y' = x^4 - 1$

34. Given that $y = 2x^3 + 6x^2 - 18x - 5$ as in equation (14), apply the theorems of Exercise 24 to verify equations (17) and (18) given in the text.

35. Do Exercise 26 again, working analytically rather than numerically. That is, write the equations for y' and y'' in each problem, and from the equations find the intervals of constant sign of y' and y'' from which to apply Table 7. Use the theorems of Exercise 24.

36. Given the function $y = x^5 - 30x^3 + 160x - 10$, write the equations for y' and y'', using the theorems of Exercise 24. From these equations verify the intervals of constant sign given in Figure 27. If we move away from the origin at $x = 0$ to the right, what is the precise value of x at which y' first vanishes? Is this point a maximum or minimum of the function y? Answer the same question if we move away from the origin to the left. Are there other maximum or minimum points of y. Where?

37. In Section 4.5 we devised an algorithm which finds an estimate of the speed of a freely falling object 2 sec after it is released. However, we were not able to estimate the error in the estimate. Change that algorithm in the following way: If the answer to the question in box 20 in Figure 7 is "yes," replace e by $10e$ and return to box 2 in Figure 6. Eventually you will leave box 21 (Figure 21) with a "yes." In that case print w_j and e. The estimate w_j should differ from v by less than e. You will need to check that e does not become too large. Stop if e becomes 1.0 or larger.

Write a FORTRAN program to carry out this new algorithm. Compare the results with those given in the text for the computer with the same number base (decimal, binary, or hexadecimal) as the one you are using.

38. Use the algorithm described in Exercise 37 with $\Delta t = 2^{-j}$. If e is increased, replace it by $2e$. Write a FORTRAN program for this new algorithm. Compare the results with those given in the text for the computer with the same number base (decimal, binary, or hexadecimal) as the one you are using.

39. Alter the FORTRAN program in Section 4.6 so that $\Delta t = \frac{1}{3}, \frac{1}{9}, \frac{1}{27}$, $\ldots,$. Compare the results with those for the computer with the same number base (decimal, binary, or hexadecimal) as the one you are using. Explain why they are better or worse.

CHAPTER FIVE

Solving Equations by Iteration

5.1 An Ancient Paradox

Suppose Speedy[1] can run twice as fast as Pokey.[1] They hold a race, and Pokey is given a 100-yd head start from the starting line. Where will Pokey be when Speedy catches up to him? Try to do this problem in your head.

Let us find the solution to this problem in a straightforward way. Let x be the number of yards Pokey runs before Speedy catches up. Then Pokey is $100 + x$ yards from the starting line. While Pokey was running x yards, Speedy ran $2x$ yards. The distance of each from the starting line must be equal when Speedy catches up; hence,

$$2x = 100 + x \tag{1}$$

Therefore,

$$x = 100 \text{ yd}$$

is the answer. Pokey runs 100 yd, Speedy runs 200 yd and catches Pokey 200 yd from the starting line.

Zeno of Elea, who lived in Greece about 500 B.C., would not have agreed with our solution. He would have argued as follows. Speedy first has to overcome Pokey's head start of 100 yd. By the time he runs 100 yd, Pokey (who runs only half as fast) is 50 yd ahead of him. When Speedy runs this additional 50 yd, Pokey has run 25 and is still 25 yd ahead. Of course, Speedy can cover that 25 yd too, but then Pokey will still be $12\frac{1}{2}$ yd ahead. Continuing the argument, it appears that Pokey will always

---

[1] In mathematics the names and symbols are arbitrary. However, good notation makes it easy to remember what the symbols refer to. "Pokey" and "Speedy" may sound childish, but you won't need to look back to recall which was the faster runner as you would if they had "names" like A and B.

be ahead of Speedy and so Speedy can never catch up! This is Zeno's famous paradox with which he wished to demonstrate that motion does not exist. Originally Zeno proposed this race as one between Achilles, the swiftest of the Greeks, and a tortoise. Even the fleet Achilles could not catch up with the tortoise according to this argument.

Questions. Suppose Achilles runs 10 times as fast as the tortoise and the tortoise is given 1000 yd as a head start. When will Achilles catch up with the tortoise? What happens according to Zeno?

The paradox disappears if we think of Zeno's argument as only an algorithm for calculating by successive approximations the distance run by Pokey. As we have seen previously with successive approximations, at each step we get closer to the answer although we never reach the exact answer in this way.

Let us translate Zeno's argument into mathematical terms. We call the time it takes Speedy to run the 100 yd to where Pokey started the first time interval. Then, as you recall, Pokey is still 50 yd ahead. The second time interval is the time it takes Speedy to run another 50 yd. At the end of the second time interval Pokey still leads by 25 yd. The third time interval is the time required for Speedy to run 25 yd, and so on. These data are tabulated in Table 1. If we let y_n be the distance run by

Table 1

	Distance Run by Speedy	Distance Run by Pokey
During *first* time interval	100	50
During *second* time interval	50	25
During *third* time interval	25	12.50
During *fourth* time interval	12.50	6.25
	...	...

Pokey during the nth time interval, where n stands for any positive integer, then we see from the last column in Table 1 that

$$y_{n+1} = \frac{y_n}{2}$$

where

$$y_1 = 50$$

Now let x_n be the *total* distance run by Pokey in the time intervals $1, 2, \ldots, n$. Then

$$x_n = y_1 + y_2 + \cdots + y_n$$

and

$$x_{n+1} = y_1 + y_2 + \cdots + y_n + y_{n+1}$$

Since $y_2 = y_1/2$, $y_3 = y_2/2$, and so on, then

$$x_{n+1} = y_1 + \frac{y_1}{2} + \cdots + \frac{y_{n-1}}{2} + \frac{y_n}{2}$$

or

$$x_{n+1} = y_1 + \frac{y_1 + y_2 + \cdots + y_n}{2}$$

But $y_1 = 50$ and the numerator of the fraction is just x_n; therefore,

$$x_{n+1} = 50 + \frac{x_n}{2} \tag{2}$$

where

$$x_1 = 50$$

and $n = 1, 2, 3, \ldots$. If we calculate a few values of x_n we get

$$x_2 = 75$$

$$x_3 = 87.5$$

$$x_4 = 93.75$$

The reader should verify that these values are indeed the total distances run by Pokey in the first two, first three, and first four time intervals.

We now let x_n be our *n*th *approximation* to the total distance run by Pokey until he is caught. From each approximation x_n we get the next one by substituting the numerical value of x_n in the right-hand side of (2) and taking the value of the right-hand side as the new approximation x_{n+1}.

We see that the successive approximations are apparently approaching the true value of x, which is 100. To visualize what is happening let us locate the successive values on a number line,[2] as in Figure 1. We can see that x_1 is halfway between 0 and 100, the true distance Pokey runs

[2] Remember that x is the distance Pokey runs, so $x = 0$ on our number line is Pokey's starting position. The actual *starting line* in the race is 100 yd to the left of this.

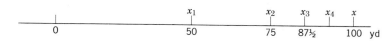

Figure 1

Distances run by Pokey

before he is caught. The next approximation x_2 is halfway between the approximation x_1 and 100. The next approximation x_3 is then halfway between x_2 and 100. In this way we continually halve the remaining distance to the true solution. Since half of the previous distance always remains, we never reach 100, but we can come as close to 100 as we please just by continuing long enough. We say that the approximations x_n **converge**[3] to the solution.

Problem.   Write a FORTRAN program to compute x_n for $n = 2, 3, 4,$ . . . , 30, starting with $x_1 = 50$.

There is a close relation between equation (2), which gives us our successive approximations, and equation (1), which is the actual mathematical equation being solved. If we divide through equation (1) by 2 to get simply x on the left-hand side, it becomes

$$x = 50 + \frac{x}{2} \qquad (3)$$

If for x on the right-hand side we put x_n and call the value of the left-hand side x_{n+1}, we get (2)

A very remarkable fact about equation (2) is that you can start with any value for x_1 and the successive values $x_2, x_3, \ldots$ will still converge to $x = 100$. For example, suppose we chose $x_1 = 150$ as an initial guess. Then we find, from equation (2),

$$x_2 = 50 + \frac{150}{2} = 125$$

$$x_3 = 50 + \frac{125}{2} = 112.5$$

$$x_4 = 50 + \frac{112.5}{2} = 106.25$$

and again the numbers will converge to 100.

[3] Recall the use of the term *convergence* on page 216 in Chapter 4.

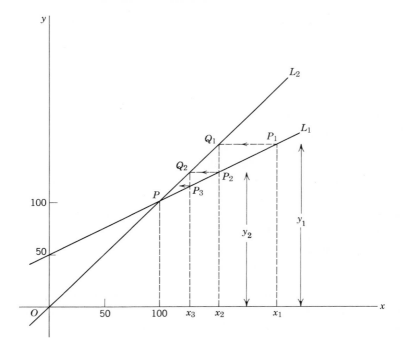

Figure 2

Successive approximations leading to intersection of $y = x/2$ (line L_1) and $y = x$
(line L_2) at $x = 100$

Problem. Write a FORTRAN program to compute x_n for $n = 2, 3,$
$\ldots, 30$, starting with $x_1 = 150$. Compare the results with the
preceding program which started with $x_1 = 50$.

To understand why this process converges, it is helpful to refer to a
geometric model. Let x now refer to an arbitrary real number and let y
denote the value of the function $50 + x/2$, giving the equation

$$y = 50 + \frac{x}{2} \qquad (4)$$

The graph of this equation for all real numbers x is the line L_1 of Figure 2.
Is there a point P on this line L_1 at which $y = x$? That is, is there a point
at which the y-coordinate, whose value by (4) is just $50 + x/2$, and the
x-coordinate, which is just the number x, are equal? If so, we have

$$x = 50 + \frac{x}{2}$$

which is just equation (3). Hence, the x-coordinate of the point P (or the y-coordinate since they are the same number) will be the solution of equation (3). Recall that P also lies on the line L_1. Now the equation

$$y = x \tag{5}$$

for all real numbers x is represented geometrically by the line L_2 in Figure 2. The intersection of this line with the line L_1 determines the desired point P. We see this as follows. Since P lies on L_1, its coordinates x and y are numbers which satisfy the equation

$$y = 50 + \frac{x}{2}$$

Because P also lies on L_2, the numbers x and y satisfy the equation

$$y = x$$

Combining, we have that the number x satisfies the equation

$$x = 50 + \frac{x}{2}$$

as desired.

We have replaced the single equation (3) by the pair of equations (4), (5) which are to be solved simultaneously, that is, as a system, for x and y (which equals x).

We now give a new interpretation of the method of successive approximations: first, algebraically, as a method of solution of the system of equations (4), (5) and, second, graphically, in terms of Figure 2.

The letters x and y now stand for the numbers which satisfy (4) and (5) [they are equal, according to (5)]. The method of successive approximations, in this problem, allows us to choose any initial estimate we like for x, say x_1. The procedure to get x_2, the next approximation, can be interpreted as an algorithm using both equations (4) and (5) as follows. We replace x in (4) by x_1. The resulting value of y we call y_1. We then replace y in equation (5) by the value y_1. The resulting value of x we call x_2. Obviously, $x_2 = 50 + x_1/2$, and the algorithm agrees with the estimate x_2 furnished by (2).

We now repeat to get x_3. The number x_2 is used in place of x in (4). The value of y which results is called y_2. We then replace y in (5) by y_2, and the resulting value of x is called x_3. Thus,

$$x_3 = 50 + \frac{x_2}{2}$$

which is the same x_3 generated by equation (2).

The procedure is repeated to obtain x_4 and all successive approximations.

Problem.   Construct a flow chart to describe this algorithm.

We now interpret the algorithm geometrically on the graph of **Figure 2** as a process of successive approximations to the point P. The algorithm locates a sequence of points P_1, P_2, . . . , on line L_1 which *converge* to the point P. By this we mean that, if n is chosen large enough, then the distance between P and the nth point P_n and all succeeding points P_{n+1}, P_{n+2}, . . . , in the sequence will be smaller than any preassigned number, no matter how small that preassigned number is.

The first step is to choose an initial estimate x_1 for x. This number is located on the x-axis. To this abscissa there corresponds the point P_1 on L_1 whose ordinate is

$$y_1 = 50 + \frac{x_1}{2}$$

This ordinate in turn determines a point Q_1 on L_2. We call the abscissa of this point x_2. It is located by dropping the perpendicular from Q_1 to the x-axis. This completes one full cycle of the algorithm.

To repeat the process we begin with the point x_2 on the x-axis. To this abscissa there corresponds the point P_2 on L_1 whose ordinate is

$$y_2 = 50 + \frac{x_2}{2}$$

This ordinate in turn determines a point Q_2 on L_2. The abscissa of this point we call x_3. It is located by dropping the perpendicular from Q_2 to the x-axis. This completes the second iteration.

Repeating the process indefinitely, we generate a sequence of points P_1, P_2, . . . , on L_1 whose abscissas are the successive numbers x_2, x_3, x_4, . . . , where x_{n+1} is given by equation (2). The convergence of the sequence x_1, x_2, . . . , to x is equivalent to the convergence of the points P_1, P_2, . . . , to the point P. We have not attempted here to prove mathematically that this convergence takes place, but to provide a model to guide and develop our intuition and to further our understanding.

The successive steps in the iteration which locate the points P_1, Q_1, P_2, Q_2, P_3, . . . , lead us along an infinite "staircase" defined by these points as shown in Figure 2. An initial guess x_1, which is too large (as $x_1 = 150$ was) leads one along a descending staircase to $x = 100$ as shown in Figure 2. An initial guess which is too small (as $x_1 = 50$ was) leads one along an ascending staircase to $x = 100$.

> **Problem.**   Draw a figure to illustrate the method when the initial guess is too small.

The method of successive approximations in this application has another very desirable characteristic besides being able to begin with any initial guess. *It is self-correcting.* If you make a mistake in arithmetic, the new (erroneous) value is treated like any other guess and will lead you eventually to as accurate an answer as you want. Of course, you cannot go on making mistakes and expect your answer to improve continually.

This self-correcting feature also helps to control round-off errors which can cause considerable difficulties in a computer. We have seen in other algorithms how the effect of one round-off error early in a calculation can become magnified in the final result. Not so in the method of successive approximations. Each value of x_j may be considered as a starting approximation. Any round-off errors it contains can be considered to be part of the approximation. They can be wiped out by the method itself as the calculations proceed.

Before your enthusiasm for this new method carries you away, we must warn you that there are dangers present. It doesn't always work! However, by studying the matter a little more deeply we can find out when it is safe to use the method of successive approximations.

Let us return to equation (1). Instead of simply dividing by 2 to get x on one side, let us subtract 100 from both sides and rewrite the equation:

$$x = -100 + 2x \qquad (6)$$

We can form successive approximations by putting an initial guess in the right-hand side and using the value of the right-hand side as the new approximation. This is the same as setting

$$x_{n+1} = -100 + 2x_n \qquad (7)$$

If we now start with our nice initial guess $x_1 = 50$ as before, we find

$$x_2 = -100 + 2(50) = 0$$

Putting $x_2 = 0$ in the right-hand side of (7), we get

$$x_3 = -100 + 2(0) = -100$$

Then

$$x_4 = -100 + 2(-100) = -300$$

Our successive approximations are getting worse and worse. The solution of (6) is still $x = 100$ as we see by substitution, but we are not approaching 100 at all. In a case like this we say that the sequence $x_1, x_2, x_3, \ldots,$ **diverges** or the approximations **diverge**.[4]

Problem.   Write a FORTRAN program to compute x_n for $n = 2, 3,$ $\ldots, 20$ from equation (7), starting with $x_1 = 50.$

To see graphically why we are diverging rather than converging we replace equation (6) by the pair of simultaneous equations

$$y = -100 + 2x \tag{8}$$

and

$$y = x$$

Plotting $y = x$ in Figure 3, we get line L_2 as before. Now, however, (8) gives the line L_3. As before, L_2 and L_3 intersect at $x = 100$.

The process of successive approximations determines a sequence of points $P_1, P_2, \ldots,$ on line L_3 as follows. The abscissa x_1 locates the point P_1 on L_3 with ordinate

$$y_1 = -100 + 2x_1$$

This ordinate in turn locates the point Q_1 on L_2. The abscissa of this point we call x_2. It is located by dropping the perpendicular from Q_1 to the x-axis. This number is the next approximation to the solution $x = 100$ and is used to repeat the process to get x_3, and so on.

The sequence of points $P_1, Q_1, P_2, Q_2, P_3, \ldots,$ obtained in this way defines successive steps in a staircase leading up and away from the solution, as the arrows indicate in Figure 3.

If we compare Figure 2 and Figure 3 we see that the difference lies in the *slope* of the lines L_1 and L_3. Line L_1 has slope *less* than that of the line $y = x$ (L_2); line L_3 has slope *greater*. These lines, we recall, are obtained from the functions appearing on the right-hand side of the equations upon which the iterations are based; that is, L_1 arises from the right-hand side of equation (3), L_3 arises from the right-hand side of equation (6).

---

[4] There is another kind of divergence, as will be seen later.

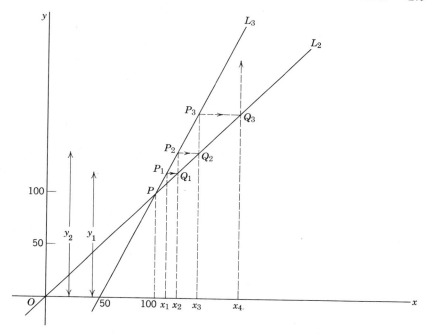

Figure 3

Successive approximations leading away from intersection of $y = -100 + 2x$ (line L_3) and $y = x$ (line L_2)

Question. What are the slopes of lines L_1, L_2, and L_3?

We conclude from this that, for the method of successive approximations to work, the slope of the function on the right-hand side of the equation upon which the method is based must be less than the slope of the function on the left-hand side. If we write the equation in the form $x = \cdots$, the slope of the function on the left-hand side is 1, and so the slope of the function on the right must be less than 1. Since we are basing our conclusions on geometric reasoning, we must be careful to recognize the limitations inherent in Figures 2 and 3. One restriction in the drawings is that all the lines have a positive slope. Accordingly, we should require more specifically that the slope of the function on the right-hand side of the iteration equation be between 0 and 1.

Question. What happens if in the equation $x = \cdots$ the slope of the function on the right is negative?

Problem.   Solve the equation

$$x = 60 - \frac{x}{2}$$

by successive approximation. What is the slope of the function on the right?

Problem.   Solve the equation

$$x = 120 - 2x$$

by successive approximation. What is the slope of the function on the right?

5.2   Nonlinear Equations

We have just learned an ingenious but undoubtedly complicated method for solving a very simple equation like $2x = 100 + x$. Why bother at all when it is so easy to find that $x = 100$ directly? This question might have occurred to you as you studied the preceding pages. The answer lies in the fact that the same method can be used to solve more complicated equations where the solution cannot be written down at all.

Suppose, as was frequently the case in your earlier courses in mathematics, that you had to solve a quadratic equation such as

$$x^2 + 6x - 3 = 0 \tag{9}$$

Using the quadratic formula, we find that there are two solutions,

$$x = -3 + 2\sqrt{3}$$

and

$$x = -3 - 2\sqrt{3}$$

The quadratic formula enabled us to write down this "answer." However, if x stands for the amount of some real quantity like a distance or an electrical current and if someone had to use this answer, it would still be necessary to calculate $\sqrt{3}$ as a decimal fraction to some desired accuracy. As we know, this requires a never-ending algorithm.

If one encounters an equation which contains the third power of the unknown as the highest power, the equation is called a *cubic* or third degree equation. Examples of cubic equations are

$$x^3 - 27 = 0$$
$$7x^3 - 3x^2 + x - 5 = 0$$
$$x^3 + 6x - 8 = 0$$

To find the values of x satisfying a cubic equation is a problem that can also be "solved" by means of a formula.[5] Now, however, the formula becomes more complicated than in the quadratic case. For example, the formula tells us that one solution of $x^3 + 6x - 8 = 0$ is

$$x = \sqrt[3]{4 + \sqrt{24}} + \sqrt[3]{4 - \sqrt{24}}$$

To find the numerical value of x from this requires that we be able to take cube roots as well as square roots. We see that a formula may not be very helpful when a numerical answer is needed.

Problem.   Give a rough estimate of the value of $\sqrt[3]{4 - \sqrt{24}}$.

You may think that adding higher powers to the equation results only in more complicated formulas for the solution. Indeed, this is true if we proceed to the next higher power, four. An equation which contains the fourth power of the unknown as the highest power is called a *quartic* or *biquadratic* equation or an equation of fourth degree. A procedure for solving quartics was given by Ferrari in 1540. The resulting formulas are even more intricate than those for the cubic equation. Noted mathematicians of the next two centuries tried to find formulas for the solution of equations involving fifth or higher powers. All so-called *quintic* or fifth-degree equations have the form

$$ax^5 + bx^4 + cx^3 + dx^2 + ex + f = 0$$

where a, b, c, d, e, f are constants. Of course, the number a cannot be zero, for then this would be an equation of fourth degree or less. What was sought was a formula giving the solution x in terms of the constant coefficients a, b, c, d, e, f. The failure of a number of outstanding mathematicians to find any such formulas led some mathematicians to suspect that such a goal might be impossible. The Norwegian mathematician Abel[6] actually proved in 1826 that formulas do not exist for the general

---

[5] Formulas for solving cubic equations were found by Italian mathematicians of the 16th century, especially Cardan (1545). The solution of quadratic equations by geometric methods was known to Euclid (300 B.C.). Formulas for solving quadratics seem first to have been given by the Hindus (600–1100 A.D.)

[6] **Niels Henrik Abel** (pronounced "ah'-bel"), 1802–1829, made substantial contributions to the theory of elliptic functions and to what are now called Abelian functions. His work received little notice until after his untimely death at the age of 27.

solution of fifth- and higher-degree equations. Only for special cases of such equations can formulas be given.

Problem.   The equation $x^5 = p$, where p is a positive number, is a special form of the equation of the fifth degree. Give a formula for a root of this equation.

The fact that formulas cannot be found does not mean that we cannot find solutions of equations of any degree. Methods of successive approximation will furnish the solutions to any desired degree of accuracy. These methods apply not only to equations involving arbitrary integer powers of the unknowns but also to more general equations involving functions other than the powers of x. Such functions as sin x, cos x, tan x, and log x can appear in the equations as well. One can combine these functions with powers to obtain complicated equations such as

$$x^2 \sin x - x^5 + 7 (\log x)^2 = 32$$

to be solved for the values of x.

To develop the method of successive approximations so that it applies to any equation we do not specify what functions appear, and simply let $f(x)$ refer to an arbitrary function of x. We suppose that the equation we wish to solve is written in the form

$$x = f(x) \tag{10}$$

For example, equation (1) can be written in this form as in (3). There $f(x)$ is simply the function $50 + x/2$. That the same equation can be written in many ways but still in the form (10), is seen from the fact that (1) was also written as (6). In (6), $f(x)$ is $-100 + 2x$. As another example, consider the equation $x^3 + 6x - 8 = 0$. It can be written in the form of (10) as follows:

$$x = -\frac{x^3}{6} + \frac{4}{3}$$

In this equation, $f(x) = -x^3/6 + 4/3$. Another way of writing the same equation is

$$x = x^3 + 7x - 8$$

Then $f(x) = x^3 + 7x - 8$.

Question.   Do the last two equations have the same solutions as the original cubic equation?

Problem.   Write the equation $x^2 - 2 = 0$ in the form $x = f(x)$. What is $f(x)$? Are there other ways to write it in this form? What is the exact positive solution of this equation? What is the positive solution correct to two decimal places?

The method of successive approximations for solving (10) consists in taking on initial estimate x_1 for the solution and substituting in the right-hand side to find the function value $f(x_1)$. This value is taken as the next estimate x_2. Then x_2 is substituted in the right-hand side to find $f(x_2)$, which is taken as the third estimate x_3, and so on. The iteration is given by

$$x_{n+1} = f(x_n), \qquad n = 1, 2, 3, \ldots . \tag{11}$$

Problem.   Consider the equation

$$x = x + \frac{1}{2}\left(\frac{8}{x} - x\right)$$

Verify that a solution of this equation is $x = \sqrt{8}$. Write a FORTRAN program to compute

$$x_{n+1} = x_n + \frac{1}{2}\left(\frac{8}{x_n} - x_n\right)$$

for $n = 1, 2, \ldots .$ Let

$$x_1 = 1.0$$

and stop when two successive x_n differ by less than 10^{-4} in absolute value.

When will the iteration process described by equation (11) converge to a solution of equation (10)? That is, when will the sequence of numbers $x_1, x_2, x_3, \ldots ,$ converge to a number x which is a solution of equation (10)? We have already seen that, even if $f(x)$ is a linear function, the process may or may not converge. Again, we turn to the geometric model for the answer.

Let $y = f(x)$ and imagine the graph of this function. In general, it will be some sort of curve. Also imagine the graph of $y = x$, which is a straight line as before. Where these two graphs cross each other we have a point P. At P the y-coordinates of both the curve and the line are equal; therefore, the value of x equals the value of $f(x)$ and we have $x = f(x)$. The x-coordinate of the point of intersection, P, is therefore a solution of (10). We focus our attention, then, on the intersection of

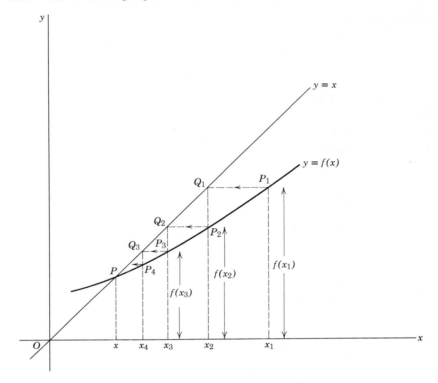

Figure 4

Successive approximations leading to solution of $x = f(x)$; at P: $f(x)$ increasing, slope less than 1, method converges

$y = x$ and $y = f(x)$. Various possibilities can occur. We distinguish first between (a) the case where $f(x)$ is increasing at P (slope positive) and (b) the case where $f(x)$ is decreasing (slope negative).

In case (a) where $f(x)$ is increasing at P, there are two subcases. First, the slope of the curve at P may be less than 1; then the curve falls below the line $y = x$. (This was the situation for the line L_1 in Figure 2.) Second, the curve's slope at P may be greater than 1; then the curve rises above the line $y = x$. (This was the situation for the line L_3 in Figure 3.)

In the first subcase where the slope at P is less than 1, the iteration technique will converge. This is shown in Figure 4. Starting with an initial estimate x_1 (too large), this locates an initial abscissa. To this corresponds the ordinate $y_1 = f(x_1)$ locating the point P_1 on the curve. The ordinate y_1 locates the point Q_1 on the line $y = x$. The abscissa of Q_1 is called x_2, which is the next estimate and is used to repeat the procedure. The abscissa x_2 determines the ordinate $y_2 = f(x_2)$ corresponding to the point P_2 on the curve. The ordinate y_2 locates the point Q_2 on the line $y = x$. The abscissa of Q_2 is called x_3, which then is the next estimate, and the process is continued. The sequence of points $P_1, Q_1, P_2, Q_2, P_3, \ldots$, obtained in this way defines successive steps in a staircase leading toward P. In this subcase, therefore, the sequence of points $P_1, P_2, P_3, \ldots$, converges to P and the sequence of numbers $x_1, x_2, x_3, \ldots$, converges to a solution x of equation (10).

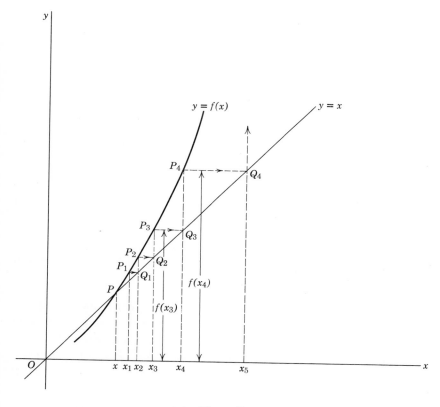

Figure 5

Successive approximations leading away from solution of $x = f(x)$; at P: $f(x)$ increasing, slope greater than 1, method diverges

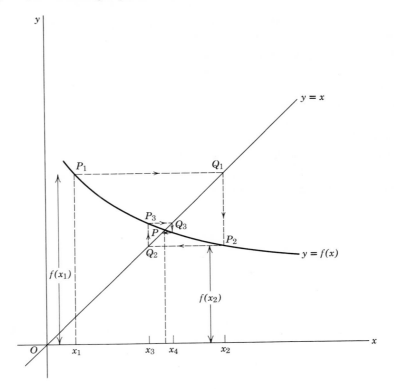

Figure 6

Successive approximations oscillating toward solution of $x = f(x)$; at P: $f(x)$ decreasing, slope between 0 and -1, method converges

Problem.   Show what happens if x_1 is initially to the left of P; that is, if x_1 is too small.

Figure 5 illustrates the second subcase where $f(x)$ is increasing and the slope of the curve $y = f(x)$ at P is greater than 1. Starting with an initial guess x_1 which is near the solution x and somewhat too large, we see that $x_2 = f(x_1)$ is still larger and $x_3 = f(x_2)$ is still larger again. The sequence x_1, x_2, x_3, ..., moves away from the solution x, and the process diverges.

Something new enters the picture in the second main case, case (b), when $f(x)$ is decreasing and the slope at P therefore is negative. Figure 6 shows what happens if the slope is not too great numerically, lying between 0 and -1. An initial estimate x_1 which is too small locates the point P_1 on the curve $y = f(x)$. The ordinate $y_1 = f(x_1)$ of this point locates the point Q_1 on the line $y = x$. The abscissa of this point serves as the new estimate x_2; it locates the point P_2 on $y = f(x)$. The ordinate of this point is $y_2 = f(x_2)$; it locates the point Q_2 on $y = x$, whose abscissa is the new estimate x_3, and so on. We see that the points P_1, P_2, P_3, ..., are alternately on opposite sides of P on the curve $y = f(x)$, but come closer to P with each step. The numbers x_1, x_2, x_3, ..., which are the abscissas of these points, oscillate between being smaller and larger than the solution x, but get closer to x in value at each step. The sequence x_1, x_2, x_3, ..., converges to x in what is called **oscillatory convergence.**

On the other hand, if the curve falls too steeply, with a slope at P more negative than -1, the process will diverge. This situation is illustrated in Figure 7. An initial guess x_1 is too small, and the value $x_2 = f(x_1)$ is too large. The critical fact is that x_2 lies farther from x than did x_1. Similarly $x_3 = f(x_2)$ is back to the left of x again, but it is even farther from x than x_2 was. Each oscillation takes us farther and farther away from the solution, and we have a kind of **divergence** called **oscillatory.**[7]

We conclude from the geometrical analysis that to have the method of successive approximations converge for equation (10) *we must have the slope of the function f(x) on the right-hand side of the equation lie between* -1 *and* $+1$ *at the solution x. If the slope is positive and less than* 1, *the approximations will converge to x from one side (left or right). If the slope is negative and lies between* 0 *and* -1, *then the approximations will converge to x while oscillating from one side to the other.* We may also say that, if the slope of the right-hand side of equation (10) is larger than $+1$ or less than -1 at P, then the method of successive approximations diverges.

Looking carefully at the diagrams upon which we based our geometric analysis, we see that the conditions on $f(x)$ for convergence implicitly go beyond what we have just stated in the last paragraph. Indeed, in Figures 4 and 6, corresponding to convergence, we see that the slope condition is satisfied by $f(x)$ not merely at the point P, but also throughout the interval on the x-axis encompassed by all the approximations x_1, x_2, x_3, ... To fulfill this condition it is sufficient to require that either $0 \leq f'(x) < 1$ or $-1 < f'(x) \leq 0$, in an interval centered at P,

---

[7] For another type of oscillatory divergence see Exercises 22 and 23.

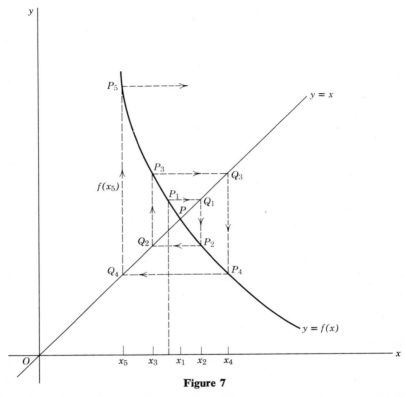

Figure 7

Successive approximations oscillating from solution of $x = f(x)$; at P: $f(x)$ decreasing, slope less than -1, method diverges

and that the initial estimate x_1 lie in this interval. [Recall that $f'(x)$ is
the derivative of $f(x)$.]

In applying the method of successive approximations we can write
the same equation in many different ways, as we have seen. Clearly, we
must write the equation $x = f(x)$ so that the slope of $f(x)$ is between -1
and 1 at the solution x. The "flatter" $f(x)$ is near P, or the nearer zero the
slope is, the faster will the staircase or the oscillation approach x. Notice
that, for the very flat curve $g(x)$ in Figure 8, even starting from the far
initial estimate x_1, the "stairs" quickly approach x. In the same figure
for comparison we have drawn a second curve $y = f(x)$ which intersects
$y = x$ at P and rises with slope nearly 1. Although the process converges,

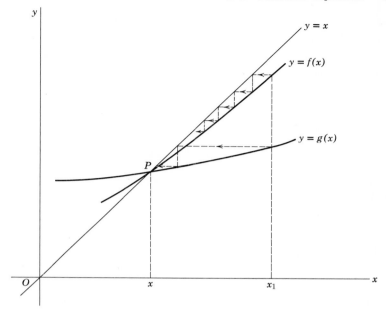

Figure 8

Comparison of number of steps required in successive approximations to P; based on $x = g(x)$ and $x = f(x)$

it takes many steps starting from the same initial approximately $x = x_1$ to achieve the same degree of approximation achieved in fewer steps with the flat curve, $y = g(x)$. This suggests that, when we write the iteration equation, we should try to do it in such a way that the slope at the intersection point is zero or as close to zero as possible.

We now find a way of setting up the method of successive approximations so that it converges and converges rapidly. Suppose that in some way or other the original equation is written in the now standard form

$$x = f(x) \tag{10}$$

Because $f(x)$ may be any function to begin with, we have no guarantee that the iteration process

$$x_{n+1} = f(x_n) \tag{11}$$

will converge to a solution of (10). Therefore, we construct a new equation obtained from the old equation as follows. Let A be any number different from 0. (Later we shall find a value for A that will be of help to us.) We multiply both sides of (10) by this number A. This, of course, does not change the problem. The new equation still has the same solution as (10). We now have the equation

$$Ax = Af(x)$$

We subtract Ax from both sides of this equation to get

$$0 = Af(x) - Ax \tag{12}$$

Of course, this is an equivalent equation and still has the same solution as (10). Now we add x to both sides of equation (12) to obtain

$$x = Af(x) - Ax + x$$

which we rearrange to the form

$$x = (1 - A)x + Af(x) \tag{13}$$

This equation is equivalent to the original one. It has the same solution as (10), having been obtained merely by multiplying both sides of (10) by a constant different from zero, rearranging terms, and then adding the same quantity to both sides. Suppose we call the right-hand side of (13) the function $g(x)$ so that

$$g(x) = (1 - A)x + Af(x) \tag{14}$$

Equation (13) then becomes

$$x = g(x)$$

and it has the same solutions as equation (10).

Now we are going to choose the number A so that the slope of $g(x)$ at the solution x is zero (or as nearly zero as possible). We estimate the slope of $y = g(x)$ at the intersection point x by the process used in Chapter 4. We take a point $x + \Delta x$ near x, where Δx is a small number, and evaluate the function $g(x)$ at this point. That is, we find the value of $g(x + \Delta x)$. We subtract $g(x)$ to find Δy, the change in the value of the function $g(x)$. We then divide Δy by Δx. This gives us the average change in $g(x)$ from x to $x + \Delta x$.

Carrying out the steps in this process for the function $g(x)$ in equation (14) we get:

Step 1: $g(x + \Delta x) = (1 - A)(x + \Delta x) + Af(x + \Delta x)$

Step 2: $\Delta y = g(x + \Delta x) - g(x) = (1 - A)(x + \Delta x) + Af(x + \Delta x)$
$- (1 - A)x - Af(x)$
$= (1 - A)\Delta x + Af(x + \Delta x) - Af(x)$

Step 3: $\dfrac{\Delta y}{\Delta x} = (1 - A) + A\dfrac{f(x + \Delta x) - f(x)}{\Delta x}$

Now we observe that the quantity

$$w = \frac{f(x + \Delta x) - f(x)}{\Delta x} \tag{15}$$

is an estimate of the slope of $f(x)$ at x. It is the slope of the chord joining the points on the curve $y = f(x)$ at x and $x + \Delta x$.

Problem. Show graphically that

$$\frac{f(x + \Delta x) - f(x)}{\Delta x}$$

is an estimate of the slope of $f(x)$ at x.

We find, then, that an estimate for the slope of $g(x)$ at the solution is given by

$$(1 - A) + Aw \tag{16}$$

To make convergence as rapid as possible, we want to choose A so that the slope of $g(x)$ is zero or near zero. Setting our estimate (16) equal to zero, we can solve for A as follows:

$$(1 - A) + Aw = 0$$

$$A(w - 1) = -1$$

$$A = \frac{1}{1 - w}, \quad \text{provided } w \neq 1 \tag{17}$$

This is what we wanted to know. It says that, if we take A to be the value given by (17), we will get a function $g(x)$ whose slope at the solution is at or near zero. Now there is a small catch to this. To calculate A we must estimate the slope of $f(x)$ at the solution of (10). However, the very purpose of the whole method is to *find* the solution of (10). How can we estimate the slope at a point when we do not know where the point is?

The way out of our difficulty is to observe that, although we may not know x exactly, we could take any reasonably close value $\bar{x}$ and use that instead. If the slope of $g(x)$ near x is zero, then the slope *at* x should still be small in value. In this case the process could still be expected to converge with reasonable speed. We get then for A the approximate value

$$\bar{A} = \frac{1}{1 - \bar{w}} \tag{18}$$

where

$$\bar{w} = \frac{f(\bar{x} + \Delta x) - f(\bar{x})}{\Delta x} \tag{19}$$

The number $\bar{w}$ is an estimate of the slope of $f(x)$ at $\bar{x}$. Putting the value of $\bar{A}$ in (13), we find the equation

$$x = \left(1 - \frac{1}{1 - \bar{w}}\right) x + \frac{1}{1 - \bar{w}} f(x)$$

or

$$x = x - \frac{x - f(x)}{1 - \bar{w}}$$

Another way of writing this is simply

$$x = x - \bar{A}[x - f(x)] \tag{20}$$

If we begin with an initial estimate x_1 for the solution of (10) and substitute in the right-hand side of (20), the value of the right-hand side becomes our new estimate x_2, and so on. Our iteration formula is

$$x_{n+1} = x_n - \bar{A}[x_n - f(x_n)] \tag{21}$$

where $\bar{A}$ is given by equations (18) and (19). If $\bar{x}$ is near the solution of (10) (for example, you could simply use the initial guess x_1, as $\bar{x}$), then this formula will generate a sequence of values $x_2, x_3, \ldots$, which converges rapidly to the solution of (10). We turn now to an example using this method.

5.3   The Square Root

Finding the square root of a number, such as $\sqrt{2}$, is the problem of finding a number x whose square is 2. In symbols we want x such that $x^2 = 2$. The equation $x^2 = 2$ is nonlinear because it involves the unknown x to a power other than the first power. It is, in fact, a quadratic equation. We can apply the machinery of the preceding section to find $\sqrt{2}$ by successive approximations.

First we must write the equation

$$x^2 = 2 \tag{22}$$

in the form $x = f(x)$. There are many ways to do this. Let us, for example, add $x - 2$ to both sides to get

$$x = x^2 + x - 2 \tag{23}$$

and define

$$f(x) = x^2 + x - 2 \tag{24}$$

If we are going to use the iteration formula (21), we need an estimate $\bar{w}$ of the slope of $f(x)$. We use the estimate given by (19). To do this we first find $f(\bar{x} + \Delta x)$. From equation (24),

$$f(\bar{x} + \Delta x) = (\bar{x} + \Delta x)^2 + (\bar{x} + \Delta x) - 2$$

Therefore,

$$\bar{w} = \frac{f(\bar{x} + \Delta \bar{x}) - f(x)}{\Delta x} = \frac{(\bar{x} + \Delta x)^2 + (\bar{x} + \Delta x) - \bar{x}^2 - x}{\Delta x}$$

or

$$\bar{w} = \frac{(\bar{x} + \Delta x)^2 - \bar{x}^2}{\Delta x} + 1 \tag{25}$$

To evaluate this we need (a) to estimate $\sqrt{2}$ and (b) to choose a small value for Δx. Let us take $\bar{x} = 1.4$ as a value close to the solution, and $\Delta x = .1$. Then for our estimate of the slope of $f(x)$ we obtain

$$\bar{w} = \frac{(1.4 + .1)^2 - (1.4)^2}{.1} + 1 = 3.9$$

Since we are only interested in an estimate, we can round off this value to 4. Taking $\bar{w} = 4$, we find from (18) that

$$\bar{A} = \frac{1}{1 - 4} = -\frac{1}{3}$$

Putting this value and $f(x)$ from (24) into (21), we have as our iteration formula

$$x_{n+1} = x_n + \frac{1}{3}(2 - x_n^2) \tag{26}$$

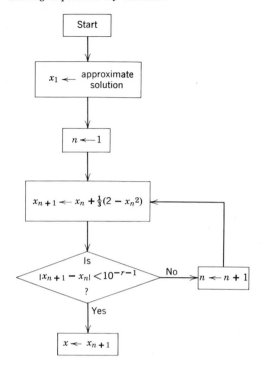

Figure 9

Flow chart for calculating $\sqrt{2}$

We can use (26) to find $\sqrt{2}$. For the initial guess x_1 we may use 1.4. Then

$$x_2 = 1.4 + \frac{1}{3}(2 - 1.4^2) = 1.4133$$

We do not know how many of these digits are correct. As with our algorithm for calculation of slopes in Figure 6 of Chapter 4, we simply continue with successive approximations, until the answer is unchanging, to $r + 1$ decimal places assuming that we wish to obtain the answer correctly rounded to r decimal places.

A flow chart for the calculation of $\sqrt{2}$ based on the iteration formula (26) is shown in Figure 9.

Problem.   Write the FORTRAN program corresponding to the algorithm of Figure 9 and use the program to calculate $\sqrt{2}$ correct to four decimal places. Use the starting value $x_1 = 1.4$. Give the solution and tell how many steps in the iteration were required to determine it.

The algorithm just found can be easily modified to find the square root of any number N. Since $\sqrt{N}$ is the value of x which satisfies the equation

$$x^2 - N = 0$$

the only change required in the choice of the function $f(x)$ of equation (24) is to replace 2 by N. This gives us

$$f(x) = x^2 + x - N \tag{27}$$

Now we would choose some rough estimate x for $\sqrt{N}$ and some small increment Δx. We use these to calculate $\bar{w}$, the approximate value of the slope of $f(x)$ from (19). Then $\bar{A}$ is found from (18), and (21) becomes

$$x_{n+1} = x_n - \bar{A}[N - x_n^2] \tag{28}$$

This is our iteration formula for $\sqrt{N}$.

Problem.   Write a program for calculating $\sqrt{N}$. Use it to calculate $\sqrt{37}$ correct to four decimal places. For the starting estimate use $x_1 = 6$.

The square root algorithm derived here is not useful as a general method for finding $\sqrt{N}$ because the coefficient $\bar{A}$ in (28) varies with the number N. We have presented it here only for the purpose of illustrating the general procedure of finding a rapidly convergent iteration technique for the solution of a specific equation. In Exercise 16 the preferred algorithm for finding square roots by the method of successive approximation is derived.

5.4 Additional Questions

We have seen that, to use the method of successive approximations for the solution of an equation $x = f(x)$, the equation must be put into an appropriate form such as

$$x_{n+1} = x_n - \bar{A}[x_n - f(x_n)] \tag{21}$$

Finding this form requires two things:

(i) An initial guess $\bar{x}$ for the solution of $x = f(x)$.

(ii) An estimate $\bar{w}$ of the slope of $f(x)$ at the solution.

We look more closely now into these two requirements.

We ask first how an initial estimate $\bar{x}$ (or for that matter x_1) of the solution of $x = f(x)$ is obtained. It would seem that one can always find an estimate simply by graphing $y = x$ and $y = f(x)$ and reading off the approximate abscissa of the intersection of the curves. However, the graphs may intersect near $x = 1$, $x = -10$, or $x = 1,000,000$. Obviously, we cannot draw the graph over a very large range of x values. Unless there is some information about where the solution lies, graphing is impractical. There are mathematical procedures which can be of help here, but they lie beyond the scope of this book. For the present, we must simply assume that we have enough information to guess approximately where the solution is.

Another point in connection with requirement (i) concerns the accuracy required in the initial estimate $\bar{x}$ (or x_1). As we have seen, the slope of $f(x)$ must lie between -1 and $+1$ at the solution x for convergence. As we go away from the point of intersection, the slope of the curve changes and may become greater than $+1$ or more negative than -1. If our guess $\bar{x}$ (or x_1) lies too far away from x, we may find ourselves in a region where the slope is too positive or too negative and the process may not converge. There is a requirement, therefore, that $\bar{x}$ (or x_1) "be sufficiently close" to x that this does not happen. Of course, if there is more than one crossing of $y = x$ and $y = f(x)$ so that there is more than one solution (as in quadratic and higher-degree equations), we must make sure that our approximation $\bar{x}$ (or x_1) lies close to the solution we are interested in.

Turning now to the second requirement, several possibilities exist. For simple functions such as polynomials, we have already seen that it is possible not merely to estimate the slope but also to give an exact formula for the slope.

In Exercise 24 of Chapter 4 you were shown how to give an explicit formula for the slope, or derivative, of a polynomial such as $2x^3 + 6x^2 - 18x - 5$. In the differential calculus, general techniques are developed for finding derivatives which enable one to find formulas for the derivatives of many other functions. Such formulas provide an easy means of finding an estimate $\bar{w}$ of the slope of $f(x)$. One simply evaluates the formula at the estimated value $\bar{x}$ of the solution.

When we do not have a formula for the slope, the estimate

$$\bar{w} = \frac{f(\bar{x} + \Delta x) - f(\bar{x})}{\Delta x}$$

can be used as previously explained. One could even calculate the slope at x very accurately by using the algorithm of Figure 6 of Chapter 4 and taking smaller and smaller values of Δx. However, since $\bar{x}$ is itself only an estimate, it is not worthwhile to calculate the slope at $\bar{x}$ very exactly.

A final refinement in calculating the slope is to take into account the improved estimates of the solution furnished by the iteration process itself. That is, we need not be satisfied with estimating the slope at $\bar{x}$. We could recalculate the slope once we have x_2 and use the new slope (at x_2) to give an improved value of $\bar{A}$. Then we would apply (21) again with the improved $\bar{A}$ value to get x_3, and so on. The algorithm which would result from this refinement was first discovered by Newton.

5.5   Errors

In Section 1.12 we discussed the effect of errors in the coefficients of a system of linear equations on the solution of those equations. We turn now to a discussion of what happens to the solution of a nonlinear equation if there is some doubt about the coefficients in the equation.

For example, suppose we wish to solve the quadratic equation

$$x^2 - 3x + 2 = 0 \qquad (29)$$

The reader should have no trouble in determining that $x = 1$ and $x = 2$ are the two solutions of this equation.

But, suppose that the constant term and the coefficients of x^2 and x are numbers which were measured in some experiment or are numbers which we calculated on a computer. In either case, they will not be exact and will contain some error. In particular, suppose each of them can be in error by as much as 0.01. That is, suppose that the coefficient of x^2 is between 0.99 and 1.01. We do not know its exact value, but we know it must lie somewhere in that range. Similarly, the coefficient of x is between -3.01 and -2.99, and the constant term is between 1.99 and 2.01. How accurate are our solutions $x = 1$ and $x = 2$?

The true equation is

$$(1 + d_2)x^2 - (3 + d_1)x + (2 + d_0) = 0 \qquad (30)$$

where each d_i is between $-.01$ and $+.01$. We would expect the solutions of equation (30) to be close to the solutions of equation (29). Therefore, we write $1 + e_1$ and $2 + e_2$ for the solutions of equation (30). We want some estimate of how large e_1 and e_2 can be.

Let us put $x = 1 + e_1$ into equation (30). Then

$$(1 + d_2)(1 + e_1)^2 - (3 + d_1)(1 + e_1) + (2 + d_0) = 0$$

Upon multiplying out and grouping terms we get

$$-e_1 + (d_2 - d_1 + d_0) + e_1^2 + 2e_1d_2 - e_1d_1 + d_2e_1^2 = 0 \qquad (31)$$

Now we make an important assumption. We assume that e_1, d_0, d_1, d_2 are all small — so small that products of any of them can be ignored. With this assumption we can throw out the last four terms in equation (31) and rewrite it

$$-e_1 + (d_2 - d_1 + d_0) = 0$$

To repeat, the assumption is that products of the errors, e_i and d_j, are small compared with the errors themselves. Although we have no way now of knowing whether that assumption is valid or not, once we have estimated e_1 we shall be able to check it.

Now,

$$e_1 = d_2 - d_1 + d_0$$

Since each d_i can be between $-.01$ and $+.01$, the largest the right-hand side can be is $.03$; therefore,

$$|e_1| \leq .03$$

Thus, one solution of the true equation lies between $.97$ and 1.03.

We now check our assumption about the smallness of products of e_1 and the d_i. Since $|e_1| \leq .03$, then

$$|e_1^2| \leq .0009$$

Similarly, since $|d_2| \leq .01$,

$$|2e_1d_2| \leq .0006$$

Continuing in this way, we find that the four terms which we neglected in equation (31) do not in total exceed $.001809$. Because this is less than e_1 and all of the d_i, our assumption is valid.

Notice, however, that changes in the coefficients of 1% or less can give rise to errors of 3% in the solution $x = 1$. Problems in which small changes in the coefficients in the equation cause large changes in the solutions can be encountered. In such cases the equation is said to be **ill-conditioned**. The reader should return to Section 1.12 and review the meaning of ill-conditioned for systems of linear equations.

If the error estimate is carried out for the solution $x = 2$, it will turn out that $|e_2| \leq .07$, and the solution actually lies between 1.93 and 2.07.

A similar analysis can be carried out for any equation $f(x) = 0$, where $f(x)$ is a polynomial, to determine the effect on the solutions x of errors in the coefficients of $f(x)$. For each case we need to make the same assumption about the products of the errors. A complete discussion is beyond the scope of this book. The interested reader is referred to Section 5.8 of *Numerical Methods and FORTRAN Programming* by Daniel D. McCracken and William S. Dorn (John Wiley & Sons, 1964).

5.6   Solution of a System of Two Linear Equations by Iteration

We return now to the problems discussed in Chapter 1 and investigate iterative algorithms for solving them. We consider, therefore, a system of linear equations in which the number of equations is the same as the number of variables. We shall investigate an algorithm for two equations in two variables in detail. We shall find that geometry again will give us some insight into when and why the algorithm converges. We then will generalize the algorithm so that it can be used for larger systems of equations.

Consider the following system of two linear equations in two variables, x and y:

$$a_{11}x + a_{12}y = b_1 \tag{32}$$

$$a_{21}x + a_{22}y = b_2 \tag{33}$$

We suppose that $a_{11} \neq 0$ and $a_{22} \neq 0$. This is an important assumption. We shall find that, before we are finished, we shall need to assume much more.

Next we "solve" equation (32) for x:

$$x = \frac{1}{a_{11}}(b_1 - a_{12}y) \tag{34}$$

and we "solve" equation (33) for y:

$$y = \frac{1}{a_{22}}(b_2 - a_{21}x) \tag{35}$$

Since $a_{11} \neq 0$ and $a_{22} \neq 0$, we can carry out the required operations without difficulty.

The solution of the system (34) and (35) by successive approximations will be entirely analogous to that carried out on equations (4) and (5) in Section 5.1; they are simply special cases of (34) and (35). The reader may wish to try to carry this out himself before reading further.

We make an initial estimate of x and y the solution of (34) and (35). We call these estimates x_1 and y_1. We use these estimates in the right-hand side of (34) to get a new estimate for x. Notice that, because x does not appear on the right in equation (34), all we really need is y_1. The new estimate for x is called x_2. It is given by

$$x_2 = \frac{1}{a_{11}} (b_1 - a_{12}y_1)$$

This new estimate of x is used in equation (35) to get a new estimate for y. It is called y_2 and is given by

$$y_2 = \frac{1}{a_{22}} (b_2 - a_{21}x_2)$$

With the estimates x_2 and y_2, we return to equation (34) to obtain a new value of x, and then to equation (35) to obtain a new value of y, and so on. Continuing in this way, we see that the nth estimates for x and y are

$$x_n = \frac{1}{a_{11}} (b_1 - a_{12}y_{n-1}) \tag{36}$$

$$y_n = \frac{1}{a_{22}} (b_2 - a_{21}x_n) \tag{37}$$

Notice that the subscript on y in equation (36) is $n - 1$, while the subscript on x in equation (37) is n.

We now ask the question: Do the sequences x_n and y_n converge to x and y, the solution of equations (32) and (33)? Before trying to answer this question, we look at a geometrical model of the process. It will follow closely the model used in Section 5.1 (see Figures 2 and 3).[8] We will find that sometimes the algorithm described in (36) and (37) converges and sometimes it does not. When it converges, the starting estimates may be anything. This again is completely analogous to the developments in Section 5.1.

Let us look at a specific example:

$$2x - y = 4 \tag{38}$$

$$-x + 2y = 1 \tag{39}$$

[8] Because equation (4) is solved for y, it plays the role of equation (35) in the present analysis, while equation (5) is to be identified with equation (34).

The solution of this system of equations is $x = 3$ and $y = 2$. We rewrite them as

$$x = \tfrac{1}{2}(4 + y) \tag{40}$$

$$y = \tfrac{1}{2}(1 + x) \tag{41}$$

We take $x_1 = 0$ and $y_1 = 0$ as our first estimate. The succeeding estimates are

$$x_2 = 2 \qquad \text{and} \qquad y_2 = 1\tfrac{1}{2}$$

$$x_3 = 2\tfrac{3}{4} \qquad \text{and} \qquad y_3 = 1\tfrac{7}{8}$$

$$x_4 = 2\tfrac{15}{16} \qquad \text{and} \qquad y_4 = 1\tfrac{31}{32}$$

Therefore, the values of x_n and y_n appear to be converging to the solution, $x = 3$ and $y = 2$.

> **Problem.** Find a pattern in the numbers x_n and y_n such that you can predict x_5 and y_5 without calculating them from equations (40) and (41)? Write a formula for x_n and y_n for any value of n. Try your formula out on $n = 2$, 3, 4. Check your prediction of x_5 and y_5 by actual calculation.

Let us now look at a geometrical model of this process. In Figure 10 the line L_1 represents equation (38) or, equivalently, equation (40). The line L_2 represents equation (39) or equation (41). Our algorithm starts with $x_1 = 0$ and $y_1 = 0$ at the origin O. We then keep y fixed at y_1 and from (40) compute

$$x_2 = \tfrac{1}{2}(4 + y_1)$$

This means that we move horizontally to the line L_1 (see dashed line). With this value of $x = x_2$ fixed, we calculate a new y value from (41):

$$y_2 = \tfrac{1}{2}(1 + x_2)$$

Thus, we move vertically to L_2 and reach the point P_2 with coordinates (x_2, y_2).

There follows a succession of horizontal and vertical moves, and we approach the intersection of the two lines on a "staircase" from the left. The reader who is not sure of this should reread the discussions in Sections 5.1 and 5.2.

Before going on, we note that the slope of L_2 is *less* than the slope of L_1. Now consider the system of equations

$$-2x + 5y = 4 \tag{42}$$

$$-x + 2y = 1 \tag{43}$$

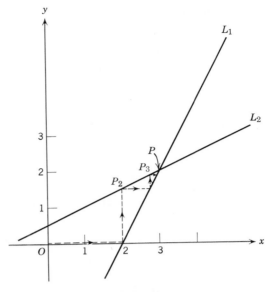

Figure 10

Method of successive approximations applied to equations (38) and (39)

Notice that equation (43) is identical with equation (39). Notice also that this system of equations has the same solution, $x = 3$ and $y = 2$, as the system given by equations (38) and (39).

To apply the method of successive approximations we "solve" equation (42) for x and we "solve" equation (43) for y:

$$x = \tfrac{1}{2}(-4 + 5y)$$
$$y = \tfrac{1}{2}(1 + x)$$

With an initial estimate x_1 and y_1, we get succeeding estimates from

$$x_n = \tfrac{1}{2}(-4 + 5y_{n-1}) \tag{44}$$

$$y_n = \tfrac{1}{2}(1 + x_n) \tag{45}$$

where $n = 2, 3, \ldots$.

A geometrical model is shown in Figure 11, where L_1 is the line corresponding to equation (42), and the line L_2 represents equation (43). If we again choose $x_1 = 0$ and $y_1 = 0$, we move horizontally to the line L_1, then vertically to L_2, and repeat this process. Notice that the horizontal moves are now to the left rather than to the right, as they were in

Figure 10. The point P_2 has coordinates (x_2, y_2), and (x_3, y_3) are the coordinates for the point P_3.

Each successive approximation is farther and farther from the solution; therefore, the algorithm *diverges* along a staircase which descends to the left.

We note that here the slope of L_2 is *greater* than the slope of L_1. This is the exact opposite of the case for equations (38) and (39) shown in Figure 10, where the algorithm converged.

Problem.   Write a FORTRAN program to compute the first 10 approximations to the solution of equations (42) and (43). Use the formula given in equations (44) and (45), where $x_1 = 0$ and $y_1 = 0$. From these results, write down a formula for x_n and y_n.

It appears, therefore, that if the slope of the line corresponding to the equation used for determining successive y estimates, that is, equation (33) or (35), is less than the slope of the line used for determining successive x estimates, that is, equation (32) or (34), then the algorithm converges. However, if the slope of the former line is greater than the slope of the latter line, it appears that the algorithm diverges. Because the equations are linear and there are only two, it is not difficult to prove the

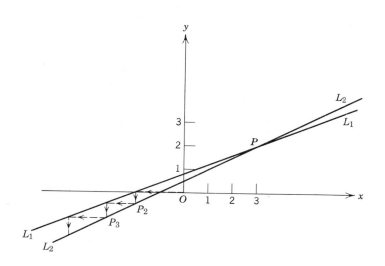

Figure 11

Method of successive approximations applied to equations (42) and (43)

truth of these statements. In the next section we indicate how the proof can be carried out.

5.7   Method of Proof of Convergence of the Iterative Method

The numbers x and y are the solution of the system of equations (34) and (35). The nth approximation to x given by the method of iteration is x_n, the nth approximation to y is y_n. The numbers x_n and y_n are given by equations (36) and (37). Subtracting equation (36) from equation (34) gives an expression for the amount by which the estimate x_n differs from x:

$$x - x_n = -\frac{a_{12}}{a_{11}}(y - y_{n-1}) \tag{46}$$

Similarly, subtracting equation (37) from equation (35) gives

$$y - y_n = -\frac{a_{21}}{a_{22}}(x - x_n) \tag{47}$$

an expression for the amount by which the estimate y_n differs from y.

The proof of the convergence of the iteration method reduces to finding estimates of $|x - x_n|$ and $|y - y_n|$ which show that under certain conditions, if n is sufficiently large, those quantities will be arbitrarily small. However, to give a complete mathematical proof would require a more precise definition of convergence than we have given, as well as precise statements of what we mean by such expressions as "sufficiently large" and "arbitrarily small." For our purposes, such a formal proof is not essential. Instead, we derive the estimates upon which the proof can be based and which clearly show the conditions under which the method converges or diverges.

Substituting for the quantity $(x - x_n)$ from (46) into (47), we get

$$y - y_n = \frac{a_{21}a_{12}}{a_{22}a_{11}}(y - y_{n-1}) \tag{48}$$

This holds for $n = 2, 3, \ldots$. Let us write down a few of these relations. We write r for the coefficient $a_{21}a_{12}/a_{22}a_{11}$:

$$y - y_4 = r(y - y_3)$$
$$y - y_3 = r(y - y_2)$$
$$y - y_2 = r(y - y_1)$$

Substituting from the last of these into the one above it and then again into the one above that, we find

$$y - y_4 = r^3(y - y_1)$$

Indeed, continuing this way we can express $(y - y_n)$, for any n, in terms of $(y - y_1)$ as follows:

$$y - y_n = r^{n-1}(y - y_1) \tag{49}$$

Now, for a fixed initial estimate y_1, which may be *any* number, $|y - y_1|$ is some fixed number which we may denote by the letter c. Hence, from (49),

$$|y - y_n| = c|r|^{n-1} \tag{50}$$

Whether $|y - y_n|$ gets smaller and smaller and approaches zero as n gets larger and larger obviously depends upon the number r. If $|r| < 1$, the numbers $r, r^2, r^3, \ldots$, become smaller and smaller and will eventually be less than any positive number, no matter how small, so that they approach zero.[9] If $|r| > 1$, the numbers $r, r^2, r^3, \ldots$, become larger and larger and will eventually be greater than any number, no matter how large, so that they approach infinity.[9] Hence, we see that for convergence of y_n to y we must have $|r| < 1$. If $|r| > 1$, the process will diverge.

Problem.   Show that $x - x_n = r^{n-1}(x - x_1)$. Tell under what conditions x_n will converge to x, and under what conditions x_n will diverge?

Now what does r represent? We have

$$r = \frac{a_{21}a_{12}}{a_{22}a_{11}}$$

a number depending on the coefficients appearing in the original equations (34) and (35). On the other hand, our geometrical model has shown that convergence and divergence are dependent upon the slopes of the

---

[9] Both of these statements seem reasonable on the basis of our experience with repeated multiplication of a *finite* number of equal numbers less than 1 or greater than 1, such as ½ × ½ × ½ × ⋯ × ½ and 2 × 2 × 2 × ⋯ × 2. However, the student should realize that this does not constitute a proof of convergence, which is a statement regarding an *infinite* sequence. A complete proof of these and similar statements is not intended here and can be found in texts on the calculus.

lines corresponding to these equations. The slope m_1 of the line corresponding to equation (34) is

$$m_1 = -\frac{a_{11}}{a_{12}} \qquad \text{(assume } a_{12} \neq 0\text{)}$$

The slope m_2 of the line corresponding to equation (35) is

$$m_2 = -\frac{a_{21}}{a_{22}}$$

Therefore, we see that

$$r = \frac{a_{21}a_{12}}{a_{22}a_{11}} = \frac{m_2}{m_1} \tag{51}$$

It follows that, if $|m_2/m_1| < 1$, the iterations converge, while, if $|m_2/m_1| > 1$, they diverge. This result agrees with the predictions made in the preceding section based on the geometrical model in Figures 10 and 11. In the case of Figure 10, both m_1 and m_2 are positive and $m_2 < m_1$; therefore, $|m_2/m_1| = m_2/m_1 < 1$ and the method converged. In the case of Figure 11, again m_1 and m_2 are both positive, but now $m_2 > m_1$; therefore, $|m_2/m_1| = m_2/m_1 > 1$ and the method diverged.

From (49) we see that, if r is negative, $y - y_n$ will be alternately positive and negative. Similarly, $x - x_n$ will alternate in sign from the corresponding formula. That is, the successive approximations y_n will oscillate about y, being alternately too small and too large. The same is true for x_n and x. If $|r| < 1$, the oscillations will converge. If $|r| > 1$, the oscillations will diverge.

To summarize, we have the following statement: If the absolute value of the ratio of the slope of equation (35) to the slope of equation (34) is less than 1, then the iterations defined by (36) and (37) will converge for any initial estimates x_1 and y_1. If the ratio is greater than 1 in absolute value, the iterations diverge.

In the next section we show how the method of successive approximations can be used to treat linear systems with more than two equations.

5.8 An Iterative Algorithm for a System of Four Linear Equations

Consider the system of four equations given in Section 1.7 and reproduced here:

$$a_{11}x_1 + a_{12}x_2 + a_{13}x_3 + a_{14}x_4 = b_1 \tag{52}$$

$$a_{21}x_1 + a_{22}x_2 + a_{23}x_3 + a_{24}x_4 = b_2 \tag{53}$$

$$a_{31}x_1 + a_{32}x_2 + a_{33}x_3 + a_{34}x_4 = b_3 \tag{54}$$

$$a_{41}x_1 + a_{42}x_2 + a_{43}x_3 + a_{44}x_4 = b_4 \tag{55}$$

We assume that $a_{11} \neq 0$, $a_{22} \neq 0$, $a_{33} \neq 0$, and $a_{44} \neq 0$, and we "solve" the first equation for x_1, the second for x_2, and so on. Doing this, we obtain

$$x_1 = \frac{1}{a_{11}} (b_1 - a_{12}x_2 - a_{13}x_3 - a_{14}x_4)$$

$$x_2 = \frac{1}{a_{22}} (b_2 - a_{21}x_1 - a_{23}x_3 - a_{24}x_4)$$

$$x_3 = \frac{1}{a_{33}} (b_3 - a_{31}x_1 - a_{32}x_2 - a_{34}x_4)$$

$$x_4 = \frac{1}{a_{44}} (b_4 - a_{41}x_1 - a_{42}x_2 - a_{43}x_3)$$

The numbers x_1, x_2, x_3, x_4 are the solution of the system. We let $x_1^{(1)}$, $x_2^{(1)}$, $x_3^{(1)}$, $x_4^{(1)}$ denote our initial estimate for the numbers x_1, x_2, x_3, x_4, respectively. The number ^{1} in parentheses written above the line is called a **superscript.**[10] The superscripts $(^1)$, $(^2)$, $(^3)$, ..., will be used to identify the successive estimates; they must not be confused with powers or exponents, which are written without parentheses.

The nth approximation is given by

$$x_1^{(n)} = \frac{1}{a_{11}} (b_1 - a_{12}x_2^{(n-1)} - a_{13}x_3^{(n-1)} - a_{14}x_4^{(n-1)}) \tag{56}$$

$$x_2^{(n)} = \frac{1}{a_{22}} (b_2 - a_{21}x_1^{(n)} - a_{23}x_3^{(n-1)} - a_{24}x_4^{(n-1)}) \tag{57}$$

$$x_3^{(n)} = \frac{1}{a_{33}} (b_3 - a_{31}x_1^{(n)} - a_{32}x_2^{(n)} - a_{34}x_4^{(n-1)}) \tag{58}$$

$$x_4^{(n)} = \frac{1}{a_{44}} (b_4 - a_{41}x_1^{(n)} - a_{42}x_2^{(n)} - a_{43}x_3^{(n)}) \tag{59}$$

Notice that all the superscripts on the right in the first equation are $n - 1$. In the second equation, however, x_1 has a superscript n, while

[10] "Super" for above and "script" for writing, thus meaning "written above the line."

the other two variables on the right have superscripts $n - 1$. This denotes the use — on the right-hand side of the second equation — of the value of x_1 calculated in the first equation. Similarly $x_1^{(n)}$ and $x_2^{(n)}$ calculated in the first two equations are used in the third equation. We must still use the $(n - 1)$st approximation for x_4 since $x_4^{(n)}$ has not been calculated as yet. Finally, all the superscripts in the last equation are n.

We can no longer discuss convergence in terms of slopes of lines because the equations no longer represent lines. Indeed, the geometry is that of four dimensions, x_1, x_2, x_3, and x_4, and is difficult to visualize. However, the algebraic arguments we have used can be extended to a system of four equations. This leads to conditions for convergence which are presented below. The proofs lie beyond the scope of this text.

The algorithm converges provided

$$|a_{11}| \geq |a_{12}| + |a_{13}| + |a_{14}|$$

$$|a_{22}| \geq |a_{21}| + |a_{23}| + |a_{24}|$$

$$|a_{33}| \geq |a_{31}| + |a_{32}| + |a_{34}| \tag{60}$$

$$|a_{44}| \geq |a_{41}| + |a_{42}| + |a_{43}|$$

and at least one of these conditions is not an equality. There is an additional requirement: it must not be possible to rearrange the equations so that some of the variables can be solved for by solving less than four equations. In that case (where the equations cannot be so rearranged), the system of equations is said to be **irreducible.** We do not discuss this third requirement further, but we shall always assume it to be satisfied. For a further discussion of this aspect the reader is referred to Section 8.6 of *Numerical Methods and FORTRAN Programming* by Daniel D. McCracken and William S. Dorn (John Wiley & Sons, 1964).

Questions. Do equations (32) and (33) satisfy (60) if $|r| < 1$? Does $|r| < 1$ hold if (32) and (33) satisfy (60)?

The condition expressed by (60) is easily extended if we have more than four equations, and in extended form it correctly sets forth conditions for convergence for a system of m equations in m variables.

We need some criterion for stopping the iterations. One convenient criterion is: If the changes in all the x_i are small enough, we stop the iterations and take the last approximation to be the solution. In more

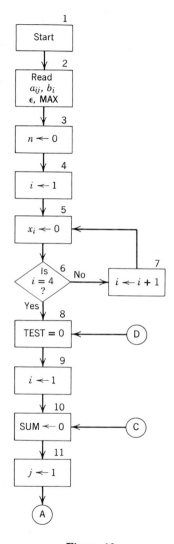

Figure 12

Flow chart for Gauss-Seidel method for a system of four equations (continued in Figures 13 and 14)

precise terms, we let ϵ (the Greek letter "epsilon") be some small positive number; then if

$$|x_i^{(n)} - x_i^{(n-1)}| < \epsilon \tag{61}$$

for $i = 1, 2, 3, 4$ we take $x_i^{(n)}$ as the solution.

We have not said what "small" means in defining ϵ. In general, we mean small compared with the solution: x_1, x_2, x_3, x_4. We might choose $\epsilon = 10^{-4}$. This does *not* guarantee that, when (61) is satisfied, the $x_i^{(n)}$ are within 10^{-4} of the solution x_i. It merely tells us that the $x_i^{(n)}$ are within 10^{-4} of the $x_i^{(n-1)}$, and we *assume* that all succeeding estimates and the actual solution will be equally close to $x_i^{(n)}$. The validity of the criterion must be tested.

We let ϵ be a number to be specified in each problem.

5.9   Flow Chart for Iterative Solution of a System of Linear Equations

A flow chart for the method is now straightforward and is given in Figures 12, 13, and 14. We first read the coefficients a_{ij} and b_i, the number ϵ which we shall use to test for convergence, and an integer MAX which is the maximum number of iterations we will perform. If n exceeds MAX, we will stop. This is insurance against the occurrence of something unforeseen.

We first set all $x_i = 0$ (boxes 4, 5, 6, 7). As we calculate $x_i^{(n)}$ for any i, we subtract it from $x_i^{(n-1)}$ to see if it is greater in absolute value than any previous $|x_i^{(n)} - x_i^{(n-1)}|$. If it is, we give its value to a variable called TEST. TEST will then be equal to the largest of the $|x_i^{(n)} - x_i^{(n-1)}|$. If TEST $< \epsilon$, then the convergence criterion is satisfied. We set TEST $= 0$ to start (box 8). Later, in boxes 17 and 18 (Figure 13), we will alter the value of TEST.

The variable SUM will contain the sum of the negative terms in the parentheses on the right-hand sides of equations (56) through (59). Therefore, we set it equal to zero to start (box 10). Boxes 11 to 15 form that sum. In box 16 we calculate $x_i^{(n)}$, which we call y_i.

Because $x_i^{(n-1)}$ has been called x_i, in box 17 we ask if $|x_i^{(n)} - x_i^{(n-1)}|$ is larger than any previous one. When $i = 1$, the answer must be "yes," for initially we set TEST $= 0$ (see box 8). Once we have calculated TEST, we no longer need both $x_i^{(n)}$ and $x_i^{(n-1)}$. In fact, the new approximation for x_i is $x_i^{(n)}$, which we have called y_i. Therefore, in box 19 we set $x_i = x_i^{(n)}$ and proceed to calculate the next variable.

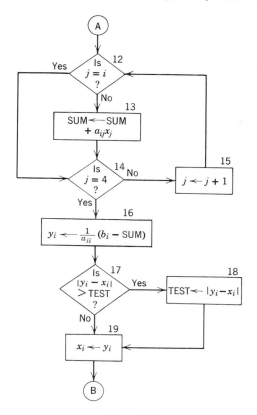

Figure 13

Continuation of Gauss-Seidel flow chart (see Figures 12 and 14)

Notice that every time we go through the loop from box 10 to box 21 we are calculating another of the variables. The first time through the loop we calculate $x_1^{(n)}$, the second time $x_2^{(n)}$, and so on. Notice also that the variable x_i always contains the latest value calculated for it. Thus, the second time through this loop x_1 is $x_1^{(n)}$, but $x_2 = x_2^{(n-1)}$, $x_3 = x_3^{(n-1)}$, and $x_4 = x_4^{(n-1)}$. These are just the values needed in equation (57), where we calculate $x_2^{(n)}$. Similarly, the third time through the loop the x_i are really $x_1^{(n)}$, $x_2^{(n)}$, $x_3^{(n-1)}$, $x_4^{(n-1)}$, which are the values required in equation (58).

In box 22 we see if the largest of the $|y_i - x_i| = |x_i^{(n)} - x_i^{(n-1)}|$ is

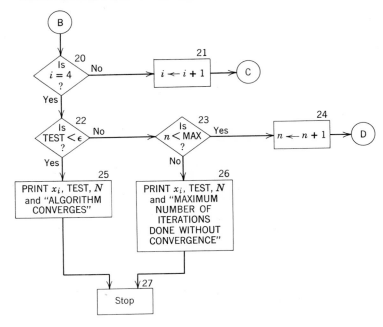

Figure 14

Continuation of Gauss-Seidel flow chart (see Figures 12 and 13)

less than ϵ. If it is not, we check to see if the number of the iteration, n, has reached the value MAX. If not, we perform another iteration.

In order to change this flow chart to solve a system of k equations the 4's in boxes 6, 14, and 20 should be changed to k's. No other changes are necessary.

Problem.   Write a FORTRAN program to solve a system of four equations in four variables using the algorithm described in the flow chart in Figures 12, 13, and 14. Use the program to solve the following system:

$$16.1x_1 - x_2 + x_3 - x_4 = 37.6$$

$$x_1 - 20x_2 - 6.2x_3 - 1.2x_4 = 19.7$$

$$5x_1 \qquad + 26.2x_3 + 1.9x_4 = 22.6$$

$$5x_2 - 2.2x_3 + 13.8x_4 = 9.8$$

Check your program by comparing the solution with the one found by using the FORTRAN program given in Section 1.10 for Gauss's method.

5.10   Comparison of Iterative Method with Gauss's Method

The algorithm we have just described is called the *Gauss-Seidel method*. It is also often referred to as *pointwise relaxation*. It is most useful in solving systems of equations which are (1) "diagonally dominant"; that is, the coefficients on the diagonal are very large compared with the other coefficients; and (2) "sparse"; that is, they have a large number of zero coefficients. The diagonal dominance guarantees convergence [see (60)]. The sparseness means that many of the numbers on the right of (56) through (59) are zero and need never be computed in any of the iterations. Therefore, the work needed is greatly reduced.

In Gauss's method, on the other hand, a sparse system of equations is of no advantage because, in the process of reducing the system to triangular form [see equations (36), (37), (40), and (42) of Chapter 1], the sparseness is lost.

Many practical problems give rise to sparse systems of equations which are diagonally dominant. For example, the weather prediction problem described in Section 1.9 is one such problem. Problems in heat conduction, bending of metal plates, and similar problems also may be described by a mathematical model which contains such systems of equations.

Finally, we should mention that not only is the work necessary to solve a sparse, diagonally dominant system of equations less when the Gauss-Seidel method is used than when Gauss's method is used, but also the round-off error generally is less in the Gauss-Seidel method.

It is important to point out, however, that the Gauss-Seidel method works only under restricted conditions. In particular, (60) and the two other conditions which follow those inequalities must be satisfied if the Gauss-Seidel method is to converge.[11] Gauss's method of Chapter 1 works for any nonsingular system of equations. Thus Gauss's method will work in cases where the Gauss-Seidel method will not. The converse is not true.

The Gauss-Seidel method, therefore, is used only in special cases to (a) reduce the amount of computing and (b) reduce the round-off error.

---

[11] Actually, these restrictions can be somewhat relaxed, but we do not discuss these refinements here.

Exercises

Answers to exercises marked * are given in Appendix A.

*1. Suppose Speedy runs three times as fast as Pokey. If Pokey is given a head start of 150 yd:

(a) How far does Pokey run before Speedy catches up?

(b) Show how the distance Pokey runs until he is caught can be found by successive approximations based on Zeno's paradox. What is the relation between successive approximations x_n and x_{n+1}?

(c) Give a graphical interpretation of the method used in (b).

2. Suppose Speedy runs p times as fast as Pokey and Pokey is given a head start of q yards (p and q are both positive numbers):

(a) How far does Pokey run before Speedy catches up? Is there any restriction on the values of p and q?

(b) Can the solution be found by successive approximations? What is the relation between successive approximations x_n and x_{n+1}?

(c) Demonstrate the method graphically.

*3. The equation $x = 3x - 90$ can also be written $x = (x/3) + 30$. Write an iteration formula corresponding to each of these two equations. Carry out five iterations with each formula, starting with the initial guess $x_1 = 60$. Which algorithm will converge to the solution of the equation? Why?

4. The equation $x = 4x - 80$ can also be written $x = x/4 + 20$. Write an iteration formula corresponding to each of these two equations. Carry out five iterations with each formula, starting with an initial guess of $x_1 = 20$. Which algorithm will converge to the solution? Why?

5. The equation $x = (\frac{1}{9})x - 2$ can also be written $x = 9x + 18$. Write an iteration formula corresponding to each of these two equations. Carry out five iterations with each formula, starting with an initial guess of $x_1 = 0$. Which algorithm will converge to the solution? Why?

6. Write an iteration formula for the equation $x = x + 20$. Carry out five iterations using this formula. Explain the behavior of the iterations. Can you do anything to induce convergence?

*7. The equation $x = f(x)$ is to be solved by successive approximations. The function $f(x)$ is increasing at the solution x, and its slope is between 0 and 1 over an interval of the x-axis between five units to the left and one unit to the right of the solution. Suppose we begin with an initial approximation x_1 approximately four units to the *left* of the solution x. Show graphically what happens to the successive approximations. Does the method converge?

8. The equation $x = f(x)$ is to be solved by successive approximations. The function $f(x)$ is decreasing at the solution x, and its slope is between 0 and -1 over an interval of the axis between four units to the left and four units to the right of the solution. Suppose we begin with an initial approximation approximately three units to the *right* of the solution x. Show graphically what happens to the successive approximations. Does the method converge?

9. What happens in Exercise 7 if the function has slope between 2 and 3 in the interval described?

10. What happens in Exercise 8 if the function has slope between -1 and -4 in the interval described?

11. The equation $x = 3x - 90$ of Exercise 3 may be cast in the form (20) taking $f(x) = 3x - 90$ and finding the slope of $f(x)$. Find the iteration formula which results and give a graphical interpretation of the algorithm. How does the speed of convergence compare to the speed of convergence of the algorithm based on the alternative form $x = (x/3) + 30$?

*12. Graph the function $y = 3x^2 - 7x - 12$ to approximately locate the solutions of the equation

$$3x^2 - 7x - 12 = 0$$

Write this equation in the form $x = f(x)$ and then derive an iteration formula in the form (21) for finding each solution. Write a FORTRAN program to calculate the values of the successive approximations and find the solutions to three decimal place accuracy. Obtain $\bar{x}$ from the graph. Use $\Delta x = .01$.

13. Finding the cube root of a number N means finding x such that $x^3 = N$. Adding $x - N$ to both sides, we have

$$x = x^3 + x - N$$

which is in the form $x = f(x)$.

(a) Derive an iteration formula in the form (21) for finding $\sqrt[3]{5}$.

(b) Write a FORTRAN program for finding $\sqrt[3]{5}$ and calculate $\sqrt[3]{5}$ correct to three decimal places. Start with $x_1 = 1.5$.

(c) Alter the program in (b) so that the cube root of any number N can be calculated.

(d) Find $\sqrt[3]{72}$ correct to three decimal places. Start with $x_1 = 4.0$.

14. Consider the cubic equation

$$x^3 - 1 = 0$$

Suppose the constant 1 can be in error by as much as 0.1. Estimate the errors in the solutions of the equation. What conclusion can you draw about the accuracy of cube roots of numbers?

15. Write an iteration formula for calculating the fifth root of 100. Start with $\bar{x} = 2.5$.

16. Finding $\sqrt{N}$ means solving the equation $x^2 = N$ for its positive solution x. This equation can be written in the form

$$x = x^2 + x - N$$

Since the function $f(x) = x^2 + x - N$ contains only powers of x, the slope v of this function can be found exactly. The formula for the slope is $v = 2x + 1$ (refer to Exercise 24, Chapter 4). This gives for the constant A in (17) the formula

$$A = \frac{1}{1-v} = \frac{1}{1-(2x+1)} = -\frac{1}{2x}$$

This means that, if we set $A = -(1/2x)$, where x is the exact value of $\sqrt{N}$, then the right-hand side of (13) will have slope exactly *zero* at the solution. This would guarantee the fastest convergence possible. Putting this formula for A and $f(x) = x^2 + x - N$ in equation (20) leads to the equation

$$x = x - \left(-\frac{1}{2x}\right)[x - (x^2 + x - N)] = x + \frac{1}{2x}(N - x^2)$$

or

$$x = x + \frac{1}{2}\left(\frac{N}{x} - x\right)$$

This equation further simplifies to

$$x = \frac{1}{2}\left(x + \frac{N}{x}\right) \tag{62}$$

which becomes the iteration equation

$$x_{n+1} = \frac{1}{2}\left(x_n + \frac{N}{x_n}\right) \tag{63}$$

This is the preferred algorithm for square root calculation by computer.

(a) Prove that equation (62) has the solution $\sqrt{N}$.

(b) Write a FORTRAN program for calculating $\sqrt{N}$ based on equation (63).

(c) Calculate $\sqrt{2}$ and $\sqrt{37}$ to four decimal places using this program. For $\sqrt{2}$ start with $x = 1.4$, and for $\sqrt{37}$ start with $x = 6$. Compare the number of steps needed to those needed in finding the same roots, using your previous square root algorithm in the text.

17. The function $f(x)$ used in Exercise 13 for deriving a cube root algorithm has slope v given exactly by the formula $v = 3x^2 + 1$. Proceed as in Exercise 16 to derive the preferred algorithm for extracting $\sqrt[3]{N}$ given by

$$x_{n+1} = \frac{1}{3}\left(2x_n + \frac{N}{x_n^2}\right)$$

Write a FORTRAN program based on this algorithm and find $\sqrt[3]{100}$ to four decimal places.

18. Use the algorithm of equation (21) to find the solutions of the equation

$$2x^3 + 6x^2 - 18x - 5 = 0$$

From Table 8 and Figure 23 of Chapter 4 we see that the equation has three solutions (roots). One solution x lies between $x = -5$ and $x = -4$. A second lies between $x = -1$ and $x = 0$. The third solution x lies between $x = 2$ and $x = 3$. These numbers will furnish you with initial estimates for each solution.

Calculate the slopes needed by writing the derivative of the polynomial you have for $f(x)$ in each case (see Exercise 24, Chapter 4).

Find the solutions correct to four decimal places.

19. Find the points where the graph of the equation

$$y = x^5 - 30x^3 + 160x - 10$$

crosses the x-axis, correct to four decimal places. The graph of this equation was sketched in Exercise 27, Chapter 4.

20. By writing all the terms in an equation on the left-hand side, it takes the form $F(x) = 0$. Plotting the graph $y = F(x)$, the solutions of the equation $F(x) = 0$ correspond to the points where the graph $y = F(x)$ crosses the x-axis. Figure 15 is an illustration of such a point P. To find the solution point x where $F(x) = 0$ we may proceed as follows by

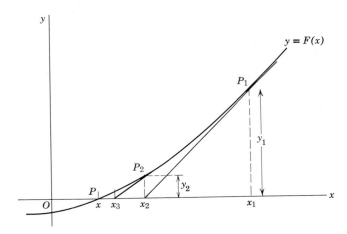

Figure 15

successive approximation based on tangents to the curve $y = F(x)$:
Let x_1 be an approximation to x. At x_1 we locate the point P_1 on the
curve. Its y-coordinate is $y_1 = F(x_1)$. Draw the tangent to the curve
at that point. The point where the tangent intersects the x-axis is nearer
to the solution than our original approximation x_1. We take this point
to be our second approximation x_2. At x_2 move vertically to the curve
where $y_2 = F(x_2)$ at the point P_2. We draw the tangent to the curve
at P_2 and find its intersection with the x-axis. This is our next approximation x_3 to the solution.

Continuing in this way, we generate an infinite sequence of approximations $x_2, x_3, x_4, \ldots$, which in general will converge to find the solution of $F(x) = 0$.

(a) Draw a flow chart describing this method.

(b) Write a FORTRAN program using this method to find the solution of

$$x^3 - 4.3x^2 + 4x - 17.2 = 0$$

near $x = 4$.

This is the *Newton-Raphson* method.

21. Prepare a flow chart describing the refinement of the method of successive approximation outlined at the end of Section 5.4.

*22. Suppose we rewrite equation (1) as

$$x = 200 - x$$

This has the solution $x = 100$, as we would expect.

(a) What happens if we try to use the iteration formula

$$x_{n+1} = 200 - x_n$$

to solve this equation? Draw a graph of this iteration procedure. While the solutions do not get farther from $x = 100$, neither do they get closer. We say the iteration procedure *diverges*.

(b) What is the slope of the right-hand side in the equation above?

23. Suppose in finding the square root of 2 we divide $x^2 = 2$ by x to obtain

$$x = \frac{2}{x}$$

(a) Use the iteration formula

$$x_{n+1} = \frac{2}{x_n}$$

to find $\sqrt{2}$. What happens? Draw a graph of the process.

(b) Estimate the slope of $2/x$ near $x = \sqrt{2}$. What does this tell you about the iteration formula above?

*24. Consider the quadratic equation in Section 5.5,

$$x^2 - 3x + 2 = 0$$

Suppose each coefficient and the constant can be in error by as much as 0.1. Estimate the errors in the two solutions $x = 1$ and $x = 2$. Check the assumption about the smallness of the errors. What conclusions can you draw?

25. Consider the quadratic equation

$$x^2 - 4 = 0$$

Suppose the constant 4 can be in error by as much as 0.05. Estimate the errors in the solutions. What conclusion can you draw about the accuracy of square roots of numbers?

26. Consider the cubic equation

$$x^3 - 2x^2 - 5x + 6 = 0$$

If the constant and each coefficient can be in error by 0.01, estimate the error in the solution $x = -2$.

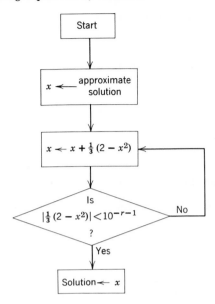

Figure 16

Flow chart for calculating $\sqrt{2}$ (Exercise 28)

27. In Figure 9 a flow chart for calculating $\sqrt{2}$ to r decimal places is given. Is the flow chart in Figure 16 equivalent to the one in Figure 9? Discuss the relative merits of the two flow charts.

28. Write a FORTRAN program to compute $\sqrt{2}$ based on the flow chart in Figure 16. Use it to compute $\sqrt{2}$ to four decimal points. Start with $x = 1.0$.

29. Attempt to solve the following system of equations by the method of successive approximations:

$$-x + 2y = 1$$
$$2x - y = 4$$

Notice that these are equations (38) and (39) in reverse order. Why does the algorithm diverge here, even though it converged before the order was reversed? Draw a graph illustrating the algorithm.

*30. (a) Apply the method of successive approximations to the following system of equations:

$$2x + y = -1$$
$$2x - 3y = 1$$

(b) Reverse the order of the equations and apply the method of successive approximations.

(c) Discuss the difference between parts (a) and (b).

31. (a) Apply the method of successive approximations to the following system of equations:

$$- x + 2y = 3$$
$$4x - y = 6$$

(b) Reverse the order of the equations, and apply the method of successive approximations.

(c) Discuss the difference between parts (a) and (b).

32. Reverse the order of equations (42) and (43) in the text, and apply the method of successive approximations. Why does the algorithm converge?

33. Accounting departments in large corporations often face the problem of determining the actual cost of operating each of the corporation's divisions. One approach to this problem is to allocate a percentage of each division's *total* expense to all divisions with which it interacts. Of course, a division's total expense generally is not known because it contains charges allocated to it by other divisions. We do know the direct cost of each division, since that is the dollar value of the resources it consumes. If we consider a firm with four divisions, we let C_1, C_2, C_3, C_4 be the direct costs, in dollars, of the four divisions.

(a) What is the cost of the entire corporation? Each of the four divisions allocates a percentage of its total cost (unknown) to the other divisions. We let P_{12} be the percentage of the total cost of division 1 which will be charged to division 2. In general, P_{ij} is the percentage of the cost of division i which is charged to division j. Of course, no division can charge more than 100% of all its expenses, although a service division may indeed charge 100% of its expenses to the other divisions. The percentages are determined by considering the portions of floor space, supplies, labor, etc., which each division supplies to the other divisions.

Let x_1, x_2, x_3, x_4 be the total costs, in dollars, of the four divisions. Then

$$x_1 = C_1 + \frac{P_{21}}{100} x_2 + \frac{P_{31}}{100} x_3 + \frac{P_{41}}{100} x_4$$

Similarly,

$$x_2 = C_2 + \frac{P_{12}}{100} x_1 + \frac{P_{32}}{100} x_3 + \frac{P_{42}}{100} x_4$$

$$x_3 = C_3 + \frac{P_{13}}{100} x_1 + \frac{P_{23}}{100} x_2 + \frac{P_{43}}{100} x_4$$

$$x_4 = C_4 + \frac{P_{14}}{100} x_1 + \frac{P_{24}}{100} x_2 + \frac{P_{34}}{100} x_3$$

This is a system of four linear equations in four variables which may be solved by the Gauss-Seidel method. Why? (*Hint:* Note that the P_{ij} are percentages.)

(b) Suppose the four divisions have direct expenses of $8000, $7000, $9000, and $12,000, respectively. What is the total cost of the firm?

(c) Suppose also that Division 1 charges 15% of its costs to Department 2, none to Department 3, and 15% to Department 4. These charges are summarized in the first column of Table 2. The last

Table 2

Charges against	Charges by			
	Div. 1	Div. 2	Div. 3	Div. 4
Div. 1	—	10%	15%	15%
Div. 2	15%	—	20%	10%
Div. 3	0	10%	—	30%
Div. 4	15%	15%	10%	—

three columns summarize the allocations of the costs of the other three divisions. Notice that Division 1 allocates 30% of its costs, while Division 2 allocates 35% of its costs. Use the FORTRAN program for the Gauss-Seidel method to find the total cost of each division.

(d) The net cost of each division is its total cost less the allocated costs. The net cost of Division 1 is

$$y_1 = X_1 - \frac{P_{12}}{100} X_1 - \frac{P_{13}}{100} X_1 - \frac{P_{14}}{100} X_1$$

In our example,

$$y_1 = X_1 - .15X_1 - .15X_1$$

Compute the net costs of all four divisions.

(e) The total cost of the firm should be the sum of the net costs of all its divisions. The firm's cost then is

$$y_1 + y_2 + y_3 + y_4$$

Find the total cost and compare it with the total cost found in part
(b). Explain the discrepancy.

The methods described above are used in many modern accounting departments, although older (precomputer) cost accounting handbooks
usually dismiss these methods as impractical. For further details the
reader is referred to *Bank Cost Accounting and Profitability Analysis*,
an IBM Data Processing Application publication. The authors are in-
debted to Dr. G. Truman Hunter of IBM for calling this application to
their attention.

*34. Use the Gauss-Seidel method to solve the following system of equa-
tions:

$$
\begin{aligned}
22.361y_1 - 1.601y_2 + 2.111y_3 &= 22.871 \\
1.621y_1 + 30.102y_2 + 1.609y_3 + 2.402y_4 &= 35.734 \\
-9.216y_1 + 2.101y_2 + 19.661y_3 + 3.216y_4 &= 15.762 \\
-1.222y_1 - 3.333y_2 - 2.109y_3 + 40.196y_4 &= 33.532
\end{aligned}
$$

35. Use the Gauss-Seidel method to solve the following system of equations:

$$
\begin{aligned}
17.4z_1 + 5.3z_2 + 3.1z_3 - 1.2z_4 &= 43.8 \\
-1.1z_1 + 12.5z_2 + 1.1z_3 + 8.1z_4 &= 35.6 \\
0.9z_1 + 0.9z_2 + 9.2z_3 + 3.1z_4 &= 33.1 \\
-4.1z_1 + 1.3z_2 + 1.1z_3 + 10.2z_4 &= 22.2
\end{aligned}
$$

CHAPTER SIX

Never-Ending Sums

In this chapter and the next we continue the study of never-ending algorithms and successive approximations. We take up first the problem of evaluating infinite sums such as $1 + \frac{1}{2} + \frac{1}{4} + \frac{1}{8} + \cdots$. Infinite sums are often calculated in order to determine the value of such quantities as sine $10°$ which you may have looked up at one time or another in a table of trigonometric functions. Did you ever wonder how such tables are made?

Problem. Find the value of sine $10°$ in a table.

6.1 Infinite Sums

In Chapter 5 we learned that, if Speedy runs twice as fast as Pokey and Pokey is given 100 yd as a head start, Speedy will catch Pokey after Pokey runs $x = 100$ yd. This value is the solution of the equation

$$x = 50 + \frac{x}{2}$$

We have seen that it can be found by successive approximation from the iteration formula

$$x_{n+1} = 50 + \frac{x_n}{2}$$

Starting with $x_1 = 50$ gives the successive approximations $x_2 = 75$, $x_3 = 87\frac{1}{2}$, etc. These can also be written

$$x_1 = 50$$

$$x_2 = 50 + \frac{x_1}{2} = 50 + \frac{50}{2}$$

$$x_3 = 50 + \frac{x_2}{2} = 50 + \frac{1}{2}\left(50 + \frac{50}{2}\right) = 50 + \frac{50}{2} + \frac{50}{4}$$

$$x_4 = 50 + \frac{x_3}{2} = 50 + \frac{1}{2}\left(50 + \frac{50}{2} + \frac{50}{4}\right) = 50 + \frac{50}{2} + \frac{50}{4} + \frac{50}{8}$$

and so on. Indeed, the nth approximation, x_n, is given by

$$x_n = 50\left(1 + \frac{1}{2} + \frac{1}{4} + \cdots + \frac{1}{2^{n-1}}\right)$$

where n stands for any one of the integers 1, 2, 3, ... We have seen that x_n approaches 100 as we take n larger and larger. That is, as the number of terms in the sum (in parentheses) approaches infinity, x_n approaches 100. This infinite sum or, as it is called, **infinite series** is denoted by

$$1 + \tfrac{1}{2} + \tfrac{1}{4} + \cdots \tag{1}$$

The $+ \cdots$ symbols at the end indicate that the process is to continue without end. To avoid ambiguity one should write enough terms so that the pattern governing succeeding unwritten terms is clear. Thus, it would be preferable to write the next term $\frac{1}{8}$ of the series (1) explicitly since the three terms written in equation (1) might just as well apply to the series

$$1 + \tfrac{1}{2} + \tfrac{1}{4} + \tfrac{1}{6} + \tfrac{1}{8} + \tfrac{1}{10} + \cdots$$

Even more explicitly one can write

$$1 + \frac{1}{2} + \frac{1}{2^2} + \frac{1}{2^3} + \cdots$$

for the series (1). Frequently one writes a formula for the "nth" term to make the law of formation specific. In equation (1) the nth term is $1/2^{n-1}$.

Question. What is the nth term of the series $1 + \frac{1}{2} + \frac{1}{4} + \frac{1}{6} + \frac{1}{8} + \cdots$?

Since we know from Chapter 5 that the approximation x_n as given above approaches 100 as n becomes large, the infinite series (1) should approach 2 as n becomes large. Let us write a FORTRAN program to test this. The following program evaluates the series (1):

```
SUM = 1.0

TERM = 1.0

DO 1 N = 1, 50
```

TERM = 0.5 * TERM

TEMP = SUM + TERM

IF (TEMP − SUM) 2, 2, 1

1 SUM = TEMP

2 PRINT 100, N, SUM

100 FORMAT (5 H ① I ① = ①, I 2, 7 H ① SUM ① = ①, F 10.5)

STOP

END

In the DO loop we multiply the previous term (called TERM) by $\frac{1}{2}$ and add it to the sum of all previous terms (called SUM). We save the new sum temporarily (in a variable called TEMP). We then check to see if the new sum (TEMP) is bigger than the old sum (SUM). If it is, we place the new sum in SUM and return to add another term. If the new sum and the old sum are the same, we know that the latest term added was so small that it did not affect the sum to the number of digits which the computer can hold. Since each succeeding term gets smaller than its predecessor, no succeeding term will change the sum either, so we stop and print the result. (We shall see later that the fact that individual terms are too small to affect the sum to the number of digits the machine holds does *not* mean that the sum computed is the actual sum of the infinite series, because adding *many* such small terms can affect the sum.)

This program was run on an IBM 7094 and the result was SUM = 2.00000 and N = 27. This means that the addition of the term $1/2^{27}$ did not change the result. On a different computer the number of terms used (which is the same as the number of times we go through the DO loop) may be different depending on how many digits there are in the mantissa of the floating-point numbers. The value of SUM should be 2 in any case.

> **Problem.** Run the preceding program on your computer. Try to figure out what the final value of N will be before you try the program. Use the data on precision given in Appendix E or in the manual for your computer.

It might seem to the reader that the statement IF (TEMP − SUM) 2, 2, 1 could be replaced by the simpler statement IF (TERM) 2, 2, 1 since the statement just preceding the IF tells us that TEMP − SUM = TERM. However, TERM will never be zero or negative, because at the beginning of the program TERM = 1.0 and each time we go through the DO loop we multiply TERM by $\frac{1}{2}$. TEMP − SUM, on the other hand, eventually becomes zero because TERM is so small that it will not affect SUM. This is the same phenomenon we encountered in Section 4.5, where Δs became zero in our computer although it was not supposed to. The culprit both here and there is the fixed and finite number of digits in the mantissa of the floating-point numbers.

In our program above we will never add more than 50 terms because of the upper limit on the range of the DO. However, suppose we wish to find the sum of the infinite series

$$1 - \frac{1}{2} + \frac{1}{3} - \frac{1}{4} + \frac{1}{5} - \cdots + (-1)^{n+1}\frac{1}{n} + \cdots \qquad (2)$$

Suppose also that we have six decimal digits in the mantissa of our floating-point numbers. Then, if the nth term is not to affect the sum, $1/n$ must be less than 10^{-6}; therefore, n must be greater than one million. Modern computers can compute and add one million terms in minutes. If we have eight or ten digits in the mantissa, however, the time becomes exorbitant. In any case we might have trouble with a DO loop since the upper limit would be one million or greater. In general, such large upper limits are not allowed although we have not discussed this problem in this text, nor shall we.

We use the following program to evaluate (2):

```
        SUM = 0.0
        N = 1
        TOP = 1.0
   1    X = N
        TERM = TOP/X
        TOP = −TOP
        SUM = SUM + TERM
        IF (TERM) 2, 3, 3
   2    IF (0.001 + TERM) 5, 5, 4
   3    IF (TERM − 0.001) 4, 5, 5
```

```
  5   N = N + 1

      IF (N − 9999) 1, 4, 4

  4   PRINT 100, SUM, TERM, N

100   FORMAT (7H ① SUM ① = ①, F6.2, 8H ① TERM ① = ①,
      F10.3, 5H ① N ① = ①, I4)

      STOP

      END
```

The variable TOP is the numerator of each term. At statement 1, the beginning of the loop, we take the number of the term, N, and convert it into a floating-point number, X. We then calculate the term, and prepare the numerator, TOP, for the next term. Next we add the term to the previous sum.

If the term is positive we go to statement 3, where we see if it is less than 10^{-3}. If it is, we print the results with statement 4. If the term is negative, we want to know if it is less in absolute value than 10^{-3}. This we determine in statement 2.

In case the term, whether positive or negative, exceeds or equals 10^{-3} in absolute value, we ask if we have added 9999 terms. This is to assure ourselves that we do not go through our loop too many times.

This program will calculate the sum of the series (2) to two decimal figures of accuracy. We have assured ourselves that the sum is no longer changing in the third place because of any one of the successive terms, but we cannot be sure that subsequent additions of several terms each of which contributes to the fourth place might not change the third place when properly rounded.

The results of this program are:

$$\text{SUM} = 0.69 \qquad \text{TERM} = -0.001 \qquad N = 1000$$

Problem.   Rewrite the program to find the sum (2) to three and then four decimal figures accuracy. Be sure to change the FORMAT statement and the IF statement following statement number 5.

The sums to three and four figures are 0.693 and 0.6928, respectively. These required 10,000 and 100,000 terms, respectively. The precise sum of this series is the natural (or Napierian) logarithm of 2 which is 0.6931471806 to ten figures.

We see that there is something suspicious about these results. The programs for two- and three-figure results do indeed produce the accuracy expected. However, the program for four-figure accuracy is in error by 3 in the fourth figure—hardly what we expected or predicted. If we extended the program to five figures, it would require a million terms and the result would be 0.68942 which is in error by 373 in the fifth place. We shall return to this dilemma and solve it later.

Before continuing, however, we evaluate the sum of yet another series which will produce some even more surprising and perplexing results. Consider the series

$$1 + \frac{1}{2} + \frac{1}{3} + \frac{1}{4} + \cdots + \frac{1}{n} + \cdots \tag{3}$$

Since, as n becomes large, the terms of this series become small, in fact equal to the absolute value of the corresponding term in (2), we should be able to evaluate its sum much as we evaluated (2). Indeed, a simplification of the last program above can be used to calculate this sum. For convenience one such simplification is given here.

      SUM = 0.0

      N = 1

  1   X = N

      TERM = 1.0/X

      SUM = SUM + TERM

      IF (TERM − 0.001) 2, 3, 3

  3   N = N + 1

      IF (N − 9999) 1, 2, 2

  2   PRINT 100, SUM, TERM, N

100   FORMAT (7H ① SUM ① = ①, F6.2, 8H ① TERM ① = ①,
      F10.3, 5H ① N ① = ①, I4)

      STOP

      END

This produces the sum to two places after the decimal point.[1] The result is

$$\text{SUM} = 7.49 \qquad \text{TERM} = 0.001 \qquad \text{N} = 1000$$

If we change the program to compute to three places after the decimal point, we get

$$\text{SUM} = 9.787 \qquad \text{TERM} = 0.0001 \qquad \text{N} = 10000$$

The surprising thing is that the sums to two and three digits after the decimal point do not agree at all!

Problem. Change the preceding program to calculate the sum of (3) to one, four, and five places after the decimal point and compare the results with the two above.

Where things seem to work nicely with the two series (1) and (2) (at least for several decimals), they do not work at all with the series (3). We now turn to a discussion of some of the mathematical aspects of infinite series which will help to explain the behavior we have encountered in these examples.

Let us use the symbol s_n to denote the sum of the first n terms of the series (1), so that

$$s_1 = 1$$
$$s_2 = 1 + \tfrac{1}{2}$$
$$s_3 = 1 + \tfrac{1}{2} + \tfrac{1}{4}$$

$$\cdot \qquad \cdot \qquad \cdot$$

$$s_n = 1 + \frac{1}{2} + \frac{1}{4} + \cdots + \frac{1}{2^{n-1}}$$

If the sequence of numbers $s_1, s_2, s_3, \ldots$ converges to a certain value s, this value is called the **sum of the series** and we say that the series converges.[2] As we know, in the case of equation (1) s_n approaches 2 as n ap-

---

[1] Not to be confused with two digits in the mantissa of the floating-point number. Here we actually have three digits of accuracy.

[2] The value approached by s_n as n approaches infinity is called the **limit** of s_n as n approaches infinity. The abbreviation "L" or "Lim" is used to denote "limit" and the symbol $\rightarrow$ is used to denote "approaches." In symbols, therefore, the statement that the limit of s_n as n approaches infinity equals 2 is usually written

$$\operatorname*{Lim}_{n \to \infty} s_n = 2$$

We shall not be concerned with this notation any further, but you will see it again in the study of the calculus.

proaches infinity. We say, therefore, that the sum of the infinite series (1) is 2. We call the numbers s_n the **partial sums** of the series.

The series (1) is a special case of what is called a **geometric series.** Each term in the sum is just equal to the preceding one times a certain fixed factor—in this case $\frac{1}{2}$. Thus, the second term is $\frac{1}{2}$ times the first term, the third term is $\frac{1}{2}$ times the second term, and so on. In general, if we take as the first term of a series some number a and choose a factor r we get the geometric series

$$a + ar + ar^2 + \cdots \tag{4}$$

Note that each term is just r times the preceding term.

Question. In the series (1) what are the values of a and r?

Set

$$s_n = a + ar + \cdots + ar^{n-1}$$

the sum of the first n terms of the series (n is any integer $n = 1, 2, \ldots$). The s_n are the partial sums of the series (4).

Problem. Show that

$$s_n = \frac{a(1 - r^n)}{1 - r} \tag{5}$$

(*Hint.* Replace s_n by the sum, multiply both sides by $(1 - r)$, and simplify.)

From (5) we can determine whether the series (4) converges or not. Convergence, we repeat, means that the sequence of numbers $s_1, s_2, \ldots$ approaches some fixed number or limit. This number, if indeed there is such a number, is *by definition* the sum of the infinite series (4). Writing

$$s_n = \frac{a}{1 - r} - \frac{ar^n}{1 - r}$$

we see that the second term is the one which is changing as n changes. Suppose $0 < r < 1$. Then the numbers $r, r^2, r^3, \ldots$ get smaller and smaller and approach zero as a limit.[3] Dividing r^n by $(1 - r)$, which is a fixed constant for a given value of r, does not alter this fact, and so $r^n/(1 - r)$ approaches 0 as n approaches infinity. We find then that s_n

[8] See footnote 9 in Chapter 5, page 305.

approaches $a/(1 - r)$ as n approaches infinity, and therefore this value is the sum of the series (4). We may write

$$a + ar + ar^2 + \cdots = \frac{a}{1 - r} \tag{6}$$

Problem. Check the value of the sum of series (1) using equation (6).

Problem. What is the sum of the geometric series $\frac{1}{3} + \frac{1}{9} + \frac{1}{27} \cdots$?

We note that (6) remains true if $-1 < r < 0$, and we leave it to the reader to show this (Exercise 8).

One can attempt to use a computer to evaluate the sum of an infinite series by calculating the sequence of partial sums, s_n, as successive approximations to the sum of the series. However, we shall see that, just as with all uses of computers, there are certain pitfalls which we must take care to avoid. We have already encountered some of them.

Let the series consist of a sum of constants $c_1 + c_2 + c_3 + \cdots$. In the series (4), $c_n = ar^{n-1}$. Then the sequence of partial sums is

$$s_1 = c_1$$

$$s_2 = c_1 + c_2 \tag{7}$$

$$s_3 = c_1 + c_2 + c_3$$

$$\cdots$$

The question which must be answered if we are to use this method of successive approximations is: When do we stop? Or, equivalently: What value of s_n should we use as the sum of the series?

This question is always encountered when using an infinite algorithm producing successive approximations. The question has two aspects. First, there is the underlying question of whether the process converges. Second, there is the immediate practical question of selecting a termination criteria for ending the calculation after a finite number of steps.

In the determination of the slope $f'(x)$ of a function $f(x)$ (Chapter 4) or in finding the solution of a properly formulated iteration equation $x = g(x)$ (Chapter 5), we *knew* that the method would converge. We repeated the process until we had reached the point where the change in successive approximations was less than the permitted error. We then stopped, assuming that all following approximations would also not differ by more than the permitted error. Even so, we had difficulties due to the limited number of digits in the mantissa of floating-point numbers in a computer.

The matter is even more complicated in the case of infinite series, for a number of reasons. First and foremost, the series may *diverge* rather than converge. That is, the sequence of partial sums $s_1, s_2, s_3, \ldots$, may not be approaching any number at all. The partial sums may approach infinity (get infinitely big) as with the series $1 + 2 + 3 + 4 + \cdots$, or they may oscillate without approaching any particular number as with the series $1 - 1 + 1 - 1 + 1 - \cdots$.

> **Problem.** (a) What are the first five terms s_1, s_2, s_3, s_4, s_5 in the sequence of partial sums for the series $1 + 2 + 3 + 4 + \cdots$?
> (b) What are the first five terms in the sequence of partial sums for the series $1 - 1 + 1 - 1 + \cdots$?

However, it is not always as obvious that a series diverges as it is in the two examples just given. You might suspect that all we need do is require that successive terms in the sum become smaller and smaller and in fact approach zero. That is, you might conjecture that if the successive terms c_n go to zero, then the series $c_1 + c_2 + c_3 + \cdots$ will converge or equivalently that the sequence of partial sums $s_1, s_2, s_3, \ldots$, given by (7) will converge. This conjecture amounts to assuming that the convergence is guaranteed by the condition $|s_n - s_{n-1}| < \epsilon$, where ϵ (epsilon) is as small a number as we please. Since, from (7), s_n is the sum of the first n terms of the series and s_{n-1} is the sum of the first $n - 1$ terms, then

$$s_n - s_{n-1} = c_n$$

and so $|s_n - s_{n-1}| = |c_n|$. Therefore, if the terms of the series approach zero, then eventually the criterion $|s_n - s_{n-1}| < \epsilon$ will be satisfied no matter how small ϵ may be. This is the type of condition that we have often employed to terminate an infinite algorithm. However, this criterion does *not* guarantee convergence of the sequence $s_1, s_2, \ldots$. That is, it does not ensure that *all* terms in the sequence after s_n will also differ by less than ϵ from s_{n-1}. This means that, although successive terms in the series may get as small as we please, the sum of enough of them may become large. Unfortunately, unless specially programmed to do so, a computer will not detect this once the individual terms no longer affect the number of digits retained in the computer.

For an example of this we take the series

$$1 + \tfrac{1}{2} + \tfrac{1}{3} + \tfrac{1}{4} + \cdots$$

which we previously tried to sum. The nth term of this series is just $1/n$. As n approaches infinity, the nth term approaches zero, and so the difference between successive partial sums approaches zero as well. But, as we shall see, the series does *not* converge. The partial sums of this series to three digits are

$$s_1 = .100 \times 10^1$$

$$s_2 = .150 \times 10^1$$

$$s_3 = .183 \times 10^1$$

$$s_4 = .208 \times 10^1$$

$$s_5 = .228 \times 10^1$$

$$s_6 = .245 \times 10^1$$

$$s_7 = .259 \times 10^1$$

If our computer has only three digits in the mantissas of its floating-point numbers, the 101st term of the series

$$\frac{1}{101} = 0.0099009900 \cdots$$

becomes $.990 \times 10^{-2}$ which will not affect the sum because before it is added it is shifted to the right three places and becomes $.000 \times 10^1$. We would mistakenly think the series had converged to the value s_{100}.

As we saw earlier, when we evaluate this series using 1000 terms we get 7.49, and when we use 10,000 terms we get 9.787. This shows the cumulative effect of these successively smaller terms and leads us to believe that the series (3) does indeed *diverge*. We now show that this is so.

Observe in (3) that the sum of $\frac{1}{3} + \frac{1}{4}$ is larger than $\frac{1}{4} + \frac{1}{4}$ and so is greater than $\frac{1}{2}$. The next four terms $\frac{1}{5} + \frac{1}{6} + \frac{1}{7} + \frac{1}{8}$ are larger than $\frac{1}{8} + \frac{1}{8} + \frac{1}{8} + \frac{1}{8} = \frac{4}{8}$ and so again the sum exceeds $\frac{1}{2}$. Continuing with larger and larger blocks of terms each block adding to more than $\frac{1}{2}$, we see that (3) must exceed in value the series $1 + \frac{1}{2} + \frac{1}{2} + \frac{1}{2} + \cdots$ which diverges.

No matter how many digits the computer can carry, the partial sums after some point will contain all the digits the machine can hold. If, then, succeeding terms are less than 1 in the last digit, the sums calculated by the computer will no longer change, and the series will appear to converge even if it does not. *The question whether a series converges is not a matter for a computer to decide.*

There are mathematical tests which often allow one to determine definitely whether a series converges or diverges. We have seen one such test for the special case of a geometric series, (4), where if $|r| < 1$ the series converges. Another type of test is given later. Generally, though, the sum of a series is not known even if it has been determined that the series converges. A formula giving the sum of the series as in (6) for the geometric series is almost never available. The sum, therefore, must usually be computed. A computer can be, and very often is, set the task of finding the sum of a *convergent series* correct to a specified number of decimal places.

If we assume that an infinite series does converge, there may still be difficulty in carrying out the evaluation of the partial sums because the series may converge extremely slowly. For example, thousands of terms might have to be added to get only two decimal places correct. Because of the large number of additions which may be needed to get a given accuracy, the round-off error may accumulate so as to overwhelm the answer and the results may be meaningless.

Recall that earlier in this section we evaluated the series

$$1 - \frac{1}{2} + \frac{1}{3} - \frac{1}{4} + \cdots + (-1)^{n+1} \frac{1}{n} + \cdots \tag{2}$$

and obtained the following results on an IBM 7094:

No. of Terms	Partial Sum
1,000	0.69
10,000	0.693
100,000	0.6928
1,000,000	0.68942

We also noted that the correct result to ten figures was 0.6931471806. The last two partial sums above are rather disturbing.

The difficulty arises from the fact that the round-off error from such a great number of additions (100,000 or more) is affecting the result adversely. However, it has been discovered that, when adding floating-point numbers, we can reduce the round-off error by adding the small numbers first.[4] However, we have done just the opposite. In calculating s_n, we have added the small numbers last.

In order to get this improved accuracy, then, we first must determine how many terms we need. For example, if we want four figures of accuracy, then we certainly want the last term not to exceed .00001. Therefore, we want to take at least 100,000 terms. Later we shall see that this number of terms is actually sufficient for the accuracy desired. We start with the term

$$-\frac{1}{100,000} = -.00001$$

and add to it

$$+\frac{1}{99,999}$$

and then

$$-\frac{1}{99,998}$$

and so on until we have added $+1$.

The following FORTRAN program does just that.

```
        SUM = 0.0

        N = 100000

        TOP = -1.0

   1    X = N

        TERM = TOP / X

        TOP = -TOP

        SUM = SUM + TERM

        N = N - 1

        IF (N) 2, 2, 1

   2    PRINT 100, SUM

  100   FORMAT (7H ① SUM ① = ①, F8.4)
```

[4] The reader is referred to Exercise 11 in Chapter 3 and Section 2.8 of the McCracken and Dorn book cited in Section 5.5, page 308.

STOP

END

The results of this program are

SUM = 0.6931

which is accurate to four figures.

> **Problem.** Write a FORTRAN program to compute the sum of the series (2) to five figures of accuracy by adding the smallest terms first. Compare your result with the natural logarithm of 2.

Series in which successive terms alternate in *sign*, such as (2), may converge or diverge. The test for convergence of an *alternating series* (as these are called) requires two conditions to be satisfied in addition to the condition that the signs alternate. We state these conditions without proof:

The alternating series

$$c_1 - c_2 + c_3 - c_4 + c_5 - \cdots$$

(where all the numbers $c_1, c_2, c_3, \ldots$, are positive) converges if

(i) $|c_n| < |c_{n-1}|$, for all $n = 2, 3, 4, \ldots$, and if
(ii) the *sequence* $c_1, c_2, c_3, \ldots$, converges to zero.

Condition (i) requires that each term in the series be numerically smaller than its predecessor. Condition (ii) requires that the terms approach zero.

A useful property of convergent alternating series is that s_n, the sum of the first n terms, differs from the sum s of the series by an amount smaller than the first term neglected; that is

$$|s - s_n| < c_{n+1}$$

Thus, it is easy to estimate how many terms are needed to provide the sum to a given accuracy. If we wish the error to be less than 10^{-r}, for some positive integer r, then we choose the number of terms, n, such that $c_{n+1} < 10^{-r}$. We have used this property in summing the series (2) to four figures of accuracy.

The alternating series (2) satisfies conditions (i) and (ii) and so is known to converge. Both of these conditions must be satisfied if a series is to converge, as can be seen from examples of alternating series that satisfy only one of these conditions and diverge. For example, the series

$$(1 + 1) - (1 + \tfrac{1}{2}) + (1 + \tfrac{1}{3}) - (1 + \tfrac{1}{4}) + \cdots$$

in which the nth term is $(-1)^{n+1}(1 + 1/n)$, alternates in sign. The terms also satisfy condition (i), since

$$\left(1 + \frac{1}{n}\right) < \left(1 + \frac{1}{n-1}\right) \qquad \text{for } n = 2, 3, \cdots .$$

However, the sequence $(1 + 1)$, $(1 + \tfrac{1}{2})$, $(1 + \tfrac{1}{3})$, $(1 + \tfrac{1}{4})$, $\ldots$, does not approach zero and, therefore, condition (ii) is not satisfied. Indeed, this sequence approaches 1, and successive partial sums $s_1, s_2, \ldots$, can never differ by less than 1; thus, convergence is impossible.

An example of an alternating series which satisfies (ii) but not (i) and which diverges is more difficult to construct. However, one such series is

$$\frac{1}{\sqrt{2}-1} - \frac{1}{\sqrt{2}+1} + \frac{1}{\sqrt{3}-1} - \frac{1}{\sqrt{3}+1} + \cdots$$

We now summarize our results for infinite series.

1. A geometric series (each term is formed by multiplying its predecessor by a factor r) converges if $-1 < r < 1$.

2. A series in which the terms alternate in sign, and in which each term is smaller in numerical value than its predecessor, and the terms approach zero, will converge. The error (exclusive of round-off error) in using a partial sum to represent the sum of the series will not exceed the first term neglected.

3. A computer should not be used to test for the convergence of a series. The tests above or others similar to them should be used for this purpose.

4. If possible, one should estimate the number of terms to be added and then start from the end and add backwards so that the smaller terms are added first. This procedure reduces the round-off error.

6.2 The Number π

Perhaps the most remarkable number in mathematics is the one which is identified by the Greek letter π. The symbol π is used to denote the ratio of the circumference of a circle to its diameter, a ratio which was known even in Biblical times to be the same for all circles. By inscribing

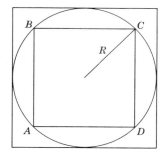

Figure 1

Inscribed and circumscribed squares used to approximate π

and circumscribing regular polygons to a circle, Archimedes[5] was able to show that

$$3\tfrac{10}{71} < \pi < 3\tfrac{1}{7} \tag{8}$$

Let us try to reconstruct Archimedes' reasoning before proceeding. A circle must have circumference greater in length than any inscribed polygon. For example, looking at the inscribed square $ABCD$ of Figure 1 we see that each side is exceeded in length by the arc of the circle joining its end points. Therefore, the entire circumference is greater than the perimeter of the square. It follows that

$$\frac{\text{perimeter of inscribed square}}{\text{diameter of circle}} < \frac{\text{circumference of circle}}{\text{diameter of circle}}$$

The right-hand side of this inequality is π. By the Pythagorean theorem each side of the square is just $\sqrt{2}R$, where R is the radius of our circle. The perimeter of the square is thus $4\sqrt{2}R$. Since the diameter of the circle is just $2R$, we have proved (as Archimedes must have once done) that $2\sqrt{2} < \pi$. To two digits this gives

$$2.8 < \pi \tag{9}$$

---

[5] **Archimedes** (approximate dates 287–212 BC) is known as the greatest scientist of ancient times. His remarkable contributions lay in mechanics as well as mathematics. The principle of the lever and the concept of density are among his discoveries. His genius placed him centuries in advance of his contemporaries. Not until Newton did a comparable scientific mind appear in history.

When we construct the circumscribed square, it is evident that the perimeter of this square *exceeds* the circumference of the circle. Since the perimeter is just $8R$, we are led to the inequality

$$\pi < 4 \tag{10}$$

What happens if we use polygons with more sides than the square? First, since we need to compute the perimeter of the polygon, it is most convenient to use regular polygons (all sides equal). The perimeter of regular polygons is easily calculated. Second, we observe that, as more and more sides are added, the edges of the polygons more and more closely approximate the arc of the circle. Therefore, we expect that, as we take more and more sides, our approximation to π will improve. This is precisely, then, a method of successive approximation for the determination of π. Archimedes used polygons with 96 sides in obtaining his estimates. The most precise value found by the Greeks was equivalent to 3.1416 and was determined by Ptolemy[6] about 150 AD.

The goal of the Greek mathematicians was to find an exact value for π, but in this they were unsuccessful. In the 16th century, progress resumed and, using arithmetic based on decimal computation and the method just described, π was determined by the Italian Viete to lie in the range

$$3.1415926535 < \pi < 3.1415926537$$

Van Ceulen (1540–1610) gave π to 35 decimal places.

Other techniques of approximation then were introduced. Of particular importance were the infinite series representations of π. Leibnitz[7] (1673) showed that

$$\frac{\pi}{4} = 1 - \frac{1}{3} + \frac{1}{5} - \frac{1}{7} + \frac{1}{9} - \cdots \tag{11}$$

A man named Sharp (1699) discovered that

$$\frac{\sqrt{3}\,\pi}{6} = 1 - \frac{1}{3 \cdot 3} + \frac{1}{3^2 \cdot 5} - \frac{1}{3^3 \cdot 7} + \cdots \tag{12}$$

[6] **Ptolemy** (pronounced "tahl'uh-me"), principal work 127–151 AD, is the Greek (or perhaps Egyptian) astronomer whose system of the universe (derived from the Greek Hypparchus) placed the earth at the center and had the sun and the planets revolve about the earth. This system with its complicated orbits is called the Ptolemaic system. It was not until Copernicus (1473–1543) that the accepted picture of the solar system emerged as one in which the planets revolved about the sun. (See reference to Galileo, footnote 11, Chapter 4, page 244.)

[7] See footnote 5 in Chapter 4, page 205.

Summing the terms of this series, he was able to find π correct to 72 decimal places. The relation

$$\frac{\pi^2}{6} - 1 = \frac{1}{1^2} + \frac{1}{2^2} + \frac{1}{3^2} + \frac{1}{4^2} + \cdots \tag{13}$$

was discovered by Euler[8] (1736). Series like the last two, equations (12) and (13), were particularly useful for computation because the terms decrease rapidly.

For computation, (12) is superior to (13) and both are far superior to (11). To see this, let us compare the nth terms of these series. The nth term of (11) is $\pm 1/(2n - 1)$, where the $+$ sign is used if n is odd and the $-$ sign if n is even. The nth term of (12) is $\pm 1/[3^{n-1}(2n - 1)]$, where the sign is again $+$ if n is odd and $-$ if n is even. The nth term of (13) is $1/n^2$.

The numerical value of the 10th term in series (11) is $1/19 = .05263$. The 10th term in series (13) is $1/10^2 = .01$. The numerical value of the 10th term in series (12), however, is $1/3^9(19) = .0000027$. If we were using these series to calculate π, we see that, after adding 10 terms, the series (11) has still not fixed π to even one decimal place. Series (13) is still changing in the second decimal place. However, (12) is no longer being affected in the 5th decimal place by the 10th term. Because (12) is an alternating series, we know that the error in stopping the summation process at any term is less than the size of the first term neglected. Therefore, we know that adding the first 9 terms of (12) gives us the sum of this series with an error of less than .0000027.

Question. How many terms of the series (11) would have to be used to find its sum correct to five decimal places?

Problem. Write a FORTRAN program to determine π from series (12). What is the value of π to five decimal places given by this program? How many terms were needed? Use $\sqrt{3} = 1.7320508076$.

The calculation of π to more and more digits continued well into the 18th century. What was the purpose of these calculations which, in the

---

[8] **Leonhard Euler** (pronounced "oi'ler," 1709–1783), a Swiss, was one of the most productive mathematicians of all time. Although blind in later life, he was able to carry out extensive calculations of great precision in his mind even to the determination of astronomical orbits. His numerous contributions range from physics to pure mathematics and even to numerical methods of importance today for computers.

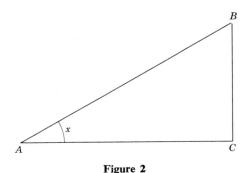

Figure 2

Right triangle definition of sin x

days before computers, could occupy much of a man's lifetime? The purpose was to discover whether π could be written exactly as a fraction. If π were a fraction (or *rational number* as it is customary to call the quotient of two integers), then the decimal for π would have to repeat after some finite number of digits as do the following.

$$\frac{7}{11} = .636363 \ldots$$

$$\frac{1357}{9999} = .135713571357 \ldots$$

$$\frac{22}{7} = 3.142857142857 \ldots$$

The hope in the calculation was that, after some number of digits, the decimal for π would repeat and so the fraction which was the exact value of π could be written down. This expectation vanished in 1761 when the German mathematician Lambert proved that π is not a rational number. However, this did not end the interest in calculating π more and more exactly. New questions arose concerning the nature of this number and, by 1873, π had been calculated correctly to 527 places. In 1882, the German mathematician Lindemann proved that π was a so-called *transcendental number*[9] and interest in calculating π appeared to have ended.

[9] A transcendental number is one which cannot satisfy an equation formed out of positive integer powers of x with integer coefficients. For example, we can be sure that $x = \pi$ does *not* satisfy the equation $x^3 - 64x^2 + 610 = 0$.

With the advent of high-speed digital computers, new interest was awakened in the calculation of π, particularly in attempting to answer statistical questions. For example, one may ask whether any one of the digits 0 to 9 occurs most frequently or whether some combination of digits occurs more frequently than others. The answers to such questions have so far appeared to be negative. In 1949, the first-high speed electronic computer, the ENIAC, was used to calculate π to 2036 figures in 70 hours of computing time. By 1961, machines and programming had improved to the point that it was possible to calculate π to 100,265 decimal places in 8 hours and 43 minutes using an IBM 7090 computer. This was done at the U. S. Bureau of Standards by two mathematicians named Shanks and Wrench.

6.3 The Series for Sine x

Infinite series play an important role in mathematics in defining and studying many functions. These include the functions you probably have already encountered (although most likely in other forms) such as the sine, cosine and logarithm. Here we take up only one of these functions, the sine. We shall find it convenient to abbreviate "sine" in the usual way by dropping the "e." That is, we shall write *sin x* for sine *x*.

We recall that sin *x*, where *x* is thought of as an angle less than 90°, can be defined in terms of a right triangle with one angle equal to *x*. The value of sin *x* is then the ratio of the length of the "opposite side" to the length of the hypotenuse or, in Figure 2,

$$\sin x = \frac{BC}{AB} \tag{14}$$

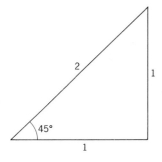
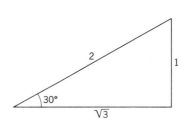

Figure 3

Diagrams to calculate sin 45° and sin 30°

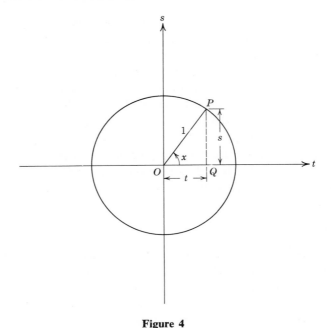

Figure 4

Circular description of trigonometric functions

where x is the angle at A. In this way you learned that, when $x = 45°$, $\sin x = \sqrt{2}/2$ and, when $x = 30°$, $\sin x = \frac{1}{2}$. The corresponding right triangles for these two cases are shown in Figure 3. The definition given in equation (14) gives us no way to compute the value of $\sin x$ for an arbitrary acute angle x. Only in special cases, such as for angles x equal to 45°, 30°, 60°, are we able to give the value of $\sin x$. Moreover, we have no definition at all for $\sin x$ if x is an angle greater than 90°.

Later you may have learned a somewhat different definition of $\sin x$ as follows. Figure 4 shows a circle of radius 1, centered at the origin O of a rectangular coordinate system. For any point P on the circumference of the circle we draw the radius joining P to O. Let the coordinates of P be (t, s). Let x be the angle made by the radius OP with the $+$ direction of the t-axis measured counterclockwise from the $+ t$ axis. Then we *define*

$$\sin x = s \tag{15}$$

This agrees with the earlier definition, as we see from the drawing since, in the right triangle OPQ,

$$\sin x = \frac{QP}{OP} = \frac{s}{1} = s$$

This definition goes beyond the previous one in that it defines $\sin x$ for angles greater than 90° and also defines such values as $\sin 90°$.

    Question.   What are the values of $\sin 0°$, $\sin 90°$, $\sin 180°$, $\sin 270°$, $\sin 360°$?

    Question.   In what quadrants for the angle x will $\sin x$ be positive? In what quadrants will $\sin x$ be negative?

While $\sin x$ is defined in this way for any angle x the definition is not useful for computing the value of $\sin x$, because s is not known except for special angles. How, then, are tables made for $\sin x$, such as the ones you have used in your books on algebra or trigonometry? The answer is that $\sin x$ can be computed from other definitions, such as the following definition of $\sin x$ as an infinite series:

$$\sin x = x - \frac{x^3}{3!} + \frac{x^5}{5!} - \frac{x^7}{7!} + \frac{x^9}{9!} - \cdots \tag{16}$$

The number x is the angle measured in *radians* now rather than degrees, as explained below. The symbol ! used in this formula is called the **factorial sign**. When this symbol follows an integer, it means that the product of all integers up to and including that integer must be taken. Thus,

$$2! = 1 \cdot 2 \qquad = 2$$
$$3! = 1 \cdot 2 \cdot 3 \qquad = 6 \tag{17}$$
$$4! = 1 \cdot 2 \cdot 3 \cdot 4 = 24$$

    Question.   How much is each of the following: 5!, 7!, 9!?

It must be understood that, as in all algebraic equations, the value of $\sin x$ for any given number x is found by substituting that number in the expression on the right-hand side of (16). This gives a series of constants to be summed.

When a series is given for a function, it is necessary to say for what values of the variable the series will converge. Amazingly, the series (16) will converge for *any* number x that may be substituted. The number

x must be the *radian measure* of the angle whose sin we wish to calculate. Thus, if we wish to find sin 20° using (16), we first convert 20° to radians. Since 360° $= 2\pi$ radians, 1° $= 2\pi/360 = \pi/180$ radians. Therefore,

$$20° = 20\,\frac{\pi}{180} = \frac{\pi}{9}\ \text{radians}$$

From (16),

$$\sin 20° = \sin\left(\frac{\pi}{9}\right) = \frac{\pi}{9} - \frac{(\pi/9)^3}{3!} + \frac{(\pi/9)^5}{5!} - \cdots$$

Adding the terms on the right will give sin 20° to any desired accuracy. Since the series for sin x alternates in sign, we know that the error will be less than the first term neglected. To get sin 20° correct to four decimal places we need only find the first term which is less than 5×10^{-5} in value and retain all the previous terms in the sum.

In summary, then: Given an angle in degrees, we divide by 57.2957795 to convert to radians. We substitute this value for x in (16) and evaluate the series.

There are, however, a few difficulties in evaluating (16). Suppose we need to use 20 terms. Then we need to calculate

$$-\frac{x^{39}}{(39)!}$$

If we try to calculate numerator and denominator of this fraction separately, we find that the denominator is approximately 2.04×10^{46}. This is too large for many computers (see range of floating-point numbers in Appendix E). Therefore, we must proceed differently.

Notice that the second term in equation (15) is $-x^2/3 \cdot 2$ times the first. Similarly, the third term is $-x^2/5 \cdot 4$ times the second. Thus, the nth term is $-x^2/[(2n-1) \cdot (2n-2)]$ times the $(n-1)$st term. Therefore, if x denotes the angle in radians, the first 20 terms in (16) can be calculated by the following program:

```
DENOM = 2.0

XSQ = X * X

TERM = X

SUM = 0.0

DO 1 I = 1, 20
```

SUM = SUM + TERM

TERM = −TERM * XSQ / (DENOM * (DENOM + 1.0))

1   DENOM = DENOM + 2.0

Of course, we always prefer to start with the smaller terms in the nth partial sum and add them first to reduce the round-off error. Because this program does just the opposite, we now develop a program which uses a similar trick to avoid computing factorials and which begins with the smaller terms. Let us take the first five terms in series (16) as shown:

$$\sin x \cong x - \frac{x^3}{3!} + \frac{x^5}{5!} - \frac{x^7}{7!} + \frac{x^9}{9!}$$

and rewrite this as

$$\sin x \cong x \left\{ 1 - \frac{x^2}{2 \cdot 3} \left[1 - \frac{x^2}{4 \cdot 5} \left(1 - \frac{x^2}{6 \cdot 7} \left(1 - \frac{x^2}{8 \cdot 9} \right) \right) \right] \right\}$$

To evaluate, we begin with the smallest term, $x^2/8 \cdot 9$, and work outward. Then the following program can be used:

DENOM = 9.0

XSQ = X * X

SUM = 1.0

DO 1 I = 1, 4

TERM = XSQ / (DENOM * (DENOM − 1.0))

SUM = 1.0 − TERM * SUM

1   DENOM = DENOM − 2.0

SUM = X * SUM

Problem.   Change the program above to sum the first ten terms of the series (16). Use the changed program to evaluate sin 30°. The result should be $\frac{1}{2}$.

Although, for any x, the series (16) converges to the sin of x radians, it is of no practical computational value for large values of x. However, the sine function repeats its values periodically as x increases (refer to the definition in terms of the circle and see, for example, that adding

$2\pi = 360°$ to x returns sin x to the same value). Therefore, if sin x is tabulated for x in the first quadrant (i.e., $0 \le x \le \pi/2$), then sin x for all other values of x can be found easily.

It can be shown (see Exercise 20) that

$$\sin(n\pi + x) = (-1)^n \sin x \tag{18}$$

where $n = 0, 1, 2, \ldots$. It can also be shown (see Exercise 21) that

$$\sin(-x) = -\sin x \tag{19}$$

We can use these results to obtain the sin of any angle (positive or negative) from the sine of an angle between 0 and $\pi/2$ radians.

As an example, let us find the series for sin 170°. First we reduce the problem to finding the sine of an angle less than 90°. Since $170° = 180° - 10° = \pi - \pi/18$, we have from equation (18) that

$$\sin 170° = \sin\left(1 \cdot \pi - \frac{\pi}{18}\right) = (-1)^1 \sin\left(-\frac{\pi}{18}\right) = -\sin\left(-\frac{\pi}{18}\right)$$

From equation (19), $\sin(-\pi/18) = -\sin(\pi/18)$ and so

$$\sin 170° = \sin\frac{\pi}{18}$$

More simply, from the definition of Figure 4, the supplementary angles 170° and 10° must have the same sine. Now from the series (16):

$$\sin 170° = \sin\frac{\pi}{18} = \frac{\pi}{18} - \frac{(\pi/18)^3}{3!} + \frac{(\pi/18)^5}{5!} - \frac{(\pi/18)^7}{7!} + \cdots$$

Question.   What are the series for sin 210°, sin 140°, sin 300°?

To tabulate the sine function we now need only consider the interval of values $0 \le x \le \pi/2$ for the series (16).

Question.   To find sin x correct to four decimal places for angles from $x = 15°$ to $x = 75°$ how many terms must be summed in the series (16)?

Problem.   Write a FORTRAN program for calculating sin x, where $0 \le x \le \pi/2$. Evaluate sin x correct to four decimal places for the angles from 15° to 75° in steps of 5°. Compare your results with those in a table of sin x.

A graph of sin x between $x = 0$ and $x = \pi/2$ is shown in Figure 5 (page 351).

Problem. From your table and the periodic behavior of sin x prepare a graph of sin x for the entire 360° interval $0 \leq x \leq 2\pi$.

Exercises

Answers to exercises marked * are given in Appendix A.

1. Speedy can run three times as fast as Pokey's cousin Shorty, but Shorty gets a 300-yd head start in a race with Speedy. Write an infinite sum for the distance Shorty runs before he is caught. What is that distance?

*2. Write the geometric series in which the first term a is equal to 100 and the factor r is equal to ⅓. Find the sum of this series using equation (6).

3. Does the following series converge?

$$1 + .1 + .01 + .001 + .0001 + \cdots$$

What is the sum? Is this a geometric series?

*4. What is the sum of the following series?

$$\frac{1}{10} + \frac{1}{100} + \frac{1}{1000} + \cdots$$

5. Does the series obtained from the series in Exercise 3 converge if every other term is omitted (i.e., omit the 2nd, 4th, 6th terms, etc.)? What is its sum? Is this a geometric series?

6. Write a geometric series with $0 < r < 1$ whose sum is
   *(a) 2   (b) 1
   (c) 3   (d) s

7. Does the series

$$1 + \tfrac{3}{4} + \tfrac{9}{16} + \tfrac{27}{64} + \cdots$$

converge? What is its sum? Is it a geometric series?

8. From equation (5) show that the sums s_n for a geometric series also converge to the value $a/(1 - r)$ if r is negative and between -1 and 0.

9. Form the geometric series with first term $a = 1$ and the factor $r = \tfrac{1}{2}$. What is the sum of the series?

10. Draw a segment of the number line and locate the first five partial sums of the series

$$1 + \tfrac{1}{2} + \tfrac{1}{4} + \tfrac{1}{8} + \cdots$$

on this graph. On a second segment locate the first five partial sums of the series

$$1 - \tfrac{1}{2} + \tfrac{1}{4} - \tfrac{1}{8} + \cdots$$

What is the difference in the type of convergence between the case where $r = +\tfrac{1}{2}$ and $r = -\tfrac{1}{2}$. Do you think this will generally be true?

11. Consider the following infinite sum:

$$1 + \frac{1}{2^2} + \frac{1}{3^2} + \frac{1}{4^2} + \cdots$$

   (a) Draw a flow chart which computes this sum until the last term added is less than .000001.

   (b) Write a FORTRAN program to carry out the calculations described by the flow chart in part (a).

   (c) Change the flow chart and FORTRAN program so that the last term added is less than .00000001. How does this change the answer?

*12. Does the series

$$1 - \frac{1}{2^2} + \frac{1}{3^2} - \frac{1}{4^2} + \cdots$$

converge or diverge? Write a FORTRAN program to compute the sum of this series to three decimal place accuracy.

13. Show that the series given in equations (11) and (12) satisfies the test for convergence of an alternating series.

14. Does the series

$$\tfrac{1}{2} + \tfrac{1}{4} + \tfrac{1}{6} + \tfrac{1}{8} + \cdots$$

converge or diverge? (*Hint:* Each term is $\tfrac{1}{2}$ the corresponding term in the series $1 + \tfrac{1}{2} + \tfrac{1}{3} + \tfrac{1}{4} + \cdots$).

15. By inscribing and circumscribing regular hexagons to a circle, find a lower and an upper bound for π.

16. The cosine of an acute angle x is defined in terms of the right triangle in Figure 2 as the ratio of the adjacent side AC to the hypotenuse AB. The circular definition (see Figure 4) of the cosine of any angle x (abbreviated cos x) is

$$\cos x = t$$

where t is the abscissa of the end point of the radius OP. The radius OP makes an angle x with the positive t-axis. Draw the radius OP cor-

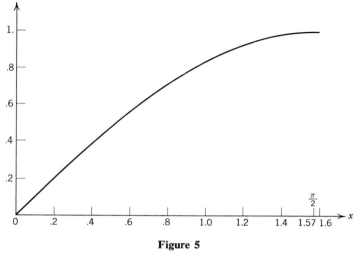

Figure 5

$\sin x$ for $0 \leq x \leq \pi/2$

responding to angles x of value $0°$, $90°$, $180°$, $270°$, and $360°$ and give the corresponding values of $\cos 0°$, $\cos 90°$, $\cos 180°$, $\cos 270°$, and $\cos 360°$ by observing the value of t in each case.

17. The value of $\cos x$ for angles in general must be obtained from a computable relation of some kind. The infinite series definition of $\cos x$ is as follows (x is the angle measured in radians):

$$\cos x = 1 - \frac{x^2}{2!} + \frac{x^4}{4!} - \frac{x^6}{6!} + \frac{x^8}{8!} - \cdots \qquad (20)$$

(a) Write a FORTRAN program for calculating $\cos x$ where $0 \leq x \leq \pi/2$.

(b) Evaluate $\cos x$ to four decimal places for angles from $15°$ to $75°$ in steps of $5°$.

(c) Compare your results with those in a table of $\cos x$.

(d) Prepare a graph of $\cos x$ between $x = 0$ and $x = \pi/2$.

18. It is of great interest to find the slope of the curve $y = \sin x$ graphed in Figure 5. The slope will again be a function of x, since at each point x along the axis between, say, $x = 0$ and $x = \pi/2$, the slope will have a definite (and different) value. This function will be the *derivative* of the sine function. What will it turn out to be? To answer this we can combine an algorithm of the kind developed in Chapter 4 for finding the slope of a function at a number of points (see Figure 10, Chapter 4) with the algorithm and program written in the present chapter for calculating sin x. We see that there is an added difficulty. In Chapter 4, the functions we dealt with could be computed directly from a formula (such as $16t^2$). Now the function is sin x, and each time it is to be evaluated we must compute a sequence of successive approximations until we have the desired accuracy. This introduces a new inner loop into the flow chart.

(a) Draw a complete flow chart for the calculation of the slope of sin x at 5° intervals from 0° to 90°.

(b) Write a FORTRAN program to compute the slope of sin x correct to two decimal places for angles from 0° to 75° in steps of 5°.

(c) Graph the derivative (slope) of sin x versus x between 0° and 75°. Compare this graph with the graph of cos x prepared in Exercise 17 or with the table of values of cos x. On the basis of this numerical experiment, what do you believe is the relation between the derivative of sin x and the function cos x?

19. Find the slope of cos x as a function of x between $x = 15°$ and $x = 90°$. To the accuracy and extent of your computations, what is the relation between the derivative of cos x and the function sin x?

20. Recall that

$$\sin (A + B) = \sin A \cos B + \cos A \sin B$$

Using this and the circular description of sin and cos (see Figure 4 and Exercise 16), show that

$$\sin (n\pi + x) = (-1)^n \sin x$$

21. Using Figure 4, show that

$$\sin (-x) = - \sin x$$

22. (a) Using the expression for sin $(A + B)$ in Exercise 20 and Figure 4, show that

$$\sin (x + \pi/2) = \cos x$$

(b) If a FORTRAN program has been written to compute the sine of an angle x, then by adding one FORTRAN statement at the beginning of the program we can change it to be a program to evaluate cos x. What is that FORTRAN statement?

23.*(a) Another convergent infinite series for the natural logarithm of 2 is

$$\frac{1}{2} + \frac{1}{2\cdot2^2} + \frac{1}{3\cdot2^3} + \cdots + \frac{1}{n\cdot2^n} + \cdots$$

Determine the value of n so that the next term added will be less than 10^{-6}. Using this series, write a FORTRAN program to find the natural logarithm of 2 to five figures. Compare the speed with which this series converges to the speed of convergence of the series used in the text.

(b) Another convergent infinite series for π is

$$2\left(1 + \frac{1}{3} + \frac{2\cdot1}{5\cdot3\cdot1} + \cdots + \frac{n!}{(2n+1)(2n-1)\cdots3\cdot1} + \cdots\right)$$

Write a FORTRAN program to determine the value of n so that the next term added will be less than 10^{-4}. Using this series, write a FORTRAN program to find π to four figures.

CHAPTER SEVEN

Algorithms for Areas

7.1 Area and Integration

The idea of area is familiar to you through such everyday questions as:

1. How many square feet or acres of land is my house situated on? (The lawn needs reseeding.)
2. How many square feet of carpet do I need to cover the floor in the living room?
3. How large is a certain reservoir? (The water reserves are being estimated.)
4. How many square yards of driveway lead to the garage? (What will it cost to have it resurfaced?)

Some areas are easily found and some are easy to estimate. Some examples of easily found areas are those which correspond to familiar geometric shapes such as squares, rectangles, circles, triangles, or figures which are formed by piecing such shapes together. Such areas are easily found because there are simple formulas for them.

Question. What is the area of a rectangle of length L and width W? Of a circle of radius R? Of a triangle of base b and altitude h?

Referring to our list of everyday questions, however, it would *not* be easy to give an accurate answer to the next-to-last question if the reservoir had the irregular shoreline of Figure 1a; or to the last question if your driveway looked like Figure 1b. If these drawings were accurately done to scale on graph paper as in Figure 2, the area of each of these figures could be estimated by counting the number of squares lying wholly within the boundaries. For the reservoir, let the scale be such that the length of a side of each square represents .1 mile so that the area of each square is .01 square mile. Then, counting squares *lying wholly inside the reservoir* and omitting the shaded squares (which lie partly outside the

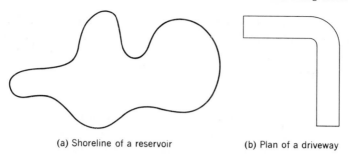

(a) Shoreline of a reservoir   (b) Plan of a driveway

Figure 1

reservoir boundary) gives a lower bound estimate of 1.33 square miles for the area covered by the reservoir. That is, the area of all the squares which lie entirely within the curve and do not touch the boundary is *less* than the area inside the curve.

If we count all the squares lying inside the boundary and *include* those which are partly inside and partly outside, then the sum of their

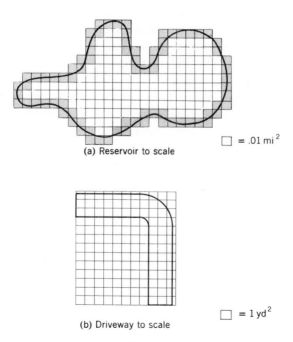

□ = .01 mi²

(a) Reservoir to scale

□ = 1 yd²

(b) Driveway to scale

Figure 2

areas will be *greater* than the area of the reservoir. There are 212 such squares (133 inside and 79 intersected by the boundary); therefore, an upper bound for the area of the reservoir is 2.12 square miles. If A denotes the area of the reservoir, then

$$1.33 < A < 2.12 \tag{1}$$

Question.   Suppose the drawing of the driveway in Figure 2b is done to a scale such that the length of the side of each square equals 1 yd. What estimate can you give for the area of the driveway?

To improve our estimates of these areas by much might hardly seem worthwhile in the case of the reservoir or the driveway. The approximate answers found are good enough for most practical purposes. Historically, such rough measurements of area must have served the needs of the human race for thousands of years as land was divided and apportioned. However, the ability to calculate areas with great accuracy is important in engineering, science, and mathematics — much more important than the need for measurements of actual physical square footage or mileage. The accurate determination of the area of a circle, for example, is equivalent to the problem of the determination of π which we considered in Chapter 6. Later we shall see that "area" frequently has an interpretation in scientific problems quite distinct from its usual meaning of land or surface area. This different interpretation arises from the use of graphs to represent such quantities as distance versus time, velocity versus time, force versus distance, and so on. In each case, area will also have physical meaning corresponding to the product of the variables being graphed, and an accurate determination of an area may be required.

Problem.   Draw a circle of radius 1 on a grid whose lines are spaced ¼ apart. Find upper and lower bounds for π. Compare the result with the one found in Section 6.2 using the inscribed and circumscribed squares?

Suppose that a more accurate determination is wanted of the area covered by the drawing of Figure 2a depicting the reservoir. How can we proceed to get better estimates than those of the inequalities (1)? We should not expect an exact answer and, as in all such cases, we look for a method of successive approximation — a never-ending algorithm.

Question.   Why should we not expect an exact answer? If the reservoir were a circle, should we expect an exact answer?

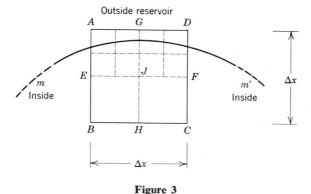

Figure 3

Subdividing a boundary square

For the time being we shall concentrate on improving the smaller estimate (lower bound) for the area. One method for improving our estimate is furnished by successively reducing the size of the squares used in counting. It might be somewhat surprising that the process of reducing the size of the squares provides better estimates of the area. One might think that using smaller squares would result in a larger number of squares being counted and the net effect would be to leave things unchanged. However, this is not so. The error in our estimates lies in the "boundary squares" — the squares through which the boundary passes. If we subdivide these squares, say by dividing each square into four equal smaller squares, then the boundary in general intersects only some of the new smaller squares. The total area of these smaller squares which are intersected by the boundary can then be less than the area of the original boundary square which was subdivided. For example, let $ABCD$ in Figure 3 represent a boundary square with side of length Δx. The curved boundary passing through this square is represented by the arc mm'. The amount contributed to the error estimate by this boundary square is $(\Delta x)^2$. If we subdivide into squares of side $\Delta x/2$, the boundary squares are now $AEJG$ and $GJFD$. The squares $EJHB$ and $JFCH$ are now wholly inside the boundary and therefore may be added to the lower area estimate. This clearly gives an improved (larger) lower bound. The area which the boundary squares now contribute to the error estimate is just the sum of the areas of the two top squares and is equal to $2[(\Delta x)^2/4]$ or $(\Delta x)^2/2$. The error in using just the inside squares is *at most* this amount. Therefore, by taking squares with half the side length, we have reduced our error estimate corresponding to this section of boundary to one-half of what it was.

If we again subdivide each square into four equal squares, now of side $\Delta x/4$, as shown in the top half of Figure 3, the error is reduced again. The lower, four smallest squares add to the area estimate inside the boundary. Now the error is at most equal to the sum of the areas of the four top small squares. These four squares have a total area of

$$4 \times \left(\frac{\Delta x}{4}\right)^2 = \frac{(\Delta x)^2}{4}$$

This is again a reduction of one-half in the error estimate.

One must not conclude from these diagrams that the error will always be reduced exactly one-half each time we cut the length of the side of each square in half. The curved boundary was shown to go through exactly two of the four subdivided squares each time. Actually, it can go through all four, or three, or two, or one of the smaller squares depending on how curved the boundary is and where the boundary is in relation to the square being subdivided. Consider, for example, the four curves shown in Figure 4. The pieces of boundary which curve more, (a) and (b), pass through four and three subdivisions, respectively. The "straighter" curves, (c) and (d), pass through only two subdivisions and one subdivision, respectively. On the other hand, depending on its location, a very "wiggly" section of arc might intersect only one of the smaller squares, or a nearly straight section of arc might intersect three or four of the smaller squares.

Problem. Illustrate with drawings the cases just described. Can a straight-line segment intersect all four of the smaller squares?

As the subdivision into smaller and smaller squares continues, however, the length of boundary passing through a single square will be shorter. Sufficiently short sections of arc will contain no "wiggles" (compare a short piece of the curve in Figure 4a with the whole length shown).[1] Such short sections of arc can, therefore, be well approximated by

---

[1] This whole discussion assumes that we are dealing with ordinary curves. However, it is possible to define functions, for example, which in any horizontal distance Δx, no matter how small, possess infinitely many "wiggles" of any height. Our conclusions would not apply to such cases. A study of these functions in mathematics is necessary to understand fully and give precise meaning to such descriptive terms as length, continuous curve, and slope.

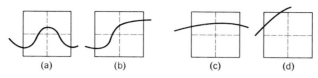

Figure 4

Possible intersections of boundary and subdivided squares

straight-line segments. A straight-line segment passing through any of the large squares in Figure 4 will cut only two of the small squares "on the average." We expect, therefore, if we continue to subdivide, that the error will eventually drop by roughly the factor one-half at each successive approximation, even if the boundary is quite curved to begin with. The method of subdivision will therefore *converge* in the usual sense that we can get as close as we please to the actual area simply by taking smaller and smaller squares.

Of course, we could use the same type of argument to show that the upper bound (the estimate which is too large) also converges to the value of the area as we subdivide the squares.

The reader will notice the similarity of these arguments to those in Section 4.3, where we found better and better estimates of the speed of a freely falling object. There we also had upper and lower bounds which came closer and closer together. The same is true of the bounds we find for the area by subdividing the squares again and again.

> **Problem.**   Find the estimate for the area A of the reservoir in the form (1) corresponding to the use of squares of side half the length of those in Figure 2a.

Although we can imagine such a process being continued, it cannot actually be carried much further if we use an actual graph of the boundary and actual squares. (Try dividing the squares in the last problem in half again!) The curve itself cannot be drawn beyond a certain accuracy, nor can the squares, simply because of the limitation of measurement and the tools used in drawing. Nevertheless, the idea itself can be carried over to a purely mathematical process where the curved boundaries we deal with are given by mathematical equations or functions. This idea of continuing the subdivisions indefinitely is the basic idea and process of the **integral calculus**.

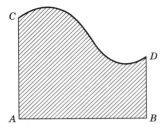

Figure 5

Typical boundary region

The problem of finding the area of plane geometric figures with curved boundaries, as we have seen, reduces to the problem of finding the area of regions like the shaded one in Figure 5. Line segments AC and BD are perpendicular to the base AB. The top of the figure is a curve such as CD. To specify the curve precisely we introduce a system of coordinates as shown in Figure 6, taking the x-axis to coincide with the base AB and the y-axis parallel to the sides AC and BD in Figure 5. The point A is at a distance a from the origin and the point B is at a distance b. The height y of the curve at a distance x from the origin is given by some function $f(x)$ so that

$$y = f(x) \tag{2}$$

What we seek is the area of the region lying "under the curve" $y = f(x)$ and above the x-axis, contained between the lines $x = a$ and $x = b$. This area under the curve has a special name given to it in calculus. It is called the **integral** of $f(x)$ from $x = a$ to $x = b$. There is also a special symbol for the integral, namely:

$$\int_a^b f(x)\, dx \tag{3}$$

The curved symbol $\int$ derives from the letter s for sum and refers to the fact that the quantity is related to a summing process—the addition of subdivisions of the area. The symbol dx is derived from the symbol Δx referring to the lengths of the sides of the subdivisions. The integral is the result of a limiting process, that is, infinitely many steps in a successive approximation algorithm. Just what this process consists of will be made clear as we continue. The letters a and b in the symbol (3) are called the **limits of integration,** and they specify the least and greatest

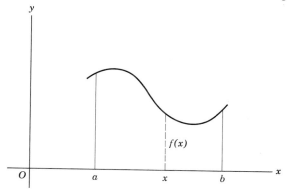

Figure 6

Graph of typical boundary region

values of x; that is, the position of the left- and right-hand sides of the "box" in Figure 6.

We are going to give a general procedure to be followed in calculating the value of $\int_a^b f(x)\,dx$ for some given curve $y = f(x)$. First, however, let us look at some other examples in which this problem arises.

Suppose we have a scientific instrument whereby some mechanism, which we need not describe here, continuously records the *speed* of a moving object. Given the record as the graph drawn by a pen on a con-

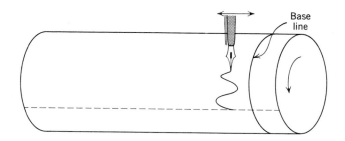

Figure 7

Device to record speed of a moving object [as the speed of the object increases, the pen moves to the left; if the object stops (speed is zero), the pen moves to the base line.]

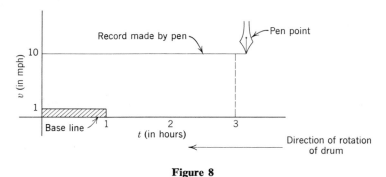

Figure 8

Instrument-recorded graph of speed versus time

tinuously turning drum,[2] can we find the *distance* traveled by the object during a given period of time? If the object moved at constant speed, the distance of the pen from the base line would not change and the graph would appear as in Figure 8. Suppose the speed v is measured in miles per hour, the time t in hours. A rectangle measuring one "unit" of time (one hour) by one "unit" of speed (one mile per hour) is drawn shaded in Figure 8. The area of this unit rectangle represents the product of the units along the two axes. Hence, one unit of area on this graph represents

$$1 \text{ mile/hour} \times 1 \text{ hour} = 1 \text{ mile}$$

The area of the region under the line drawn by the pen, lying above the t-axis and between the times $t = 0$ and $t = 3$, is given by the total number of units of area contained in this figure. Since the speed v is constant and equal to 10 mph, the figure is a rectangle and the number of units of area contained is given by $10 \times 3 = 30$. Since each unit of area represents 1 mile, the area under the "curve" represents 30 miles. This is exactly the distance traveled by the moving object during the elapsed time.

Question. Can you calculate the distance traveled in another way to check the answer just found by determining the area under the curve?

[2] In a typical instrument of this type (see Figure 7) the paper is wrapped around a circular cylinder which rotates at a slow fixed speed. The pen moves back and forth along a line parallel to the axis of the cylinder. The distance of the pen point from the base line (a circle around the cylinder) corresponds to the speed of the object being observed. The result is a graph in which distance along the base line corresponds to time, and height above the base line corresponds to speed of the moving object.

In the language of calculus we would say that the integral of v from $t = 0$ to $t = 3$ was equal to 30. In symbols we would write

$$\int_0^3 v\,dt = 30$$

or, since $v = 10$ throughout,

$$\int_0^3 10\,dt = 30$$

In the foregoing example, we have seen that the area of the region under the curve (or integral as the area is called) represented distance. Let us look next at a simple case of *varying* speed and see whether we are again justified in equating the integral with the distance traveled.

In Chapter 4 we studied the motion of an object freely falling under gravity. Taking the acceleration due to gravity to be 32 ft/sec², we found that, starting from rest, the speed v after t seconds of fall is given by the equation

$$v = 32t \tag{4}$$

Graphing $v = 32t$, we get the straight line shown in Figure 9. We are interested in the area of the region lying under this line and above the t-axis between, say, $t = 0$ and $t = 2$. That is, we want the integral of v from $t = 0$ to $t = 2$. In symbols, we wish to find the value of

$$\int_0^2 v\,dt \tag{5}$$

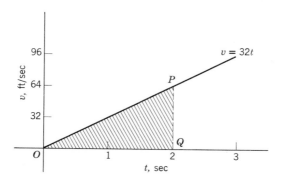

Figure 9

The region whose area is $\displaystyle\int_0^2 v\,dt$

Replacing v by $32t$ from equation (4), we can also write

$$\int_0^2 32t\, dt \tag{6}$$

for the area in question.

We find the area as follows. First, we note that the unit of area is the product of the unit in the t-direction (which is 1 sec) and the unit in the v-direction (which is 1 ft/sec). The unit of area, the area of a rectangle one unit long by one unit high, represents therefore

$$1 \text{ ft/sec} \times 1 \text{ sec} = 1 \text{ ft}$$

The area or integral in (6) is given by the number of units of area contained in the triangle OPQ. Since PQ is 64 units high and OQ is 2 units long, the total area is $\frac{1}{2} \times 2 \times 64 = 64$ units of area. Since each unit of area represents 1 ft, the total area represents 64 ft. We have found, then, that

$$\int_0^2 v\, dt = \int_0^2 32t\, dt = 64 \text{ ft}$$

Is 64 ft the distance traveled by the freely falling object during the first 2 sec? The task of checking the distance as calculated from the integral is not quite so simple now as in the case of constant speed. Fortunately, however, we can check our answer because we already know a formula relating distance and time for free fall. From equation (1) of Chapter 4 we have

$$s = 16t^2 \tag{7}$$

For $t = 2$ we find the distance traveled to be 64 ft, the same value as found by *integration*.[3]

Problem.   Find the value of

$$\int_0^3 v\, dt$$

for a freely falling object. What does this answer represent? Compare your answer with the distance found from equation (7).

---

[3] The process of evaluating an integral is called *integration*. Similarly, the process of finding the derivative of a function is called *differentiation*.

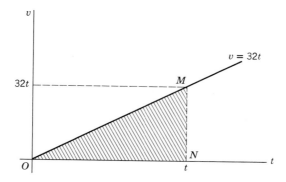

Figure 10

The region whose area is $\displaystyle\int_0^t v\,dt$

If we calculate

$$\int_0^t v\,dt$$

where t is any time, we will be finding the distance fallen in the first t seconds. Referring to Figure 10, we need the area contained in the triangle OMN. Since $ON = t$ and $MN = 32t$, the area is just

$$\tfrac{1}{2} \times t \times 32t = 16t^2$$

We see that the distance found by integration is just that given by equation (7). Therefore, the *integral* of the function $v = 32t$ (between the limits 0 and t) is just the function $s = 16t^2$. You will recall, from Chapter 4, that the function $v = 32t$ is the *derivative* of the function $s = 16t^2$. Evidently, in this example, the effect of integration following differentiation is to bring us back to the original function, that is, to undo what we did. This is very generally true, and for that reason integration and differentiation are called *inverse processes.*

7.2   The Area under a Curve

We are ready now to work out the integral of a function whose graph is not a straight line. This requires finding the area of a region under an actual curve such as that sketched in Figure 5. To be specific, suppose that

$$v = t^2 \tag{8}$$

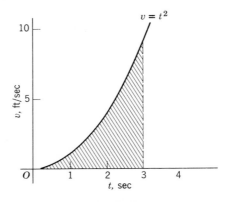

Figure 11

The region with area $\displaystyle\int_0^3 t^2\, dt$

is the record of the changing speed v with time t of a rapidly accelerating object such as a rocket. The speed v is measured in feet per second, and time t in seconds. The graphical record of the first few seconds of flight is shown in Figure 11. The curve is a parabola. We want the area of the region under this curve for some time interval, say from $t = 0$ to $t = 3$. In symbols, we want to evaluate

$$\int_0^3 t^2\, dt \tag{9}$$

We also want to verify that the value of this integral is actually equal to the distance traveled by the rocket in the first 3 sec. Both of these tasks are complicated by the fact that we have been given no simple formula (from elementary geometry) to tell us the area under a parabolic segment. In our previous examples we were able to apply formulas for the area of a rectangle and triangle. Now, in fact, if we are successful in evaluating (9), we will be led to a formula for the area under a parabolic segment.

Basically, our approach to the evaluation of (9) and to finding the area of the shaded region in Figure 11 is to go back to the technique of successive approximation which we used to estimate the area of the reservoir in Figure 2a. This required a subdivision of the figure into squares. Because of the box-like shape of Figure 11 (curved only on top), it is more convenient to divide it into vertical strips of equal width Δt. Figure 12a shows the area divided into three strips of width $\Delta t = 1$ unit each.

Drawing horizontal line segments to the right, from the points of intersection of the sides of the strip with the curve, we get the two shaded
rectangles in Figure 12b. These are the largest rectangles that can be
found in the strips and which lie wholly under the curve. Adding the
areas of these rectangles gives us a lower bound for the area under the
curve. The height of the first rectangle is the height of the curve at $t = 1$
or 1^2, from (8). The height of the second rectangle is the height of the
curve at $t = 2$ or 2^2. The width of each rectangle is $\Delta t = 1$. Let A be
the value of the area under the curve [the value of the integral (9)]. Then,

$$1^2 \cdot 1 + 2^2 \cdot 1 < A \tag{10}$$

In each strip in Figure 12a we can also draw the smallest rectangle that
wholly contains the boundary of the curve. These are found by drawing
horizontal line segments to the left from the points on the curve lying on
the sides of the strips. We get the three shaded rectangles of Figure 12c.
Adding the areas of these rectangles we get an *upper bound* for A as
follows:

$$A < 1^2 \cdot 1 + 2^2 \cdot 1 + 3^2 \cdot 1 \tag{11}$$

Combining this estimate and the preceding one, we have

$$5 < A < 14 \tag{12}$$

Comparing Figures 12b and 12c, we find that the excess of the upper-
bound estimate over the lower-bound estimate is precisely the area of

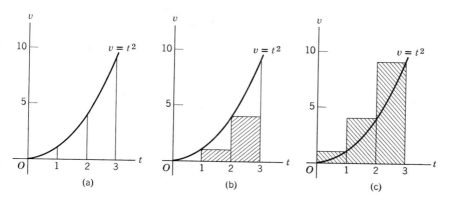

Figure 12

Division into strips; approximation by rectangles

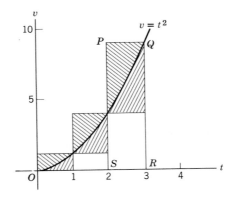

Figure 13

Boundary rectangles and error

three shaded rectangles (shown in Figure 13) through which the boundary passes. If we slide all the "boundary rectangles" in Figure 13 to the right so that they line up one above the other, we see that the sum of the areas of these "boundary rectangles" is equal to the area of the rectangle *PQRS*. The area of *PQRS* is $3^2 \cdot 1 = 9$. If the strips were of width Δt, the area of the last rectangle would become

$$3^2 \cdot \Delta t$$

since the height would still be 3^2. This again would equal the total area contained in the boundary rectangles of width Δt. Accordingly it seems reasonable to conclude that the gap between the upper and lower bounds for A will shrink toward zero if we take more and more strips to approximate the area between $t = 0$ and $t = 3$ in such a way that Δt gets smaller and smaller and approaches zero. If we use N strips (N may be any integer), then the width of each strip is given by

$$\Delta t = \frac{3}{N} \tag{13}$$

As the number of strips, N, increases, the width Δt of each strip decreases. Letting N approach infinity (i.e., Δt approaches zero), our upper and lower bounds should both converge to the desired area A. This is indeed the case, although a proof of this statement is beyond our scope and intent here.

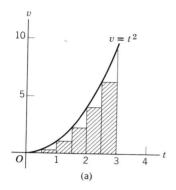

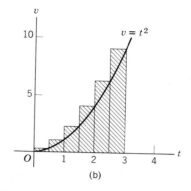

(a)   (b)

Figure 14

Division into $N = 6$ strips ($\Delta t = \frac{1}{2}$); approximation of $\displaystyle\int_0^3 t^2\, dt$

Comparing the upper bound estimate given by the shaded rectangles in Figure 12c and the "boundary rectangles" in Figure 13, we see that the error in the upper bound is just equal to the shaded parts of the "boundary rectangles" lying *above* the curve. Similarly, the lower-bound estimate is too low by an amount equal to the shaded parts of the boundary rectangles lying *below* the curve. The error, therefore, in using either the upper or the lower estimate is actually less (roughly by one-half) than the combined areas of the boundary rectangles. Thus, we can estimate the error in the lower or upper bound by calculating the areas of the "boundary rectangles."

Next we proceed to find improved estimates of A by increasing the number N of strips. If we take $N = 6$, from (13) the width of each strip is $\Delta t = \frac{1}{2}$. Figure 14a shows the approximating rectangles whose area furnishes a lower bound for A. Figure 14b shows the approximating rectangles whose area furnishes an upper bound for A. The points on the curve which give the heights of these rectangles correspond to the points

$$1 \cdot \Delta t, \ 2 \cdot \Delta t, \ 3 \cdot \Delta t, \ 4 \cdot \Delta t, \ 5 \cdot \Delta t, \ 6 \cdot \Delta t$$

along the t-axis. The heights of the rectangles are found by substituting these values for t in (8) to get

$$(1 \cdot \Delta t)^2, \ (2 \cdot \Delta t)^2, \ (3 \cdot \Delta t)^2, \ (4 \cdot \Delta t)^2, \ (5 \cdot \Delta t)^2, \ (6 \cdot \Delta t)^2$$

Summing the areas of the rectangles in Figure 14a, we get

$$\Delta t[(1 \cdot \Delta t)^2 + (2 \cdot \Delta t)^2 + (3 \cdot \Delta t)^2 + (4 \cdot \Delta t)^2 + (5 \cdot \Delta t)^2]$$

where the width Δt, being the same for each rectangle, has been written in front as a factor. Since $\Delta t = \frac{1}{2}$, this gives for the lower-bound estimate

$$(\tfrac{1}{2})^3[1^2 + 2^2 + 3^2 + 4^2 + 5^2] < A \tag{14}$$

Summing the areas of the rectangles in Figure 14b gives the upper-bound estimate,

$$A < (\tfrac{1}{2})^3[1^2 + 2^2 + 3^2 + 4^2 + 5^2 + 6^2] \tag{15}$$

Combining and evaluating these estimates gives

$$6.875 < A < 11.375 \tag{16}$$

As we anticipated, the gap between upper and lower estimates is now 4.5, just half of the previous gap of 9 in (12). This has resulted from cutting the strip width from $\Delta t = 1$ to $\Delta t = \frac{1}{2}$.

Generalizing to the case where there are N strips, N standing for any integer greater than 1, we have the following situation. Each strip has width $\Delta t = 3/N$. The heights of the approximating rectangles are given by

$$(1 \cdot \Delta t)^2, (2 \cdot \Delta t)^2, \ldots, [(N - 1) \cdot \Delta t]^2, (N \cdot \Delta t)^2$$

The sum of the areas of all these but the last one gives a lower bound to A. The sum of all the areas gives an upper bound. Since $(\Delta t)^2$ appears in every height and Δt is the width, we can factor out $(\Delta t)^3$ or $(3/N)^3$. We get

$$\left(\frac{3}{N}\right)^3 [1^2 + 2^2 + \cdots + (N - 1)^2] < A$$

$$< \left(\frac{3}{N}\right)^3 [1^2 + 2^2 + \cdots + (N - 1)^2 + N^2] \tag{17}$$

Problem. Write a FORTRAN program for finding the upper bound for A corresponding to a division of the area into N strips. Using this program, find the upper bounds corresponding to $N = 10$, 50, and 100.

A formula can be written for the sum of the squares of the first K integers (where K stands for any one of the numbers 1, 2, 3, . . .). This formula is derived in Appendix C. It states that

$$1^2 + 2^2 + 3^2 + \cdots + K^2 = \frac{K(K + 1)(2K + 1)}{6} \tag{18}$$

Question. What is the sum of the squares of the first 10 integers? Of the first twenty integers? Check the result obtained from equation (18).

Applying equation (18) with $K = N - 1$, we are able to rewrite the lower bound for A in (17) as

$$\left(\frac{3}{N}\right)^3 \frac{(N-1)(N)(2N-1)}{6}$$

This simplifies to give

$$\frac{3^3}{6}\left(1 - \frac{1}{N}\right)\left(2 - \frac{1}{N}\right) < A \tag{19}$$

Similarly, applying (18) with $K = N$ and simplifying, we have the upper bound for A given by

$$A < \frac{3^3}{6}\left(1 + \frac{1}{N}\right)\left(2 + \frac{1}{N}\right) \tag{20}$$

The use of formula (18) not only allows us to calculate bounds more easily for A for different values of N, but, more important, it enables us to see what happens as the number of approximating strips, N, approaches infinity. Indeed, we can exactly find the area A, the limit both of the sequence of upper bounds and of the sequence of lower bounds. As N approaches infinity, $1/N$ approaches 0. Therefore,

$$\left(1 - \frac{1}{N}\right) \text{ approaches 1}, \qquad \left(2 - \frac{1}{N}\right) \text{ approaches 2}$$

$$\left(1 + \frac{1}{N}\right) \text{ approaches 1}, \qquad \left(2 + \frac{1}{N}\right) \text{ approaches 2}$$

Both the lower bounds and the upper bounds therefore approach

$$\frac{3^3}{6} \cdot 2 = \frac{3^3}{3} = 9$$

and we conclude that $A = 9$ exactly.

Once again we caution the reader that, although the argument just completed is convincing intuitively and makes clear what happens, it does *not* constitute a complete mathematical proof. This would require precise definitions of the descriptive terms we have used in our discussion such as limit, approach infinity, approach zero, etc., and precise estimates for N, $1/N$, and the other quantities. This kind of proof is presented in courses in calculus.

Replacing $t = 3$ in the preceding paragraphs by $t = b$, we would be led to the area under the parabola from $t = 0$ to $t = b$, or

$$\int_0^b t^2 \, dt$$

The only change that occurs is caused by replacing $\Delta t = 3/N$ by $\Delta t = b/N$ for the width of the strip. Now (17) becomes

$$\left(\frac{b}{N}\right)^3 [1^2 + 2^2 + \cdots + (N-1)^2] < \int_0^b t^2 \, dt$$
$$< \left(\frac{b}{N}\right)^3 [1^2 + 2^2 + \cdots + N^2]$$

Using the formula (18) again this becomes

$$\frac{b^3}{6}\left(1 - \frac{1}{N}\right)\left(2 - \frac{1}{N}\right) < \int_0^b t^2 \, dt < \frac{b^3}{6}\left(1 + \frac{1}{N}\right)\left(2 + \frac{1}{N}\right)$$

Taking the limit as N approaches infinity, we find that both the left- and the right-hand sides approach $b^3/3$, so that

$$\int_0^b t^2 \, dt = \frac{b^3}{3} \tag{21}$$

This derivation of the area under a parabola, based on approximation of the area by increasing numbers of narrower and narrower rectangular strips, and the use of the formula for the sum of the squares of the first K integers, is essentially the same as that given by Archimedes.[4]

In Chapter 4 we found that the derivative of the function t^3 is the function $3t^2$. Multiplying by $\frac{1}{3}$, we see that the derivative of the function $t^3/3$ is just t^2 (see Theorem I, Exercise 24, Chapter 4). Now we have found that the integral of the function t^2 from $t = 0$ to t is $t^3/3$, bringing us back to the original function. This demonstrates once again that differentiation and integration are inverse processes. This knowledge, which came with the discovery of the calculus by Newton and Leibnitz, made the finding of the integral of functions, that is, the area under curves, easy for simple functions like t^2, t^3, ..., t^m, ..., and the combination of

---

[4] See footnote 5, Chapter 6 (page 339)

such functions as in polynomials. Until that time, however, integrals were evaluated exactly only with great difficulty and depended upon the discovery of formulas such as the one in equation (18) for the sum of the squares of integers. Indeed, after Archimedes' discovery of the formula for the area under the parabola as shown above, it was not until the time of Cavalieri[5] that the exact area under the cubic $y = t^3$ was found.

We return now to the question of the distance traveled by the rocket, given $v = t^2$ as the record of its velocity. We found that $\int_0^3 v \, dt = 9$. The number 9 signifies 9 units of area under the curve. Since each unit of area represented 1 foot, the integral represents 9 feet. We must now decide whether we can accept this as the distance traversed by the rocket. Let $s(t)$ be the distance traversed in t seconds, so that $s(3)$ is the distance traveled in 3 seconds. We can estimate $s(3)$ in the same way we estimated the area under the curve from $t = 0$ to $t = 3$. Referring to Figure 12c, the speed of the rocket in the first second is less than the speed at $t = 1$; therefore, the distance traveled in the first second is less than $1^2 \cdot 1$. In the interval between $t = 1$ and $t = 2$ the speed is less than the speed at $t = 2$; hence, the distance traveled is less than $2^2 \cdot 1$. In the third second the speed is less than the speed at $t = 3$, and the distance traveled is less than $3^2 \cdot 1$. Adding, we have as an upper bound

$$s(3) < 1^2 \cdot 1 + 2^2 \cdot 1 + 3^2 \cdot 1$$

which is the same as we found for A in equation (11).

Similarly, from Figure 12b we find that the speed in the time from $t = 1$ to $t = 2$ is greater than the speed 1^2 at $t = 1$. Therefore, the distance traveled in that time is greater than $1^2 \cdot 1$. In the interval from $t = 2$ to $t = 3$ the speed is greater than the speed at $t = 2$; thus, the distance traveled is greater than $2^2 \cdot 1$. Moreover, $s(3)$ also contains the distance traveled in the first second, which we know must be greater than 0. Therefore, as a lower bound for $s(3)$ we have

$$1^2 \cdot 1 + 2^2 \cdot 1 < s(3)$$

This is the same lower bound that we found for A in equation (10).

[5] **Bonaventura Cavalieri** (pronounced "ca-val-yer'-ee"), 1598–1647, studied under Galileo and was a professor of mathematics at the University of Bologna. He was an influential mathematician of his day and wrote on optics and astronomy as well as mathematics. His most famous contribution to mathematics was a treatise published in 1635 on the *method of indivisibles,* a method which enabled him to calculate certain volumes and areas before the development of the integral calculus.

Dividing up the interval from $t = 0$ to $t = 3$ into N strips of width $\Delta t = 3/N$, we can in each time interval Δt overestimate the distance traveled by using the value of v at the end of the time interval (getting a rectangle corresponding to too large a constant speed and so containing the curve). Similarly, we can underestimate the distance traveled in the time interval Δt by using the value of v at the beginning of the time interval (getting a rectangle too small). Adding these estimates, we get the same estimates for $s(3)$ as given by (17) for A. Since both the upper and lower estimates converge to the same number, this number is precisely $s(3)$, and we conclude that $s(3)$ and A are the same.

The same argument shows us that $s(t)$, the distance traveled in t seconds, and $\int_0^t t^2 \, dt$ are the same. We, therefore, have found the formula for the distance traveled by the rocket given that its speed was $v = t^2$. Since $\int_0^t t^2 \, dt = t^3/3$, we have that

$$s = \frac{t^3}{3} \tag{22}$$

Question. How far does the rocket go in 60 secs?

7.3 Approximate Integration

The process which we followed in estimating the area under the curve $v = t^2$ through the use of approximating rectangles may be followed with any other curve as well. For any number N of approximating strips we can get an estimate of the area. Generally, we do not get both upper and lower estimates. Since both will come as close as we please to the actual area, we may use either in estimating the area. By taking larger and larger values of N we can obtain the area to any desired degree of accuracy.

As we remarked earlier, we assume in our discussion that we are dealing with ordinary curves. Functions for which this limiting process does not converge can be found; of such functions it is said that the integral of the function does not exist. The existence of the integral and the determination of conditions on functions such that the integral exists are matters which are studied in advanced mathematics courses on the theory of functions of a real variable.

Let $y = f(x)$ be the function we wish to integrate. The graph of $y = f(x)$ depends on the actual function $f(x)$ you select. In general, it will be some

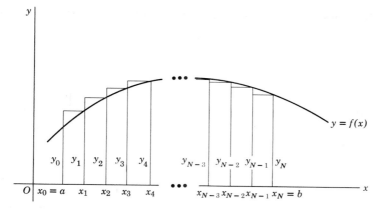

Figure 15

Approximation to $\displaystyle\int_a^b f(x)\,dx$

curve such as that shown in Figure 15. Suppose we want the area under the curve from $x = a$ to $x = b$, or symbolically,

$$\int_a^b f(x)\,dx \tag{23}$$

To estimate this integral we divide up the interval from $x = a$ to $x = b$ into N strips of width $\Delta x = (b - a)/N$. The points $x_1, x_2, x_3, \ldots, x_{N-1}$ shown along the x-axis in Figure 15 locate the x-coordinates of the sides of the dividing strips. The actual distances of these points from the origin are given by

$$
\begin{aligned}
x_1 &= a + \Delta x \\
x_2 &= a + 2 \cdot \Delta x \\
& \quad \cdot \quad \cdot \quad \cdot \quad \cdot \\
x_{N-1} &= a + (N - 1) \cdot \Delta x
\end{aligned}
\tag{24}
$$

For consistency of notation we may also denote the abscissa $x = a$ by x_0 and the abscissa $x = b$ by $x_N = a + N \cdot \Delta x$. The heights of the curve at these points will be denoted by $y_0, y_1, \ldots, y_N$, so that

$$
\begin{aligned}
y_0 &= f(a) = f(x_0) \\
y_1 &= f(x_1) \\
& \quad \cdot \quad \cdot \quad \cdot \quad \cdot \\
y_{N-1} &= f(x_{N-1}) \\
y_N &= f(b) = f(x_N)
\end{aligned}
\tag{25}
$$

For the sum of the areas of the approximating rectangles we may take

$$y_1 \cdot \Delta x + y_2 \cdot \Delta x + \cdots + y_N \cdot \Delta x$$

or

$$\Delta x(y_1 + y_2 + \cdots + y_N) \qquad (26)$$

This corresponds to using the height of the curve on the right side of each strip as the height of the corresponding rectangle as shown in Figure 15. If the height of the curve on the left side of each strip is used as the height of the corresponding rectangle, then the estimate of the area under the curve is given by

$$\Delta x(y_0 + y_1 + \cdots + y_{N-1}) \qquad (27)$$

If the curve is rising throughout a strip, the use of the right side as height gives an overestimate, and the use of the left side as height gives an underestimate. If the curve is rising throughout the interval from a to b, then (26) gives an upper bound and (27) gives a lower bound. This was the case for the function $v = t^2$.

Both (26) and (27) are estimates of (23). As N approaches infinity (making Δx approach 0), these estimates converge to give the value of (23). For any finite value of N, we may use the value furnished by either (26) or (27) as an approximation to (23).

As a further example, let us take $f(x)$ to be the function $1/x$ and integrate from $x = 1$ to $x = 10$. In symbols we seek to evaluate

$$\int_1^{10} \frac{1}{x}\,dx \qquad (28)$$

The ends of the interval being 1 and 10, we have $x_0 = a = 1$ and $x_N = b = 10$ in our previous notation. Dividing this interval into N subintervals, each has length $\Delta x = (10 - 1)/N = 9/N$. The edges of the rectangles are at

$$
\begin{aligned}
x_0 \quad &= 1 \\[4pt]
x_1 \quad &= 1 + \frac{9}{N} \\[4pt]
x_2 \quad &= 1 + 2 \cdot \frac{9}{N} \\[4pt]
&\cdot \quad \cdot \quad \cdot \\[4pt]
x_{N-1} &= 1 + (N - 1) \cdot \frac{9}{N} \\[4pt]
x_N \quad &= 1 + N \cdot \frac{9}{N} = 10
\end{aligned}
\qquad (29)
$$

The heights of the rectangles are

$$y_0 \quad = \frac{1}{x_0} = \frac{1}{1}$$

$$y_1 \quad = \frac{1}{x_1}$$

$$\cdot \quad \cdot \quad \cdot \tag{30}$$

$$y_{N-1} = \frac{1}{x_{N-1}}$$

$$y_N \quad = \frac{1}{x_N} = \frac{1}{10}$$

Using (26), we get the estimate

$$\frac{9}{N}\left(\frac{1}{x_1} + \cdots + \frac{1}{x_N}\right) \tag{31}$$

for (28).

Question.   Is the value furnished by (31) an upper bound or a lower bound for the integral? What do you estimate the error in this value to be when $N = 1000$?

The following FORTRAN program evaluates (28) using the formula given in (31).

```
       READ   100, N
 100   FORMAT  (I4)
       XN = N
       DELX = 9.0/XN
       X = 1.0
       SUM = 0.0
       DO 1  I = 1, N
       X = X + DELX
   1   SUM = SUM + 1.0/X
       SUM = DELX * SUM
       PRINT 200, SUM
```

200 FORMAT (12H①INTEGRAL① = ①, F12.8)

STOP

END

We first read in an integer which tells us how many intervals we will use between $x = 1$ and $x = 10$. The variable XN is the floating-point representation of N. The variable DELX is Δx. We set $x = 1$ and SUM, which will eventually be the result, equal to zero. The DO loop adds Δx to x to get x_1, then divides 1 by x_1 to get y_1 and adds it to SUM. It then adds Δx to x_1 to get x_2. Then y_2 is $1/x_2$, and this is added to SUM, and so on. Finally, after $1/x_N$ is added, the SUM is multiplied by Δx and the result is printed.

The program was run on an IBM 7094 with various values of N with the following results:

N	Integral
5	1.71492368
10	1.96021436
20	2.11647716
50	2.22424927
100	2.26275215
200	2.28250101

The correct value of this integral is the natural logarithm of 10, which is 2.30258509. As we expected, as N increases the value computed comes closer and closer to the correct result. However, even with 200 intervals we have only two accurate digits, because our method is not very suitable for use on a computer. We now develop a more accurate method that will yield substantially better results.

Problem. The integral

$$\int_1^2 \frac{1}{x}\,dx$$

is the natural logarithm of 2 which we calculated in Chapter 6 using an infinite series. Change the preceding FORTRAN program to evaluate this integral and test it for 5, 10, 20, 50, and 100 intervals. This can be done by changing one statement. How many digits of accuracy does each case produce?

Using the same points of subdivision $x_0, x_1, \ldots, x_{N-1}, x_N$ of the interval from $x = a$ to $x = b$ and the same function values $y_0 = f(x_0)$,

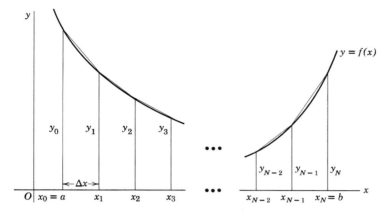

Figure 16

Approximation to $\displaystyle\int_a^b f(x)\, dx$ using N trapezoids of width Δx

$y_1 = f(x_1), \ldots, y_{N-1} = f(x_{N-1})$, $y_N = f(x_N)$ as in the rectangular approximations just given for $\displaystyle\int_a^b f(x)\, dx$, it is possible to get substantially better approximations. One such improved method of approximate integration is called the *trapezoidal rule*.

The trapezoidal rule is based on the simple idea of capping each strip with a line segment joining the points on the curve corresponding to the end points of the strip. This segment replaces the horizontal segment previously used to form a rectangle. In Figure 16 we see the area under $y = f(x)$ divided into strips of equal width Δx. The first strip is capped by the line segment joining the point (x_0, y_0) on the curve to the point (x_1, y_1) on the curve. The second strip is capped by the line segment joining the points (x_1, y_1) and (x_2, y_2) on the curve. Finally, the Nth strip is capped by the line segment joining the points (x_{N-1}, y_{N-1}) and (x_N, y_N) on the curve. The approximation consists in replacing the area under the curve by the area under the line segments. The area under the jth line segment ($j = 1, \ldots, N$) is equal to the area of a trapezoid with base Δx and sides y_{j-1} and y_j. The area of this trapezoid is equal to

$$\frac{\Delta x}{2}(y_{j-1} + y_j) \tag{32}$$

From the geometric picture we would expect the trapezoids to give a better approximation to the area under the curve than do the simple rectangles. Indeed, this can be proved as well as tested by examples, such as the one below.

A simple formula results if we add the areas of the individual trapezoids. From the first to the Nth, the areas are successively given by

$$\frac{\Delta x}{2}(y_0 + y_1)$$

$$\frac{\Delta x}{2}(y_1 + y_2)$$

.
.
.

$$\frac{\Delta x}{2}(y_{N-2} + y_{N-1})$$

$$\frac{\Delta x}{2}(y_{N-1} + y_N)$$

Adding, we find the formula, known as the **trapezoidal rule,** for estimating area:

$$\int_a^b f(x)\, dx = \frac{\Delta x}{2}(y_0 + 2y_1 + 2y_2 + \cdots + 2y_{N-1} + y_N) \qquad (33)$$

Problem.   Write a FORTRAN program for evaluating $\int_1^{10} \frac{1}{x}\, dx$ using the trapezoidal rule. Find the approximate values given by the rule for $N = 5, 10, 20,$ and 50. Compare these results with those given in the text where (31) was used.

Exercises

Answers to exercises marked * are given in Appendix A.

*1. An irregularly shaped region is drawn to scale on square ruled graph paper. The boundary of the region intersects exactly 75 of the squares. Each square represents 1 square foot. Inside of the boundary there are 119 squares.

(a) Give a lower bound for the area A of the region.

(b) Give an upper bound for the area of the region.

Upon subdividing each boundary square into four equal squares, it is found that the boundary intersects 160 of the smaller squares and 60 of the smaller squares lie wholly outside the region.

(c) Give an improved lower bound for A.

(d) Give an improved upper bound for A.

Suppose that each of the small squares is again subdivided into four equal squares.

(e) What is the maximum possible accuracy with which A is now determined (i.e., what is the smallest possible gap between the new upper and lower bounds)?

(f) What do you expect the accuracy to be?

2. By counting squares on a graph (1 square = 10 square feet) it is found that the area A of a region is given by

$$9600 \text{ ft}^2 < A < 11{,}400 \text{ ft}^2$$

(a) Taking A to be 10,500 ft², the average of these bounds, what is the maximum percent error in this value?

Suppose the boundary squares are each subdivided into four equal squares.

(b) What is the least amount by which the new upper and lower bounds can differ?

(c) What percent accuracy in the determination of A would this correspond to?

3. Using the *integral notation*, give the *symbol* for each of the following areas (do *not* evaluate these areas):

*(a) The area of the region under the line $y = x$ lying above the x-axis and between $x = 0$ and $x = 4$.

(b) The area of the region under the line $y = 6x$ lying above the x-axis and between $x = 0$ and $x = 10$.

(c) The area of the region under the line $y = 2x + 1$ lying above the x-axis and between $x = 0$ and $x = 3$.

(d) The area of the region under the line $y = 10 - x$ lying above the x-axis and between $x = 5$ and $x = 10$.

4. What is the numerical value of the area of each of the regions in Exercise 3?

5. What is the region of integration corresponding to each of the following integrals:

*(a) $\displaystyle\int_{1}^{3} (3x + 1) \, dx$?

(b) $\displaystyle\int_{-1}^{1} x^2\, dx$?

(c) $\displaystyle\int_{0}^{10} 2\, dx$?

(d) $\displaystyle\int_{2}^{4} (5 - x)\, dx$?

6. An instrument recording the speed v, in feet per second, of a moving object shows that between $t = 0$ sec and $t = 5$ sec the graph is the straight line $v = t + 100$. Express the distance traveled in these 5 sec by an integral. How far did the object travel?

7. The speed v of a freely falling object which starts at rest at $t = 0$ is given approximately by $v = 32t$ after t seconds. Express the distance fallen after 6 sec as an integral. What is this distance? Check your answer, using the known relation between distance and time for a freely falling object.

*8. In physics we learn that, if a constant force F acts on an object, and if, because of this force, the object moves a distance x in the direction of application of the force, then the *work* W done by the force F is given by the product of F and x or

$$W = Fx$$

If x is measured in feet and F in pounds, then the work W is measured in foot-pounds (the product of the units), abbreviated ft-lb.

(a) A force of 60 lb applied to a sled moves it a distance of 7 ft in the direction of the applied force. How much work is done?

(b) Express the work done as an integral.

(c) An object weighing 150 lb falls 12 ft. What is the work done? Express this work as an integral. What is the force acting?

9. Consider a steel spring with one end fastened to a rigid wall and having its length perpendicular to the wall. We push the other end of the spring along the line toward the wall so that the spring is compressed. A certain force is required to compress the spring 1 in. If we wish to compress the spring another inch, a greater force is required. In fact, the force F required to compress the spring x inches will be approximately proportional to x if x is not too large. This is called Hooke's law, and it gives us the formula

$$F = cx$$

In this formula c is a constant (called the "spring constant") and equals the force required to compress the spring by 1 in.

(a) Let $c = 50$ lb/in., and suppose that a spring having this spring constant is compressed 3 in. Graph the force F required against the compression x as x varies from 0 to 3. Express the area of the region under the graph from $x = 0$ to $x = 3$ as an integral. What is the value of the area (in pound-inches)?

(b) Justify the assertion that this area is actually equal to the work done in compressing the spring 3 in.

10. How much work is required to compress a spring by 3 in. if the spring constant is 4 lb/in.? (Refer to Exercise 9.)

11. A spring obeying Hooke's law is compressed 2 in. by a force of 15 lb. How much force is required to compress it 4 in.? Graph force F versus compression x for this spring from $x = 0$ to $x = 4$. How much work must be done to compress the spring 4 in.? (Refer to Exercise 9.)

12. Estimate the value of the integral

$$\int_0^3 t^3 \, dt$$

by dividing the region under the curve $y = t^3$ into three equal vertical strips and finding upper and lower bounds to the area.

13. If the interval $0 \le t \le b$ is divided into N equal vertical strips of width $\Delta t = b/N$, what upper and lower bounds do you get for the value of

$$A = \int_0^b t^3 \, dt$$

using rectangles for approximation?

14. Write a FORTRAN program for finding the value of the upper bound in the previous problem. Apply this program to find the numerical value of the bound for $b = 3$ when $N = 10, 50, 100$.

15. Following an argument similar to that used in Appendix C, prove that the sum of the cubes of the first K integers is given by

$$1^3 + 2^3 + \cdots + (K - 1)^3 + K^3 = \frac{K^2(K + 1)^2}{4}$$

16. Use the formula in the preceding exercise and the bounds found in Exercise 13 to show that

$$\frac{b^4}{4}\left(1 - \frac{1}{N}\right)^2 \le \int_0^b t^3 \, dt \le \frac{b^4}{4}\left(1 + \frac{1}{N}\right)^2$$

17. Letting N approach infinity in the preceding exercise, what number does the upper bound approach? The lower bound? What is the exact value of

$$\int_0^b t^3 \, dt?$$

*18. In this chapter it has been found that

$$\int_0^t t \, dt = \frac{t^2}{2}$$

$$\int_0^t t^2 \, dt = \frac{t^3}{3}$$

$$\int_0^t t^3 \, dt = \frac{t^4}{4}$$

Can you see in this a pattern which predicts the value of

$$\int_0^t t^4 \, dt?$$

What do you believe to be the value of this integral? What will be the value of

$$\int_0^t t^{n-1} \, dt$$

where n is any integer?

19. Compare the results of the preceding exercise with Exercise 19 in Chapter 4. What is the relation between the slope of the curve $y = t^4/4$ and the integral of the function $3t^2$? Between the slope of the curve $y = t^n/n$ and the integral of the function $(n-1)t^{n-1}$?

20. The following two theorems aid us in the calculation of the integral of more complicated functions. They are analogous to the theorems of Exercise 24, Chapter 4, for derivatives.

   I. The integral of $c \cdot f(x)$, where c is a constant and $f(x)$ a given function is equal to c times the integral of $f(x)$; that is,

$$\int_a^b cf(x) \, dx = c \int_a^b f(x) \, dx$$

   II. The integral of the sum of two functions, $f(x) + g(x)$, is equal to the sum of the integrals of the functions; that is,

$$\int_a^b (f(x) + g(x)) \, dx = \int_a^b f(x) \, dx + \int_a^b g(x) \, dx$$

Make use of I and II and the fact that $\int_0^x x^m \, dx = x^{m+1}/(m+1)$ for $m = 0, 1, 2, \ldots$ to calculate the following integrals:

*(a) $\displaystyle\int_0^x (x^2 + x^3) \, dx$

(b) $\displaystyle\int_0^2 (x^2 + x^3) \, dx$

(c) $\displaystyle\int_0^x dx$

(d) $\displaystyle\int_0^5 1 \, dx$

*(e) $\displaystyle\int_0^x (4x^2 - 3x + 7) \, dx$

(f) $\displaystyle\int_0^1 (4x^2 - 3x + 7) \, dx$

(g) $\displaystyle\int_0^x x^{100} \, dx$

(h) $\displaystyle\int_0^1 101 x^{100} \, dx$

21. Check the validity of theorem II (Exercise 20) for the integral

$$\int_0^b (x^2 + x^3) \, dx$$

(*Hint:* Divide the interval $0 \leq x \leq b$ into N vertical strips of width $\Delta x = b/N$. Obtain upper and lower bounds for this integral using the formula in Exercise 15 and formula (18). Let N go to infinity to find the value of the integral. Compare with $\displaystyle\int_0^b x^2 \, dx$ and $\displaystyle\int_0^b x^3 \, dx$.)

22. Dividing the region under the curve

$$y = \frac{1}{1 + x^2}$$

between $x = 0$ and $x = 1$ into N strips of width $1/N$, we may use rectangles to approximate the area of this region. Show that

$$\int_0^1 \frac{1}{1 + x^2} \, dx$$

is approximately given by

$$\frac{1}{N}\left[\frac{1}{1^2} + \frac{1}{1 + (1/N)^2} + \cdots + \frac{1}{1 + ((N-1)/N)^2}\right]$$

Write a FORTRAN program to compute this expression and evaluate it, using $N = 10, 50, 100$.

23. Compare the rectangles used in Exercise 22 with the actual region under the curve $y = 1/(1 + x^2)$. Are the estimates found too small or too large? Give an upper bound for the error in each of the estimates using $N = 10, 50, 100$. (*Hint:* Refer to Figure 13 and the accompanying text.)

24. The exact value of

$$\int_0^1 \frac{dx}{1 + x^2}$$

is known to be $\pi/4$. Compare the actual error in the estimates of Exercise 22 to your error bounds given in the previous exercise.

25. Write a FORTRAN program for evaluating

$$\int_0^1 \frac{dx}{1 + x^2}$$

using the trapezoidal rule of equation (33). Find the approximate value of this integral to four decimals given by this rule for $N = 10$, 100, 1000. What do you find for the value of π using this method of computation and $N = 1000$? To how many places is π found correctly by this method with $N = 1000$?

26. In Chapter 6, Exercise 18, you found by numerical calculation that the derivative of the function sin x is cos x. That is, the slope of the graph of $y = \sin x$ at any x is just equal to the value of cos x. Having been told that integration is the inverse process to differentiation, you would expect that integrating the function cos x will once again give back sin x. Indeed it does, and for any positive number t.

$$\int_0^t \cos x \, dx = \sin t$$

In particular, then, the integral of cos x from $x = 0$ to $x = \pi/2$ (or 90°) must equal sin $(\pi/2)$ or 1. That is, the area of the region lying under the curve $y = \cos x$ and above the x-axis, between $x = 0$ and $x = \pi/2$ is exactly 1.

(a) Divide this region $x = 0$ to $x = \pi/2$ into six strips of width $\Delta x = (\pi/2)/6$ and use the values of cos x found in Exercise 17b of Chapter 6 to estimate

$$\int_0^{\pi/2} \cos x \, dx$$

using rectangles first and then trapezoids. Compare your approximate answers with the exact answer, 1.

(b) Prepare a flow chart for the calculation of

$$\int_0^{\pi/2} \cos x \, dx$$

using the trapezoidal rule, where the interval is divided into N strips of width $\pi/2N$, and the function $\cos x$ is to be computed at the points of division from the infinite series of equation (20) of Exercise 17, Chapter 6.

(c) Prepare a FORTRAN program to carry out this calculation and find the estimated value of

$$\int_0^{\pi/2} \cos x \, dx$$

using $N = 50$ and $N = 100$.

27. Since, for curves which rise, (26) gives an upper bound to the integral and (27) gives a lower bound, we might expect that the *average* of (26) and (27) gives a better approximation. Show that the average of (26) and (27) is the trapezoidal rule given in (33).

*28. Use the trapezoidal rule, equation (33), to estimate the natural logarithm of 2 by evaluating

$$\int_1^2 \frac{1}{x} \, dx$$

Use 5, 25, 50, 100, and 500 intervals.

CHAPTER EIGHT

Mathematical Logic —
Switching Circuits

8.1 The Light Switch Problem

In homes or schools there often is a stairway light which is controlled by two switches, one at the bottom of the stairs and one at the top of the stairs. If the light is off, it can be turned on by flipping the switch at either place. Similarly, when the light is on, it can be turned off by throwing either switch.

Switches used in such a way do not have an "on" or an "off" position. They are "up" or "down." When the downstairs switch is "up," the light may be either on or off depending on the position of the upstairs switch.

Before discussing these switches we examine a more elementary type of switch. We can represent a simple switch by the diagram in Figure 1. The line *BC* is either in the position shown or is horizontal so that *C* touches *D*. As shown, no current can flow from *A* to *E*. The switch is said to be "open" or "off." In the other position where *C* and *D* coincide, it is said to be "closed" or "on" and current can flow from *A* to *E*. Switches normally are assumed to be set to be open.

A more complex kind of switch is shown in Figure 2. This switch normally is set as shown so that current can flow from *A* to *D*. If the switch is flipped down to *C*, then current can flow from *A* to *E*, but *not*

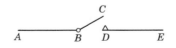

Figure 1

A simple switch

388

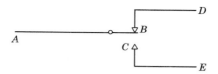

Figure 2

A double-throw switch

from A to D. This is sometimes called a *single-pole, double-throw switch.*[1]

We can use two of these single-pole, double-throw switches to turn on a stairway light from two different places.

Let us look at the circuit shown in Figure 3. We assume that there is a source of electrical power in the line where the light is shown. As it stands, the light will be off because there is no closed circuit which includes the light. However, if we flip the switch at A so that it connects A to C, then current can flow from L to A to C to E to F and back to L. In this case the light will be on. If we next flip the switch at F we get the arrangement shown in Figure 4. Again there are no closed circuits so the light is off. The reader should assure himself that if, starting from the arrangement in Figure 4, we again flip the switch at A to return that switch to its original position the light will be on.

The circuit in Figure 3 behaves just as we want it to behave in order to operate the stairway light. If we flip either switch, the condition of the light changes. That is, if the light is on, flipping either switch turns it off; if the light is off, flipping either switch turns it on.

[1] There is only one movable part (a single pole) which can be flipped or thrown either of two ways (double throw) so as to close either one or the other of two contacts.

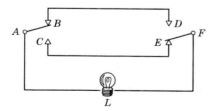

Figure 3

A circuit for the two-switch problem

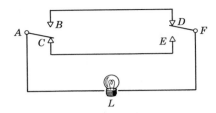

Figure 4

Two-switch circuit with both switches flipped

This is a reasonably easy circuit to design, and we might expect to arrive at it by scratching our heads and experimenting a little. Suppose, however, we have a light at the top of a stairwell which goes between *three* floors. And suppose we want to put a switch on each floor so that by flipping any one of the three switches we can turn the light on or off.

This is a much more difficult problem, and it is less likely that we could find a solution to it by trial and error. In this chapter we discuss some mathematics which will allow us to design a circuit which will solve this *three-switch problem*, as well as other switching problems.

8.2   A Boolean Algebra

In this section we construct a mathematical model of switching circuits. We use variables x, y, $\ldots$, to represent the variable positions of the switches. However, instead of the operations of "addition," "subtraction," "multiplication," and "division" (represented by $+$, $-$, $\times$, and $\div$), we define new operations of "and," "or," and "not" (represented by $\wedge$, $\vee$, and $\sim$).

Switching circuits are made up of switches with one or more contacts. The switch in Figure 1 has one contact at D, while the switch in Figure 2 has two contacts, one at B and one at C. The switches and their contacts are connected by wires. We assume that current can flow in either direction in a wire. Figure 3 is an illustration of a switching circuit.

We confine our mathematical discussion to the simple "on-off switch" in Figure 1. Of course, the physical circuits themselves may be constructed from more complex switches such as the one in Figure 2. Because we are concerned only with the mathematical aspects of circuits, we deal with the simplest switches since they are adequate for our purposes.

Such simple on-off switches must always be in either one or the other of two positions. They are, therefore, often referred to as *bi-stable* or *two-state* devices. We distinguish between the two states (or two positions) of such devices by means of the numerals "0" and "1." The actual state of any such switch is represented by means of variables $x, y, \ldots$, which may take on only the values 0 or 1. For example, if we assign the variable x to the switch in Figure 1, then we write: $x = 0$ whenever the switch is open, and $x = 1$ whenever the switch is closed. This choice is quite arbitrary, and we could just as well have chosen to let $x = 0$ when the switch is closed, and $x = 1$ when the switch is open. For on-off switches of the type in Figure 1, we use the first alternative. Such a switch is referred to as *normally open;* this means that it is open when $x = 0$.

Sometimes two switches are "coupled" so that the state of either of them depends on the state of the other. For example, in Figure 5a, the two switches are either both open or both closed. Thus, when $x = 0$, $y = 0$. Similarly, when $x = 1$, it must be that $y = 1$. In this case we quite naturally write

$$y = x$$

On the other hand, in Figure 5b, whenever switch x is open, it follows that switch y is closed and vice versa. Therefore, when $x = 0$, $y = 1$. Moreover, when $x = 1$ it follows that $y = 0$. In this case we write

$$y = \sim x \tag{1}$$

The expression $\sim x$ is called the "negation of x" or the "complementation of x." It is read "not x."

Notice that, if we think of x in Figure 5b as normally open, then y in Figure 5b is normally closed.

(a)　　　　　　　　(b)

Figure 5

Two examples of coupled simple switches (the heavy lines are nonconducting, rigid bars)

Figure 6

Two switches in series

Suppose we put two switches in series with each other as shown in Figure 6. Switches x and y are both normally open. We let $x = 0$ and $y = 0$ when both switches are open. No current can flow from A to B. If we close x ($x = 1$) and leave y open ($y = 0$), still no current can flow from A to B. Only when both x *and* y are closed can current flow from A to B.

We express such an arrangement of switches as

$$x \wedge y \tag{2}$$

which is read "x and y." If, in Figure 6, A and B are joined to form a circuit, it is called an **AND circuit.**

In other textbooks the expression $x \wedge y$ sometimes is referred to as the "intersection of x and y," or the "meet of x and y," or the "conjunction of x and y." The symbol $\wedge$ is sometimes called "cap." However, in this text we refer to the symbol $\wedge$ as "and," and to $x \wedge y$ as "x and y."

Just as we assign variables x and y to simple switches, we can assign variables to circuits consisting of combinations of switches. Suppose we let s represent the AND circuit in Figure 6. Then we write

$$s = x \wedge y$$

The variable s is assigned the value 0 if no current can flow in the circuit, and it is assigned the value 1 if current can flow. Thus we can think of s as a switch which is open if $s = 0$ and closed if $s = 1$.

However, while we can arbitrarily assign values to x and y simply by choosing the positions of the switches, we cannot arbitrarily assign a value to s. Once we choose values for x and y, the value of s is determined. Thus, when $x = 1$ and $y = 1$, it follows that $s = 1$.

Suppose now we put two normally open switches in parallel with each other as shown in Figure 7. No current can flow from A to B as long as both contacts remain open. However, if w is closed ($w = 1$), the current can flow along the upper branch from A to B regardless of the position of *z*. Similarly, if *z* is closed, then current can flow along the lower branch.

Question. Can current flow if both contacts are closed?

Thus, current can flow from *A* to *B* if either *w or z* is closed. We express this arrangement of switches as

$$w \lor z$$

and read it "*w* or *z*." If *A* and *B* are joined to form a circuit it is called an **OR circuit.**

The expression $w \lor z$ is also referred to as the "union of *w* and *z*," or the "join of *w* and *z*," or the "disjunction of *w* and *z*." The symbol $\lor$ is sometimes referred to as "cup." Here we refer to the symbol $\lor$ as "or," and we refer to $w \lor z$ as "*w* or *z*."

Again, if we let *p* represent the circuit in Figure 7, then

$$p = w \lor z$$

Once again *p* is 0 or 1 depending on whether no current flows or current flows in the circuit. We can choose values for *w* and *z* quite arbitrarily, for these values are determined by the position of the switches which we can set at will. Once we have chosen *w* and *z*, however, *p* is determined and cannot be chosen arbitrarily. Again by way of example, if $w = 1$ and $z = 0$, then it must be that $p = 1$.

The arrangements in Figures 6 and 7 are examples of rather simple switching circuits. It may seem strange to refer to such an arrangement as a *circuit* since the paths (or wires) at *A* and *B* are not connected to anything. However, we always assume that *the two loose ends are joined to complete the circuit.* In order to avoid unnecessary complication of the diagrams, the lines to accomplish this are not drawn.

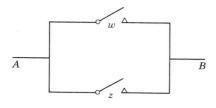

Figure 7

Two switches in parallel

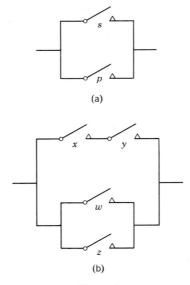

(a)

(b)

Figure 8

Two representations of a switching circuit

We have placed switches in series and parallel with each other. We can also place circuits in series and parallel with each other. We can, in fact, think of circuits as switches except for the fact that their positions cannot be arbitrarily chosen but depend on the settings of other switches.

For example, suppose again we let p be the parallel circuit in Figure 7, and we let s be the series circuit in Figure 6. Now we connect the *mathematical* switches p and s in parallel as shown in Figure 8a. Replacing p and s by their detailed circuits, we arrive at the circuit in Figure 8b.

The switching circuits we shall discuss are made up of switches and other switching circuits connected in series and parallel. Each circuit can be represented by a *logical expression* made up of variables (representing the switches) and the symbols $\sim$ and $\wedge$ and $\vee$.

We say that two circuits are **equivalent** if the circuit variables always have the same value whenever each of the switches in common to the two circuits have given values. One or both of the two equivalent circuits may have switches not present in the other. In that case, the value of the first circuit variable must not depend on the values of those of its switches which are not present in the second circuit. Similarly, the positions of the switches in the second circuit which do not appear in the first circuit must have no effect on the value of the second circuit variable.

The logical expressions corresponding to equivalent circuits are said to be equivalent. We shall be able to make these statements of equivalence more precise in the next section after we have discussed truth tables.

We now discuss some fundamental properties of switching circuits. We find that our mathematical model of these circuits forms a Boolean[2] algebra. We can use this algebra to help us analyze and design circuits.

A switch is either open or it is closed. That is,

$$\text{Either} \quad x = 0 \quad \text{or} \quad x = 1 \tag{3}$$

Consider next two switches in series as shown in Figure 6. The logical expression for this circuit is $x \wedge y$.

Now, if y is open ($y = 0$), then the value of the circuit is 0 regardless of the value of x. That is, $s = 0$. From equation (2) then,

$$x \wedge 0 = 0 \tag{4}$$

On the other hand, if y is closed ($y = 1$), then the value of the circuit is 1 if $x = 1$ and is 0 if $x = 0$. The value of the circuit then is equal to the value of x.

$$x \wedge 1 = x \tag{5}$$

Consider now the circuit represented by $x \wedge x$. If $x = 0$ we get $0 \wedge 0$ which, from (4) is 0. If $x = 1$, we get $1 \wedge 1 = 1$ from (5). Thus

$$x \wedge x = x \tag{6}$$

This is called an **idempotent law.** Physically it can be realized by two single-contact switches in series and tied together by a nonconducting, rigid bar so that both contacts are either open or closed (see Figure 9). Clearly this could be replaced by a single switch.

We turn now to parallel circuits and follow a similar discussion. If a switch is placed in parallel with an open switch, then current can flow only when the first switch is closed. This can be expressed by

$$x \vee 0 = x \tag{7}$$

---

[2] **George Boole** (pronounced "bool"), 1815–1864, was born into a very poor English family. Although he received no formal education, at 16 he was teaching mathematics and at 24 he joined the faculty of Queen's College in Cork, Ireland, where he remained until his death. In 1847 he discovered that logic could be carried out using symbols and operations similar to those used in algebra. While his ideas were slow in gaining attention, they became the cornerstone for many of the subsequent developments in the philosophy of mathematics.

Figure 9

Switches representing $x \wedge x$ (the heavy line represents a nonconducting, rigid bar)

Similarly, if a switch is placed in parallel with a closed switch, then current can always flow; that is,

$$x \vee 1 = 1 \qquad (8)$$

Setting $x = 0$ in (7), we obtain

$$0 \vee 0 = 0$$

Setting $x = 1$ in (8), we have

$$1 \vee 1 = 1$$

Combining these results gives

$$x \vee x = x \qquad (9)$$

This also is called an **idempotent law.**

> **Problem.** Draw a circuit which represents the circuit on the left in equation (9).

We repeat that when we have a simple on-off switch which is normally open, we label it with a variable x. When $x = 0$ the switch is open, and this gives rise to the term "normally open" since 0 has been chosen to represent the normal state.

Because some switches are normally closed, we want $x = 0$ to correspond to a closed position of such a switch. To achieve this we label a normally closed switch $\sim x$. That is, if we take a switch x and change its normal state to the opposite of what it was, we place the symbol $\sim$ before the variable name.

Suppose, therefore, that we have a normally closed switch, $\sim x$, and we change its normal state. We place before it a $\sim$ sign to get $\sim(\sim x)$. But

Figure 10

Graphical description of a normally open switch

Figure 11

Simplified diagram of a normally open switch

Figure 12

Graphical description of a normally closed switch

——————— $\sim x$ ———————

Figure 13

Simplified diagram of a normally closed switch

——————— x ——————— y ———————

——————— y ——————— x ———————

Figure 14

Two equivalent series circuits illustrating one of the commutative laws

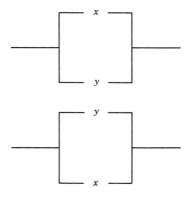

Figure 15

Two equivalent parallel circuits illustrating one of the commutative laws

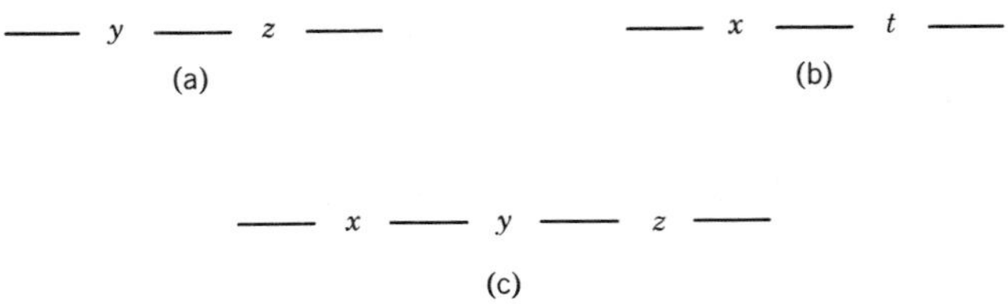

—— y —— z ——   —— x —— t ——

(a)   (b)

—— x —— y —— z ——

(c)

Figure 16

Three switches in series to display the associative law

the normal state of this switch is now open. In fact, the switch becomes just x again. Therefore

$$\sim(\sim x) = x \tag{10}$$

This is called the **involution law**.

Before going on we pause to discuss how we may simplify the diagrams we will draw. We do this because our diagrams will soon become more complicated and difficult to read or draw if some simplifications are not made. We assume that a switch is normally open unless it is preceded by a $\sim$, so we need not draw the details of the switch. That is, instead of drawing the switch shown in Figure 10, we can draw the one shown in Figure 11, and we will understand that it is a normally open switch. We can have current flowing in such a circuit if $x = 1$.

Similarly, instead of a normally closed switch (Figure 12), we can have the switch shown in Figure 13 with no confusion. If $x = 1$ no current flows in this circuit.

We have assumed that all switches are simple on-off switches. Of course, when we wish to construct one of our circuits we may not really use such simple switches, but, as we said before, we are interested only in the mathematics of switching circuits and not their construction.

We proceed to develop the laws of our Boolean algebra using our simplified diagrams of switches. If two switches are placed in series, it makes no difference in which order they appear. That is, the two circuits in Figure 14 are equivalent. This can be represented by

$$x \wedge y = y \wedge x \tag{11}$$

Similarly, if two switches are parallel with each other, it makes no difference which is in the top branch and which is in the bottom branch (see Figure 15). Therefore,

$$x \vee y = y \vee x \tag{12}$$

Equations (11) and (12) are the **commutative laws.**

Consider now two switches, y and z, in series as shown in Figure 16a. We label this circuit t and think of t as a switch. Of course, t is not independent of y and z. Its value is determined uniquely by the values of y and z. In fact,

$$t = y \wedge z$$

We place the switch t (which is really a circuit) in series with a new switch x as shown in Figure 16b. This circuit is represented by $x \wedge t$. From the expression for t, however,

$$x \wedge t = x \wedge (y \wedge z)$$

The circuit this represents can be obtained by replacing t in Figure 16b by the circuit in Figure 16a. The result is shown in Figure 16c.

Had we started with x and y in series and placed z in series with them on the right, the resulting logical expression would be

$$(x \wedge y) \wedge z$$

However, this circuit is equivalent[3] to the one shown in Figure 16c; hence

$$x \wedge (y \wedge z) = (x \wedge y) \wedge z$$

Therefore, *the parentheses are not needed* and we can write

$$x \wedge (y \wedge z) = (x \wedge y) \wedge z = x \wedge y \wedge z \qquad (13)$$

Similarly, we place two switches, y and z, in parallel (see Figure 17a). We define a switch p which is really the circuit $y \vee z$ and place p in parallel with a switch x as shown in Figure 17b. The logical expression representing this last circuit is

$$x \vee p = x \vee (y \vee z)$$

The circuit represented by the logical expression on the right is shown in Figure 17c. If, on the other hand, we place x and y in parallel and then z in parallel with the result, we arrive at the circuit shown in Figure 17d. The logical expression for this circuit is

$$(x \vee y) \vee z$$

---

[3] Equivalence of two circuits means that the variables for both circuits are the same for any given set of values for x, y, and z.

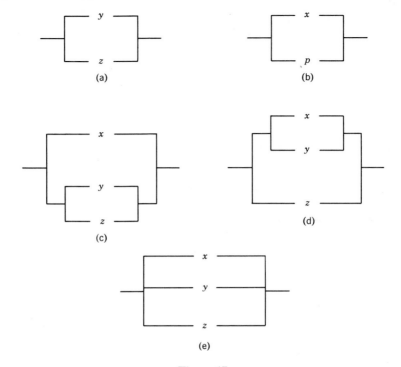

(a)

(b)

(c)

(d)

(e)

Figure 17

Three switches in parallel to display one of the associative laws

The circuits in Figures 17c and 17d are equivalent[3] to the one in Figure 17e. The circuit in Figure 17e is represented by

$$x \lor y \lor z$$

so

$$x \lor (y \lor z) = (x \lor y) \lor z = x \lor y \lor z \qquad (14)$$

Equations (13) and (14) represent the **associative laws.** They allow us to remove or ignore parentheses in logical expressions when only one of the symbols $\lor$ and $\land$ appears and where no $\sim$ symbols appear.

Next we turn to the distributive laws. Suppose we place y and z in parallel and x in series with the resulting circuits (see Figure 18a). The logical expression for this circuit is

$$x \land (y \lor z)$$

We can obtain an equivalent[3] circuit by placing x in each branch of the parallel circuits as shown in Figure 18b. The reader should assure himself that the circuits in Figures 18a and 18b are indeed equivalent.

The top branch of the circuit in Figure 18b is represented by $x \wedge y$. Similarly, the bottom branch is represented by $x \wedge z$. The entire circuit then is

$$(x \wedge y) \vee (x \wedge z)$$

Since the two circuits are equivalent,

$$x \wedge (y \vee z) = (x \wedge y) \vee (x \wedge z) \tag{15}$$

Problem.   Show that

$$x \vee (y \wedge z) = (x \vee y) \wedge (x \vee z) \tag{16}$$

Draw the circuits represented by both sides of this equation.

Equations (15) and (16) represent the **distributive laws.**

Notice that, while parentheses are not needed when all the symbols ($\wedge$ or $\vee$) in an expression are the same [see equations (13) and (14)], the parentheses in all other cases are important [see equations (15) and (16)].

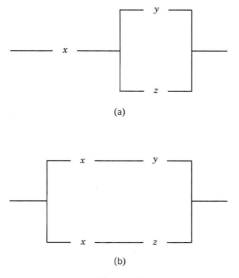

(a)

(b)

Figure 18

Circuits to illustrate one of the distributive laws

We turn next to the complementarity laws. Suppose we place a switch x in parallel with a related switch, $\sim x$. Physically this can be accomplished as shown in Figure 19a where the two switches are tied together so that one of them is closed when the other is open. Schematically it can be diagrammed as shown in Figure 19b. In such a diagram it is assumed that, when x is closed, $\sim x$ is open and vice versa.

In any case current can always flow in this circuit, so

$$x \vee \sim x = 1 \tag{17}$$

Problem.   Show that

$$x \wedge \sim x = 0 \tag{18}$$

Equations (17) and (18) are called the **complementarity laws.**

Finally, we turn to the dualization laws. Consider two normally closed switches, $\sim x$ and $\sim y$, in parallel as shown in Figure 20a. The logical expression for this circuit is

$$\sim x \vee \sim y$$

Current flows in all cases *except when $x = y = 1$.*

Now consider two switches, x and y, in series as shown in Figure 20b. The logical expression for this circuit is

$$x \wedge y$$

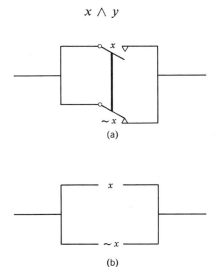

(a)

(b)

Figure 19

Circuit to show one of the complementarity laws (the solid line (a) is a nonconducting, rigid bar)

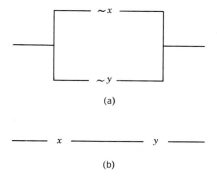

(a)

———— x ———————— y ————

(b)

Figure 20

Circuits to illustrate a dualization law

Current flows *only when* $x = y = 1$. Therefore, this circuit is the exact opposite of the one in Figure 20a in the following sense: If

$$p = \sim x \vee \sim y$$

and

$$s = x \wedge y$$

then, when $p = 0$, it follows that $s = 1$. Similarly, when $p = 1$, then $s = 0$. It follows that

$$p = \sim s$$

or

$$\sim x \vee \sim y = \sim(x \wedge y) \tag{19}$$

Problem.   Show that

$$\sim x \wedge \sim y = \sim(x \vee y)$$

Equations (19) and (20) are called the **dualization laws** or de Morgan's laws.

Variables $x, y, z, \ldots$, together with symbols $\sim, \vee, \wedge$ which satisfy equations (3) through (20) form a **Boolean algebra.** Such a mathematical model for switching circuits was first proposed by Claude Shannon[4] in

---

[4] **Claude E. Shannon,** 1916—, attended the University of Michigan and received his Ph.D. from M.I.T. in 1940. He joined the Bell Telephone Laboratories in 1941 and in 1956 returned to M.I.T. He is the founder of the field of information theory, i.e., the mathematical representation of the transmission of signals. These ideas have proved useful not only in circuit design and communications but also in such fields as biology, psychology, and semantics.

1938 while he was a graduate student at M.I.T. It marked the birth of a new branch of mathematics: information theory.

We might have started our discussion by defining a Boolean algebra as variables and symbols which satisfy these eighteen equations. We then could have shown that switching circuits obey these equations. Many developments of this subject do just that. Instead, we chose to obtain the equations as natural consequences of switching circuits. These equations, (3) through (20), often are referred to as the *basic postulates* of a Boolean algebra.

We summarize these basic postulates here in a slightly different order for ready reference. Any variable x satisfies

$$\text{Either} \quad x = 0 \quad \text{or} \quad x = 1 \tag{3}$$

There are two elements, 0 and 1, satisfying

$$x \wedge 0 = 0 \tag{4}$$

$$x \vee 1 = 1 \tag{8}$$

$$x \wedge 1 = x \tag{5}$$

$$x \vee 0 = x \tag{7}$$

There are two idempotent laws,

$$x \wedge x = x \tag{6}$$

$$x \vee x = x \tag{9}$$

There is an involution law,

$$\sim(\sim x) = x \tag{10}$$

There are two commutative laws,

$$x \wedge y = y \wedge x \tag{11}$$

$$x \vee y = y \vee x \tag{12}$$

There are two associative laws,

$$x \wedge (y \wedge z) = (x \wedge y) \wedge z \tag{13}$$

$$x \vee (y \vee z) = (x \vee y) \vee z \tag{14}$$

There are two distributive laws,

$$x \wedge (y \vee z) = (x \wedge y) \vee (x \wedge z) \tag{15}$$

$$x \vee (y \wedge z) = (x \vee y) \wedge (x \vee z) \tag{16}$$

There are two complementarity laws,

$$x \vee \sim x = 1 \tag{17}$$

$$x \wedge \sim x = 0 \tag{18}$$

There are two dualization laws,

$$\sim x \vee \sim y = \sim(x \wedge y) \tag{19}$$

$$\sim x \wedge \sim y = \sim(x \vee y) \tag{20}$$

Any variables x, y, z, . . . which satisfy these postulates are the elements of a Boolean algebra. Other Boolean algebras can be constructed, and many interesting and important theorems regarding such algebras can be proved. Some of these extensions are considered in Chapter 9 (Probability).

There also is much, much more to discuss about mathematical logic. However, it is beyond the scope of this book.

For our purposes we now have a mathematical model of switching circuits. We can write a logical expression which describes a circuit, or we can find a circuit which represents any such logical expression. We also have a set of rules, equations (3) to (20), which tell us how we can combine logical expressions.

Therefore, we shall study circuits by studying the Boolean algebra we have just defined. We shall learn how to carry out calculations using variables x, y, . . . and the symbols $\vee$, $\wedge$, $\sim$ just as we carry out calculations in our more familiar algebra using the same variables but different symbols, $+$, $-$, $\times$, $\div$. We shall also learn how to use a computer to help us with the Boolean algebra calculations. We proceed to these things now, keeping in mind that our objective is to analyze and design switching circuits.

8.3   Truth Tables

We have now constructed a mathematical model of switching circuits. We let each switch be a variable, say, x. If we want the switch to be normally closed, we represent the switch by $\sim x$. Two switches, x and y, in parallel are represented by $x \vee y$ and are called an OR circuit. Two switches, r and t, in series are represented by $r \wedge t$ and are called an AND circuit. We can represent any switching circuit by a logical expression made up of variables representing the switches and the symbols $\sim$, $\vee$, $\wedge$.

We now use our mathematical model of switching circuits to help us describe the behavior of circuits. In particular, we want to know whether or not current can flow in a circuit for any given settings of the switches. To do this we construct "truth tables."

Recall that a normally open switch x is open when $x = 0$ and is closed when $x = 1$. On the other hand, $\sim x$ is closed when $x = 0$ and open when $x = 1$.

Consider the two switches, x and y, in series as shown in Figure 6. Current cannot flow in this circuit except when both switches are closed. Thus the circuit has a value 0 except when $x = y = 1$, in which case the circuit has a value of 1. Representing the circuit by $x \wedge y$ as before, we summarize this information in Table 1. The first row of numbers tells

Table 1   Truth Table for an AND Circuit

x	y	$x \wedge y$
0	0	0
0	1	0
1	0	0
1	1	1

us that, when $x = 0$ and $y = 0$, then $x \wedge y = 0$ and current cannot flow. Similarly, the second line of numbers tells us that, when $x = 0$ and $y = 1$, then still $x \wedge y = 0$. The last two lines are read in a similar way.

Such a table is called a **truth table.** The name is derived from the fact that logic problems often concern themselves with true and false statements. Usually 0 represents a false statement and 1 represents a true statement. The statement "x and y" is true ($= 1$) when and only when both of the statements "x" and "y" are true. We are not concerned with these aspects of logic in this text, but we shall retain the name truth table.

There is one row in the truth table for each and every combination of settings of the switches. The AND circuit of Figure 6 has two switches each with two possible settings. There are, therefore, four combinations of switch settings: (1) both off, (2) the first off and the second on, (3) the first on and the second off, and (4) both on. The four rows of Table 1 correspond to these switch settings.

Question.   If there were *three* switches, x, y, and z, in a circuit, how many rows would there be in the truth table for that circuit?

We now construct the truth table for two switches in parallel (Table 2).

Table 2   Truth Table for OR Circuit

x	y	$x \lor y$
0	0	0
0	1	1
1	0	1
1	1	1

Consider now the truth table for the circuit $x \land \sim x$. This will have only two rows corresponding to the two possible values of x. In the second column we write the values of $\sim x$ corresponding to the two x values. In the third column, $x \land \sim x$, we place a 1 if both of the first two columns contain a 1 and 0 otherwise. The resulting table is shown in Table 3. We see that

$$x \land \sim x = 0$$

Table 3   Truth Table for $x \land \sim x$

x	$\sim x$	$x \land \sim x$
0	1	0
1	0	0

regardless of the value of x. This is precisely the complementarity law in equation (18).

Problem.   Construct the truth table for $x \lor \sim x$ and compare the results with equation (17).

We now consider a slightly more complicated circuit,

$$x \land (x \lor y)$$

The truth table is given in Table 4. The first two columns show the values which x and y can take. (The reader familiar with binary arithmetic will notice that the binary numbers represented by the entries in

Table 4   Truth Table for $x \land (x \lor y)$

x	y	$x \lor y$	$x \land (x \lor y)$
0	0	0	0
0	1	1	0
1	0	1	1
1	1	1	1

the first two columns are 00, 01, 10, and 11 which, in decimals, are 0, 1, 2, 3.) The third column represents the corresponding values of $x \vee y$. This third column has an entry 1 if either x or y or both are 1. It is 0 only when $x = y = 0$. The last column is the first column (x) combined with the third column $(x \vee y)$ by an "and" operation. Thus, the fourth column contains a 1 in the rows where *both* the first and third columns contain a 1. The fourth column has zeros elsewhere.

Problem.   Construct the truth table for $x \vee (x \wedge y)$ and compare it with Table 4.

We are now in a position to define equivalent circuits much more rigorously than we did in Section 8.1. We say that two circuits are **equivalent** if the last column of their truth tables are identical or can be made identical by renaming the switches.

Question.   Show that $x \vee (x \wedge y) = x \wedge (x \vee y)$.

Circuits with three variables are slightly more complex. Consider first $x \wedge y \wedge z$. (Why are no parentheses needed?) The truth table is shown in Table 5. It contains a 1 only when all three columns contain a 1.

Table 5   Truth Table for AND Circuit with Three Switches

x	y	z	$x \wedge y \wedge z$
0	0	0	0
0	0	1	0
0	1	0	0
0	1	1	0
1	0	0	0
1	0	1	0
1	1	0	0
1	1	1	1

(Notice that the digits in the eight rows of the first three columns contain the numbers 0, 1, ... , 7 in binary.)

Next we consider $x \vee (y \wedge z)$. The truth table is shown in Table 6. The fourth column $(y \wedge z)$ is 1 where both the second and third columns are 1. The fifth column is 1 where either or both the first and fourth columns are 1.

Let us now construct the truth table for $(x \vee y) \wedge (x \vee z)$. It is given in Table 7. Here the fourth column is 1 if either the first or second column

Table 6   Truth Table for x ∨ (y ∧ z)

x	y	z	$y \wedge z$	$x \vee (y \wedge z)$
0	0	0	0	0
0	0	1	0	0
0	1	0	0	0
0	1	1	1	1
1	0	0	0	1
1	0	1	0	1
1	1	0	0	1
1	1	1	1	1

is 1. The fifth column is 1 if either the first or third column is 1. Finally, the last column is 1 if both the fourth and fifth columns are 1.

Notice that the last columns of Tables 6 and 7 are identical. Thus, the two circuits they represent are equivalent, and we write

$$x \vee (y \wedge z) = (x \vee y) \wedge (x \vee z)$$

This is equation (16).

Problem.   Using truth tables, show that

$$(\sim x \vee y) \vee (y \vee z) = \sim x \vee y \vee z.$$

If the circuits get very complex, the computation of a truth table becomes very tedious and error prone. Consider, for example, the circuit represented by the logical expression

$$(x_1 \wedge \sim x_2) \vee (x_1 \wedge x_3 \wedge x_4) \vee (\sim x_1 \wedge x_2 \wedge x_4)$$
$$\vee (x_1 \wedge \sim x_2 \wedge x_3 \wedge \sim x_4) \tag{21}$$

Table 7   Truth Table for (x ∨ y) ∧ (x ∨ z)

x	y	z	$x \vee y$	$x \vee z$	$(x \vee y) \wedge (x \vee z)$
0	0	0	0	0	0
0	0	1	0	1	0
0	1	0	1	0	0
0	1	1	1	1	1
1	0	0	1	1	1
1	0	1	1	1	1
1	1	0	1	1	1
1	1	1	1	1	1

The truth table for this circuit will contain sixteen rows and many columns. It should be obvious that, in order to compute it with ease and accuracy, we should turn to the computer for assistance.

When we wish to analyze and design even moderately complex circuits, we need to be able to compute rather complex truth tables with some facility. Therefore, before continuing our study of circuits and Boolean algebra, we pause to discuss how we can compute truth tables using FORTRAN.

8.4   FORTRAN and Boolean Algebra

Since the variables in our Boolean algebra are integers, if we are to represent them as FORTRAN variables their names must begin with one of the letters I, J, K, L, M, or N. Suppose we let IX be the value of the variable x. Then either IX $= 0$ or IX $= 1$. Similarly, let IZ be the value of the variable z. Again, either IZ $= 0$ or IZ $= 1$. We shall always restrict FORTRAN variables in Boolean algebra to be 0 or 1.

Now suppose

$$z = \sim x$$

Then, if IX $= 0$, we want IZ $= 1$. On the other hand, if IX $= 1$, we want IZ $= 0$. If we let

$$IZ = 1 - IX \tag{22}$$

we accomplish our purpose.

Now suppose

$$z = x \wedge y$$

Then if we let

$$IZ = IX * IY \tag{23}$$

it follows that IZ $= 1$ if IX $=$ IY $= 1$ and is zero otherwise.[5] Referring to the truth table in Table 1, we see that this is precisely the desired result.

Finally we turn to

$$z = x \vee y$$

This is slightly more difficult than NOT or AND and requires more than one FORTRAN statement.[6] If we let

$$IZ = IX + IY$$

[5] Recall that IX and IY can be 0 or 1 but nothing else.
[6] See Exercises 23 and 26 for two ways of doing this in one FORTRAN statement.

the following four cases arise:

$$IX = 0 \text{ and } IY = 0 \quad \text{then} \quad IZ = 0$$
$$IX = 0 \text{ and } IY = 1 \quad \text{then} \quad IZ = 1$$
$$IX = 1 \text{ and } IY = 0 \quad \text{then} \quad IZ = 1$$
$$IX = 1 \text{ and } IY = 1 \quad \text{then} \quad IZ = 2$$

Reference to the truth table in Table 2, shows that the first three produce the correct value of IZ. However, the last produces a value of 2 for IZ where what is really required is IZ = 1. We get around this difficulty by testing to see if IZ is greater than 0. If it is, we automatically set it equal to 1. The following statements do just that.

$$IZ = IX + IY$$
$$IF \quad (IZ) \quad 1, 1, 2$$
$$2 \quad IZ = 1 \tag{24}$$
$$1 \quad Continue$$

The value of IZ will now equal the value of the variable $z = x \lor y$.

Question. Would the following statements work just as well for $z = x \lor y$?

$$IZ = IX + IY$$
$$IF \quad (IZ - 1) \ 1, 1, 2$$
$$2 \quad IZ = 1$$
$$1 \quad Continue$$

Why?

If we start with integer variables with values of 0 or 1 and use the statements in (22), (23), and (24) to combine them, then the results also will be integer variables with values of 0 or 1. Since Boolean algebra uses only the symbols NOT, AND, and OR, our FORTRAN Boolean algebra will produce only the values 0 or 1 for any expression. Moreover, we now have all the FORTRAN statements we need to evaluate any expression in our Boolean algebra.

Let us use the above FORTRAN statements to compute a simple truth table. Let

$$z = x \land (x \lor y)$$

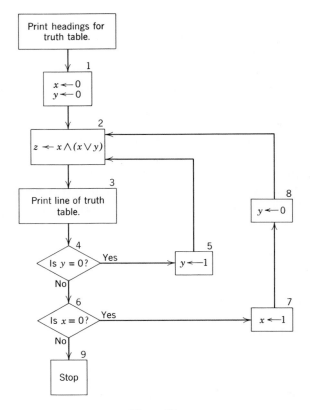

Figure 21

Flow chart for computing truth table for $x \wedge (x \vee y)$

The flow chart for computing the truth table is shown in Figure 21. We set both switches to zero and compute z and print the line of the truth table corresponding to these switch settings.

Keeping x fixed, we increase y to 1 and repeat the calculations. Next we increase x to 1, reset $y = 0$ and recompute. Finally, we let $x = y = 1$ and compute z once more. After this computation the answer to both questions in the flow chart is "no," so we stop.

A FORTRAN program to compute this truth table is shown in Figure 22.[7] The printed results are shown in Figure 23.

---

[7] The statement numbers from 1 to 9 correspond to the box numbers in the flow chart of Figure 21.

```
        PRINT 100
100 FORMAT (15H     X      Y      Z)
  1 IX=0
    IY=0
  2 IT=IX+IY
    IF (IT)20,20,21
 21 IT=1
 20 IZ=IX*IT
  3 PRINT 200,IX,IY,IZ
200 FORMAT (I5,I5,I5)
  4 IF (IY)6,5,6
  5 IY=1
    GO TO 2
  6 IF (IX)9,7,9
  7 IX=1
  8 IY=0
    GO TO 2
  9 STOP
    END
```

Figure 22

FORTRAN program to compute the truth table for $x \wedge (v \vee y)$

Problem. Write a program to compute the truth table for

$$z = x \wedge (x \vee y)$$

using the flow chart in Figure 21 and DO loops. Recall that the index in a DO loop must be positive.

In the succeeding sections of this chapter we use these computer techniques to analyze more complex circuits.

Problem. Compute the truth table for

$$t = x \vee (x \wedge y)$$

Is $x \vee (x \wedge y) = x \wedge (x \vee y)$?

Problem. Suppose that we wish to compute

$$t = x \vee y \vee z$$

X	Y	Z
0	0	0
0	1	0
1	0	1
1	1	1

Figure 23

Truth table for $x \wedge (x \vee y)$ resulting from program in Figure 22

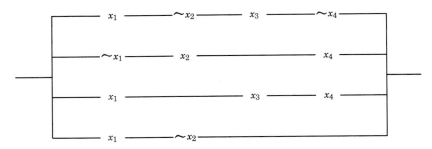

Figure 24

Circuit with four independent switches

Does the following FORTRAN program accomplish this?

$$IT = IX + IY + IZ$$

$$IF \quad (IT) \quad 1, 1, 2$$

$$2 \quad IT = 1$$

$$1 \quad Continue$$

Tell how you would evaluate

$$p = x_1 \lor x_2 \lor x_3 \lor x_4 \lor x_5 \lor x_6$$

8.5 Analysis of Circuits

We turn now to the important problem of analyzing a given circuit. We want to predict how a circuit will behave under all possible settings of its switches. To do this we compute the truth table for the circuit and examine the results. In the next section we take up the more diffi-cult problem of *designing* a circuit which behaves in a way we specify. In the design problem we start with a truth table, and find a circuit which has that truth table. In this section we start with the circuit and find the truth table.

Consider the circuit shown in Figure 24. Notice that there are only four independent switches. The logical expression for the circuit in Figure 24 is given by expression (21) at the close of Section 8.3. Let

$$y_1 = x_1 \land \sim x_2$$

$$y_2 = x_1 \land x_3 \land x_4$$

$$y_3 = \sim x_1 \land x_2 \land x_4$$

```
       I1=0
14     I2=0
11     I3=0
 8     I4=0
 5     J1=I1*(1-I2)
       J2=I1*I3*I4
       J3=(1-I1)*I2*I4
200    J4=I1*(1-I2)*I3*(1-I4)
201    J=J1+J2+J3+J4
       IF (J)1,1,2
 2     J=1
 1     PRINT 100,I1,I2,I3,I4,J
       IF (I4)3,3,4
 3     I4=1
       GO TO 5
 4     IF (I3)6,6,7
 6     I3=1
       GO TO 8
 7     IF(I2)9,9,10
 9     I2=1
       GO TO 11
10     IF (I1)12,12,13
12     I1=1
       GO TO 14
13     STOP
100    FORMAT (I2,I2,I2,I2,I4)
       END
```

```
0 0 0 0    0
0 0 0 1    0
0 0 1 0    0
0 0 1 1    0
0 1 0 0    0
0 1 0 1    1
0 1 1 0    0
0 1 1 1    1
1 0 0 0    1
1 0 0 1    1
1 0 1 0    1
1 0 1 1    1
1 1 0 0    0
1 1 0 1    0
1 1 1 0    0
1 1 1 1    1
```

Figure 25

FORTRAN program and truth table for circuit in Figure 24

$$y_4 = x_1 \land \sim x_2 \land x_3 \land \sim x_4$$

$$y = y_1 \lor y_2 \lor y_3 \lor y_4$$

Then y is equal to the expression in (21).

In order to write a FORTRAN program to evaluate y we let $I1 = x_1, \ldots, I4 = x_4$, $J1 = y_1, \ldots, J4 = y_4$ and $J = y$. A FORTRAN program to compute the truth table together with the truth table itself

0	0	0	0	0
0	0	0	1	0
0	0	1	0	0
0	0	1	1	0
0	1	0	0	0
0	1	0	1	1
0	1	1	0	0
0	1	1	1	1
1	0	0	0	1
1	0	0	1	1
1	0	1	0	1
1	0	1	1	1
1	1	0	0	0
1	1	0	1	0
1	1	1	0	0
1	1	1	1	1

Figure 26

Truth table for circuit in Figure 24 with top branch missing

is shown in Figure 25. No headings were printed on the truth table, but
the columns are x_1, x_2, x_3, x_4, y, in that order. The reader should study
the program and understand it in detail. In particular, the reader should
examine the statement numbered 201 which represents

$$y = y_1 \lor y_2 \lor y_3 \lor y_4$$

and understand why it is possible to do all three additions and then test
to see if y (or J) is positive rather than testing after each addition.

Now suppose the top branch in the circuit in Figure 24 is removed.
What is the effect on the circuit's behavior? To answer this question all
we need to do is modify the two statements 200 and 201 in the program
in Figure 25. Statement 200 is removed and statement 201 is changed
to read

$$J = J1 + J2 + J3$$

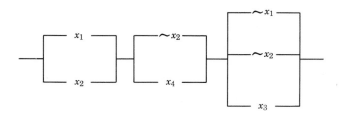

Figure 27

Seven-switch circuit which is equivalent to the one in Figure 24

```
      PRINT 200
200   FORMAT (24H X(1)   X(2)   X(3)    C   S)
      I1=0
22    I2=0
21    I3=0
20    IT=I1+I2
      IF (IT)1,1,2
2     IT=1
1     IT=IT*(1-I1*I2)
      IS=IT+I3
      IF (IS)3,3,4
4     IS=1
3     IS=IS*(1-IT*I3)
      IC=IT*I3+I1*I2
      IF (IC)5,5,6
6     IC=1
5     PRINT 100,I1,I2,I3,IC,IS
      IF (I3)7,7,8
7     I3=1
      GO TO 20
8     IF (I2)9,9,10
9     I2=1
      GO TO 21
10    IF (I1) 11,11,12
11    I1=1
      GO TO 22
12    STOP
100   FORMAT (I4,I6,I6,I5,I3)
      END
```

Figure 28

FORTRAN program to compute truth table from equations (25), (26), (27)

The results of running the modified program are shown in Figure 26.

We now note the remarkable fact that the truth tables in Figures 25 and 26 are *identical*. Therefore, the circuit in Figure 24 can have its top branch removed without affecting its behavior. Our truth tables have shown us that we can replace the circuit in Figure 24 by one with fewer switches and accomplish the same result. The first circuit (Figure 24) has twelve switches. The second circuit has eight switches.

We can find still a third circuit with only seven switches which is equivalent to the circuit in Figure 24. It is shown in Figure 27. The reader will find it instructive to construct the truth table for this seven-switch circuit in Figure 27 and to compare it with Figures 25 and 26.

We close this section by computing some truth tables which we will find useful later. We let

$$t = (x_1 \lor x_2) \land \sim(x_1 \land x_2) \tag{25}$$

$$s = (t \lor x_3) \land \sim(t \land x_3) \tag{26}$$

$$c = (t \land x_3) \lor (x_1 \land x_2) \tag{27}$$

X(1)	X(2)	X(3)	C	S
0	0	0	0	0
0	0	1	0	1
0	1	0	0	1
0	1	1	1	0
1	0	0	0	1
1	0	1	1	0
1	1	0	1	0
1	1	1	1	1

Figure 29

Results of FORTRAN program of Figure 28 for truth table for equations (25), (26), (27)

The variable t is not important itself but it is needed to compute s and c, which are important.

We again let our FORTRAN variables be $I1 = x_1, \ldots, I4 = x_4$ and

$$IT = t$$

$$IS = s$$

$$IC = c$$

The FORTRAN program to compute the truth table for c and s is shown in Figure 28 and the truth table is given in Figure 29.

Question.   What relationship do the *numbers* c and s have to the sum $x_1 + x_2 + x_3$?

8.6   Design of Circuits — The Light Switch Problem Revisited

We come now to the more important (and more difficult) problem of designing a circuit. We suppose that we know how many independent switches we want in our circuit and how we want the circuit to behave for all given switch settings. The problem is to construct a circuit to accomplish the assigned task.

The behavior of a circuit is completely specified by its truth table. Therefore, we want to find a circuit which has a truth table which we will specify ahead of time. For example, let us return to the two-switch light problem which we posed at the beginning of this chapter. We have already given a solution to this problem without any explanation of how we arrived at the solution. We now proceed to find that solution in a way which will allow us to solve more difficult problems as well.

Our two-switch light problem has two independent switches which we call x_1 and x_2. When both are off, we want no current to flow. If we throw either switch, we want current to flow. Thus, if $x_1 = 0$ and $x_2 = 1$ or if $x_1 = 1$ and $x_2 = 0$, we want the truth table entry to be 1 (see Table 8). If both switches are thrown, we want no current to flow; therefore, the last entry in the truth table is 0.

We can summarize all this by saying that if, starting with the light off, an odd number of changes are made in the switch settings, the light should be on. On the other hand, an even number of switch changes should leave the light off.

We want to find a logical expression involving x_1 and x_2 which results in the truth table of Table 8.

Table 8

x_1	x_2	Light
0	0	0
0	1	1
1	0	1
1	1	0

First we note that the truth table of the AND of any two variables has all zeros in its truth table except for one place. For example, the truth table for $x_1 \wedge x_2$ is shown in Table 9a. It has a 1 in the last row and zeros elsewhere. As a further example, consider $x_1 \wedge \sim x_2$. This is zero except when $x_1 = 1$ and $\sim x_2 = 1$. That is, $x_1 \wedge \sim x_2 = 1$ only when $x_1 = 1$ and $x_2 = 0$. The truth table is shown in Table 9b. Similarly, the truth tables for $\sim x_1 \wedge x_2$ and $\sim x_1 \wedge \sim x_2$ are given in Tables 9c and 9d. Each of the truth tables in Table 9 has a 1 in one and only one row, and each has its 1 in a different row from the others.

Secondly, we note that the truth table of the OR of any number of variables has a 1 where *any* of the variables has a 1. Suppose, for example, we use the last columns of the truth tables in Table 9b and 9c as values for two variables. We call these variables b and c, since they come from parts (b) and (c) of Table 9. We let a variable $l = b \vee c$. The truth table is shown in Table 10.

The column l of Table 10 corresponds exactly to the column "light" of Table 8. Now the b values in Table 10 are just the values of $x_1 \wedge \sim x_2$. Similarly, the c values are the values of $\sim x_1 \wedge x_2$. Therefore,

$$l = (x_1 \wedge \sim x_2) \vee (\sim x_1 \wedge x_2) \tag{28}$$

Table 9

x_1	x_2	$x_1 \wedge x_2$
0	0	0
0	1	0
1	0	0
1	1	1

(a)

x_1	x_2	$x_1 \wedge \sim x_2$
0	0	0
0	1	0
1	0	1
1	1	0

(b)

x_1	x_2	$\sim x_1 \wedge x_2$
0	0	0
0	1	1
1	0	0
1	1	0

(c)

x_1	x_2	$\sim x_1 \wedge \sim x_2$
0	0	1
0	1	0
1	0	0
1	1	0

(d)

The expression on the right represents the circuit we are seeking. That is, it has the truth table specified in Table 8.

This circuit, is often called an **exclusive OR circuit.** It allows current to flow if either switch is on but not if both are. Therefore, it "excludes" the case where both switches are on. The OR circuit we have used previously (two switches in parallel) allows current to flow if either or both switches are closed. Therefore, it is often called an **inclusive OR circuit** since it "includes" the case in which both switches are on.

The procedure for designing any two-switch circuit should now be clear. We have four basic AND circuits described by the truth tables in Table 9. We take the truth table we want to obtain (such as Table 8) and note in which rows it has a 1 in the last column. We find basic AND circuits with 1's in those rows and form the OR of all of them.

Problem.   Find a two-switch circuit which allows current to flow in two and only two situations: when x_1 is open and x_2 closed; and when both switches are closed.

Table 10

b	c	$l = b \vee c$
0	0	0
0	1	1
1	0	1
0	0	0

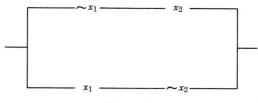

Figure 30

Circuit for the two-switch light problem

The circuit for the two-switch light problem is given by the right side of equation (28). It is represented schematically in Figure 30. This diagram does not look very much like the diagram in Figure 3. The reason is that Figure 30 is purely mathematical and does not imply any particular physical embodiment of the circuit. However, in this case at least, the reader should have no trouble translating Figure 30 into Figure 3. In later problems the translation to a physical circuit may not be so easily accomplished. However, as we noted previously, we do not discuss physical circuits but content ourselves with mathematical circuits.

We return now to the three-switch light problem which we posed in Section 8.1 but which as yet we have not solved. Recall that, if an odd number of switches are "on," we want the light to be "on." However, if an even number of switches are "on," we want the light to be "off." We let the three switches be represented by x_1, x_2, and x_3. The truth table is given in Table 11. We want to design a circuit with this truth table. We again look for four basic AND circuits: (a) one with a 1 in the second row and nowhere else, (b) one with a 1 in the third row and nowhere else, (c) one with a 1 in the fifth row and nowhere else, and

Table 11 Truth Table for Three-Switch Light Problem

x_1	x_2	x_3	Light
0	0	0	0
0	0	1	1
0	1	0	1
0	1	1	0
1	0	0	1
1	0	1	0
1	1	0	0
1	1	1	1

(d) one with a 1 in the eighth row and nowhere else. If we form the OR of these four basic AND circuits we will obtain the truth table of Table 11.

An AND circuit has a 1 in the row where all its variables have the value 1. For example, $x_1 \wedge x_2 \wedge x_3$ has a 1 in the row where $x_1 = 1$ and $x_2 = 1$ and $x_3 = 1$. Therefore, this is one of the AND circuits we need for this three-switch light problem. The truth table for this AND circuit is shown in Table 12d.

Table 12

x_1	x_2	x_3	$\sim x_1 \wedge \sim x_2 \wedge x_3$
0	0	0	0
0	0	1	1
0	1	0	0
0	1	1	0
1	0	0	0
1	0	1	0
1	1	0	0
1	1	1	0

(a)

x_1	x_2	x_3	$\sim x_1 \wedge x_2 \wedge \sim x_3$
0	0	0	0
0	0	1	0
0	1	0	1
0	1	1	0
1	0	0	0
1	0	1	0
1	1	0	0
1	1	1	0

(b)

x_1	x_2	x_3	$x_1 \wedge \sim x_2 \wedge \sim x_3$
0	0	0	0
0	0	1	0
0	1	0	0
0	1	1	0
1	0	0	1
1	0	1	0
1	1	0	0
1	1	1	0

(c)

x_1	x_2	x_3	$x_1 \wedge x_2 \wedge x_3$
0	0	0	0
0	0	1	0
0	1	0	0
0	1	1	0
1	0	0	0
1	0	1	0
1	1	0	0
1	1	1	1

(d)

The AND circuit $\sim x_1 \wedge \sim x_2 \wedge \sim x_3$ will be 1 in the row where $\sim x_1$ and $\sim x_2$ and $\sim x_3$ are all 1. That is the row where x_1, x_2, and x_3 are all 0. Although this is not a row where we want a 1 in our truth table, it shows us how to find AND circuits that give us the desired results.

Referring to Table 11, notice that we want a 1 in row two where $x_1 = 0$ and $x_2 = 0$ and $x_3 = 1$. Since $x_1 = 0$, it follows that $\sim x_1 = 1$. Similarly, since $x_2 = 0$, then $\sim x_2 = 1$. Therefore, in row two, $\sim x_1$ and

$\sim x_2$ and x_3 are all 1. This leads us to the AND circuit $\sim x_1 \wedge \sim x_2 \wedge x_3$. Its truth table is shown in Table 12a. It does have a 1 in row two and nowhere else.

We also want an AND circuit with a 1 in row three where $x_1 = 0$ and $x_2 = 1$ and $x_3 = 0$ (Table 11). In this row, then, $\sim x_1 = 1$ and $x_2 = 1$ and $\sim x_3 = 1$, so we use $\sim x_1 \wedge x_2 \wedge \sim x_3$. The truth table for this AND circuit is given in Table 12b. The reader should have no trouble in determining that $x_1 \wedge \sim x_2 \wedge \sim x_3$ has a 1 in the fifth row. The truth table is shown in Table 12c.

The rules for finding the basic AND circuits are:

(i)   Note the variable values in the row where a 1 is desired.

(ii) If the variable value is 1, use that variable in the AND circuit.

(iii) If the variable value is 0, use that variable preceded by a NOT symbol ($\sim$) in the AND circuit.

Each basic AND circuit contains every variable x either as x itself or as $\sim x$. The number of basic AND circuits is equal to the number of 1's in the truth table.

Once we have found the basic AND circuits, we form an OR circuit with each basic AND circuit as an element. The solution to the three-switch light problem then is

$$l = (x_1 \wedge x_2 \wedge x_3) \vee (\sim x_1 \wedge \sim x_2 \wedge x_3) \vee (\sim x_1 \wedge x_2 \wedge \sim x_3)$$
$$\vee (x_1 \wedge \sim x_2 \wedge \sim x_3) \qquad\qquad (29)$$

Problem. Write a FORTRAN program to compute the truth table for the expression for l and check that it indeed does solve the three-switch light problem.

This circuit uses twelve switches although only three are independent. A simpler circuit which uses ten switches and accomplishes the same objective is given by

$$p = \{x_1 \wedge [(x_2 \wedge x_3) \vee (\sim x_2 \wedge \sim x_3)]\} \vee \{\sim x_1 \wedge [(\sim x_2 \wedge x_3)$$
$$\vee (x_2 \wedge \sim x_3)]\}$$

The circuit corresponding to this expression is shown in Figure 31. Notice the similarity of part of the lower branch of Figure 31 to the diagram in Figure 30 for the two-switch circuit.

In general, our design procedure produces circuits with a large number of switches. It usually is desirable to reduce the number of switches to a

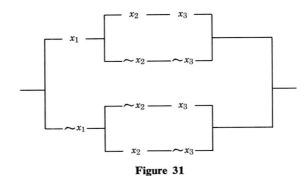

Figure 31

Ten-switch circuit for the three-switch light problem

more reasonable number in order to reduce the cost and difficulty of actually constructing the circuit.

Techniques for systematically simplifying circuits are available and are in widespread use. A discussion of these simplification methods is beyond the scope of this text. The interested reader is referred to either *Boolean Algebra and Its Application* by H. Graham Flegg (John Wiley & Sons, 1964) or *Applied Boolean Algebra, An Elementary Introduction* by Franz E. Hohn (Macmillan, 1960).

The important thing is that we can now design a circuit to perform any switching problem which we want to solve. We have a straightforward algorithm for accomplishing this design task, and we have applied it successfully to both the two-switch and the three-switch stairwell light problems. In the next section we use this technique to design a simple computer.

8.7   Design of a Simple Computer

Digital computers perform four basic arithmetic operations: addition, subtraction, multiplication, and division. In this section we consider the design of a device which will add two integers. Such a device can be used to perform the other three arithmetic operations as well, since subtraction is addition with the sign changed, multiplication is repeated addition, and division is repeated subtraction. Most computers actually perform all their arithmetic operations by repeated use of adding devices.

Because the numbers 0 and 1 can be handled conveniently by switching circuits, we use a binary number system.[8] The number 11 in decimal

[8] The reader unfamiliar with binary numbers should read a text which describes them (see e.g., Appendix I of *Applied Boolean Algebra* by Franz E. Hohn).

is 1011 in binary, while the decimal number 3 is 11 in binary. If we wish to add 3 to 11 using binary numbers, we write

$$1011$$
$$+ \quad 11$$
$$\overline{1110}$$

The details of the addition are as follows: We add the two digits in the right-most (one's) place. We write the right-most digit, 0, and carry the left-most digit, 1, to the next place to the left.

$$1$$
$$1011$$
$$+ \quad 11$$
$$\overline{0}$$

We then add the two digits in the second place from the right (two's place) together with the carry digit ($1 + 1 + 1 = 11$). We write down the right-most digit of the sum, 1, and carry the left-most digit, also 1, to the next place to the left.

$$1$$
$$1011$$
$$+ \quad 11$$
$$\overline{10}$$

The remainder of the procedure should be clear.

> **Problem.**   Draw a flow chart to describe addition of positive binary integers digit-by-digit as described above. Assume that two six-place integers are to be added. You must allow for seven digits in the sum.

At any given place we need to add up to three digits (the two from the given numbers and a carry digit) each of which can be 0 or 1. We shall design a device which adds *three* one-place binary numbers and produces *one* two-place binary number as the sum. The low-order digit (one's place) of the sum will be called the sum digit, s. The high-order digit (two's place) will be called the carry digit, c. If we place n devices of the type just described in series with one another, we will have constructed a device which adds two integers each with n digits.

Let us first construct a truth table for the simple device which adds three one-place digits. We let x_1 and x_2 and x_3 be the one-place binary digits which we want to add. These variables can take on the values 0 or 1. Therefore, they can be treated as Boolean variables just like the switches discussed earlier in this chapter. The truth table for adding these three variables is shown in Table 13. If all variables are 0, then

Table 13   Truth Table for One-Place Adder

x_1	x_2	x_3	c	s
0	0	0	0	0
0	0	1	0	1
0	1	0	0	1
0	1	1	1	0
1	0	0	0	1
1	0	1	1	0
1	1	0	1	0
1	1	1	1	1

both the sum digit and the carry digit are 0 (line 1). If only one variable is 1, then the sum digit is 1 and the carry digit is 0 (lines 2, 3, and 5). If exactly two variables are 1, then the sum digit is 0 and the carry digit is 1 (lines 4, 6, and 7). Finally, if all three variables are 1, then both the sum and carry digits are 1 (line 8).

We shall construct two logical expressions which involve the variables x_1, x_2, and x_3 and which have the same truth tables as those shown for c and s in Table 13. We already know how to design such expressions from Section 8.6. After we have obtained these logical expressions, we shall discuss their implementation briefly.

Notice first that the truth table for the sum digit (s column of Table 13) is the same as the truth table for the three-switch light problem (Table 11). Thus the logical expression on the right side of equation (29) can be used for the sum digit. That is,

$$s = (x_1 \wedge x_2 \wedge x_3) \vee (\sim x_1 \wedge \sim x_2 \wedge x_3) \vee (\sim x_1 \wedge x_2 \wedge \sim x_3)$$
$$\vee (x_1 \wedge \sim x_2 \wedge \sim x_3) \quad (30)$$

To obtain a logical expression for the carry digit we need basic **AND** circuits which are 1 in the fourth, sixth, seventh, and eighth rows. The fourth row indicates $x_1 = 0$, $x_2 = 1$, and $x_3 = 1$. Therefore, for this row, $\sim x_1 = 1$, $x_2 = 1$, and $x_3 = 1$. The basic **AND** circuit is

$$\sim x_1 \wedge x_2 \wedge x_3$$

Similarly, for the other three rows the circuits are

$$x_1 \wedge \sim x_2 \wedge \quad x_3$$

$$x_1 \wedge \quad x_2 \wedge \sim x_3$$

$$x_1 \wedge \quad x_2 \wedge \quad x_3$$

respectively. The carry digit is the logical OR of these four AND circuits, or

$$c = (\sim x_1 \wedge x_2 \wedge x_3) \vee (x_1 \wedge \sim x_2 \wedge x_3) \vee (x_1 \wedge x_2 \wedge \sim x_3)$$
$$\vee (x_1 \wedge x_2 \wedge x_3) \qquad (31)$$

We turn now to an implementation of these logical expressions. We could think of constructing a circuit with switches which would produce a current in a line s when $s = 1$ and no current when $s = 0$. Similarly, we could construct a circuit with c as its current. Computers, however, are so constructed that current flows in only one direction in a line.[9] Instead of switches, "gates" are used. A **gate** has one or two lines carrying current into it and only one line carrying current out. There are three types of gates of interest to us: AND gates, OR gates, and INVERTERS. They are represented by the symbols $\wedge$ and $\vee$ and $\sim$, respectively.

AND and OR gates have two[10] lines carrying current into them and only one line carrying current out (see Figure 32). If currents flow in on both lines to an AND gate, then current flows out. Otherwise, no current leaves the AND gate. Similarly, if current flows in on either of the lines to an OR gate, then current flows out. Only if both of the incoming lines have no current does no current flow out of an OR gate.

INVERTERS have only one entering line and one exiting line. If there is a current in the entering line to an INVERTER, then there is no current in the exiting line. Conversely, if no current enters an INVERTER, then current does exit.

---

[9] Recall that in our previous circuits we said nothing about the *direction* in which the current could flow. The direction was immaterial.

[10] AND and OR gates are sometimes constructed with more than two entering lines. For example, $x \wedge y \wedge z$ might be represented by one gate. According to the procedures defined above, however, we would use two AND gates: (a) one with x and y on the incoming lines and $t = x \wedge y$ on the outgoing line, and (b) one with t and z on the incoming lines and $t \wedge z = x \wedge y \wedge z$ on the outgoing line. We restrict ourselves to the simple AND gates with two incoming lines to make easier our comparisons of the relative complexity of different circuits.

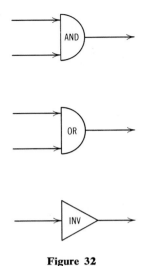

Figure 32

AND, OR, and INVERTER gates

A circuit with three INVERTERS, seven AND gates, and three OR gates is shown in Figure 33. The line c leaving the OR gate has a current if the carry digit from the sum of $x_1 + x_2 + x_3$ is 1. Otherwise it carries no current. This circuit follows the logical expression given by equation (31).

Problem. Using gates, construct a circuit to produce the sum digit s given by the logical expression in equation (30).

The circuits we have just constructed are rather complex. If we placed a lot of them in series, we would have a complicated circuit indeed. And all this just to add two integers! Therefore, we look for simpler circuits. Notice that together the two circuits for s and c required eleven AND gates, six OR gates, and three INVERTERS.

Problem. Verify the number of gates needed for s and c. (*Hint:* Notice that $x_1 \wedge x_2 \wedge x_3$ appears in both s and c but needs to be evaluated only once.)

Return now to equations (25), (26), and (27) at the end of Section 8.5. The truth tables for s and c in those equations are identical with the truth tables in Table 13. Therefore, those circuits can be used to add three one-place binary integers. A circuit is shown in Figure 34. Notice that four AND gates, three OR gates, and two INVERTERS are needed. This results in a saving of seven AND gates, three OR gates, and one INVERTER over the circuit in Figure 33. The reader should study the circuit in Figure 34 along with equations (25), (26), and (27) and assure himself of its validity.

Now suppose we wished to add two *three*-place binary integers and obtain a four-place binary number as the sum. We would need three circuits like the one shown in Figure 34. The first adds the one's place

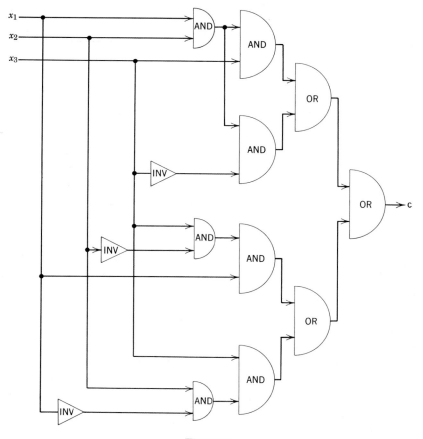

Figure 33

Circuit to produce the carry digit in the sum of three binary digits

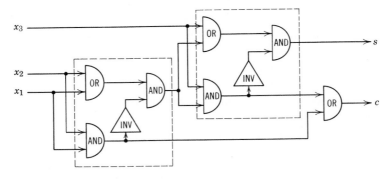

Figure 34

Circuit to add three one-place binary integers (x_1, x_2, x_3) and produce one two-place binary sum (c, s)

and would have no current in line x_3.[11] The x_1 and x_2 lines will carry the one's place of the two integers being added. The s line will carry the one's place of the sum. The c line holds the carry digit and will enter as x_3 in the second circuit which will add the two's place.

The second circuit would have the two's places from the two integers being added on the x_1 and x_2 lines. The x_3 will connect to the c line from the first circuit. The s line from the second circuit contains the two's place digit in the sum.

The third circuit would have the four's places from the two integers to be added entering on the x_1 and x_2 lines. It would have its x_3 line connected to the c line from the second circuit. This third circuit would produce the four's place of the sum on its s line. It would produce the eight's place of the sum on its c line.

Now notice that we have used a rather large number of gates to add two three-digit numbers. In fact, we have used twelve AND gates, nine OR gates, and six INVERTERS.[12] We can reduce the number of gates if we are willing to take a little longer to perform the addition.

Recall that all three circuits we used were identical with Figure 34. If we make the second circuit wait until the first circuit has completed its job (added x_1 and x_2 and produced s and c), then we can use those

[11] We could simplify this first circuit because $x_3 = 0$. Can you draw the simplified circuit? It will have two AND gates, one OR gate, and one INVERTER.
[12] If we make use of the simplification suggested in footnote 11, we still require ten AND gates, seven OR gates, and five INVERTERS.

same physical gates and wires for circuit two. Similarly, if we make the third circuit wait even longer until the second circuit has completed its assignment, we can use the original circuit again. What we should do then is to place a timing device in our computer which holds up adding the two's place until the one's place has been summed. It also holds up adding the three's place until the one's place and the two's place have been added. The reader should stop to notice that this is precisely what we usually do when we add with paper and pencil.

One more economy can be achieved at the expense of time. Notice that the two circuits in dotted boxes in Figure 34 are identical. The lower left box produces t [equation (25)] on the line leaving the uppermost AND gate. Therefore, if we delay adding the carry from the previous place (x_3 line) until t has been computed, we can re-use the circuit in the lower left box to perform the operations to be done in the upper right box.

All the economies we have suggested require us to delay certain things. This means that, if we wish to use less hardware (gates), we must do so at the expense of time. This is a common trade-off in the design of computers. If we wish to build an inexpensive computer, then we should not expect it to be exceptionally fast in performing its work. On the other hand, if we wish to build a very fast computer, then we should expect it to be rather expensive.

Exercises

Answers to exercises marked * are given in Appendix A.

*1. Using truth tables show that

$$(x \wedge y) \vee (\sim x \wedge y) \vee (x \wedge \sim y) = x \vee y$$

2. Verify the following equations using truth tables:

(i) $(a \wedge b) \vee (\sim a \wedge c) \vee (b \wedge c) = (a \wedge b) \vee (\sim a \wedge c)$

(ii) $(\sim a \wedge \sim b) \vee (b \wedge c) \vee (a \wedge \sim c) =$

$$(\sim a \wedge c) \vee (a \wedge b) \vee (\sim b \wedge \sim c)$$

*3. Design a circuit with three switches and the truth table shown in Table 14. What is the smallest number of switches possible?

4. Draw a diagram of a circuit which solves the three-switch light problem using equation (29). Compare your result with Figure 31.

Table 14

x_1	x_2	x_3	
0	0	0	0
0	0	1	1
0	1	0	0
0	1	1	1
1	0	0	0
1	0	1	1
1	1	0	0
1	1	1	1

*5. Show that the circuits shown in Figures 35 and 36 are equivalent.

6. Show that we need only two symbols, $\sim$ and $\vee$, to construct a Boolean algebra by showing that

$$x \wedge y = \sim(\sim x \vee \sim y)$$

Why does this show that we need only two symbols? Could we use $\sim$ and $\wedge$ as the two symbols? Could we use $\wedge$ and $\vee$ without $\sim$?

*7. Using the dualization law, equation (19), and the associative law, equation (13), show that

$$\sim(a \wedge b \wedge c) = (\sim a) \vee (\sim b) \vee (\sim c)$$

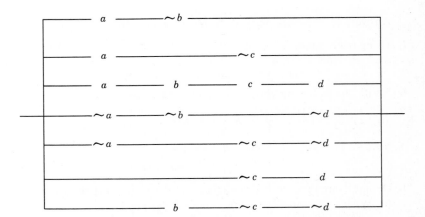

Figure 35

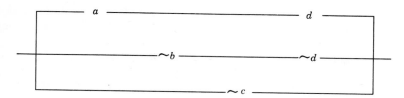

Figure 36

8. Using the dualization law, equation (20), and the associative law, equation (14), show that

$$\sim(a \vee b \vee c) = (\sim a) \wedge (\sim b) \wedge (\sim c)$$

*9. Construct a truth table to verify the equation in Exercise 7.

10. Construct a truth table to verify the equation in Exercise 8.

*11. Using truth tables, determine which of the following logical expressions are equivalent.

(a) $(x \wedge y) \vee (x \wedge z)$ (b) $x \vee (y \wedge \sim z)$

(c) $(x \wedge y) \vee (z \wedge \sim x)$ (d) $x \wedge (y \vee z)$

(e) $(x \vee y) \wedge (\sim x \vee z)$ (f) $(x \vee y) \wedge (x \vee \sim z)$

(g) $(x \wedge z) \vee (\sim x \wedge y)$ (h) $(x \wedge y) \vee (y \wedge z) \vee (z \wedge \sim x)$

12. Without using truth tables, show that

(a) $z \wedge (y \vee z) = z$ (b) $(y \wedge \sim z) \vee z = y \vee z$

*13. Using truth tables, verify the equations in Exercise 12.

14. Just as we constructed basic AND circuits whose truth tables had a 1 in one and only one row, we can construct basic OR circuits whose truth tables have a 0 in one and only one row.

(a) Construct the truth tables for the four basic OR circuits:

$$x_1 \vee x_2, x_1 \vee \sim x_2, \sim x_1 \vee x_2, \sim x_1 \vee \sim x_2.$$

(b) Form a circuit as the AND of two of these basic OR circuits so that the truth table is 1, 0, 0, 1.

(c) From the result of part (b) find an expression for the exclusive OR which solves the two-switch light problem.

(d) Using the dualization laws, equations (19) and (20), show that the expression obtained in part (c) is equivalent to the expression obtained in the text, equation (28).

*15. The NAND (NOT-AND) operation is represented by $a \mid b$ where $\mid$ is the **Sheffer stroke.** It has the truth table shown in Table 15.

Table 15

a	b	$a \mid b$
0	0	1
0	1	1
1	0	1
1	1	0

Design a NAND circuit.

16. In a railroad yard there is a switch x which is usually closed. There are two men, a and b, each with a switch in front of him. In the event of a possible collision either man can close his switch, with the result that the yard switch x is opened. Of course, if both men close their switches the yard switch should also be open. Design a circuit to provide for this safety measure. This circuit performs what is sometimes called the NOR operation (NOT-OR) and is expressed as $a \downarrow b$, where $\downarrow$ is called the **Pierce arrow.**

*17. (a) Using three switches, how many basic AND circuits are there?
(b) What are they?

18. (a) Using four switches, how many basic AND circuits are there?
(b) What are they?

*19. Without using truth tables, show that

(a) $(x \wedge y) \vee (x \wedge \sim y) = x$ (b) $(x \vee y) \wedge (x \vee \sim y) = x$

(*Hint:* Use the distributive and complementarity laws.)

20. Verify the equations in Exercise 19, using truth tables.

21. Without using truth tables, show that

$$(x \wedge y) \vee (\sim x \wedge z) \vee (y \wedge z) = (x \wedge y) \vee (\sim x \wedge z)$$

[*Hint:* Replace $y \wedge z$ by $y \wedge z \wedge (x \vee \sim x)$.]

*22. Verify the equation in Exercise 21 using truth tables.

23. Show that if we let

$$IZ = (IX + IY + 1)/2$$

then

$$IZ = IX \lor IY$$

The method in the text for computing $IX \lor IY$ requires three FOR-TRAN statements. Nevertheless, it is often preferable to the one-statement method given here because division is often a relatively time-consuming operation on a computer.

*24. Rewrite the FORTRAN program in Figure 22, using the one-statement method for computing $x \lor y$ given in Exercise 23. How many FORTRAN statements are saved?

25. Rewrite the FORTRAN program in Figure 28, using the one-statement method for computing $x \lor y$ given in Exercise 23. How many FORTRAN statements are saved?

*26. Show that if we let

$$IZ = IX + IY - IX * IY$$

then

$$IZ = IX \lor IY$$

The three-statement method given in the text for computing $IX \lor IY$ is often preferable to this because multiplication is often a relatively time-consuming operation on a computer.

27. Rewrite the FORTRAN program in Figure 22, using the one-statement method for computing $x \lor y$ given in Exercise 26.

28. Rewrite the FORTRAN program in Figure 28, using the one-statement method for computing $x \lor y$ given in Exercise 26.

CHAPTER NINE

Probability —
The Laws of Chance

9.1 A Problem in Heredity

Inheritable characteristics depend on special carriers called *genes*. We assume that genes appear in pairs and that each gene can take on one of two forms. We will call these two forms X and x.

A given individual may possess two X genes or two x genes or one X gene and one x gene. Thus, all individuals fall into one of three *genotypes: XX, xx,* or *Xx.* We confine our discussions to this simple case where an inherited characteristic is completely determined by one pair of genes and where each individual must be one of three genotypes.

For some inheritable characteristics, one type of gene is *dominant* and the other is *recessive.* Suppose, for example, X is a dominant gene and x is a recessive gene. Then XX individuals cannot be distinguished from Xx individuals because the X gene dominates and suppresses any effect the x gene may have. However, xx individuals are easily distinguished since nothing suppresses the x characteristic.

Generally, in any mating, each offspring receives *one* gene of a particular characteristic from each parent. A parent can pass on only the kinds of genes it possesses itself. For example, if one parent is an XX genotype and the other is an xx genotype, then the offspring must receive one X gene from the first parent since that is the only kind of gene that parent has to transmit. Similarly, the offspring receives one x gene from the second parent. The offspring of such a mating must be an Xx genotype. On the other hand, if both parents are Xx genotypes, then the offspring may receive an X gene from each parent or it may receive an X from one and an x from the other or it may receive an x from each parent. Such an offspring may be an XX or an Xx or an xx genotype.

Suppose now that we are animal breeders and do considerable inbreeding (mating of close relatives) to strengthen our breed. However, there is one characteristic which we wish to eliminate from the animals.

It is carried by a recessive gene, x. An animal which is an xx genotype is easily detected (there may be a change in the physical appearance such as the color of the eye). Such an xx animal is not used further for breeding purposes. However, it is not possible to distinguish between XX and Xx individuals. They are considered identical from our point of view.

If we start with a population of animals with an unknown but "evenly distributed" number of Xx genotypes, what is our best strategy to keep the number of xx genotypes in successive generations as small as possible? We ask the more simple question which answers the preceding question in part: Which is more likely to produce an xx genotype offspring, a brother-sister mating or a mother-son mating?

We shall find that, regardless of the percentage of Xx genotypes present in the original population, one of these pairings is always preferable. We return to this problem in Section 9.6.

9.2 Algebra of Events

We turn now to a discussion of the mathematical theory of probability. Probability deals with events whose outcome is not certain. For example, when we toss a coin, usually we do not know whether it will land with heads or tails showing. Similarly, when two animals of Xx genotype are mated, we do not know whether the offspring will be XX, Xx, or xx.

We call the outcome of a simple experiment a **simple event**. Heads is a simple event when the experiment is tossing a coin. An XX genotype offspring is a simple event when the experiment is the mating of two Xx genotypes.

It is convenient to think of each simple event as a point in space. Such points are called **sample points** since they represent a "sample" of the total number of possible events. The collection of all the sample points of an experiment is called the **sample space**. The notion of sample space is due to von Mises.[1]

For example, if we toss a coin, there are two sample points, one for

---

[1] **Richard von Mises** (pronounced "fohn mee'-ses"), 1883–1953, was born and educated in Austria. He became distinguished as an engineer, mathematician, philosopher, and authority on the poet Rainer Maria Rilke. During World War I he served as an officer in the Flying Corps of the Austro-Hungarian Army. He came to the United States to Harvard University in 1939. Mises made substantial contributions to many fields of mathematics including the theory of flight, fluid mechanics, plasticity (the study of solids stressed beyond their elastic range), and probability. His widow, Hilda Geiringer, is a prominent applied mathematician in her own right.

$H \bullet$ $\bullet\, T$

Figure 1

Sample space for the toss of one coin

heads and one for tails. In Figure 1 these two points are represented
graphically by the points H and T. The sample space is made up entirely
of the two points H and T. There is no significance to the place where
the points are drawn. They could just as well be one over the other as
side by side. If we toss two coins there are four possible outcomes:
(1) both coins may be heads; (2) the first coin may be heads and the
second tails; (3) the first coin may be tails and the second heads, and
(4) both coins may be tails. These possibilities are shown in Figure 2
where the first letter designates the first coin (H for heads and T for
tails) and the second letter designates the second coin. The entire sample
space consists of four points. Again there is no significance to where the
points are placed in the diagram. The salient fact is that there are *four
distinct points*. Notice that we have distinguished between the case
where the first coin is heads and the second is tails (HT) and the case
where the first coin is tails and the second coin is heads (TH). One might
argue that, since both of these outcomes result in one head and one
tail, they are really the same case. For some purposes we shall treat
them in that way. However, we want each simple event to be "equally
likely to occur." It turns out that in our experiment (tossing two coins)
there are four "equally likely" outcomes. They are the ones indicated
in Figure 2 and described above.

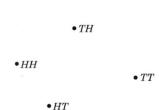

Figure 2

Sample space for the toss of two coins

To reassure ourselves on this point we consider another experiment which is, roughly speaking, equivalent to tossing two coins. This experiment consists in tossing one coin twice. The first toss results in either a head or a tail, and each is equally likely. That is, each occurs half the time. If the first toss results in a head, then the second can also result in a head or a tail with equal likeliness. Thus, *HH* and *HT* are equally likely and each occurs one-fourth of the time. The first toss results in a tail one-half the time and, when this occurs, the second toss results in a head or a tail with equal likeliness. Thus *TH* and *TT* occur one-fourth the time. Therefore, the four events in Figure 2 are all equally likely.

We conclude, therefore, that in our coin-tossing experiments the order of the events *H* and *T* is important. It is not true that in all experiments the order of the events is important. Many physical phenomena behave as if there were no difference. We must use care in deciding such an issue. Our intuition (and the experiment involving one toss of two coins) tells us that in coin tossing the order of the heads and tails is important.

In all the problems which we study there will be a *finite* number of sample points. Moreover, we will consider only the cases in which *each sample point (simple event) is just as likely to occur as any other.* For example, in Figure 1 we would expect to get *H* one-half of the time and *T* one-half of the time. In Figure 2 we would expect each of the outcomes to occur one-fourth of the time.

The assumption of the equal likelihood of all sample points is an important and extreme assumption. The results we derive can be extended to more general cases, but such extensions are beyond the scope of this book.

We can use the terminology and powerful ideas of the theory of sets to help us develop laws of probability, and we turn to that now. We think of the sample space as a set of points, and we think of the sample points as elements or members of the set.

Any subset of the sample space defines an **event.** An event may contain one point, several points, or no points. For example, consider Figure 2. The event "at least one tail appears" contains three points: *HT, TH,* and *TT.* The event "precisely one tail appears" contains two points: *HT* and *TH.* On the other hand, the event "two tails appear and one head appears" contains no points.

Problem. Name four different events each of which contains only one point. These are the *simple* events.

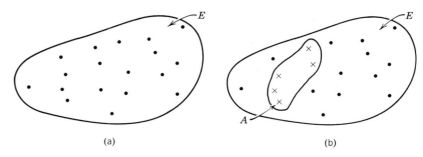

Figure 3

Venn diagrams for a sample space *E* and an event *A*

Schematically, we may think of the sample space as the region *E* in Figure 3a. The dots represent the sample points (simple events). Again their exact physical location is unimportant. The event *A* may be represented by the region *A* in Figure 3b. The simple events of which the event *A* is comprised are represented by the five points marked ×. Diagrams such as those in Figures 3a and 3b are called Venn[2] diagrams. For the case of tossing two coins the set *E* is shown in Figure 4a. The event *A* in Figure 4b represents "precisely one tail appears." The sample points of which this event are comprised are marked ×.

[2] **John Venn,** 1834–1923, an English logician, came from a long line of scholars. He represented the eighth consecutive generation of his family to attend Cambridge. Venn was ordained a deacon of the Church of England in 1858 and a priest the following year. At the age of 50 he resigned his holy orders to devote himself to the study and teaching of logic.

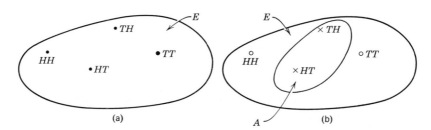

Figure 4

Venn diagrams for tossing two coins

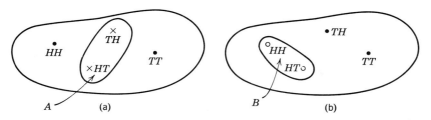

Figure 5

Venn diagrams for (a) one tail and (b) first coin is a head

The **complement** of an event is the set of outcomes for which the event does *not* occur. For example, the complement of A in Figure 4b is the set of points HH and TT. These are the points where "precisely one tail does *not* appear." Geometrically the sample points in the complement of A are those points of E which do not lie in A. In Figure 4b the sample points in the complement of A are the two points marked ○. The complement of A is written $\sim A$ and read "not A."

The **union** of two events is the set of outcomes for which *either* of the two events occurs. Consider the event A: "precisely one tail appears" in Figure 5a; and the event B: "the first coin is a head" in Figure 5b. The sample points in event A are labeled ✕. The sample points in event B are labeled ○. The union of these two sets consists of the simple events where *either* the first coin is a head *or* precisely one coin is a tail. That is, the points in the union of A and B are the points labeled with either an ✕ or an ○. There are three such points. These three points are HH, HT, and TH. They are either in the set A or the set B or in both. The union of A and B is written $A \cup B$ and is read "union of A and B" or "A union B."

If we do not write down the sample points themselves, then the sets A and B may be represented as in Figure 6. The vertically lined area is the set A and the horizontally lined area is the set B. $A \cup B$ is represented by the area with lines either horizontal, vertical, or both.

The **intersection** of two events is the set of outcomes for which *both* events occur. Using the same sets A and B as we used above, the intersection is the points where both precisely one tail appears *and* the first coin is a head. Geometrically, the intersection of A and B is composed of the points labeled with both an ✕ and an ○ in Figure 5. There is only one such point. That single point is the point HT. The intersection

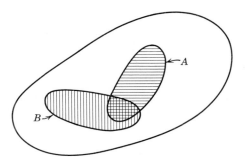

Figure 6

Venn diagram of $A \cup B$ and $A \cap B$

of A and B is written $A \cap B$ and is read "the intersection of A and B" or "A intersect B." In Figure 6, $A \cap B$ is the region which is lined *both* horizontally and vertically.

There are two sets which require special attention. They are the sure set and the empty set. The **sure set** (or sure event) contains all events. It derives its name from the fact that at least one of the outcomes in that set (or event) is certain to occur. Therefore, the event is sure to occur. We express the sure event as E. In Figure 4 or 5 it is represented by all four points.

The **empty set** contains no events. It is usually expressed by the Greek letter ϕ (pronounced "fee").

The union of an event A and its complement, $\sim A$, is the sure event E. That is,

$$A \cup \sim A = E \tag{1}$$

This expression says that either an event occurs or it does not occur. Similarly,

$$A \cap \sim A = \phi \tag{2}$$

This expression tells us that an event cannot occur and also not occur. The reader unsure of these last two results should reread the definitions of complement, union, intersection, sure and empty sets, and then draw Venn diagrams representing $A \cup \sim A$ and $A \cap \sim A$.

We come now to one last concept of sets, the cardinal number. The **cardinal number** of a set is the number of members or elements of the set. For example, the set A in Figure 5a has the cardinal number 2 because there are two points in that set. They are the two points marked $\times$

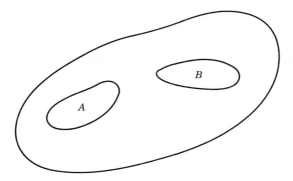

Figure 7

Venn diagram for nonoverlapping sets

in Figure 5a. The set $A \cup B$ where A and B are shown in Figure 5 has the cardinal number 3. The three points in $A \cup B$ are *HH, TH,* and *HT.*

We express the cardinal number of the set A by $n(A)$. Notice that $n(\phi) = 0$ since ϕ is empty. Consider any member (sample point) of E. If it is not a member of A, then it must be a member of $\sim A$ (since $\sim A$ consists of all the sample points not in A). Moreover, any member of E cannot be simultaneously in A and in $\sim A$. Therefore,

$$n(A) + n(\sim A) = n(E)$$

or

$$n(\sim A) = n(E) - n(A) \tag{3}$$

Therefore, if we know the cardinal numbers of E and A, we can compute the cardinal number of the complement of A.

Next we turn to the cardinal number of $A \cup B$. Consider first two events A and B which have no members in common (Figure 7). Clearly,

$$n(A \cup B) = n(A) + n(B) \tag{4}$$

Now consider two events which do have some simple events (members) in common (Figure 8). The cardinal number of $A \cup B$ is the number of members in A or B. If we try to use equation (4), we will be counting the members in the cross-hatched area of Figure 8 twice when we add $n(A)$ and $n(B)$. Thus, we need to subtract the cardinal number of the cross-hatched area from the right-hand side of equation (4). The cross-hatched area is just $A \cap B$; therefore,

$$n(A \cup B) = n(A) + n(B) - n(A \cap B) \tag{5}$$

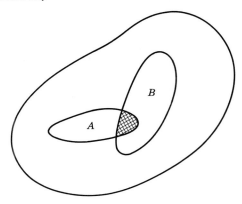

Figure 8

Venn diagram for overlapping sets

When the two sets A and B do not overlap, then $A \cap B = \phi$ and, since $n(\phi) = 0$, equations (4) and (5) produce the same result.

As an example, consider once more the events A and B in Figure 5. The cardinal numbers of A and of B are 2; hence,

$$n(A) = n(B) = 2$$

The intersection of A and B is the single point, HT; so

$$n(A \cap B) = 1$$

Equation (5) then tells us that

$$n(A \cup B) = 2 + 2 - 1 = 3$$

The reader should verify that there are three points in $A \cup B$.

Now equation (5) tells us the cardinal number of the union of A and B provided we know the cardinal numbers of both A and B and also the cardinal number of their intersection. If, on the other hand, we knew $n(A)$, $n(B)$, and $n(A \cup B)$, then we could use equation (5) to find $n(A \cap B)$. In general, equation (5) is the only equation we can find relating the cardinal number of the union of two events with the cardinal number of the intersection of two events. In Section 9.4 we shall obtain an expression for $n(A \cap B)$ for a special case which is of great importance. We shall then use equation (5) to find $n(A \cup B)$.

We close this section by noting that the idea of cardinal numbers can be extended to sets with an infinite number of members (such as all the points in a plane). This gives rise to the theory of **transfinite** numbers and is a result of the work of the German mathematician, Georg Cantor.[3]

9.3 Simple Probabilities

Suppose we repeat a given experiment *e* a large number of times. We might, for example, toss a die 6000 times. We count the number of times a given event occurs. Again by way of example, we might note that a 3 occurs on the top face of the die 997 times and a 4 occurs 1005 times, and so on. If we divide the number of occurrences of a given event by the number of experiments, we get the **frequency** of the event. The frequency of an event then is that fraction of the experiments which produce the given event. The frequency of 3 in our example is $997/6000 = .166166 \ldots$.

The process of repeating the experiment *e* a large number of times is itself an experiment. We can call this bigger experiment *E*. In our example, *E* consists in tossing a die 6000 times. If we perform the bigger experiment *E* several times, how will the frequency of an event vary? Again using our example, if we toss a die 6000 times and repeat this process 10 times (a total of 60,000 tosses of the die), how will the number of 3's in the 10 big experiments vary? We obtained 997 three's in the first big experiment. The second may produce 1002. The third big experiment may produce 998, and so on. We have purposely written down numbers (997, 1002, 998) which do not vary much since this is typical of the outcomes of such experiments.

The **law of large numbers** tells us that, if the number of small experiments performed in each big experiment is large enough, then the frequency of any event will not vary much from one big experiment to another. A precise definition of "much" in the law of large numbers can be given, but it is beyond the scope of this book. For our purposes it is sufficient to observe that in the long run the frequency of an event is practically constant. This long-run frequency is called the **probability** of the event. This remarkable and important law of large numbers was

[3] **Georg Cantor,** 1845–1918, was born in Russia but lived in Germany from the time he was 11 years old. He took the position that "in mathematics the art of properly stating a question is more important than solving it." He studied at Berlin and late in his life suffered from mental breakdowns. Upon recovery from such attacks, he often entered his most productive periods.

first discovered by James Bernoulli.[4] When we say the probability of an event e_1 is P_1, we mean that, if we perform an experiment many times, then "on the average" a fraction P_1 of those experiments will produce the event e_1. For example, in tossing a coin, "on the average" half of the tosses will result in a head. Thus, the probability of a head appearing is ½. This does not mean that if we toss a coin 10 times we should expect precisely five of the tosses to result in a head. Nor does it mean that in 10,000 tosses we should expect 5000 heads. It means that in 10,000 tosses of a coin it is "unlikely" that the number of heads will differ from 5000 by "much." The words "unlikely" and "much" are necessarily vague here. It is possible to be more precise about them if a more precise statement of the law of large numbers is used. As we have pointed out, a more precise statement of this law is beyond the scope of this book.

We are now prepared to discuss probability models or mathematical models of experiments.

A **probability model** consists of a sample space E which is a set of simple events, $e_1, e_2, \ldots, e_n$. To each simple event e_i we attach a number $P(e_i)$ called the **probability** of the event. The numbers $P(e_i)$ satisfy

$$0 \leq P(e_i) \leq 1 \tag{6}$$

for $i = 1, \ldots, n$ and

$$P(e_1) + P(e_2) + \cdots + P(e_n) = 1 \tag{7}$$

The inequalities (6) say that the number of appearances of each simple event is between 0 and the total number of experiments. Equation (7) says that the total number of appearances of all simple events is the total number of experiments.

As an example of a probability model consider a toss of one die. The events $e_1, \ldots, e_6$ are the appearances of $1, 2, \ldots, 6$ on the top face of the die. Since each face of a die is equally likely to appear, we let

$$P(e_1) = P(e_2) = \cdots = P(e_6) = 1/6$$

---

[4] **James Bernoulli** (pronounced "ber-noo'-lee"), 1654–1705, a Swiss mathematician, was the first in a long line of Bernoullis who made significant contributions to mathematics. The most famous were James, his brother Jean, and one of Jean's sons, Daniel. However, eight members of the family distinguished themselves as mathematicians. James first studied theology at his father's urging. However, he soon turned to mathematics and took up the study of the new calculus of Leibnitz. He contributed to mensuration of curves as well as probability. His treatise on probability, *Ars Conjectandi,* was published posthumously in 1715.

For the probability models which we shall consider, each simple event has the same long-run frequency as any other. That is, all simple events have the same probability. Thus, equation (7) becomes

$$n(E) \cdot P(e) = 1$$

where $n(E)$ is the number of simple events in E or, what is the same, the cardinal number of E. The probability of a simple event then is $1/n(E)$. Such probability models are called **uniform.**

Because of the assumption that each simple event has the same long-run frequency we are able to define the probability of an event in terms of cardinal numbers of sets.

We first note that the long-run frequency of any *simple* event is $1/n(E)$ since that is the probability of any simple event.

Next consider an event A with a cardinal number $n(A)$. The event A occurs whenever any simple event in A occurs. Therefore, the long-run frequency of A is the sum of the long-run frequencies of the simple events in A. The long-run frequency of A then is

$$n(A) \cdot \frac{1}{n(E)}$$

The probability of A is

$$P(A) = \frac{n(A)}{n(E)} \tag{8}$$

For example, suppose we toss a die. Let the event A be the appearance of an even number on the top face of the die. Three even numbers can occur (2, 4, or 6), so $n(A) = 3$. The number of possible outcomes is 6, so $n(E) = 6$ and

$$P(A) = 3/6 = 1/2$$

which tells us that one-half of the time an even number will appear.

Problem.   Using Figure 4, determine the cardinal number of the event "at least one head appears." What is the probability of that event?

9.4 Compound Probabilities

We turn now to a discussion of two-part experiments. One type of two-part experiment is tossing a single die twice or, what is equivalent, one toss of two dice. We already have discussed some two-part experiments, but we look at them more closely in this section.

The two parts of a two-part experiment are said to be unrelated if the particular outcome of one does not affect the frequency of the outcome of the other. For example, when we toss two dice the number showing on the first die has nothing whatsoever to do with the frequency with which a 4 (or any other number) appears on the face of the second die. The two parts of this experiment are unrelated. On the other hand, suppose in an urn we have three marbles, one red, one white, and one black. We conduct the following two-part experiment: (1) draw a marble from the urn and (2) draw a second marble from the urn without replacing the first. The probability that the first marble drawn is red (or black or white) is 1/3. However, if the first marble drawn is red, then the probability that the second one is red is 0. The probability that the second marble is white (or black) is ½ if the first marble drawn is red. These probabilities change if the result of the first drawing changes. Therefore, the two parts of this experiment are **related.**

We confine our discussion in this section to **unrelated experiments.**

> **Question.** What is the probability that the second marble is red if the first marble is white? If the first marble is black? If the first marble is red?

Now let E be the sample space for an unrelated two-part experiment. Using the example of the toss of two dice again, the sample space E is shown in Figure 9. It contains 36 points. Each row corresponds to a particular number on the first die, and each column corresponds to a particular number on the second die. Thus the point in the fourth row and third column represents a 4 on die 1 and a 3 on die 2. It is marked $(4, 3)$. As we have pointed out repeatedly, the precise arrangement of the points on the paper is immaterial. The reason why the arrangement is immaterial is that the 36 simple events are unrelated. We have arranged these points by rows and columns for our own later convenience.

Let A be an event which corresponds to some fixed set of outcomes of the first part of the experiment and *any* outcome of the second part of the experiment. If A is the event "the number on the face of the first die is less than or equal to 3," then A is the set of 18 sample points in the first three rows (Figure 9). Any event A then will pick out certain rows of the sample space.

> **Question.** What columns of E correspond to the event "the face of the second die shows an even number"?

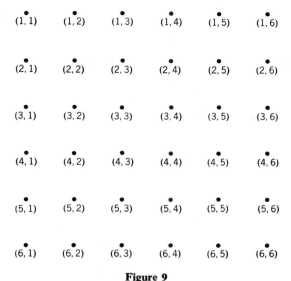

Figure 9

Sample space for toss of two dice

Let B, on the other hand, be an event which corresponds to *any* outcome of the first experiment and a fixed set of outcomes of the second experiment. If B is the event "the number on the face of the second die is greater than or equal to 3," then B is the set of 24 sample points in the last four columns of E (Figure 9).

Let $n(E)$, $n(A)$, and $n(B)$ be the cardinal numbers of E, A, and B, respectively. In our dice example,

$$n(E) = 36, \quad n(A) = 18, \quad n(B) = 24$$

Let the number of rows in E be r. Let c be the number of columns in E. Then

$$r \cdot c = n(E)$$

Now an event A consists of a set of *rows* of E. Since each row contains c points, the number of rows in A is $n(A)/c$. From the last equation then

$$\frac{n(A)}{c} = \frac{n(A)}{n(E)} \cdot r$$

Thus the fraction of the total number of rows which are in A is

$$\frac{n(A)}{n(E)} \tag{9}$$

Next we note that an event B consists of a set of *columns* of E. How many sample points which are in these columns also lie in the rows of A? These points are the points in $A \cap B$.

If we look at any one column of B, only a fraction of the sample points in that column also are in A. That fraction is the fraction of the rows which are in A. It is given by (9).

Looking now at *all* the columns of B, only a fraction of the total number of sample points in B also lie in A. That fraction also is given by (9). Therefore, the number of sample points in $A \cap B$ is

$$n(A \cap B) = \frac{n(A)}{n(E)} \cdot n(B) \tag{10}$$

Returning to our example in which $n(A) = 18$, $n(B) = 24$, and $n(E) = 36$, we have

$$n(A \cap B) = \frac{18}{36} \cdot 24 = 12$$

This tells us that there are 12 sample points where the first die is less than or equal to 3 and the second die is greater than or equal to 3. Can you find them?

Problem.   Let A be the event "the number on the face of the first die is even" and let B be the event "the number on the face of the second die is odd." Describe the events A and B in terms of rows and columns of Figure 9. What are $n(A)$ and $n(B)$? Compute $n(A \cap B)$ from equation (10). Find the sample points in $A \cap B$ and describe the event $A \cap B$ in words.

We can now compute probabilities of the intersection, union, and complement of events *provided the events are unrelated*. Recall that the probability of an event is the cardinal number of the event divided by the cardinal number of the sample space. For example,

$$P(A) = \frac{n(A)}{n(E)} \tag{11}$$

and

$$P(B) = \frac{n(B)}{n(E)} \tag{12}$$

These equations are valid only if each simple event (sample point) is *equally likely*. Now, using equation (10),

$$P(A \cap B) = \frac{n(A \cap B)}{n(E)} = \frac{n(A)}{n(E)} \cdot \frac{n(B)}{n(E)}$$

From equations (11) and (12) then,

$$P(A \cap B) = P(A) \cdot P(B) \tag{13}$$

This is often referred to as the **product law.** Two events, A and B, which obey the product law are called **independent.**

We have derived the product rule for the case where (a) the two parts of an experiment are unrelated and where (b) each point in the sample space is equally likely. The law is valid even when (b) is not true, but we do not prove it here. Part (a), on the other hand, is essential. The product law is not valid in general if the two parts of the experiment are related.

We now ask: What is the probability that either event A *or* event B will occur? From equation (5),

$$n(A \cup B) = n(A) + n(B) - n(A \cap B)$$

Dividing by $n(E)$ and using equations (11), (12), and (13), we obtain

$$P(A \cup B) = P(A) + P(B) - P(A) \cdot P(B)$$

It is important to remember that this law is valid *only if the events A and B satisfy the product law*, equation (13). However, we can always write

$$P(A \cup B) = P(A) + P(B) - P(A \cap B) \tag{14}$$

Returning to our example again, the probability that the first die is ≤ 3 *or* the second die is ≥ 3 is

$$P(A \cup B) = \frac{18}{36} + \frac{24}{36} - \frac{18}{36} \cdot \frac{24}{36} = 5/6$$

This means that $5/6$ of the sample points should be in $A \cup B$. What points are they? How many of them are there?

Finally we recall from equation (3) that

$$n(\sim A) = n(E) - n(A)$$

therefore,

$$P(\sim A) = 1 - P(A) \tag{15}$$

We can compute many compound probabilities using (13), (14), and (15). For example, if A, B, and C are independent events, then from (13)

$$P(A \cap (B \cup C)) = P(A) \cdot P(B \cup C)$$

From (14) then

$$P(A \cap (B \cup C)) = P(A)[P(B) + P(C) - P(B) \cdot P(C)]$$

Multiplying out the terms gives

$$P(A \cap (B \cup C)) = P(A) \cdot P(B) + P(A) \cdot P(C) - P(A) \cdot P(B) \cdot P(C) \quad (16)$$

As an example of the last relationship, suppose we toss three coins. We ask: What is the probability that we will get a head on the first coin and also either a head on the second coin or the third coin or both?

We let A be the event "first coin is a head," we let B be the event "second coin is a head," and we let C be the event "third coin is a head." The probability of each of these events is $1/2$. From (16) then

$$P(A \cap (B \cup C)) = \tfrac{1}{2} \cdot \tfrac{1}{2} + \tfrac{1}{2} \cdot \tfrac{1}{2} - \tfrac{1}{2} \cdot \tfrac{1}{2} \cdot \tfrac{1}{2}$$
$$= 3/8$$

Question. Is the last probability the same as the probability of getting at least two heads on the three coins? Would you expect the probability of getting two heads to be greater than, less than, or equal to 3/8?

The reader might wonder why we have bothered with the laws (13), (14), and (15) when it appears that we must construct the entire sample space in any case. The fact is that we do not need to construct the whole sample space. We can construct the sample spaces for experiments leading to events A and B independently. After we compute $P(A)$ and $P(B)$, then we can get the probabilities for more complex experiments from the laws (13), (14), and (15). For example, in the case where three coins are tossed the sample space consists of eight points. The reader should write them down. To find the probabilities of events in that sample space, however, we need construct only the sample space for the toss of one coin. This sample space has only two points and the probabilities of its events are easily calculated. We can then calculate the probabilities of events in our eight-point sample space from our laws.

We now use one of the laws we have derived in this section to compute the probability of getting a consecutive string of heads if we toss a coin a number of times. That is, we want to find the probability that "the first toss produces a head" *and* "the second toss produces a head" *and* "the third toss produces a head," and so on. If we let H_i be the event that "a head occurs on toss i," then we wish

$$P(H_1 \cap H_2 \cap \cdots \cap H_n)$$

This is the probability that n consecutive heads will appear. But, from (13),

$$P(H_1 \cap H_2 \cap \cdots \cap H_n) = P(H_1) \cdot P(H_2 \cap H_3 \cdots H_n)$$

Similarly,

$$P(H_2 \cap H_3 \cdots H_n) = P(H_2) \cdot P(H_3 \cap \cdots \cap H_n)$$

so that

$$P(H_1 \cap H_2 \cap \cdots \cap H_n) = P(H_1) \cdot P(H_2) \cdot P(H_3 \cap \cdots \cap H_n)$$

Continuing in this way, we have

$$P(H_1 \cap H_2 \cap \cdots \cap H_n) = P(H_1) \cdot P(H_2) \cdots P(H_n)$$

But

$$P(H_i) = 1/2 \tag{17}$$

for all i; therefore,

$$P(H_1 \cap H_2 \cap \cdots \cap H_n) = (1/2)^n$$

The probability of two consecutive heads ($n = 2$) is $1/4$. The probability of three consecutive heads is $1/8$, of four consecutive heads $1/16$, and so on.

It is easy to be misled by these results. For example, we note that the probability of four consecutive heads is much lower than that of three consecutive heads. The difference between these probabilities is $1/16$. We might conclude, therefore, that if we do get three consecutive heads the probability of getting another head on the fourth toss is very slight. Actually, the probability of getting a head on the fourth toss is $1/2$ regardless of what happens on the first three throws. This is what we mean when we say that the parts of the experiment are unrelated. It was for this reason that we wrote equation (17), which in turn verifies the fact that the probability of getting a head on any given toss is $1/2$.

Problem. What is the probability of getting heads and tails alternately on six tosses of a coin?

Problem.   Suppose we toss a single die four times. What is the probability that the face of the die will be an even number on all four tosses? What is the probability that an even number will appear on the face of the die at least once in the four tosses?

We close this section by computing the probabilities of certain events occurring in a special compound experiment. We shall find these results helpful when we analyze the heredity problem posed in Section 9.1 and when we analyze the game of dice (Section 9.9).

Notice first that, in any experiment where each sample point is equally likely, the number of sample points in an event is proportional to the probability of the event. Indeed, for an event A, from equation (8),

$$n(A) = n(E) \cdot P(A) \tag{18}$$

Similarly, for the event B,

$$n(B) = n(E) \cdot P(B) \tag{19}$$

The proportionality factor is always the same and is $n(E)$.

Now suppose we repeat this experiment over and over again until either the event A or the event B occurs. The intersection of A and B is assumed to be empty. That is, events A and B have no sample points (simple events) in common. Thus A and B are two distinct events between which we can easily distinguish. We then ask the question: What is the probability that the event A will occur before the event B? We write this probability as

$$P(A \mid A \cup B)$$

which we read "probability of A given that A or B occurs." That is, we ask for the probability of the event preceding the bar given that the event following the bar occurs.

We let m be the maximum number of experiments conducted before either A or B occurs. Of course, we do not know what m is, and indeed it may be infinite. Nevertheless, the number of sample points in all m experiments is $m \cdot n(E)$.

However, some of these sample points can be ignored because in our experiment we ignore them. In fact, all sample points which are not included in $A \cup B$ are ignored. Therefore, we might just as well construct a sample space consisting only of the sample points in A or B. The number of points in that space is $m \cdot n(A \cup B)$. Since $A \cap B = \phi$, we get from equation (4)

$$m \cdot n(A \cup B) = m \cdot n(A) + m \cdot n(B)$$

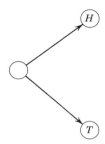

Figure 10

"Star" representing a toss of one coin

as the number of sample points in $A \cup B$. Of these, $m \cdot n(A)$ correspond to the occurrence of the event A; hence, the probability that event A occurs rather than event B is

$$\frac{m \cdot n(A)}{m \cdot n(A) + m \cdot n(B)}$$

Using (18) and (19), this becomes

$$\frac{P(A)}{P(A) + P(B)}$$

Therefore,

$$P(A \mid A \cup B) = \frac{P(A)}{P(A) + P(B)} \tag{20}$$

9.5 Stochastic and Markov Processes

We now continue our study of compound probabilities. We shall derive a graphical method of analyzing probabilities and be able to use it even when different parts of an experiment are related. Of course, the use of the sample space is one graphical method for analyzing probabilities. We turn now to another graphical method which is, in certain cases, more practical.

We first define a **stochastic process** as any sequence of experiments whose outcomes have probabilities of occurring attached to them. Several tosses of a coin represent a stochastic process. So do several tosses of a die.

When we toss a coin, two possible outcomes appear, heads or tails. We represent this graphically by the diagram in Figure 10. The diagram

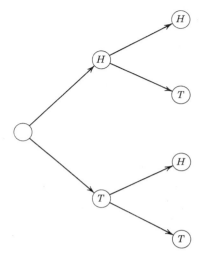

Figure 11

Diagram for toss of two coins

says that, starting from the empty circle, we can go in two directions. One direction leads us to heads (*H*) and the other leads to tails (*T*). This diagram is called a **star.**

Now if we toss the coin a second time we may also get a head or a tail regardless of the outcome of the first toss. This is represented in Figure 11. By following each *chain* of arrows we can determine the four possible outcomes of the experiment. The diagram for three tosses of a coin is shown in Figure 12. Such diagrams are referred to as **trees** because of their tree-like structure. The arrows are called the **branches** of the tree. Each circle with arrows or branches emerging from it is called a *star* as before. If we start at any circle and follow an arrow to a second circle and an arrow from the second circle to a third, and so on, we construct a **chain** of arrows.

The tree in Figure 12 represents three experiments. Each experiment is the toss of a coin. The second experiment cannot be carried out until the first is completed. Therefore, we call the part of the tree to the left of the left-most dashed line the first **stage** of the experiment. The part of the diagram between the two dashed lines is the second stage. The part to the right is the third stage. Notice that the number of stars increases as the number of the stage increases.

In general, we represent stochastic processes by *trees*. As we move from left to right we refer to the successive *stages* of the process. We can visualize time increasing as we move from left to right, but that is not essential and may not always be correct. For example, Figure 12 could represent three coins all thrown at the same time, in which case all stages correspond to the same time.

The reader should notice that there is a correspondence between the chains in a tree and the sample points in the sample space. Each chain corresponds to one sample point. There are eight sample points (simple events) in the experiment of tossing three coins and there are eight chains in the tree in Figure 12.

Before going on we draw one more tree representing a simple stochastic process. Suppose we toss two dice. The tree is shown in Figure 13.

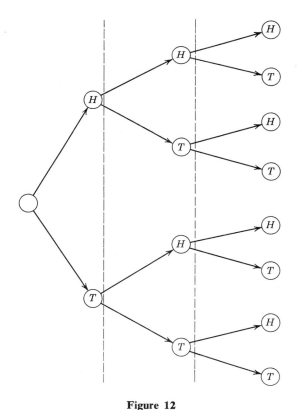

Figure 12

Diagram for toss of three coins

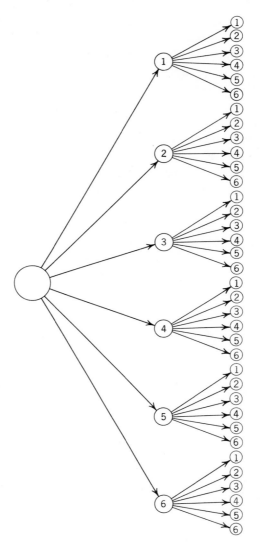

Figure 13

Tree diagram for toss of two dice

There are two stages and each star has six branches. The 36 circles at the end of stage two represent the 36 points in the sample space (see Figure 9). The top star in the second stage corresponds to the first row in Figure 9.

> **Question.** How many chains (points in the sample space) would there be if we tossed three dice? Four dice? How many stages would there be in the tree representing each case?

We now label each branch of the tree with the probability that the event at the end of the arrow will occur given *that the event at the tail of the arrow has occurred.* That is, we look at any star and assume that the event at its origin has occurred. We then label the arrows (branches) emerging from that star with the probabilities that the events at their ends will occur. For example, all the branches in Figure 12 should be labeled $1/2$, so that we get the result shown in Figure 14. These labels are used because the probability of obtaining a head on any single toss of a coin is $1/2$. All of the branches in Figure 13 should be labeled $1/6$. The labels on the branches are called the **branch weights.**

We now ask the question: What is the probability that a given chain will occur? For instance, in Figure 14 we ask for the probability of a tail followed by a head followed by a tail. This is the chain marked with double lines.

One-half of the time we will get a tail on the first coin. Of those times that we do get a tail on the first coin, one-half of them also will result in a head on the second coin. Thus one-fourth of the time we will get a tail followed by a head. Of all the times we get a tail followed by a head, one-half of them will result in a tail on the third coin. Thus one-eighth of the time we will get tail-head-tail.

What we effectively did was to multiply all the branch weights on the chain. We can always do this to find the probability of any chain occurring. In Figure 14 all chains with three branches have a probability of $1/8$. In Figure 13 all chains with two branches have a probability of $1/36$. That all chains have the same probability results from the fact that each chain corresponds to a simple event (point in the sample space) and each simple event is equally likely.

We can use this technique for computing probabilities of chains even if the branch weights are not equal. Suppose, for example, we toss a weighted coin twice. The coin is so weighted that heads appears twice

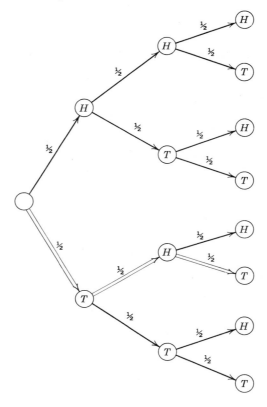

Figure 14

Tree for toss of three coins, with branches labeled

as often as tails. The tree diagram is shown in Figure 15. The probability of two heads is $(2/3) \cdot (2/3)$ or $4/9$. The probability of two tails is $1/9$.

Question. What is the probability of one head followed by one tail?

The only requirements placed on the branch weights are (a) that they be numbers between 0 and 1 and (b) that the branch weights on any star add to 1. That is, the branch weights on the arrows pointing away from any star are probabilities satisfying (6) and (7) in Section 9.3 (page 446).

So far all the branches in our trees have led to simple events, but that is not a necessary restriction. We could replace Figure 15 with the tree in Figure 16. Here we have replaced a two-stage process by a one-

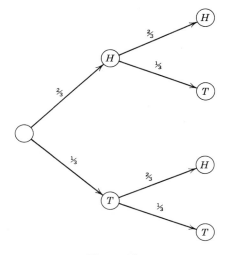

Figure 15

Tree diagram for two tosses of a weighted coin

stage process. This is somewhat analogous to the process in Chapter 8, where we replaced a circuit by a switch. In both cases it is only a convenience and does not give rise to any difficulties except that some of the details of the process are lost in the condensation procedure.

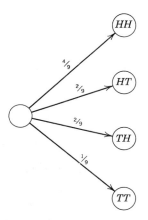

Figure 16

Tree for toss of two weighted coins with two stages reduced to one stage

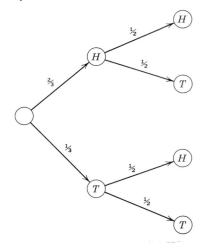

Figure 17

Tree for toss of weighted coin followed by toss of fair coin

The trees we have seen so far have all had their branch labels assigned independently of the outcomes of the previous stages. These are called **independent processes** because they refer to unrelated parts of experiments. Moreover, all our examples have had identical stars throughout the tree. That is, all stars had the same number of branches and the same branch weights. Such processes are called **independent trials processes.**

Not all independent processes are independent trials processes. For example, suppose we toss our weighted coin followed by a fair coin. The tree is shown in Figure 17. This is an independent process (branch weights on any star do not depend on previous outcomes), but it is not an independent trials process (all stars are not identical).

There also are processes which are neither independent nor independent trials processes. Some of these are extremely important, and we turn now to the discussion of one of them, Markov processes.[5]

In a **Markov process** the probabilities assigned to the branches of any

[5] **Andrei Andreevich Markov,** 1856–1922, was a famous Russian mathematician who made valuable contributions to the theory of numbers and approximation theory, as well as to probability. Most of his career was spent at Petrograd University, where he was named Honored Professor in 1905. His son, A. A. Markov (1903—) is an outstanding Soviet mathematician today.

star depend on the outcome at the origin of that star but not on the outcomes of any previous stages. In other words, the probabilities of the outcomes of a given stage depend on the outcome of the stage immediately preceding it but not on other preceding stages.

By way of example, suppose we toss our weighted or biased coin. If a head results, we toss a fair coin. However, if a tail results from the first toss then we toss the weighted coin again. The tree is shown in Figure 18. This is a Markov process because the probabilities assigned at the second stage depend on the outcomes of the previous stage.

Problem. From the tree in Figure 18 find the probability of obtaining two heads, one head and one tail, and two tails.

Problem. Continue the tree in Figure 18 two more stages. The rule for assigning branch weights is: If a head appeared on the previous toss, use a fair coin. If a tail appeared on the previous toss, use a weighted coin. This is a Markov process.

Of course, we can imagine processes in which the probabilities assigned as branch labels depend on the outcomes of several previous stages. The urn problem at the top of page 448 is one such process. However, we do not concern ourselves with such processes.

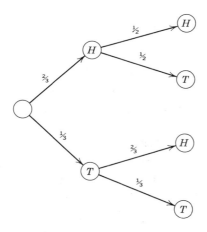

Figure 18

Tree for toss of a weighted coin followed by toss of weighted coin or fair coin, depending on the outcome

We now return to our problem in heredity (Section 9.1) which, we shall see, is a Markov process.

9.6   The Heredity Problem Revisited

In Section 9.1 we posed the following problem. Suppose we are animal breeders and do considerable inbreeding to refine the breed.[6] There is one characteristic, however, which we wish to eliminate and which is carried by a recessive gene. Is it less likely that this characteristic will appear in the offspring resulting from a mating of a brother and sister or from a mating of a mother and son?

Of course, if the undesirable characteristic appears in any animal we shall not use that animal for breeding purposes. In that case the animal is an *xx* genotype and is easily distinguished. Therefore, the animals used for breeding are either *XX* or *Xx* genotypes, since we cannot detect any difference between these two genotypes.

Suppose that a certain fraction of the unrelated (or distantly related) animals used for breeding purposes are *Xx* genotypes. Let that fraction be λ (the Greek letter "lambda") where $0 \leq \lambda \leq 1$. Then the fraction which is *XX* genotype is $1 - \lambda$. Of any sufficiently large sample of the animals, then, the proportion which are *Xx* is likely to be very close to λ. In general, we will not know the value of λ. However, we shall find that the answer to our question is the same regardless of what value λ has.

The undesirable characteristic can appear in an animal only if both its parents are *Xx* genotypes. If at least one parent is *XX*, then the offspring cannot be *xx*. We call an *Xx* genotype a *carrier* since it "carries" the recessive gene but does not give any visible evidence of that fact. In any mating, what we want to know is: What is the probability that both parents are carriers? The probability that an offspring is an *xx* genotype is directly proportional to the probability that both its parents are carriers. We first compute the probability that both partners in a mother-son mating are carriers.

The tree for the mother-son mating is shown in Figure 19. We first select a father from the general population of animals which is at our disposal. The probability that he is *Xx* is λ, and the probability that he is *XX* is $1 - \lambda$. The first stage of the tree in Figure 19 indicates this.

---

[6] The inquisitive reader might ask why selective inbreeding refines a breed. The answers to the questions at the close of this section should help to clarify this concept.

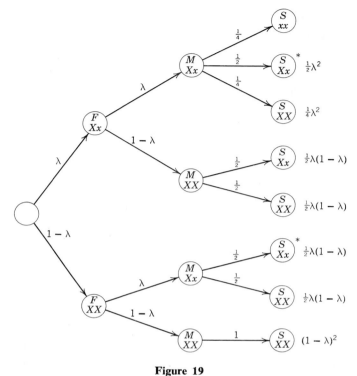

Figure 19

Tree for transmission of genes in mother-son mating

The symbols "*F Xx*" in the circle indicate that the circle represents the outcome of a father (*F*) which is a carrier (*Xx*).

The second stage of the process is the choice of a mother (*M*). Again the probability that she is a carrier is λ. The second stage indicates this choice.

Notice that so far this is an independent trials process. Notice also that the probability that both father and mother are carriers is λ^2. We now wish to go on to the third stage where the outcomes will be the genotype of an offspring. In this case the offspring is assumed to be a son (*S*).

Let us look at the upper star in stage three. Clearly, the son may be any one of three genotypes. Actually, four combinations of genes are possible: (1) the son may receive an *X* gene from both parents; (2) the son may receive an *X* gene from his father and an *x* gene from his mother; (3) the son may receive an x gene from his father and an X gene from his mother; or (4) the son may receive x genes from both parents. We assume that each of these is equally likely. Two of them produce an Xx offspring, so the probability of an Xx offspring is 1/2. The probability that the son is XX or xx is 1/4. These are indicated as branch weights on the top star.

In the second and third stars in stage three, one parent is XX and one is a carrier. The son must receive an X gene from one parent. One-half of the time he will receive an x from the other parent and one-half of the time he will receive a second X. Thus the branch weights are 1/2. Finally, in the last star in stage three, both parents are XX; therefore, the son must be also and the branch weight is 1.

There are now eight chains. If we mate the mother with the son, any one of the eight chains might have been the one which occurred. There is one exception. The uppermost chain could not have occurred because then the son would have been an xx genotype and we would not have allowed the mating.

Two of the chains would result in both mother and son being carriers. They are marked with asterisks at the end of stage three. The other five chains have at least one of the mother and son as XX genotypes.

The expressions to the right of stage three are the probabilities that each of those chains occur. These expressions are the products of the branch weights of each chain.

The probability that both mother and son are carriers is the sum of the probabilities of the two chains ending in an asterisk or

$$P_A = \tfrac{1}{2}\lambda^2 + \tfrac{1}{2}\lambda(1 - \lambda) = \lambda/2$$

The probability of one or neither of the mother and son being a carrier is the sum of the probabilities on the other five chains with expressions to their right. That sum is

$$P_B = 1 - \lambda/2 - \lambda^2/4$$

We wish to know the probability that mother and son are both carriers given that either both are carriers or one is a carrier or neither is a carrier. From equation (20) this is $P_A/(P_A + P_B)$. Thus the probability P_1 that both are carriers is

$$P_1 = (\lambda/2)/(1 - \lambda^2/4) \tag{21}$$

We now turn to the more complicated case of a brother-sister mating. Then we shall compare the two results.

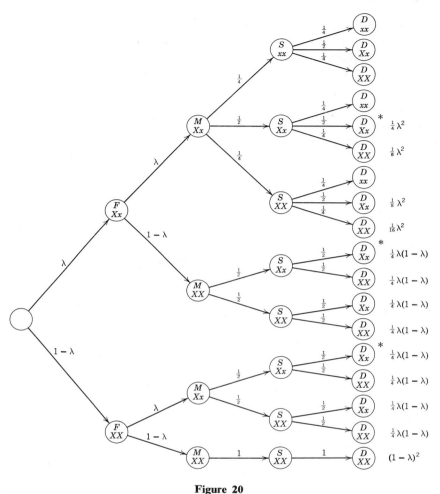

Figure 20

Tree for transmission of genes in brother-sister mating

The tree for this second mating is shown in Figure 20. The first three stages are identical with Figure 19. The fourth stage represents the possible genotypes of the daughter (*D*). Notice that the daughter's genotypes do not depend on the son but on the father and mother. In other words, the branches and branch weights in stage four are identical with those in stage three.

There are eighteen possible chains. Five of them are of no interest to us since either the son or daughter or both are *xx* genotypes. Those five chains are identified by the fact that no expression is written to the right of their tails.

The remaining thirteen chains represent possible outcomes from which we might choose the son (*S*) and the daughter (*D*) for a brother-sister mating. The probability of each of these chains occurring is given by the expression to the right of the chain in Figure 20. The probability that both brother and sister are carriers is the sum of the expressions at the tails of the chains bearing asterisks. It is

$$P_A = (\lambda/2)(1 - \lambda/2)$$

The probability that either or both the brother and the sister are *XX* (noncarriers) is the sum of the other eight chains with expressions at their tails. It is

$$P_B = 1 - (\lambda/2) - (3\lambda^2/16)$$

From equation (20), then, the probability P_2 that brother and sister are carriers given that neither is an *xx* genotype is $P_A/(P_A + P_B)$; therefore,

$$P_2 = \frac{(\lambda/2)(1 - \lambda/2)}{1 - 7\lambda^2/16} \tag{22}$$

Now we would like to know whether P_2 is greater than, equal to, or less than P_1. We will show now that, for $0 < \lambda \leq 1$, $P_1 > P_2$. If $\lambda = 0$, of course, $P_1 = P_2 = 0$.

Problem.   Write a FORTRAN program to compute P_1 and P_2 for $\lambda = 0$, 0.1, 0.2, . . . , 0.9, 1.0 and compare the results.

Consider the following quadratic expression in λ:

$$2\lambda^2 + 3\lambda - 8$$

The reader should have no trouble assuring himself that for $0 < \lambda \leq 1$ this quadratic expression is negative. Thus, we may write

$$2\lambda^2 + 3\lambda - 8 < 0$$

Since $\lambda > 0$, we may multiply this inequality by λ and not affect the inequality sign.

$$2\lambda^3 + 3\lambda^2 - 8\lambda < 0$$

We now add $16 - 7\lambda^2$ to both sides and divide by 16:

$$\frac{2\lambda^3 - 4\lambda^2 - 8\lambda + 16}{16} < \frac{16 - 7\lambda^2}{16}$$

or, upon factoring on the left-hand side,

$$\frac{(4 - \lambda^2)(2 - \lambda)}{8} < \frac{16 - 7\lambda^2}{16}$$

This can be rewritten

$$(1 - \lambda^2/4)(1 - \lambda/2) < 1 - 7\lambda^2/16 \tag{23}$$

Now both $1 - \lambda^2/4$ and $1 - 7\lambda^2/16$ are positive because $0 < \lambda \leq 1$; therefore, we can divide the inequality (23) by both of them, obtaining

$$\frac{1 - \lambda/2}{1 - 7\lambda^2/16} < \frac{1}{1 - \lambda^2/4}$$

Finally, multiplying both sides by the positive number $\lambda/2$, we get

$$\frac{(\lambda/2)(1 - \lambda/2)}{1 - 7\lambda^2/16} < \frac{\lambda/2}{1 - \lambda^2/4}$$

Referring to equations (21) and (22), this tells us that

$$P_2 < P_1$$

(except, of course when $\lambda = 0$, in which case $P_2 = P_1$).

We conclude, therefore, that the probability of both a brother and sister being carriers is always less than the probability of both a mother and son being carriers. There is one exception. If there are no carriers at all in the original population ($\lambda = 0$), then our conclusion is not valid.

Assuming that we start with a mother and father picked at random, it will be safer to mate a brother and sister than to mate a mother and son if we wish to avoid a characteristic carried by a recessive gene.

We make one final remark before leaving this subject. This process is a Markov process although our tree diagrams (Figures 19 and 20) might lead us to think otherwise. The first two stages in each can be combined into one stage with four outcomes. Those four outcomes are: F and M are Xx; F is Xx and M is XX; F is XX and M is Xx; F and M are both XX. Similarly, the last two stages in Figure 20 can be condensed into one stage. When these condensations have been made, it is clear that the processes are Markov processes.

Problem.   The probability of the mother and father selected at random from the population both being carriers is λ^2. Write a FORTRAN program to compare λ^2 with P_1 and P_2 for a sequence of values of λ between 0 and 1. What can you conclude about the propagation of characteristics through random breeding as compared to inbreeding? Can you use this information to explain why animal breeders use inbreeding a great deal?

9.7   Monte Carlo Methods

So far we have talked about experiments which we were able to analyze in detail. We could go on to analyze even more complicated experiments. Indeed, in Section 9.9 we analyze the game of dice and determine the chances of winning that game. However, there are experiments too complicated for the type of analysis we have discussed so far.

Suppose, for example, we wish to design a nuclear reactor. Although it is possible to construct a mathematical model of a reactor, the geometry of an actual reactor is usually so complicated that the model defies solution. However, we can think of the reactor as billions and billions of neutrons moving about and colliding with the nuclei of various atoms. Each collision can result in the emission of new nuclear particles, in a change in direction and energy of the neutron, in the absorption of the neutron by a nucleus, and so on. We can think of the travels of each neutron as a series of experiments. With a certain probability it strikes a nucleus, and with certain other probabilities the different physical phenomena described above will occur. Some of these phenomena may actually produce a new neutron and thus initiate a new set of experiments.

At any given point in time (when the reactor is started, for example) there are billions of neutrons scattered "randomly" throughout the reactor. They are moving in various directions with a variety of energies. If we could trace the history of these neutrons we could determine the energy and other properties of the reactor at any given time. Of course, we cannot do this, but we can approximate such a tracing of history.

If, using the law of large numbers, we trace a large enough number of neutron histories, we will be able to find out all we want to know fairly closely. But we do not know the position, direction, and energy of even one neutron at the start. Again using the law of large numbers, we can say that, if we pick enough neutrons, scatter them "randomly" throughout the reactor, and start them off in "random" directions with "random" energies, the results will not be far from the true results.

It should be obvious that this is a job for a computer because of the tremendous volume of calculation involved. However, the important word in the paragraphs above is "random." It implies some element of chance, and we need to examine its meaning more closely. Roughly speaking, when something is random we are not able to see any pattern in it.

Let us first consider a simpler problem and discuss how we would analyze it by the type of techniques outlined above for a reactor. Suppose we want to know our chances of winning at the game of dice. In this game two dice are thrown. If the total of the numbers on the faces of the dice is 7 or 11 we win. If it is 2, 3, or 12 we lose. If it is any other number (4, 5, 6, 8, 9, 10) the number is called our "point," and we toss the dice again. On the second toss, if the number is our point we win. If it is a 7 we lose. If it is any other number we toss the dice a third time. The process is repeated until either our point or a 7 appears.

While this game can be analyzed in detail as we shall see, it is easier to conceive of determining our chances in another way. We could, of course, actually toss a pair of dice thousands or millions of times and record the wins and losses. From the law of large numbers, we could then estimate the probability of winning. This would be very time consuming and would entail a great deal of bookkeeping.

Another way to find the probability of winning at the game of dice would be to use a computer to "randomly" generate integers between 1 and 6. We could take two of these "randomly" generated numbers and take their sum to be the sum showing on a toss of the dice. We then take two more such "random" integers and use them as another toss of the dice. Using the rules of the game, we could *simulate* thousands of games of dice in a computer. Again we could employ the law of large numbers to estimate the probability of winning. Now, of course, the work and bookkeeping are done by the computer for us. We shall do just that for the game of dice later and compare the results with our more theoretical analysis.

The technique of simulating many chance experiments and drawing inferences from the results of the simulated experiments is called the **Monte Carlo method.** It was first used by the French naturalist, Buffon, in 1773 to estimate the value of π. Buffon took a stick of length L and threw it onto a large flat piece of paper ruled with straight lines a distance $2L$ apart. The experiment was repeated many times, and each time it was noted whether the stick intersected one of the lines or not.

Let N be the number of tosses of the stick. Let X be the number of times the stick lands so that it crosses a line. Then, if N is large enough (law of large numbers),

$$N = \pi X$$

This usually is referred to as the *Buffon needle problem*.

> **Problem.** Try the Buffon needle problem. Combine your results with those of other students and see how close you can estimate π. Usually it takes a large number of experiments to get a reasonably accurate answer.

Monte Carlo methods were given their first systematic development and their colorful name about 1944 by von Neumann[7] and Ulam.[8] These two scientists simulated random neutron diffusion in fissionable material while working on the atomic bomb at Los Alamos Scientific Laboratory in New Mexico. Since then work has continued in these methods, and the most recent work has been directed toward reducing the number of experiments required to obtain a given accuracy.

We have referred to "randomness" many times in our discussion, and it should be clear that it is a pivotal notion in Monte Carlo methods. Let us look at three-digit numbers. When we say a sequence of such three-digit numbers is "random" we mean that any number between 000 and 999 is equally likely to appear in the sequence. But we mean more than that, because in the ordered sequence 0, 1, 2, 3, . . . , 999, 0, 1, 2, 3, . . . each number appears as often as any other and, therefore, each number is equally likely. That sequence, however, is certainly not random. In a random sequence there should be *no pattern in the order in which the numbers appear* and each number should be equally likely to appear. A more precise definition of randomness requires concepts of statistics which are beyond the scope of this text.

---

[7] See footnote 12 in Chapter 1, page 23.
[8] **Stanislaw M. Ulam** (1909—) was born in Poland and came to the United States when he was 27. By then he had received a Doctor of Science degree from the Polytechnic Institute at Lwow. He was a member of the Institute for Advanced Studies at Princeton and a member of the faculties at Harvard and Wisconsin before going to Los Alamos in 1943. It is reported that during the work leading up to the construction of the hydrogen bomb Ulam, with paper and pencil, produced a critically needed result before the computer program to find the result could even be written. He is now a professor of mathematics at the University of Colorado in Boulder.

Suppose we have a sequence of three-digit random numbers. How can we use them in Monte Carlo calculations? We could let the first three numbers (9 digits) describe the position of a neutron using Cartesian coordinates. The next three might specify the direction in which the neutron starts to move. The seventh random number could represent the energy. If the neutron collides with a nucleus the next (or eighth) random number might be used to decide if another atomic particle is released from the nucleus. One possible rule is that, if the eighth random number is even, a particle is released; if it is odd, no particle is released.[9] The succeeding random numbers determine the directions and energies of the neutrons after collision. The process continues until any given state or time occurs.

Suppose we wanted to use random numbers to analyze the game of dice using Monte Carlo methods. We might divide a three-digit random number by 6 and add 1 to the remainder. Then the numbers 1, 2, 3, 4, 5, 6 are all equally likely to appear. We can use these remainders to represent the numbers on the faces of a die and simulate the playing of many games.

In any case it is clear that we need a large number of "random numbers" and that we need to use them to help us simulate many experiments. In the next section we discuss how we can generate random numbers in a computer, and we write a FORTRAN program to generate them. In essence we create an "electronic roulette wheel." We use those programs in Section 9.9 to simulate the game of dice.

Before going on, however, we note another way in which Monte Carlo methods can help us solve problems. Recall that in our heredity problem we did not know the fraction λ of carriers in our original population. We can see from the first two stages of Figure 19 that the probability that an offspring of an unrelated mating will exhibit the undesirable property[10] is λ^2. Suppose we observe that of m offspring from such unrelated matings u of them are xx genotypes. Then, for m sufficiently large, u/m will be very close to λ^2, and we can estimate λ. Although there was no way we could use a computer to assist us directly in this particular genetic experiment, nevertheless we are able to use the ideas of Monte Carlo to extract an important piece of information, the value of λ.

---

[9] This rule supposes that it is equally likely that a particle is released or it is not. Other rules can be devised for other situations.
[10] That is, the offspring is xx.

9.8   *Random Number Generators*

We have seen that to use Monte Carlo methods we need a great quantity of "random numbers." In the preceding section we talked mainly of random numbers each of which had three digits, but we can think of a sequence of random numbers each having as many digits as we like. Suppose, for example, we wanted a sequence of random numbers between 1 and 10. The following sequence is such a random sequence:

$$8, 5, 10, 9, 7, 3, 6, 1, 2, 4, \ldots \tag{24}$$

The dots mean we start again with 8, 5, 10, ..., and repeat the ten numbers again and again. Each of the integers from 1 to 10 appears precisely once each time the sequence in (24) appears (each is equally likely) and the arrangement of the numbers is "scrambled" (there is no apparent pattern).

Of course, once we have written down the sequence (24) it is no longer random because we can reproduce it. For the moment it suffices to say that this sequence "behaves" like a sequence of random numbers.

As a matter of fact, there *is* a pattern to the sequence (24). Suppose we take any number in the sequence and add it to itself. If the result is less than 11, it is the next number in the sequence. If the result is 11 or greater, we subtract 11 from the sum and this difference becomes the next number in the sequence. This algorithm is shown in Figure 21.

As we have pointed out, these numbers are not random in the same sense that the sequence of numbers appearing on the face of a die in repeated tosses of that die are random. We can repeat these numbers merely by repeating the algorithm. We have little hope that we can repeat a sequence of numbers obtained by tossing a die. For this reason, numbers such as those in sequence (24) are called **pseudo-random numbers.** The important point is that they behave somewhat like random numbers. We could use them in Monte Carlo experiments, but it is not advisable since they are not sufficiently random. Shortly we shall see how to obtain a better sequence for use in Monte Carlo work.

Let us take one more example. We use the algorithm in Figure 21 except that we will substitute the number 13 for 11 in boxes 4 and 6. We start with 4 as our first x. The sequence of random numbers is

$$8, 3, 6, 12, 11, 9, 5, 10, 7, 1, 2, 4, \ldots \tag{25}$$

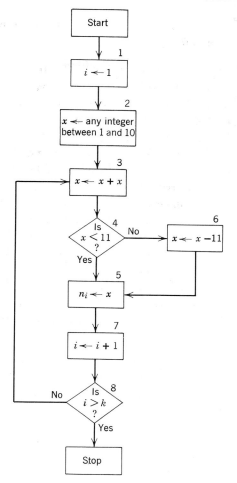

Figure 21

Flow chart to calculate a sequence of k random numbers

Here there are twelve numbers: the integers from 1 to 12 in scrambled order. As we continue the algorithm, we obtain the sequence shown in (25) again and again.

When a sequence of pseudo-random numbers begins to repeat itself, we say it has completed a **cycle.** The cycle length is the number of numbers before repetition begins. The sequence (25) has a cycle length of 12.

Problem.   Continue the sequence (24) for four more terms. What is its cycle length?

It should be obvious that we would like to obtain sequences of pseudo-random numbers with long cycle lengths, although this is not the only requirement we place on our sequences. We can increase the cycle length by increasing the integer used in boxes 4 and 6. We have used 11 and 13 so far. In each case we obtained all the integers up to and including one less than that number (11 or 13) in scrambled order.

To determine what numbers, other than 11 and 13, we can use in boxes 4 and 6 of Figure 21 we need to discuss a few ideas of the branch of mathematics known as *number theory*. We digress from our discussion of random numbers now to discuss those ideas of number theory.

A **prime number** is an integer greater than 1 which, when divided by any other positive integer other than itself or 1, does not result in a quotient which is also an integer. For example, 11 is a prime number because only 11 and 1 divide it exactly. On the other hand, 10 is not a prime since 2 and 5 divide it exactly. The number we choose to use in boxes 4 and 6 of Figure 21 must be a prime number, but not all prime numbers may be used.

Problem.   Use the prime number 17 in boxes 4 and 6 of Figure 21 and choose $x = 1$ in box 2. Show that we do not get the integers 1, 2, . . . , 16 in scrambled order. How many integers do we get? How long is the cycle?

Suppose now we take a prime number and divide it into 2, 2^2, 2^3, . . . , 2^n, ... In general, we get a remainder r_n, so that

$$\frac{2^n}{p} = a + \frac{r_n}{p}$$

or, multiplying both sides of the equation by p,

$$2^n = ap + r_n \tag{26}$$

where $r_n < p$.

Readers familiar with modular arithmetic will notice that the information in equation (26) is contained in the expression

$$2^n \equiv r_n \pmod{p}$$

which is read "2^n is congruent to r_n modulo p."

A famous theorem due to the part-time mathematician, Pierre de

Fermat,[11] proves that, when $n = p - 1$, then $r_n = r_{p-1} = 1$. If $r_n \geq 2$ for all $n = 1, 2, \ldots, p - 2$, then 2 is said to be a **primitive root of** p.

For example, 2 is a primitive root of 5 because

$$2 = 0 \cdot 5 + 2$$
$$2^2 = 0 \cdot 5 + 4$$
$$2^3 = 1 \cdot 5 + 3$$
$$2^4 = 3 \cdot 5 + 1$$

Here $p - 1 = 4$, and r_n is not 1 until $n = p - 1$. However, 2 is not a primitive root of 7 since

$$2^3 = 1 \cdot 7 + 1$$

and here $p - 1 = 6$ not 3, yet $r_3 = 1$.

We now show that, if 2 is a primitive root of p, then the process described in Figure 21 where p is used in place of 11 in boxes 4 and 6 produces all the integers $1, 2, \ldots, p - 1$ in scrambled order.

Notice first that, if we start with $x = 1$, then the integers produced by the algorithm in Figure 21 are the remainders r_n described above. To see this, notice that in Figure 21 we multiply the preceding number by 2, divide by p, and take the remainder as the next integer. From equation (26), however,

$$2^{n+1} = 2ap + 2r_n = bp + r_{n+1}$$

If $2r_n < p$, then $b = 2a$ and $r_{n+1} = 2r_n$. If, on the other hand, $2r_n > p$, then $b = 2a + 1$ and $r_{n+1} = 2r_n - p$. This is exactly the algorithm described above.

Question. Why is it not possible that $2r_n = p$?

We now suppose that at least one of the integers $1, 2, \ldots, p - 1$ is missing from the sequence generated by Figure 21. We shall show that this contradicts the assumption that 2 is a primitive root of p.

[11] **Pierre de Fermat** (pronounced "fair'-mah"), 1601–1665, was a French magistrate (or jurist) who gave no serious thought to mathematics until he was over 30 years old. Although he was only a part-time mathematician, he was one of history's greatest contributors to the theory of numbers, and he discovered the theory of maxima and minima. He once wrote that the equation $x^n + y^n = z^n$, where n is a positive integer, has no solutions where x, y, and z are integers except when $n = 1$ or $n = 2$. This statement remains unproved to this day and is now a classical problem in mathematics. It is usually referred to as "Fermat's last theorem."

If one of the integers 1, 2, ..., $p - 1$ is missing in the first $p - 1$ integers produced by the algorithm of Figure 21, then some other integer must appear at least twice. Suppose the integer m, which is less than p, appears at least twice. We start with $x = 1$ and write down the sequence until the second appearance of m:

$$1, 2, 4, \ldots, m, \ldots, m$$

Now we can determine the integer preceding m in the following way: If m is even, the preceding integer is $m/2$. If m is odd, the preceding integer is $(m + p)/2$. (Recall that all primes, except 2, are odd.) Thus we can reconstruct the sequence by computing the integers to the left of each m. The sequences from right to left starting with each m will be identical since they start from the same value and use the same rule. Thus we get

$$1, 2, 4, \ldots, i, j, k, m, \ldots, i, j, k, m \tag{27}$$

We assume that all the integers preceding the first appearance of m are different. If they are not, we choose the first two that are equal, use their value for m, and start over again.

Now all the integers which precede the first m must also appear between the first and second m. This is so because we use the same rule computing backwards from each m and because the integers preceding the first m are all different. (If all integers preceding the first m were not different, computing backwards from the second m might produce a loop where only some of the integers were computed over and over.)

Since all the integers preceding the first m also appear between the two m's, the integer 1 must appear between the two m's. In fact, 1 immediately follows the first m and the sequence is

$$1, 2, 4, \ldots, i, j, k, m, 1, 2, \ldots, i, j, k, m$$

This implies that some remainder in equation (26) is 1 for $n < p - 1$ which contradicts the assumption that 2 is a primitive root of p.

Therefore, if 2 is a primitive root of p, we will get all the integers from 1 to $p - 1$ in some scrambled order when we use the algorithm in Figure 21 with p replacing 11 in boxes 4 and 6. This argument proceeds without change if we start with any x (rather than $x = 1$), although we have carried it through only for $x = 1$. A complete flow chart for any p is given in Figure 22.

We already have seen that 11 and 13 have 2 as a primitive root. The next five prime numbers of which 2 is a primitive root are 19, 29, 37, 53,

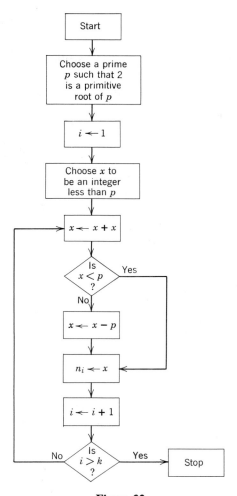

Figure 22

Flow chart to produce sequence of k pseudo-random numbers with cycle length of $p - 1$

and 59. Two other larger primes which have 2 as a primitive root and which we shall find useful later in this section are 941 and 947.

Many texts on number theory contain tables of those prime numbers which have 2 as a primitive root. One such text is *A Second Course in Number Theory* by Harvey Cohn (John Wiley & Sons, 1962). An extensive list including all primes less than or equal to 25,409 can be found in the Proceedings of the London Mathematical Society, Vol. 21, pp. 350–358 (1921).

We now return to our discussion of random numbers where we make use of Figure 22 to produce sequences of integers in scrambled order. We can get longer and longer cycle lengths by increasing p in Figure 22. However, there is a much more clever way to increase the cycle length and at the same time to introduce more "randomness" into the sequence. Suppose we use two different prime numbers both of which have 2 as a primitive root and generate two sequences of random numbers. We create a third sequence by summing the corresponding entries in the first two sequences. We use 11 and 13 as examples and take the sequences (24) and (25). The results are shown in Table 1. The integers in the sum column are again pseudo-random numbers. They can now be as large as $10 + 12 = 22$. Their cycle length is 60. If we carried this sequence out

Table 1

Sequence 1	Sequence 2	Sum
8	8	16
5	3	8
10	6	16
9	12	21
7	11	18
3	9	12
6	5	11
1	10	11
2	7	9
4	1	5
8	2	10
5	4	9
10	8	18
9	3	12
7	6	13
3	12	15
6	11	17
1	9	10
2	5	7
4	10	14
.	.	.
.	.	.
.	.	.

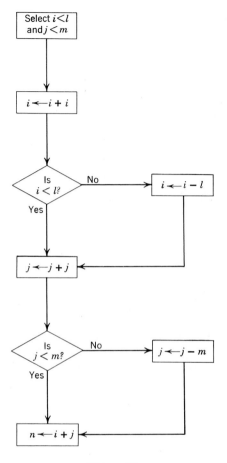

Figure 23

Flow chart for generating *n*, one of a sequence of pseudo-random numbers (the numbers *l* and *m* are prime numbers both of which have 2 as a primitive root)

to 60 terms we would find that 30 are even numbers and 30 are odd numbers. This is precisely what we would like.

Problem.   Continue the sequence of pseudo-random numbers for 40 more terms. Can you see that the cycle has been completed?

In general, this process (described in Figure 23) will produce pseudo-random numbers *n* between 2 and *l* + *m* − 2. The cycle length will be the least common multiple of *l* − 1 and *m* − 1. Here *l* and *m* are prime

```
DIMENSION N(5000)
     L=947
     M=941
     I=400
     J=401
     DO 7 K=1,5000
     IF (I-L) 1,2,2
   2 I=I-L
   1 IF (J-M) 3,4,4
   4 J=J-M
   3 N(K)=I+J
     IF (N(K)-1000) 5,6,6
   6 N(K)=N(K)-1000
   5 I=I+I
   7 J=J+J
```

Figure 24

FORTRAN program to generate 5000 pseudo-random numbers between 0 and 999

numbers of which 2 is a primitive root. We have used variables i, j, l, m, and n in anticipation of a FORTRAN program where these will have to be integers.

Suppose now that we wish to write a FORTRAN program to compute 5000 pseudo-random digits between 0 and 999. We use the flow chart in Figure 23. For l and m we use the prime numbers 941 and 947. To keep the numbers below 1000 we test each number n. If it exceeds 1000, we subtract 1000 from it.

The program is shown in Figure 24. The first 960 of the pseudo-random numbers it produces are shown in Figure 25. They should be read by rows from left to right.

A program such as the one in Figure 24 is called a **random number generator** since it generates random numbers. Strictly speaking, it generates only pseudo-random numbers, but the name "random number generator" is in common usage.

We close this section with a more precise description of what we mean by a sequence of random numbers. We always assume that the numbers are integers.

So far we have said only that every number should be equally likely to appear and that there should be no apparent pattern to the sequence. Actually, a sequence of random numbers should satisfy certain statis-

```
801  602  316  744  488   88  288  576  211  422  844  741  541   82  223  505
122  356  712  483  966  991   35  129  370  740  533   66  191  441  994   47
147  353  755  639  372  856  771  542  196  451   14  140  280  560  179  358
716  485   29   58  116  232  464  928  909  371  795  649  357  714  487  974
  1   55  163  385  882  823  646  404  920  899  857  767  593  245  490  980
 19   97  253  618  236  584  168  389  890  839  731  521  101  202  404  808
675  403  806  612  336  784  568  248  549  210  479   70  193  445    2   63
179  417  946  945  949  957  973  999   51  155  422  844  747  553  165  330
669  320  699  510  132  323  705  522  156  365  842  737  533   66  185  423
958  975    9  130  260  520   40  139  390  780  613  285  570  199  398  796
651  361  722  444    0   59  177  413  938  935  923  905  869  791  635  270
652  363  726  511   22   97  253  618  289  578  156  371  854  767  587  174
460  920  893  845  743  539   78  209  530   60  179  417  946  945  949  957
967  987   33  119  297  647  406  924  907  873  799  598  308  728  509   18
 95  249  551  214  548   80  219  491   94  241  541  194  500    0   59  171
454  908  875  803  659  371  742  537  133  266  532   64  181  415  942  937
933  919  891  841  735  529   58  175  462  924  907  867  787  627  254  561
234  586  160  373  858  769  591  235  470  940  939  937  933  919  897  847
753  565  183  366  732  464   40  139  331  774  548  208  469   50  153  418
836  725  509   18   89  237  586  172  403  918  895  843  686  484   80  272
544   88  235  529  170  399  910  873  799  657  314  681  474   60  173  399
910  873  805  669  338  735  582  276  611  334  730  613  285  570  193  386
772  597  194  441  994   47  153  418  836  672  456   24  107  326  652  357
714  481  962  983   25  109  277  666  391  782  617  234  527  166  444  888
835  729  458   28  109  271  601  314  740  480   72  197  447    6   71  201
461   34  121  301  714  428  968   48   96  192  384  768  589  231  462  924
901  861  775  603  206  524   48  155  422  844  747  547   94  300  600  259
518   36  184  368  736  472   56  165  442  884  821  642  396  904  861  722
556  224  560  120  299  710  473  946  945  943  945  943  939  931  921  901
861  781  621  242  596  192  437  986   25  103  318  636  272  656  312  683
478   68  189  490  980   13   79  211  534   68  195  443  998   49  151  361
834  727  507   14   81  215  542   84  280  560  173  346  692  443  886  825
703  406  924  907  814  740  592  296  645  402  863  838  788  688  488   88
288  576  152  363  779  670  452   16  144  288  576  152  416  832  717  487
974    7   67  187  433  978    9   71  195  443  998   49  157  426  852  757
573  146  345  749  616  332  717  546  204  520   40  133  378  756  571  195
390  780  619  291  582  164  440  880  813  685  423  846  692  496  104  320
640  339  678  356  765  642  396  904  861  775  603  259  518   36  125  362
724  507   14   87  233  578  209  418  836  672  456   24  107  267  587  286
684  368  848  696  504  120  293  639  390  892  837  727  507   14   81  215
542   84  221  501  114  340  680  360  832  664  440  992   37  127  313  738
535   70  193  439  990   39  131  321  754  508  128  315  742  543   86  284
568  136  325  762  577  154  367  846  745  549   98  308  616  285  570  140
339  790  633  266  644  347  694  388  888  829  711  481  962  983   19  150
300  600  200  512   24  107  267  646  292  643  398  908  875  809  618  348
755  622  356  324  701  461  922  903  865  783  625  250  612  224  501  114
281  621  354  820  699  457  914  881  821  701  402  916  891  841  741  541
 82  217  487   86  225  562  124  301  661  434  980   19   91  235  582  164
440  880  819  691  441  882  823  705  410  932  923  899  851  761  575  150
353  818  695  443  886  825  709  477  954  961  975    3   59  177  466  932
923  907  862  779  617  293  586  231  462  924  907  867  787  627  307  614
228  568  136  331  721  554  220  499  110  332  664  381  762  524  160  432
864  781  615  230  519  150  359  830  719  491  982   17   87  227  507  126
311  734  521   42  137  386  772  544  200  453   18  148  296  592  184  480
960  979   70  140  280  560  120  293  698  449  898  855  763  526  164  387
833  778  568  448    8   75  209  471   54  167  446  892  843  739  478   68
189  437  986   25  109  271  601  314  681  474   60  179  411  934  921  901
861  781  615  230  572  203  406  812  677  413  826  652  416  944  947  953
959  977   13  138  276  552  104  261  575  262  577  266  644  288  688  435
870  799  557  314  740  533   66  185  482  964  987   33  125  362  724  507
```

Figure 25

960 pseudo-random numbers generated by the program in Figure 24

tical tests. For example, half of the numbers should be even. We have already noted, in the sequence we generated by summing (24) and (25), that there were 30 even numbers and 30 odd numbers. This sequence, therefore, satisfies this simple test. Another test is to see how often the center digit of any three digits is greater than either of the outside digits. If we look at the first 480 three-digit numbers in Figure 25, we find that in 143 of them the center digit exceeds both outside digits. Ideally this would occur in 137 cases.

There are many other more complicated statistical tests which random number sequences or pseudo-random number sequences should pass if they are to be used with any degree of reliability. We cannot go into them here, but the reader interested in an elementary discussion is referred to Section E of the excellent book, *Problems for Computer Solution* by Fred Gruenberger and George Jaffrey (John Wiley & Sons, 1965). We hasten to point out, however, that the simple sequences (24) and (25) used earlier in this section do *not* satisfy these tests. They were used only to introduce the basic concepts of pseudo-random numbers and should not be used in Monte Carlo calculations. The numbers generated in Figure 23, however, can be used in many problems and will be used in the next section to find the probability of winning at the game of dice.

9.9 The Game of Dice

We return to the game of dice described in Section 9.7. We analyze the game as a Markov process, using trees and branch weights, and find the probability of winning. We then use the random number generator in the last section (Section 9.8) to analyze the game using Monte Carlo methods. Finally we compare our two analyses of the game.

It is appropriate that the study of such a dice game be included in this chapter since it was a similar game that gave birth to the theory of probability. In about 1651 or 1652 a young philosopher-scientist, Blaise Pascal,[12] met a nobleman-gambler, the Chevalier de Méré. de Méré raised the question of the fair way to split the remaining stakes on the table when a game of dice was discontinued. Pascal corresponded with a part-time mathematician, Pierre de Fermat,[13] about the problem, and

---

[12] **Blaise Pascal,** 1623–1662, was the son of an able French mathematician, Etienne Pascal. The younger Pascal was always in ill health, and it has been said that he never went through a day beyond his eighteenth birthday without enduring some pain. Pascal was forbidden the study of mathematics by his father who tutored him in ancient languages. Consequently, as a child he rediscovered much of Euclidean geometry himself. At 19 he invented a mechanical adding machine which was one of the world's first calculating machines. At 23 he became interested in physics and established a reputation for himself in that field as well. At 25 Pascal abandoned science and devoted the remainder of his life to a study of philosophy and religion. Only occasionally did he return to mathematics. He died at the age of 39.

[13] See footnote 11, page 477.

it finally was solved by these two men in 1654. This marked the beginning of mathematical probability.[14]

The rules of the game of dice we discuss are as follows:

1. Two dice are tossed. If the sum of the numbers on the faces of the dice is 7 or 11, we win. If the sum is 2, 3, or 12, we lose. If the sum is any other number (4, 5, 6, 8, 9, or 10), the sum is called the "point" and the result is a draw.

2. If we draw on the first toss, the dice are tossed again. If the sum of the numbers on the faces of the dice is the "point" from the first throw, we win. If the sum is 7, we lose. If the sum is neither the "point" nor 7, the result is a draw.

3. In the event of a draw we toss the dice again and repeat the process in (2) until either the "point" or a 7 appears.

Clearly, this game could go on indefinitely for there is no guarantee that we will ever see either our "point" or a 7 appear. We assume, however, that eventually one or the other does appear and consequently the game ends after a finite number of tosses.

We start our analysis by computing the probability of any given sum appearing on the faces of the two dice on any *one* toss.

Question. What are the possible sums that can occur if we add the numbers on the faces of two dice?

Looking back at Figure 13 in Section 9.5, we can see the tree diagram for one toss of two dice. There are 36 sample points each of which we assume to be equally likely. Since each of these 36 sample points (chain ends in Figure 13) is assumed to be equally likely, each has a probability of 1/36 of occurring. The sum of the numbers on the faces of the dice is the sum of the integers in the circles on the respective chains. We look at the chains starting at the top of Figure 13 and proceeding downward. The 36 sums are:

$$2, 3, 4, \quad 5, \quad 6, \quad 7$$
$$3, 4, 5, \quad 6, \quad 7, \quad 8$$
$$4, 5, 6, \quad 7, \quad 8, \quad 9$$
$$5, 6, 7, \quad 8, \quad 9, \quad 10$$
$$6, 7, 8, \quad 9, \quad 10, \quad 11$$
$$7, 8, 9, \quad 10, \quad 11, \quad 12$$

[14] Actually, Galileo and Cardan had investigated some games of dice some years earlier but not until Pascal and Fermat was probability investigated in depth.

Table 2

Sum	No. of Sample Points
2	1
3	2
4	3
5	4
6	5
7	6
8	5
9	4
10	3
11	2
12	1

From this the reader can easily count the number of sample points corresponding to each sum. They are shown in Table 2. The event "a sum of 7 appears on the faces of the dice" consists of 6 sample points. If we let $\{7\}$ denote this event, then

$$n(\{7\}) = 6$$

Therefore, the probability that a sum of 7 appears is, from equation (8),

$$P(\{7\}) = \frac{n(\{7\})}{n(E)} = 6/36 = 1/6$$

We can compute the probabilities of other events corresponding to the appearance of other possible sums. A tree with branch weights is shown in Figure 26. The numbers in the circles represent the sums appearing on the faces of the dice. The branch weights are the probabilities that those sums will occur. This represents a condensation of the tree shown in Figure 13 much as Figure 16 represented a condensation of the tree in Figure 15. We perform the condensation as a convenience to keep our trees from spreading out too much. We shall perform further condensations in the succeeding discussion.

The three circles marked L in Figure 26 represent the event "we lose on the first throw." This event consists of the three events: "a sum of 2 appears," "a sum of 3 appears," and "a sum of 12 appears." We let $\{2\}$ be the event that a sum of 2 appears. Similarly, $\{3\}$ and $\{12\}$ represent the events that a sum of 3 or a sum of 12 appears. Finally, we let L_1 denote the event that we lose on the first toss. Then

$$L_1 = \{2\} \cup \{3\} \cup \{12\}$$

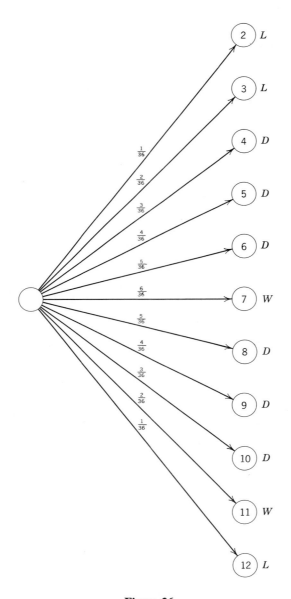

Figure 26

Tree showing probabilities of different sums in one toss of two dice

That is, we lose if 2 *or* 3 *or* 12 occurs. Now 2 and 3 are mutually exclusive events; if 2 occurs, then 3 does not and conversely. Similarly 2, 3, and 12 are all mutually exclusive. In the language of sets,

$$\{2\} \cap \{3\} \cap \{12\} = \phi$$

Using equation (14), then

$$P(L_1) = P(\{2\} \cup \{3\} \cup \{12\}) = P(\{2\}) + P(\{3\}) + P(\{12\})$$

These last probabilities are read off the tree in Figure 26 and

$$P(L_1) = \tfrac{1}{36} + \tfrac{2}{36} + \tfrac{1}{36} = 1/9$$

The probability of winning on toss 1 is calculated in a similar way. It is the sum of the branch weights on 7 and 11, or

$$P(W_1) = \tfrac{6}{36} + \tfrac{2}{36} = 2/9$$

We can, therefore, condense and simplify our tree further to the one shown in Figure 27.

This completes the first stage of our Markov process. The first two chains (win and lose) will end at this first stage. The other six chains can continue. Let us analyze one of these continuations in detail. The analyses of the other chains will be easily deducible from our first detailed analysis.

At the close of Section 9.4 we discussed the following problem: Suppose we conduct an experiment over and over again until either event A or event B occurs. (Events A and B were mutually exclusive.) What is the probability that event A will occur first? The result given in equation (20) was

$$P(A \mid A \cup B) = \frac{P(A)}{P(A) + P(B)}$$

where $P(A)$ and $P(B)$ are the probabilities that A and B, respectively, occur on one experiment, and the notation $P(A \mid A \cup B)$ means the probability that A occurs given that either A or B will occur.

The remaining stage of our dice game is precisely this type of problem. Suppose, for example, our "point" is 4. Then we continue to toss the dice until either a sum of 4 or a sum of 7 appears on the faces of the dice. These two events are mutually exclusive. Therefore, the probability of winning on the second or succeeding throws is

$$P(\{4\} \mid \{4\} \cup \{7\}) = \frac{P(\{4\})}{P(\{4\}) + P(\{7\})} \tag{28}$$

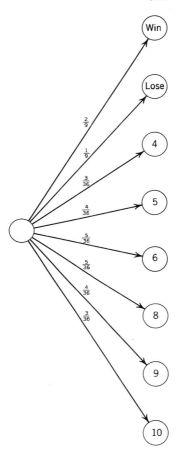

Figure 27

Tree showing probabilities of win, loss, or draw on first toss of dice

where $\{x\}$ is the event "a sum of x" appears on the faces of the dice. But the probability of any given sum appearing is the same on all throws and can be read from the tree in Figure 26. For example, $P(\{4\}) = 3/36$ and $P(\{7\}) = 6/36$. Thus, the probability P_4 of winning if the point is a 4 is, from equation (28),

$$P_4 = \frac{3/36}{3/36 + 6/36} = 1/3$$

Similarly, we can find the probability of winning for other points as follows.

If the point is 5:

$$\frac{P(\{5\})}{P(\{5\}) + P(\{7\})} = \frac{4/36}{4/36 + 6/36} = 2/5$$

If the point is 6:

$$\frac{P(\{6\})}{P(\{6\}) + P(\{7\})} = \frac{5/36}{5/36 + 6/36} = 5/11$$

If the point is 8:

$$\frac{P(\{8\})}{P(\{8\}) + P(\{7\})} = \frac{5/36}{5/36 + 6/36} = 5/11$$

If the point is 9:

$$\frac{P(\{9\})}{P(\{9\}) + P(\{7\})} = \frac{4/36}{4/36 + 6/36} = 2/5$$

If the point is 10:

$$\frac{P(\{10\})}{P(\{10\}) + P(\{7\})} = \frac{3/36}{3/36 + 6/36} = 1/3$$

Notice that we have calculated the probability of winning *if we know the "point."* This implies that we did not win or lose on the first toss and, moreover, we know the sum that appeared on that first toss. We now proceed to use these results to calculate the probability of winning the entire game starting with the first toss.

With the results obtained above we can complete the Markov process tree which we started in Figure 27. The result is shown in the condensed tree in Figure 28. From this tree we can calculate the probability of winning the game. Since the events leading to a win are mutually exclusive (the intersection of their sets of sample points is the empty set), the probability of winning is the sum of the probabilities of each chain which ends in a "win." The individual chain probabilities are the products of the branch weights on the chain.

The probability of winning then is

$$2/9 + (1/12) \cdot (1/3) + (1/9) \cdot (2/5) + (5/36) \cdot (5/11)$$
$$+ (5/36) \cdot (5/11) + (1/9) \cdot (2/5) + (1/12) \cdot (1/3)$$

or

$$244/495 = .4929292 \ldots$$

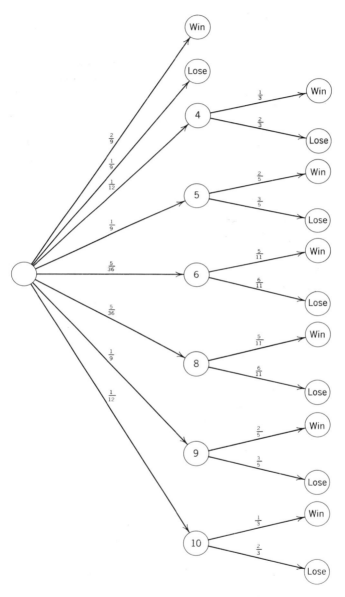

Figure 28

Markov chain for the game of dice

The probability of winning is just slightly less than 1/2. Out of 495 games we should expect that "on the average" we will win 244 and lose 251.

> **Problem.**   From the Markov process tree in Figure 28 compute the probability of losing the game. Compare this result with the probability of winning.

We now summarize our results. We have assumed that on any toss of the dice each of the sample points in Figure 13 is equally likely. We also have assumed that eventually the game ends. With these assumptions we have found that "on the average" out of any group of 495 games there will be 244 wins and 251 losses.

> **Question.**   Is the game of dice a "fair" game? Would you be inclined to bet "with" or "against" the thrower?

Our analysis is not at all simple and there are many pitfalls. Suppose we asked the more complicated question: How many times of the 495 games should we expect to win in 3 or less tosses? We would find difficulty in finding an answer, although a similar analysis could certainly be carried out. The reader no doubt can think of equally interesting questions about the game of dice which would tax his ability to analyze the game.

In order to answer these more complicated questions we turn now to a Monte Carlo analysis of the game of dice. Although the results will be approximate (since that is the very nature of Monte Carlo methods), they will be much easier to obtain with the aid of a computer. Moreover, more complicated questions do not complicate the analysis very much. The beauty of Monte Carlo methods is that the formulation of the method of solution is straightforward and uncomplicated. Its drawback is that its results are approximate and also may use a great deal of computer time.

A crude flow chart of a Monte Carlo method for analyzing the game of dice is shown in Figure 29. We first generate two random integers each of which is between 1 and 6. They represent the numbers appearing on the faces of the two dice in the first toss. These numbers could be generated by actually tossing two dice or by generating the numbers in a computer. We shall do the latter, and we will make use of the random number generator described in Section 9.8 to do so.

We then see if we have won (a 7 or an 11 appears) or lost (a 2, 3, or

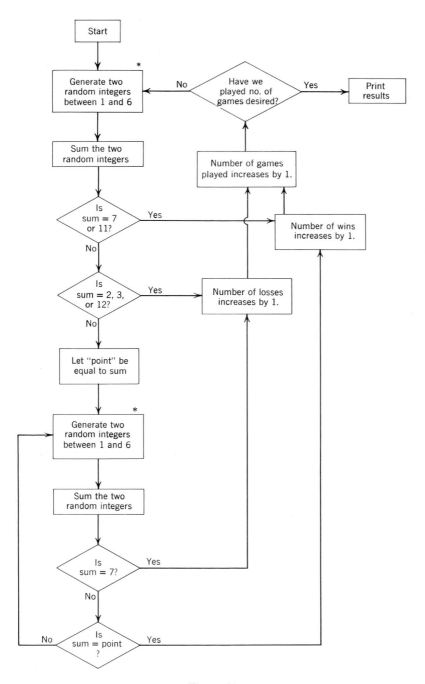

Figure 29

Crude flow chart for playing the game of dice

493

12 appears). If so, we increase the number of wins or losses by 1 and check to see if we have played as many games as we set out to play. If we have not, we play another game.

If the sum of the two dice is not 2, 3, 7, 11, or 12, then we set the sum equal to our point and "toss" the dice again. To do this we generate two more random integers between 1 and 6 and add them together. Now, if the sum is 7, we add 1 to our total of losses. If the sum is our point, we add 1 to our total of wins. If it is neither 7 nor our point, we "toss" the dice again. Of course, if we have either won or lost, we check to see if we have played enough games.

This completes the description of the Monte Carlo method for the game of dice. Compare this procedure with the analysis we described earlier for the game of dice. The Monte Carlo method is much simpler, but it produces only approximate results. In many practical problems the exact analysis is too complicated to handle in any way, whereas Monte Carlo methods are still possible. In those cases we most certainly use Monte Carlo. When a more theoretical analysis is possible, it usually is preferable to a Monte Carlo method.

There are details in the Monte Carlo procedure for the game of dice which need to be filled in later, but they are rather straightforward. Before doing that we pause to note that our algorithm in Figure 29 may never end. Suppose we toss a "4" on the first throw. We then test each succeeding toss for a "4" or a "7." If neither occurs, we continue to toss the dice. Because there is no guarantee that either will ever occur, we may never reach a conclusion. When we write our FORTRAN program, we will have to guard against this eventuality.

In order to write a FORTRAN program for the algorithm outlined in Figure 29 we look first at the details of generating two random integers between 1 and 6 (boxes marked * in Figure 29).

In Figure 23 of Section 9.8 we produced an algorithm for generating a sequence of three-digit random numbers. Suppose now we take such a sequence and divide each number in the sequence by 6. The possible remainders of such a division are the six integers 0, 1, 2, 3, 4, 5. More-over, *each of these remainders is equally likely to occur.* Therefore, if we take the remainders obtained by dividing a sequence of random numbers by 6 and add 1 to each of the remainders, we will obtain a random sequence of the integers 1, 2, . . . , 6.

In Section 3.12 we learned how to use FORTRAN to calculate the remainder when two positive integers are divided. If, using those results, we divide I by 6 the remainder is given by

$$I - 6* (I/6)$$

We now turn to Figure 30, which is a flow chart for generating two random integers between 1 and 6. The following meanings are attached to the variables:

K = loop index (either 1 or 2)

I = first three-digit random number generated from the prime number L

J = second three-digit random number generated from the prime number M

L = prime number of which 2 is a primitive root

M = prime number of which 2 is a primitive root

N(K) = three-digit random number with longer cycle than I or J

NN(K) = quotient less remainder when N(K) is divided by 6

NO(K) = random integer between 1 and 6

The reader should have no trouble following the flow chart. The first part follows Figure 23 quite closely. The index K is used to generate precisely two random integers. A 1 is added on the right side of the expression in the box marked * so that the numbers NO(K) are between 1 and 6 rather than between 0 and 5.

Problem. Write a FORTRAN program to follow the flow chart in Figure 30. Use L = 947 and M = 941. Start with any I and J you wish. Write a loop to execute the program 50 times. You will produce 100 random integers between 1 and 6. See if they appear random. How many games of dice would you win and lose if you used these numbers and Figure 29?

We now turn to a detailed flow chart of the Monte Carlo method for the game of dice. We use the following notation:

NW = number of games won

NL = number of games lost

I and J = starting random numbers

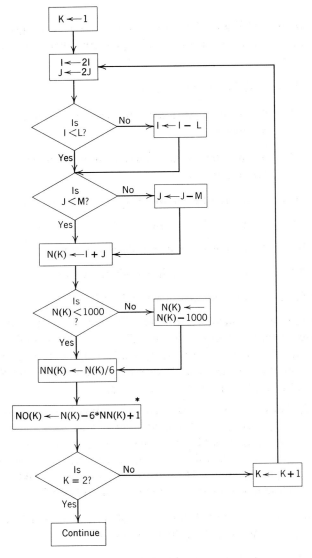

Figure 30

Flow chart to generate two random integers between 1 and 6

496

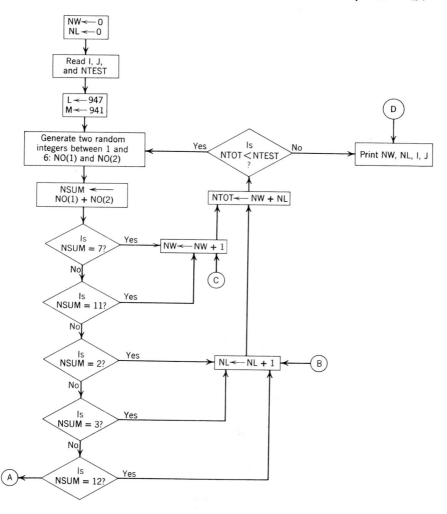

Figure 31

Part 1 of detailed flow chart for game of dice

NTEST = total number of games we want to play

NSUM = number appearing on one toss of dice

NTOT = total number of games played to date

NPT = "point" we are trying to toss

INDEX = number of tosses in a game

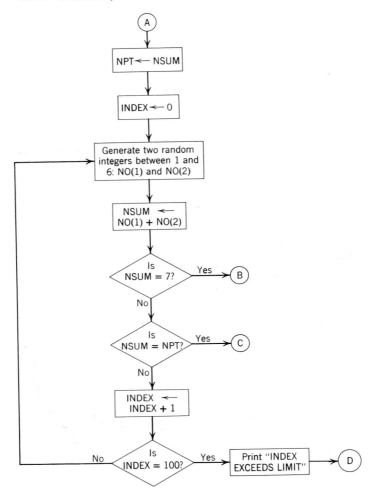

Figure 32

Part 2 of detailed flow chart for game of dice

The flow chart is given in Figures 31 and 32. There are two boxes which read "Generate two random integers between 1 and 6: NO(1) and NO(2)." Each of these should be replaced by the flow chart in Figure 30.

The FORTRAN program for accomplishing the algorithm described in Figures 31 and 32 is given in Figure 33.

The reader should have no trouble following either the flow chart or

```
      DIMENSION N(2),NN(2),NO(2)
      NW=0
      NL=0
      READ 100,I,J,NTEST
100   FORMAT (I5,I5,I10)
      L=947
      M=941
25    DO 7 K=1,2
      I=I+I
      J=J+J
      IF (I-L) 1,2,2
2     I=I-L
1     IF (J-M) 3,4,4
4     J=J-M
3     N(K)=I+J
      IF (N(K)-1000) 5,6,6
6     N(K)=N(K)-1000
5     NN(K)=N(K)/6
7     NO(K)=N(K)-6*NN(K)+1
      NSUM=NO(1)+NO(2)
      IF (NSUM-7) 9,8,9
9     IF (NSUM-11) 10,8,10
10    IF (NSUM-2) 12,11,12
12    IF (NSUM-3) 13,11,13
13    IF (NSUM-12) 14,11,14
14    NPT=NSUM
      INDEX=0
27    DO 15 K=1,2
      I=I+I
      J=J+J
      IF (I-L) 16,17,17
17    I=I-L
16    IF (J-M) 18,19,19
19    J=J-M
18    N(K)=I+J
      IF (N(K)-1000) 20,21,21
21    N(K)=N(K)-1000
20    NN(K)=N(K)/6
15    NO(K)=N(K)-6*NN(K)+1
      NSUM=NO(1)+NO(2)
      IF (NSUM-7) 26,11,26
26    IF (NSUM-NPT) 22,8,22
22    INDEX=INDEX+1
      IF (INDEX-100) 27,27,28
8     NW=NW+1
      GO TO 23
11    NL=NL+1
23    NTOT=NL+NW
      IF (NTOT-NTEST) 25,24,24
24    PRINT 200,NW,NL,I,J
200   FORMAT (8H WINS = ,I5,11H   LOSSES =,I5,7H   I = ,I4,6H   J = ,I4)
      STOP
28    PRINT 300
300   FORMAT (20H INDEX EXCEEDS LIMIT)
      GO TO 24
      END
```

Figure 33

FORTRAN program to play the game of dice using Monte Carlo methods

the FORTRAN program. We have assumed that the number of tosses of the dice in each game should not exceed 100. We shall print out the number of wins, the number of losses, and the final values of I and J. The latter will be useful if we decide to play more games starting where we left off. If we wish to do so, we merely read in the number of additional games we wish to play (NTEST) along with the values of I and J printed out in the previous results.

This was, in fact, done. The first set of games started with I = 400 and J = 401, and we let NTEST = 495. The results were

$$\text{Wins} = 234 \qquad \text{Losses} = 261$$

and

$$I = 934 \qquad J = 35$$

We then played another set of games with I and J equal to those last values (934 and 35) and NTEST again equal to 495. The results of this second set of games were

$$\text{Wins} = 230 \qquad \text{Losses} = 265$$

These two sets of games were equivalent to one set of games with I = 400, J = 401, and NTEST = 990. Had we played such a set of 990 games, we would have won 464 and lost 526.

Succeeding sets of 495 games produced 217, 231, and 219 wins each. The results are summarized in Table 3, where they are compared with

Table 3

	Theoretical Result		Monte Carlo Result	
No. of Games	Wins	Losses	Wins	Losses
495	244	251	234	261
990	488	502	464	526
1485	732	753	681	804
1980	976	1004	912	1068
2475	1220	1255	1131	1344

the theoretical results. After 2475 games, the number of wins using Monte Carlo is 89 less than the expected number.[15]

Problem.   Recompute Table 3 using different starting values for I and J. Does the law of large numbers hold for this set of results?

---

[15] The number of wins is consistently low.

The reader should note that in experiments of 495 games the number of wins varied from a low of 217 to a high of 234. This gives us some idea of how much we can expect the number of wins to vary from its expected value of 244, although there is no guarantee that the very next set of 495 might not produce fewer wins than 217 or more wins than 234. If we played more games, the number of wins should vary less.

One might ask many other questions about the game of dice and modify the program to answer them. For example, we might like to know the length of the longest winning and losing streaks in the 2495 games.

> **Problem.** A winning streak of length m is a succession of m wins immediately preceded by and followed by a loss. (A succession of wins starting with the first game played and followed by a loss is also considered a winning streak, as is a succession of wins which concludes with the last game played.) Change the FORTRAN program to count the number of winning streaks of length two or more wins. Run the modified program with I = 400, J = 401, and NTEST = 2475.

The reader no doubt can think of questions regarding the game of dice which he could not analyze theoretically but which he could compute with minor changes to the program in Figure 33. Some questions of this type appear in the exercises at the close of the chapter.

9.10 Some Practical Considerations

We close this chapter with a discussion of some of the practical aspects of and common misconceptions about probability.

First, the probabilities we have discussed are *mathematical* probabilities. That is, we have assumed that coins, dice, and genes behave in a certain way. Suppose we actually play thousands and thousands of games of dice and find that our results disagree with the results we found in Section 9.9. What have we proved? That our analysis is incorrect? That the dice are unfair?

If the results do not differ from our analysis by "much," then we can assume that our mathematical model is reasonably accurate for the actual game we are playing. If not, all we can conclude is that we do not have a very good mathematical model for *that particular game*. It may be that the dice are unfair. It may be that we are tossing them in a peculiar way. It may be any one of a number of things. Neither the game nor our probability analysis is wrong. They just do not agree.

Exercise 4 at the close of this chapter discusses different mathematical models for the same experiment. It points out that for some physical quantities (in this case sub-atomic particles) one model is preferable to another. The preference arises because one model more closely predicts the actual behavior of the experiment.

Secondly, we have always assigned probabilities ahead of time. We said that a head and a tail were equally likely when we flipped a coin. We also said that the probability of any number from 1 to 6 appearing on the face of a die was 1/6. To indicate the difficulties this kind of assumption may lead to we take a simple example due to J. L. Watling.[16]

Suppose we follow a man along a road and reach a place where the road divides into three paths. Two paths climb the hillside and one goes into the valley. The man is now out of sight. What is the probability that he took the path in the valley?

Using our usual approach, we would assume that each of the three paths was equally likely, so the probability that he took the path in the valley is 1/3. However, we might reason that it was equally likely that he would go into the hills or into the valley. In that case the probability that he took the path in the valley is 1/2. Without any further information at our disposal it is not possible to decide which of these analyses is "correct."

The point is, of course, that we must choose our probabilities ahead of time on the basis of whatever knowledge we have. However, at best, our results will be only as valid as was our choice of probabilities.

Finally, we turn to the so-called "Monte Carlo fallacy." We have noted earlier that the probability of tossing n consecutive heads when tossing a coin is $(1/2)^n$. Suppose we have just tossed 10 consecutive heads. What is the probability that the next toss will result in a head? The answer, as we also noted previously, is 1/2. However, using the "law of averages," a gambler is tempted to bet heavily against another head occurring. This is the Monte Carlo fallacy.[17]

The gambler argues that "on the average" there will be just as many heads as tails. Since there recently has been a preponderance of heads, tails is a better bet right now. However, the number of heads and tails will be equal only after an infinite number of tosses. In any finite num-

---

[16] See the interesting article "Chance" by A. J. Ayer in the October, 1965, issue of *Scientific American*.

[17] The term "Monte Carlo" as used here does not refer to the Monte Carlo method. It is again a case where the same term is used in related but different senses.

ber of tosses we cannot say they will be equal. The law of large numbers tells us only that in a large number of tosses it is "unlikely" that the number of heads will differ by "much" from the number of tails. The words "unlikely" and "much" are important.

To illustrate this final point more clearly we draw once again on the *Scientific American* article by A. J. Ayer. Suppose we draw cards from an ordinary deck containing 26 black cards and 26 red cards. As we draw each card, it is cast away and not returned to the deck. If we draw a succession of black cards, with each drawing the probability that the next card drawn will be red increases. In fact, if we draw 26 straight black cards, then the probability that the next card will be red is 1. We *know* that in a finite number of draws the number of black cards drawn and the number of red cards drawn will be equal. Indeed, after 52 cards are drawn, then 26 of the cards drawn will be red and 26 will be black.

On the other hand, suppose that after each drawing the card which is drawn is returned to the pack. Then we could continue to draw black cards indefinitely. Starting with a complete deck, the probability that the next card will be red is always 1/2.

The Monte Carlo fallacy amounts to equating the two preceding experiments (one where the card is replaced and one where it is not). The fallacy in this case is clear.

Exercises

Answers to exercises marked * are given in Appendix A.

*1. Suppose we are transmitting binary numbers over wires in a computer. That is, a 0 or a 1 is being transmitted along each wire. Because of the quality of the devices a 0 is sometimes interpreted as a 1 when it reaches the other end of the wire. Similarly, a 1 may be misinterpreted to be a 0. The probability of such a misinterpretation (or error) is 0.1. (This means that "on the average" 1 out of 10 signals is interpreted incorrectly.) To improve the accuracy of the transmission we replace each wire by three wires. If we wish to transmit a 1, we transmit a 1 on all three wires. If we wish to transmit a 0, we transmit a 0 on all three wires. Thus a 1 is represented by 111, and a 0 is represented by 000. The probability that each 0 or 1 is transmitted incorrectly is still 0.1. The following eight combinations may be received:

000	110
001	101

010	011
100	111

Those on the left are interpreted as a 0 since most of the digits are 0. The four combinations on the right are interpreted as 1.

What is the probability that a signal (000 or 111) is misinterpreted upon receipt? (*Hint:* The only way for a signal to be misinterpreted is for *two* or *three* digits to be received incorrectly.) This is another problem arising in information theory (see Chapter 8). It is a problem in the reliability of information systems.

2. Suppose the probability that a 0 signal is interpreted as a 1 is 0.01 while the probability that a 1 signal is interpreted as a 0 is 0.02.

   (a) What is the probability that a three-wire 0 signal as described in Exercise 1 is misinterpreted as a 1?

   (b) What is the probability that a three-wire 1 is misinterpreted as as 0?

*3. Condense the tree in Figure 20 so that each stage corresponds to one generation. This will demonstrate that the process is a Markov process.

4. Consider two marbles which we place in three urns in a random way. We consider three cases: (1) the marbles can be distinguished from one another, (2) the marbles cannot be distinguished from one another, and (3) the marbles can be distinguished but at most one can be placed in the same urn.

   (a) In the first case we label the marbles A and B and we label the urns 1, 2 and 3. The following nine arrangements are possible:

Case	Urn		
	1	2	3
i	A, B	—	—
ii	A	B	—
iii	A	—	B
iv	B	A	—
v	—	A, B	—
vi	—	A	B
vii	B	—	A
viii	—	B	A
ix	—	—	A, B

   Because each arrangement is equally likely, the probability of each arrangement is $1/9$. The probability of two marbles appearing in one urn is $1/3$. What is the probability that the first urn is empty?

What is the probability that the third urn contains precisely one marble? These are called *Maxwell-Boltzmann statistics*.[18] Although they appear quite logical when we are dealing with marbles and urns, if we think of the marbles as being atomic or sub-atomic particles there apparently are no particles which obey these statistics.

(b) In the second case where the marbles are indistinguishable, we cannot tell arrangement ii from arrangement iv. Similarly, arrangements iii and vii cannot be separated nor can arrangements vi and viii.

There are only six recognizable arrangements. They are

	Urn	
1	2	3
X, X	—	—
X	X	—
X	—	X
—	X, X	—
—	X	X
—	—	X, X

Each of these arrangements is equally likely and has a probability of $1/6$ of occurring. The probability of two marbles appearing in the same urn is now $1/2$ as compared with $1/3$ in part (a). What is the probability that the first urn is empty? What is the probability that the third urn contains precisely one marble? Compare your results with those in part (a).

These are called *Bose-Einstein statistics*.[18] They are obeyed by atoms, nuclei, and photons.

(c) Finally we return to distinguishable marbles, but we do not allow two marbles to appear in the same urn. This is the same as part (a) except that arrangements i, v, and ix are not allowed. There are six possible arrangements each with a probability of $1/6$. The probability of two marbles appearing in one urn is 0 compared to $1/3$ in (a) and $1/2$ in (b). What is the probability that the first urn is empty? What is the probability that the third urn contains precisely one marble? Compare your results with those in parts (a) and (b).

[18] The use of the word "statistics" here is peculiar to physics and is not to be confused with its more general use in mathematics.

These are called *Fermi-Dirac statistics*.[18] They are obeyed by electrons, neutrons, and protons.

5. Consider three marbles and three urns. An urn may contain 0, 1, 2 or 3 marbles. Construct tables to illustrate the Maxwell-Boltzmann statistics, the Bose-Einstein statistics, and the Fermi-Dirac statistics (see Exercise 4). What is the probability that each urn contains precisely one marble? Compare the results using the three types of statistics.

6. Suppose we are playing the game of dice and we toss a 4 on the first toss. The probability that we will win on the second toss is $1/12$. The probability that we will lose is $1/6$. Therefore, the probability that the second toss will result in a draw is $3/4$. The same probabilities will hold for a win, a loss, or a draw on the third and succeeding tosses. We can represent the stochastic process of tossing the dice when the point is a 4 by the tree shown in Figure 34. Of course, the tree extends

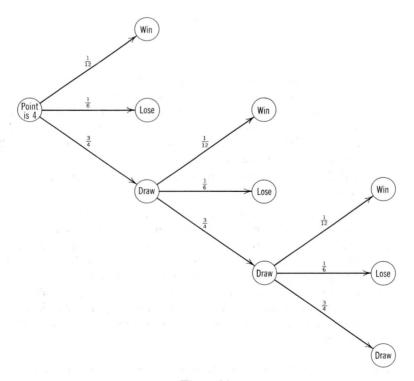

Figure 34

indefinitely to the right with a star emanating from each draw. We can win by following any chain which ends at a circle containing a Win. The probabilities of winning is the sum of the probabilities of all such chains. Therefore, the probability of winning is

$$\tfrac{1}{12} + \tfrac{3}{4} \cdot \tfrac{1}{12} + \tfrac{3}{4} \cdot \tfrac{3}{4} \cdot \tfrac{1}{12} + \cdots = \tfrac{1}{12}(1 + \tfrac{3}{4} + (\tfrac{3}{4})^2 + \cdots)$$

(a) Sum this geometric series (see Chapter 6) to show that, if the point is a 4, the probability of winning is $1/3$.

(b) Draw a tree diagram and write a geometric series for the probability of winning if the point is a 5. Sum the series and compare the result with the probability obtained in the text (Section 9.9).

(c) Repeat part (b) for a point of 6.

*7. Modify the game of dice so that a 3 is a draw rather than a loss on the first toss. What is the probability of winning this modified game of dice?

8. Write a FORTRAN program to estimate the probability of winning the modified game of dice (Exercise 7) using Monte Carlo methods.

*9. Consider two dice in the shape of pyramids. They have four identical sides in the shape of equilateral triangles. The four sides contain the numbers 1, 2, 3, and 4.

(a) If each side is equally likely to appear, draw a tree and show that the probabilities of the respective sums appearing is

Sum	Probability
2	1/16
3	1/8
4	3/16
5	1/4
6	3/16
7	1/8
8	1/16

(b) Consider a game of four-sided dice using the following rules: On the first toss a sum of 5 wins; while either a 2 or an 8 loses. All other results are a draw and the sum appearing is called the point. On the second and succeeding tosses, if a sum of 5 appears we lose, while if the point appears we win. All other numbers result in a draw and another toss of the dice. Show that the probability of winning this game is $83/168$.

10. Write a FORTRAN program to play the game of four-sided dice described in Exercise 9. Use Monte Carlo methods to estimate the probability of winning. You will need random integers between 1 and 4.

*11. Suppose we toss two of the pyramid-shaped dice described in Exercise 9 until a sum of either 4 or 7 appears. What is the probability that a 7 will appear first?

12. Suppose we toss two of the pyramid-shaped dice described in Exercise 9 until a sum of either 3 or 7 appears. What is the probability that a 7 will appear first?

*13. In tossing two six-sided dice there are eleven possible sums. They are 2, 3, . . . , 12. Assume that each of these sums is equally likely to appear (see description of Bose-Einstein statistics in Exercise 4). What is the probability of winning the game of dice under these conditions? Do you think this probability is more or less accurate than the probability found in the text? Why?

14. Write a FORTRAN program to toss a coin using Monte Carlo methods.
    (a) Count the number of times a head appears followed immediately by a tail.
    (b) Count the number of times two heads followed by a tail occurs.
    (c) Count the number of times three heads appear followed by a tail.
    (d) What are the theoretical probabilities of each of these events?

*15. Among the three digits 1, 2, and 3, first one is chosen at random. Next a second is chosen at random from the remaining two digits. There are six possible outcomes.
    (a) Draw a tree describing this process and label its branches. Is this an independent trials process? Is this a Markov process?
    (b) What is the probability that the first digit selected is odd?
    (c) What is the probability that the sum of the first two digits selected is even?
    (d) What is the probability that the third digit is even?
    (e) Compare the results in parts (c) and (d). What is the relationship between the two results? Explain why this should be so.

16. Consider the three letters *A, B,* and *T.* Choose one at random. Then choose a second at random from the remaining two letters. Finally choose the remaining unchosen letter. There are six possible outcomes.
    (a) Draw a tree describing this process and label its branches. Is this an independent trials process? Is this a Markov process?

(b) What is the probability that the first letter selected is not a vowel?

(c) What is the probability that the letters taken in the order chosen form an English word?

*17. Consider the three letters A, B, and T. Choose one at random from the three. Choose a second at random from all three. Finally choose a third at random from all three letters.

(a) Draw a tree describing this process and label its branches. Is this an independent trials process? Is it a Markov process?

(b) What is the probability that the first letter selected is not a vowel?

(c) What is the probability that the letters taken in the order chosen form an English word?

18. Consider five marbles labeled 1, 2, 4, 6, 8. Choose one at random. Then choose a second at random from the remaining four marbles.

(a) Draw a tree describing this process and label its branches. Is this an independent trials process? Is this a Markov process?

(b) What is the probability that the label on the first marble drawn is even?

(c) What is the probability that the label on the second marble drawn is even?

(d) What is the probability that the sum of the labels on the two marbles drawn is even?

19. If $n(A)$ is the cardinal number of the set A, show that

$$n(A \cup B \cup C) = n(A) + n(B) + n(C)$$
$$- n(A \cap B) - n(A \cap C) - n(B \cap C)$$
$$+ n(A \cap B \cap C)$$

Hint. Use equation (5) and the equations

$$A \cap (B \cup C) = (A \cap B) \cup (A \cap C)$$
$$(A \cap B) \cap (A \cap C) = A \cap B \cap C$$

20. Consider three events A, B, and C which obey the product law, equation (13). Using the result of Exercise 19, find the probability of A or B or C occurring in terms of $P(A)$, $P(B)$, and $P(C)$.

*21. A letter is chosen at random from the word "probability." What is the probability that the letter chosen is one of the five vowels? That it is a vowel in the first half of the alphabet?

22. A card is drawn at random from a deck of 52 playing cards.

(a) What is the probability that it is a heart?

(b) What is the probability that it is a face card (jack, queen, king, or ace)?

(c) What is the probability that it is a heart and a face card?

(d) What is the probability that it is either a heart or a face card?

*23. The integers 877 and 941 both have 2 as a primitive root. Write a random number generator in FORTRAN using the flow chart in Figure 23 and these two numbers for the prime numbers *l* and *m*. Would you expect the cycle of this random number generator to be longer or shorter than the cycle for the random number generator in Figure 24. Why?

24. Write a FORTRAN program to play the game of dice using the random number generator in Exercise 23. You will need to change only the value of L in the program in Figure 33. Play 495 games starting with I = 400 and J = 401. Compare your results with those shown in the text for the program in Figure 33.

*25. Write a FORTRAN program to find out how many tosses of the dice are needed to play a game. The number of tosses varies from game to game. The program should count the number of games which end in one toss, the number ending in two tosses, three tosses, etc.

26. What is the probability that the game of dice is won on the first toss? That it is lost on the first toss? Write a FORTRAN program to estimate these probabilities using Monte Carlo methods and compare the estimates with the theoretical results.

27. Suppose we toss one die until either a 3 or a 4 appears. What is the probability that a 4 will appear first?

*28. Use the flow chart in Figure 22 to generate a sequence of random numbers with a cycle of 4.

29. Use the flow chart in Figure 23 with *l* = 5 and *m* = 11. What is the length of the cycle? What are the maximum and minimum values of the integers in the sequence?

*30. Show that 2 is a primitive root of 11.

31. Show that 2 is a primitive root of 13.

32. Show that 2 is *not* a primitive root of 17.

33. In 1907 Paul and Tatiana Ehrenfest originated the following game. Suppose we start with two containers, *A* and *B*. We have a "large"

number of marbles which are numbered consecutively and are in container *A*. Container *B* is empty.

Choose a number at random and move the marble with that number from the container it is in (*A* or *B*) to the other. (Of course, the first move will be from *A* to *B*, but thereafter some marbles may move from *B* back to *A*.) This is a Markov process.

Start with 1000 marbles in container *A* and make 20,000 "random" moves. Write a FORTRAN program to do the work, and record the number of marbles in container *A* after each 1000 moves. Draw a graph of the results. Plot the number of marbles in container *A* on the vertical axis and the number of moves on the horizontal axis.

This is a simplified model of what occurs when a valve is suddenly opened in a tube connecting two jars, one containing a gas and the other a vacuum. The marbles represent molecules of the gas. According to the second law of thermodynamics, gas rushes into the vacuum until the pressure in the two jars is the same. Does your experiment with the Ehrenfest game confirm this?

Answers to Selected Exercises

Chapter 1

2. $x = 2$, $y = 1$, $z = 2$.

5. There is no one correct flow chart. One correct flow chart is given in Figures 1 and 2. This chart is divided into two parts. The first (Figure 1) reduces the equations from their original form to the form shown in equations (vii), (viii), and (ix) in Exercise 4. The second (Figure 2) finds the solution from those equations. Compare these with Figures 13 and 14 of Chapter 1.

6. $-1.2333 \leq x \leq -.7667$
   $1.9333 \leq y \leq 2.0667$

   The bound on x is different because, when we obtained bounds on y, we substituted them into a different inequality than we did in the text.

8. (a) $1.44 \leq x \leq 2.56$ (b) $1.84 \leq x \leq 2.16$
        $0.88 \leq y \leq 1.12$ $0.88 \leq y \leq 1.12$

12. For each equation substitute the values of x_1, x_2, x_3, and x_4 in the left-hand side and see if this is equal to the right-hand side. One possible flow chart is given in Figure 3.

14. There are many possible solutions. We give one here.

   (i) There is no solution to

$$2x_1 + 3x_2 + 6x_3 = 11$$
$$x_1 - x_2 + 2x_3 = 2$$
$$3x_1 + 2x_2 + 8x_3 = 10$$

   (ii) There is one solution, $x_1 = 1$, $x_2 = 1$, $x_3 = 1$ to

$$2x_1 + 3x_2 + 6x_3 = 11$$
$$x_1 - x_2 + 2x_3 = 2$$
$$-2x_1 + x_2 - x_3 = -2$$

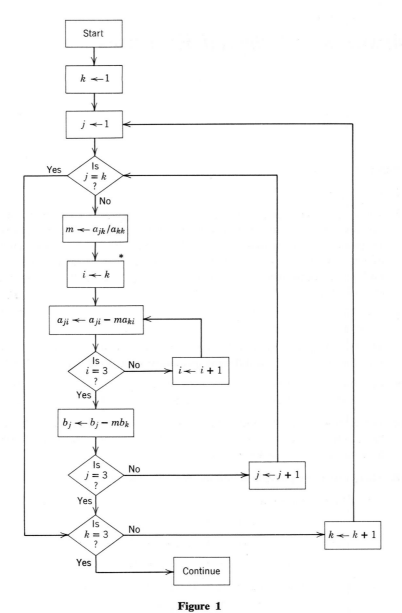

Figure 1

Part 1 of flow chart for Gauss-Jordan method (Exercise 5, Chapter 1)

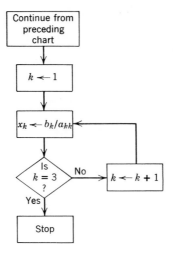

Figure 2

Part 2 of flow chart for Gauss-Jordan method (Exercise 5, Chapter 1)

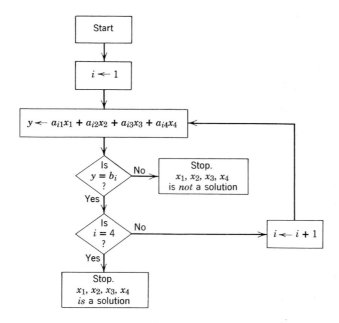

Figure 3

Solution to Exercise 12, Chapter 1

(iii) There are infinitely many solutions to

$$2x_1 + 3x_2 + 6x_3 = 11$$
$$x_1 - x_2 + 2x_3 = 2$$
$$3x_1 + 2x_2 + 8x_3 = 13$$

17. The following statement is inserted between statements numbered 5 and 6:

$$IF(Y)6,11,6$$

18. We add the two equations $M = 0$ and $S = 0$ to the two equations (10) and (11). These comprise four equations in four variables. The program begins with

DIMENSION A(4,4), B(4), X(4)

A(1,1) = 20.0

A(1,2) = 1.0

A(1,3) = 0.0

A(1,4) = 0.0

B(1) = 35.0

A(2,1) = 0.0

A(2,2) = 15.0

A(2,3) = 0.0

A(2,4) = 0.0

B(2) = 30.0

A(3,1) = 0.0

A(3,2) = 0.0

A(3,3) = 1.0

A(3,4) = 0.0

B(3) = 0.0

A(4,1) = 0.0

A(4,2) = 0.0

A(4,3) = 0.0

A(4,4) = 1.0

B(4) = 0.0

2   K = 1

The remainder of the program is unchanged.

20. (a) $x = 0$ and $y = 0$. There are no other solutions.

(b) An infinite number. For example, $x = 0$, $y = 0$, or $x = -3$, $y = 2$, or $x = 3$, $y = -2$, etc.

(c) Homogeneous equations have a nontrivial solution only if the system of equations is singular. The corresponding nonhomogeneous equations will have either no solution or infinitely many. It is informative to draw graphs for the examples in (a) and (b). The lines always pass through the origin. If the system is nonsingular, the lines are not parallel; therefore, $x = 0$ and $y = 0$ is the only solution. If the system is singular, the lines are parallel. Since they both pass through the origin, they must be one and the same line. Therefore, the system has an infinite number of solutions.

23. (a) and (d) are singular. (b) and (c) are nonsingular.

24. (b) $I = 4$ and $X = 0.0$.

26. (b) $x_1 = 1$, $x_2 = 0$, $x_3 = 0$, and $x_4 = 0$.

27. 600 grams of salad and 150 grams of roast beef.

30. $i = 6$.

32. One solution is $x_1 = 100$, $x_2 = 0$, $x_3 = 25$, and $x_4 = 125$. Another is $x_1 = 90$, $x_2 = 10$, $x_3 = 35$, and $x_4 = 115$. There are an infinite number of solutions. The FORTRAN program will not work because the system is singular, and we will attempt to divide by zero during the calculation.

33. (a) $0 = 0$. The system of four equations (i), (ii), (iii), and (iv) is singular.

(b) $0 = 0$. The system of three equations (v), (vi), and (vii) is singular. We can ignore one equation from each system because one equation from each system can be obtained by properly combining the others. For example, adding (i), (ii), and (iii), we get the negative of (iv).

(c) The currents are $x_1 = 1$, $x_2 = 1$, $x_3 = 0$, $x_4 = 1$, $x_5 = 1$. The voltages are $y_1 = 1$, $y_2 = 1$, $y_3 = 0$, $y_4 = 1$, $y_5 = 1$.

(d) The currents are $x_1 = {}^{18}\!/_{17}$, $x_2 = {}^{16}\!/_{17}$, $x_3 = {}^{4}\!/_{17}$, $x_4 = {}^{12}\!/_{17}$, and $x_5 = {}^{22}\!/_{17}$. The voltages are $y_1 = {}^{18}\!/_{17}$, $y_2 = {}^{16}\!/_{17}$, $y_3 = {}^{2}\!/_{17}$, $y_4 = {}^{24}\!/_{17}$, and $y_5 = {}^{22}\!/_{17}$.

34. (a) A = "a floating-point number."

        IF (A) 1,3,3

     3   PRINT 100

   100   FORMAT (9H POSITIVE)

        STOP

     1   PRINT 200

   200   FORMAT (13H NOT POSITIVE)

        STOP

(b) Use A = .5, A = −1.0, and A = 0.0 as the first statement.

37. Adds 11 numbers: $x_1, x_2, \ldots, x_{11}$. When the indicated change is made, it adds 10 numbers: $x_1, \ldots, x_{10}$.

39.   I = 1

        K = 1

   1 I = I + 1

        K = K * I

        IF (I − 5) 1,2,2

   2 PRINT 200, K

   200 FORMAT (I10)

        STOP

        END

40. Sets $Y = |X|$.

41. (a)   I = ?

         J = ?

         IF (I * I −J) 1,2,1

   2 PRINT 100

   100 FORMAT (4H YES)

        STOP

   1 PRINT 200

200 FORMAT (3H NO)

STOP

(b) YES should be printed when (i) and (iii) are used. NO should be printed in the other two cases.

Chapter 2

1. Figure 4 is a geometrical model of the inequalities in Exercise 1. The extreme points are $O(x = 0, y = 0)$; $A(x = 10, y = 1)$; $B(x = 15, y = 2)$, and $C(x = 20, y = 7)$. The solution is unbounded because x_2 may be as large as we please.

4. (a) $\begin{aligned} x_3 &= 3 - x_1 - x_2 \\ x_4 &= 10 - x_1 - 5x_2 \\ x_5 &= 3 - 2x_1 \\ x_6 &= 40 - 16x_1 - 5x_2 \end{aligned}$

(b) We solve the equation for which b_i/a_{i2} is smallest from among those for which $a_{i2} > 0$. In this case, we solve the second of the four equations in (a) above since $10/5$ is less than $3/1$ and $40/5$.

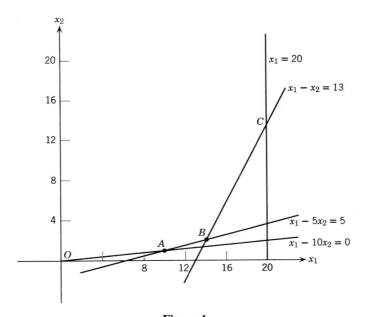

Figure 4

Solution to Exercise 1, Chapter 2

(c) $x_3 = 1 - \frac{4}{5}x_1 + \frac{1}{5}x_4$

$x_2 = 2 - \frac{1}{5}x_1 - \frac{1}{5}x_4$

$x_5 = 3 - 2x_1$

$x_6 = 30 - 15x_1 + x_4$

(d) $2 + \frac{9}{5}x_1 - \frac{1}{5}x_4$

(e) x_1

(f) x_3

(g) $x_1 = \frac{5}{4} - \frac{5}{4}x_3 + \frac{1}{4}x_4$

$x_2 = \frac{7}{4} + \frac{1}{4}x_3 - \frac{1}{4}x_4$

$x_5 = \frac{1}{2} + \frac{5}{2}x_3 - \frac{1}{2}x_4$

$x_6 = \frac{45}{4} + \frac{75}{4}x_3 - \frac{11}{4}x_4$

(h) The objective is $\frac{9}{4} - \frac{9}{4}x_3 + \frac{1}{4}x_4$; therefore, x_4 will become basic.

(i) x_5

(j) $x_1 = \frac{3}{2} \quad - \frac{1}{2}x_5$

$x_2 = \frac{3}{2} \quad - x_3 + \frac{1}{2}x_5$

$x_4 = 1 \quad + 5x_3 - 2x_5$

$x_6 = \frac{17}{2} + 5x_3 + \frac{11}{2}x_5$

(k) The objective is $\frac{9}{2} - x_3 - \frac{1}{2}x_5$. Since the coefficients of x_3 and x_5 are both negative, the objective cannot be increased.

6. See Figures 5 and 6.

9. (a) $x_3 = 0 - x_1 + x_2$

$x_4 = 2 - x_1$

$x_5 = 2 \qquad - x_2$

$x_6 = 3 - x_1 - x_2$

(b) There are three nonzero variables, but there are four basic variables.

(c) The objective does not increase at all. The new basic feasible solution is

$$x_1 = 0 - x_3 + x_2$$

$$x_4 = 2 + x_3 - x_2$$

$$x_5 = 2 \qquad - x_2$$

$$x_6 = 3 + x_3 - 2x_2$$

(d) The objective increases by $\frac{9}{2}$. The new basic feasible solution is

$$x_1 = \frac{3}{2} - \frac{1}{2}x_3 - \frac{1}{2}x_6$$

$$x_4 = \frac{1}{2} + \frac{1}{2}x_3 + \frac{1}{2}x_6$$

$$x_5 = \frac{1}{2} - \frac{1}{2}x_3 + \frac{1}{2}x_6$$

$$x_2 = \frac{3}{2} - \frac{1}{2}x_3 - \frac{1}{2}x_6$$

```
      DIMENSION A(4,2),B(4),ITAB(4),JTAB(2),C(2)
      A(1,1)=1.0
      A(1,2)=-10.0
      A(2,1)=1.0
      A(2,2)=-5.0
      A(3,1)=1.0
      A(3,2)=-1.0
      A(4,1)=1.0
      A(4,2)=0.0
      B(1)=0.0
      B(2)=5.0
      B(3)=13.0
      B(4)=20.0
      C(1)=1.0
      C(2)=1.0
    1 J=1
    2 JTAB(J)=J
    3 IF (J-2)4,5,100
    4 J=J+1
      GO TO 2
    5 I=1
    6 ITAB(I)=I+2
    7 IF (I-4)8,9,100
    8 I=I+1
      GO TO 6
    9 J=1
   10 IF (C(J))11,11,13
   11 IF (J-2)12,14,100
   12 J=J+1
      GO TO 10
   13 K=J
   15 I=1
      N=0
      RATIO= 1 000 000.
   16 IF (A(I,K))17,17,19
   17 IF (I-4)18,22,100
   18 I=I+1
```

Figure 5

First part of the solution to Exercise 6, Chapter 2

(e) The objective is $\frac{9}{2} - \frac{1}{2}x_3 - \frac{3}{2}x_6$. Since the coefficients of x_3 and x_6 are negative, this is the maximum solution.

(f) A geometrical model is given in Figure 7. The constraint set is the quadrilateral $OABC$. Three lines ($x_1 = 0$, $x_2 = 0$, and $x_1 - x_2 = 0$) all intersect at O. Therefore, one of the basic variables, x_3 ($= x_1 - x_2$) is zero at the start. For this reason the objective does not increase during the first step.

(g) $x_1 \leq 2$ and $x_2 \geq 0$.

12. (a) Three pounds of beef and four pounds of pork. (b) Ten pounds of pork and no beef.

17. (a) A geometrical model is given in Figure 8 where x_1 is the percentage of investment in stocks and x_2 is the percentage of investment in

```
        GO TO 16
 19 T=B(I)/A(I,K)
 20 IF (T-RATIO)21,17,17
 21 RATIO=T
        N=I
        GO TO 17
 22 IF (N)100,23,24
 24 ISAV=ITAB(N)
        ITAB(N)=JTAB(K)
 25 JTAB(K)=ISAV
 26 A(N,K)=1.0/A(N,K)
 27 J=1
 28 IF (J-K)31,29,31
 29 IF (J-2)30,32,100
 30 J=J+1
        GO TO 28
 31 A(N,J)=A(N,J)*A(N,K)
        GO TO 29
 32 B(N)=B(N)*A(N,K)
 33 I=1
 34 IF (I-N)37,35,37
 35 IF (I-4)36,44,100
 36 I=I+1
        GO TO 34
 37 J=1
 38 IF (J-K)39,40,39
 39 A(I,J)=A(I,J)-A(I,K)*A(N,J)
 40 IF (J-2)41,42,100
 41 J=J+1
        GO TO 38
 42 B(I)=B(I)-A(I,K)*B(N)
 43 A(I,K)=-A(I,K)*A(N,K)
        GO TO 35
 44 J=1
 45 IF (J-K)46,47,46
 46 C(J)=C(J)-C(K)*A(N,J)
 47 IF (J-2)49,48,100
 48 C(K)=-C(K)*A(N,K)
        GO TO 9
 49 J=J+1
        GO TO 45
100 STOP
 14 PRINT 200,ITAB(1),B(1)
        PRINT 200,ITAB(2),B(2)
        PRINT 200,ITAB(3),B(3)
        PRINT 200,ITAB(4),B(4)
        STOP
 23 PRINT 201
        STOP
200 FORMAT (3H X(,I1,3H) =,F10.4)
201 FORMAT (10H UNBOUNDED)
        END
```

Figure 6

Second part of the solution to Exercise 6, Chapter 2

bonds. The constraint set is the interior and boundary of the quadrilateral *ABCD*. Note that the total investment cannot exceed 100% of the funds; therefore,

$$x_1 + x_2 \leq 100$$

In addition the problem requires

$$x_1 \leq 50$$

$$x_2 \geq 40$$

$$x_1 \leq \tfrac{2}{3}x_2$$

and, of course, $x_1 \geq 0$ and $x_2 \geq 0$.

(b) Never, because the quadrilateral *ABCD* lies to the left of $x_1 = 50$.

(c) One of the constraints, $x_2 \geq 40$, is in the wrong form. If we change it to read $-x_2 \leq -40$, then the right-hand side is negative. The FORTRAN program requires all right-hand sides to be positive.

18. TEMP = T(3)

T(3) = S(6)

S(6) = TEMP

Continue

20. I = 0

1 I = I + 1

J = 11 − I

TEMP = T(I)

T(I) = T(J)

T(J) = TEMP

IF (I − 5) 1,2,2

2 Continue

23. Y = X

IF (Y) 1,2,2

1 Y = −Y

2 Continue

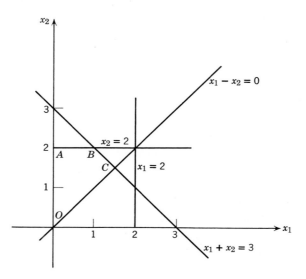

Figure 7

Geometrical model for Exercise 9, Chapter 2

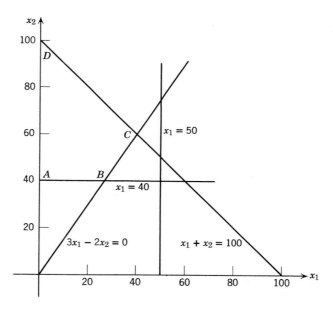

Figure 8

Solution to Exercise 17, Chapter 2

25. K = ?

A = ?

B = ?

C = ?

Y = ?

IF (K − 1) 1,2,3

1 X = A * Y * Y + B * Y + C

GO TO 4

2 X = C * Y * Y + A * Y + B

GO TO 4

3 X = B * Y * Y + C * Y + A

4 PRINT 100,K,X

100 FORMAT (5H①K① = ①,I2,5H①X① = ①,F9.4)

STOP

END

Chapter 3

1. (a) $x = -1, y = -1$

(b) $x = 1, y = 1, z = 2$

(c) $a = 2, b = -1, c = 4, d = 3$

3. READ 1,R

1 FORMAT (F10.2)

IF (R − 100.0) 4,4,5

5 STOP

4 AREA = 3.1416 * R ** 2

CIRC = 6.2832 * R

PRINT 2,R,AREA, CIRC

2 FORMAT (8H①RADIUS = ,F10.2,7H①AREA①,F10.2,
7H①CIRC = ①,F10.2)

GO TO 3

END

5. (a) $.1762315 \times 10^5$.   (b) $-.326592 \times 10^3$.   (c) $-.23 \times 10^{-3}$.
  (d) $.869288 \times 10^3$.   (e) $.1000035 \times 10^1$.   (f) $-.100265 \times 10^3$.

6.

	Mantissa	Exponent
(a)	17623	5
(b)	32659	3
(c)	23000	-3
(d)	86928	3
(e)	10000	1
(f)	10026	3

7. (a) Expression on the left of the equals sign. Only a single variable is allowed there.

  (b) Integer variable and floating-point constant. (*Note:* Some FOR-TRANs allow this.)

  (c) Integer variables cannot be raised to a floating-point power.

  (d) Comma after the 5 should be removed.

  (e) GO is not a legal variable name (Section 3.3).

9.   DO 1 I = 1,3

     PRINT 2

   2   FORMAT (1H ①)

   1   CONTINUE

     STOP

     END

11. (a) $A + B = .3652 \times 10^4$

     $S = .3652 \times 10^4$

   $B + C = .1000 \times 10^1$

     $R = .3653 \times 10^4$

  Addition is not associative on a computer. Both B and C are so small that individually they do not contribute to the sum. When they are added together first, however, their sum does contribute.

  (b) R would change, but S would not. In this case R = S.

  (c) No. Any number with an exponent of zero will be shifted four places right before being added to A. Therefore, such a number does not contribute to the sum.

14. We assume that N, the number of equations, never exceeds 10. A program then is:

```
      DIMENSION  A(10,10),B(10),X(10)
      READ 1,N
   1  FORMAT (I2)
      DO 2 I = 1,N
      DO 3 J = 1,N
      READ 4, A(I,J)
   4  FORMAT (F10.2)
   3  CONTINUE
      READ 4,B(I)
   2  CONTINUE
      DO 5 J = 1,N
      READ 4,X(J)
   5  CONTINUE
      IFLAG = 0
      DO 6 I = 1,N
      ERR = B(I)
      DO 7 J = 1,N
   7  ERR = ERR − A(I,J) * X(J)
      IF (ERR) 8,9,9
   8  ERR = −ERR
   9  IF (ERR − .0001) 6,6,11
  11  PRINT 12,I
  12  FORMAT (28H①NOT①A①SOLUTION①OF①
      EQUATION①,I2)
      IFLAG = 1
   6  CONTINUE
      IF (IFLAG) 10,13,10
```

13   PRINT 14

14   FORMAT (17H ① SOLUTION ① CORRECT)

10   STOP

    END

If this program is used to test whether $x_1 = 3$, $x_2 = 1$, $x_3 = 5$ is a solution of

$$2x_1 - x_2 + x_3 = 5$$
$$x_1 + x_2 + x_3 = 9$$
$$-x_1 + 2x_2 + 4x_3 = 20$$

it will print

NOT A SOLUTION OF EQUATION 1

NOT A SOLUTION OF EQUATION 3

17. (a)   DIMENSION X(20)

    READ 5,N

5   FORMAT (I5)

    DO 7 I = 1,N

    READ 6, X(I)

6   FORMAT (F8.2)

7   CONTINUE

    INDEX = 1

    DO 1 I = 2,N

    IF(X(I) − X(INDEX)) 1,1,2

2   INDEX = I

1   CONTINUE

    PRINT 3,INDEX,X(INDEX)

3   FORMAT (3H①X(,I2,3H)① = ,F8.2,15H①IS①THE① LARGEST)

    STOP

    END

18. (a) I = 3

20.   PRINT 2

   2 FORMAT (3H ② 2)

     DO 7 INT = 3,99

     I = 1

   4 I = I + 1

     IQUO = INT/I

     IREM = INT − IQUO * I

     IF(IREM)1,7,3

   1 STOP

   3 IF(IQUO − I)5,4,4

   5 PRINT 6,INT

   6 FORMAT (I3)

   7 CONTINUE

     STOP

     END

23. (a) See Figure 9 for flow chart.

   (b) DIMENSION IR(28)

       READ 1,IR(1),IR(2)

   1 FORMAT (I5,I5)

      IF(IR(1) − IR(2))3,2,2

   3 I = IR(1)

      IR(1) = IR(2)

      IR(2) = I

   2 I = 0

   5 I = I + 1

   3 FORMAT (3H①X(,I2,3H)① = ,F8.2,15H①IS①THE①

      IF(IR(I + 2))100,4,5

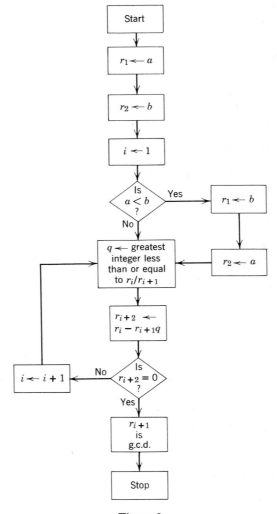

Figure 9

Solution to Exercise 21a, Chapter 3

4   PRINT 6, IR(1),IR(2),IR(I + 1)

6   FORMAT (11H①G.C.D.①OF① ,I5,5H①AND① ,I5,
     4H①IS①,I5)

100   STOP

      END

25. IP = 5 * 12 * 20

JP = (2 * 12 + 3) * 20 + 17

KP = IP − JP

IF(KP)5,6,6

5 PRINT 7

7 FORMAT (25H①PAYMENT①WAS①INSUFFICIENT)

STOP

6 KLB = KP/240

KP = KP −240 * KLB

KS = KP/20

KP = KP − KS * 20

PRINT 8,KLB,KS,KP

8 FORMAT (I3,8H①POUNDS,,I3,11H①SHILLINGS,,I3,6H① PENCE)

STOP

END

27. (a) $m = 11$, $d = 22$, $y = 53$, $c = 19$; therefore, $A = 28$, $B = 13$ and $C = 4$.

(b) The program prints out the number of the day of the week using Monday as No. 1, Tuesday as No. 2, etc.

READ 1,M,ID,IYEAR

1 FORMAT (I2,I2,I4)

M = M − 2

IF (M) 2,2,3

2 M = M + 12

IYEAR = IYEAR −1

ICEN = IYEAR/100

IY = IYEAR − 100 * ICEN

IA = (13 * M − 1)/5

IB = IY/4

    IC = ICEN/4

    K = IA + IB + IC + ID + IY − 2 * ICEN

    KREM = K − (K/7) * 7

    PRINT 4,KREM

4   FORMAT (20H①DAY①OF①THE①WEEK①NO.,I2)

    STOP

    END

(d)   Thursday (Day No. 4).

Chapter 4

2. (a) $T = s/1088 + \sqrt{s/4}$.

(b) $s = 311.52$ ft. The error would be 13.4%.

(c) $T = 23.029$ sec.

5. (a) Slope $= 1$. Equation is $y - x = 0$.

(c) Slope $= 1$. Equation is $y - x = 7$.

13. (a)

x	y	x	y
0	0	6	36
1	1	7	49
2	4	8	64
3	9	9	81
4	16	10	100
5	25		

(b) See Figure 10.

(c)   DIMENSION Y(50),W(50),X(50)

    DO 25 I = 1,6

    E = 0.0001

    XZ = I − 1

    P = XZ ** 2

    DELX = 0.1

    X(1) = XZ + DELX

    Y(1) = X(1) ** 2

    DELY = Y(1) − P

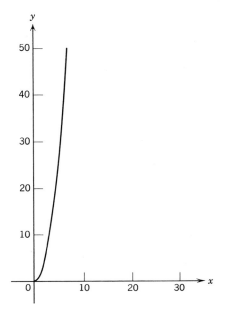

Figure 10

Solution to Exercise 13b, Chapter 4

W(1) = DELY/DELX

DO 16 J = 2,50

DELX = 0.1 * DELX

X(J) = XZ + DELX

Y(J) = X(J) ** 2

DELY = Y(J) − P

W(J) = DELY/DELX

IF(J − 2)20,21,20

20   A = W(J − 1) − W(J)

B = W(J − 2) − W(J − 1)

IF(A − B)21,22,22

21   IF(W(J − 1) − W(J) − E)23,16,16

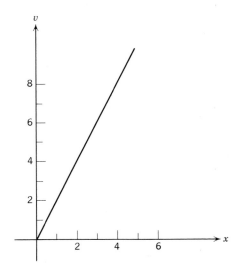

Figure 11

Solution for Exercise 13d, Chapter 4

16   CONTINUE

22   V = W(J − 1)

GO TO 24

23   V = W(J)

24   PRINT 100,XZ,V

25   CONTINUE

100   FORMAT (4H②V(,F3.1,4H)① = ①,F6.2)

STOP

END

(d)   See Figure 11.

(e) $v = 2x$, where v is the slope.

19.

Function $y =$	x^2	x^3	x^4
Slope $=$	$2x$	$3x^2$	$4x^3$

Slope of $y = x^5$ is $5x^4$. The slope of $y = x^m$ is mx^{m-1}. When $m = 1$, this formula produces $1 \cdot x^0 = 1$ and indeed the slope of $y = x$ is a constant equal to 1. When $m = 0$, the formula produces $0 \cdot x^{-1} = 0$, and the slope of $y = 1$ is 0. The formula, therefore, is correct for $m = 1$ and $m = 0$.

24. (a) $2x + 3x^2$

   (e) $4x^3 + 3x^2 + 2x + 1$

30. The sign of y'' is minus $(-)$ because the slope is changing from positive values to negative values and is, therefore, decreasing.

Chapter 5

1. (a) 75 yd.   (b) $x_{n+1} = 50 + x_n/3$.   (c) See Figure 12.

3. First iterative formula is $x_{n+1} = 3x_n - 90$. The second iterative formula is $x_{n+1} = x_n/3 + 30$.

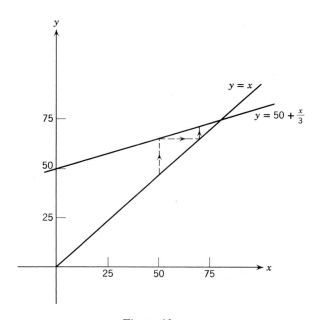

Figure 12

Solution to Exercise 1c, Chapter 5

	Formula 1	Formula 2
x_1	60	60
x_2	90	50
x_3	180	46 2/3
x_4	450	45 5/9
x_5	1260	45 5/27
x_6	3690	45 5/81

The second formula converges because the slope of $y = 30 + x/3$ is ⅓ (less than 1) while the slope of $y = 3x - 90$ is 3 (greater than 1).

7. The method converges with each iterate lying to the left of the solution. See Figure 13.

12. See Figure 14. The solutions are near -1 and $+3.5$. We write $f(x) = 3x^2 - 6x - 12$. Then, for $x = -1$ and $\Delta x = .01$,

$$\overline{w} = -12.03$$

Taking $\overline{w} = -12$, then $\overline{A} = \frac{1}{13}$; therefore,

$$x_{n+1} = x_n + \frac{1}{13}(3x_n^2 - 7x_n - 12)$$

We start with $x_1 = -1.0$

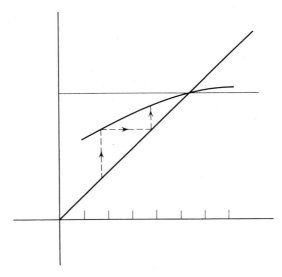

Figure 13

Solution to Exercise 7, Chapter 5

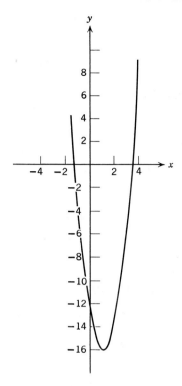

Figure 14

Solution to Exercise 12, Chapter 5

For $x = 3.5$ and $\Delta x = .01$, we get

$$\overline{w} = 15.03$$

Taking $\overline{w} = 15$, then $\overline{A} = -\frac{1}{14}$; therefore,

$$x_{n+1} = x_n - \frac{1}{14}(3x_n^2 - 7x_n - 12)$$

We start with $x_1 = 3.5$.

To find the solution near $x = -1$ use the following program.

DIMENSION X(50)

X(1) = -1.0

DO 1   I = 1,49

Y = X(I) + (3.0 * X(I) ** 2 - 7.0 * X(I) - 12.0)/13.0

$$Z = Y - X(I)$$

IF(Z)2,3,3

2   $Z = -Z$

3   IF(Z − 0.0001)4,1,1

1   X(I) = Y

4   PRINT 100,Y

100   FORMAT (F7.3)

STOP

END

To find the solution near $x = 3.5$ change the second line to read

$$X(1) = 3.5$$

and change the fourth line to read

$$Y = X(I) - (3.0 * X(I) ** 2 - 7.0 * X(I) - 12.0)/14.0$$

No other changes are needed.   •

22. (a)   First $x_1 = 200 - x_0$. Then $x_2 = 200 - x_1 = 200 - (200 - x_0) = x_0$. Then $x_3 = x_1$ and $x_4 = x_0$ and so on. See Figure 15.

(b) -1

24. At $x = 1$ the error estimate is $|e_1| \leq .3$. Because the terms neglected in the equation leading to these errors total .189, our assumption is not so good as it was when the errors in the coefficients were 0.01 (see the text). At $x = 2$ the error estimate is $|e_2| \leq .7$. Here the terms neglected total 0.889; hence, the estimate is very poor indeed. When the coefficients have a large relative error (when the error is fairly large compared to the coefficient), the estimating procedure used here breaks down.

30. (a) $x_{n+1} = \frac{1}{2}(-1 - y_n)$
$y_{n+1} = \frac{1}{3}(1 - 2x_{n+1})$

	0	1	2	3	4
x	0	$-\frac{1}{2}$	$-\frac{5}{6}$	$-\frac{17}{18}$	$-\frac{53}{54}$
y	0	$\frac{2}{3}$	$\frac{8}{9}$	$\frac{26}{27}$	$\frac{80}{81}$

This converges to $x = -1$ and $y = 1$.

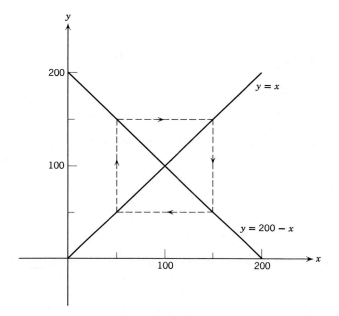

Figure 15

Solution to Exercise 22a, Chapter 5

(b) $x_{n+1} = \frac{1}{2}(1 - 3y_n)$

$y_{n+1} = -1 - 2x_{n+1}$

	0	1	2	3
x	0	$\frac{1}{2}$	$\frac{7}{2}$	$25\frac{1}{2}$
y	0	-2	-8	-26

This diverges.

(c) In the first case, part (a),

$$r = \frac{a_{21}a_{12}}{a_{22}a_{11}} = \frac{2 \cdot 1}{3 \cdot 2} = \frac{1}{3} < 1$$

However, in the second case, part (b),

$$r = 3 > 1$$

Thus we would expect (a) to converge and (b) to diverge, as they do.

34. $y_1 = 1.0$, $y_2 = 1.0$, $y_3 = 1.0$, $y_4 = 1.0$.

Chapter 6

2. $100\left(1 + \dfrac{1}{3} + \dfrac{1}{9} + \dfrac{1}{27} + \cdots + \dfrac{1}{3^{n-1}} + \cdots\right)$

The sum is $100/(1 - \frac{1}{3}) = 150$

4. $\frac{1}{9}$

6. (a) There are many solutions. Two possible ones are

$$1 + \frac{1}{2} + \frac{1}{4} + \cdots + \frac{1}{2^{1-n}} + \cdots$$

and

$$\frac{4}{3} + \frac{4}{9} + \frac{4}{27} + \cdots + \frac{4}{3^n} + \cdots$$

12. It converges because (i) the terms alternate in sign, (ii) each term is smaller in absolute value than its predecessor, and (iii) the nth term approaches zero. To get four figures of accuracy we want $1/n^2 < 10^{-4}$ so $n > 100$. Therefore, a program to evaluate this series is

```
       SUM = 0.0

       N = 101

       TOP = 1.0

    1  X = N

       TERM = TOP/(X ** 2)

       TOP = -TOP

       SUM = SUM + TERM

       N = N - 1

       IF (N) 2,2,1

    2  PRINT 100,SUM

  100  FORMAT (7H①SUM① = ①,F8.4)

       STOP

       END
```

Note the similarity with the program in Section 6.1 to evaluate (2).

23. (a) $15 \cdot 2^{15} = 491,620$ and $16 \cdot 2^{16} = 1,048,576$; therefore, we must start with $n = 16$. A program is

    SUM = 0.0

    N = 16

1   X = N

    TERM = 1.0/(X * 2.0 ** X)

    SUM = SUM + TERM

    N = N − 1

    IF(N) 2,2,1

2   PRINT 100,SUM

100   FORMAT (7H ① SUM ① =①,F9.5)

    STOP

    END

The series (2) used in the text would require one million terms to achieve this accuracy. Here we needed only 16 terms. The series in this exercise converges much more rapidly than does the series in (2).

Chapter 7

1. (a) 119 ft.²   (b) 194 ft.²   (c) 139 ft.² (d) 179 ft.²   (e) 0 ft.² because the entire boundary may coincide with some of the line segments bounding the smaller squares.   (f) 20 ft.² since "on the average" two squares will be boundary squares for each one that was a boundary square before.

3. (a) $\int_0^4 x \, dx$

5. (a) The trapezoid bounded on the left by the line $x = 1$, on the right by the line $x = 3$, on the bottom by the x-axis, and on the top by the line $y = 3x + 1$.

8. (a) 420 ft-lb

(b) $W = \int_0^7 F \, dx = \int_0^7 60 \, dx$

(c) 1800 ft-lb

$W = \int_0^{12} 150 \, dx$

The force is the force of gravity and is equal to 150 lb in this case.

18. $\displaystyle\int_0^t t^4\,dt = \frac{t^5}{5}$ $\displaystyle\int_0^t t^{n-1}\,dt = \frac{t^n}{n}$

20. (a) $\displaystyle\frac{x^3}{3} + \frac{x^4}{4}$

(e) $\displaystyle\frac{4}{3}x^3 - \frac{3}{2}x^2 + 7x$

28.

```
        READ  100,N
100     FORMAT  (I4)
        XN = N
        DELX = 1.0/XN
        X = 1.0
        SUM = 0.0
        M = N − 1
        DO 1 I = 1,M
        X = X+DELX
  1     SUM = SUM+1.0/X
        SUM = (1.0+2.0 * SUM+0.5) * (DELX/2.0)
        PRINT 200,SUM
200     FORMAT (12H ① LOG ① OF ① 2 ① = ① , F10.6)
        STOP
        END
```

Read cards with 5, 25, 50, 100 or 500 punched in the first four columns. The results of five runs on the computer (IBM 7094) are

N	LOG 2
5	.695635
25	.693247
50	.693172
100	.693153
500	.693147

The last result is accurate to six figures.

Chapter 8

1.

x	y	$\sim x$	$\sim y$	$x \wedge y$	$\sim x \wedge y$	$x \wedge \sim y$	$(x \wedge y) \vee (\sim x \wedge y) \vee (x \wedge \sim y)$	$x \vee y$
0	0	1	1	0	0	0	0	0
0	1	1	0	0	1	0	1	1
1	0	0	1	0	0	1	1	1
1	1	0	0	1	0	0	1	1

3. $(\sim x_1 \wedge \sim x_2 \wedge x_3) \vee (\sim x_1 \wedge x_2 \wedge x_3) \vee (x_1 \wedge \sim x_2 \wedge x_3)$
$\vee (x_1 \wedge x_2 \wedge x_3)$

However, from the truth table this is equivalent to x_3. Thus, we can use one switch, x_3, by itself.

5. The first circuit is $(a \wedge \sim b) \vee (a \wedge \sim c) \vee (a \wedge b \wedge c \wedge d)$
$\vee (\sim a \wedge \sim b \wedge \sim d) \vee (\sim a \wedge \sim c \wedge \sim d) \vee (\sim c \wedge d)$
$\vee (b \wedge \sim c \wedge \sim d)$.

Letting $t_1 = a \wedge \sim b$, $t_2 = a \wedge \sim c$, $t_3 = a \wedge b \wedge c \wedge d$, $t_4 = \sim a \wedge \sim b \wedge \sim d$, $t_5 = \sim a \wedge \sim c \wedge \sim d$, $t_6 = \sim c \wedge d$, $t_7 = b \wedge \sim c \wedge \sim d$, and $s = t_1 \vee t_2 \vee t_3 \vee t_4 \vee t_5 \vee t_6 \vee t_7$, we get the following truth table.

a	b	c	d	t_1	t_2	t_3	t_4	t_5	t_6	t_7	s
0	0	0	0	0	0	0	1	1	0	0	1
0	0	0	1	0	0	0	0	0	1	0	1
0	0	1	0	0	0	0	1	0	0	0	1
0	0	1	1	0	0	0	0	0	0	0	0
0	1	0	0	0	0	0	0	1	0	1	1
0	1	0	1	0	0	0	0	0	1	0	1
0	1	1	0	0	0	0	0	0	0	0	0
0	1	1	1	0	0	0	0	0	0	0	0
1	0	0	0	1	1	0	0	0	0	0	1
1	0	0	1	1	1	0	0	0	1	0	1
1	0	1	0	1	0	0	0	0	0	0	1
1	0	1	1	1	0	0	0	0	0	0	1
1	1	0	0	0	1	0	0	0	0	1	1
1	1	0	1	0	1	0	0	0	1	0	1
1	1	1	0	0	0	0	0	0	0	0	0
1	1	1	1	0	0	1	0	0	0	0	1

The second circuit is

$$(a \wedge d) \vee (\sim b \wedge \sim d) \vee (\sim c)$$

Letting $r_1 = a \wedge d$, $r_2 = {\sim}b \wedge {\sim}d$, $r_3 = {\sim}c$, and $u = r_1 \vee r_2 \vee r_3$, we get the following truth table.

a	b	c	d	r_1	r_2	r_3	u
0	0	0	0	0	1	1	1
0	0	0	1	0	0	1	1
0	0	1	0	0	1	0	1
0	0	1	1	0	0	0	0
0	1	0	0	0	0	1	1
0	1	0	1	0	0	1	1
0	1	1	0	0	0	0	0
0	1	1	1	0	0	0	0
1	0	0	0	0	1	1	1
1	0	0	1	1	0	1	1
1	0	1	0	0	1	0	1
1	0	1	1	1	0	0	1
1	1	0	0	0	0	1	1
1	1	0	1	1	0	1	1
1	1	1	0	0	0	0	0
1	1	1	1	1	0	0	1

Since the u and s columns are identical, the circuits are equivalent.

7. ${\sim}(a \wedge b \wedge c) = {\sim}(a \wedge b) \vee ({\sim}c)$

But ${\sim}(a \wedge b) = ({\sim}a) \vee ({\sim}b)$; so ${\sim}(a \wedge b \wedge c) = ({\sim}a) \vee ({\sim}b) \vee ({\sim}c)$.

9. Let $s = a \wedge b \wedge c$ and let $t = ({\sim}a) \vee ({\sim}b) \vee ({\sim}c)$; then

a	b	c	s	${\sim}s$	${\sim}a$	${\sim}b$	${\sim}c$	t
0	0	0	0	1	1	1	1	1
0	0	1	0	1	1	1	0	1
0	1	0	0	1	1	0	1	1
0	1	1	0	1	1	0	0	1
1	0	0	0	1	0	1	1	1
1	0	1	0	1	0	1	0	1
1	1	0	0	1	0	0	1	1
1	1	1	1	0	0	0	0	0

11. (a) and (d) are equivalent; (c) and (h) are equivalent; (e) and (g) are equivalent; (b) and (f) are equivalent.

13. (a)

y	z	$y \vee z$	$z \wedge (y \vee z)$
0	0	0	0
0	1	1	1
1	0	1	0
1	1	1	1

(b)

y	z	$y \wedge \sim z$	$(y \wedge \sim z) \vee z$	$y \vee z$
0	0	0	0	0
0	1	0	1	1
1	0	1	1	1
1	1	0	1	1

15. $a \mid b = (\sim a \wedge \sim b) \vee (\sim a \wedge b) \vee (a \wedge \sim b)$ or $a \mid b = \sim (a \wedge b)$

17. (a) There are eight basic AND circuits.

(b) $a \wedge b \wedge c,\ a \wedge b \wedge \sim c,\ a \wedge \sim b \wedge c,\ a \wedge \sim b \wedge \sim c,\ \sim a \wedge b \wedge c,$
$\sim a \wedge b \wedge \sim c,\ \sim a \wedge \sim b \wedge c,\ \sim a \wedge \sim b \wedge \sim c.$

19. (a) $(x \wedge y) \vee (x \wedge \sim y) = x \wedge (y \vee \sim y)$ using (15). But $y \vee \sim y = 1$;
therefore, $(x \wedge y) \vee (x \wedge \sim y) = x \wedge (1) = x$.

(b) $(x \vee y) \wedge (x \vee \sim y) = x \vee (y \wedge \sim y)$ using (16). But $y \wedge \sim y = 0$;
hence, $(x \vee y) \wedge (x \vee \sim y) = x \vee (0) = x$.

22. Let $t_1 = x \wedge y$, $t_2 = \sim x \wedge z$, $t_3 = y \wedge z$, and $s = t_1 \vee t_2 \vee t_3$. Then let
$r = t_1 \vee t_2$.

x	y	z	t_1	t_2	t_3	s	r
0	0	0	0	0	0	0	0
0	0	1	0	1	0	1	1
0	1	0	0	0	0	0	0
0	1	1	0	1	1	1	1
1	0	0	0	0	0	0	0
1	0	1	0	0	0	0	0
1	1	0	1	0	0	1	1
1	1	1	1	0	1	1	1

24.

```
        PRINT 100
100     FORMAT (15H ④ X ④ Y ④ Z)
  1     IX = 0
        IY = 0
  2     IZ = IX * ((IX + IY + 1)/2)
        PRINT 200,IX,IY,IZ
200     FORMAT (I5,I5,I5)
  4     IF (IY) 6,5,6
  5     IY = 1
```

```
    GO TO 2

6   IF (IX) 9,7,9

7   IX = 1

8   IY = 0

    GO TO 2

9   STOP

    END
```

Three statements are saved.

26. The possible values of IX, IY, and IZ are given in the following table.

IX	IY	IX*IY	IZ
0	0	0	0
0	1	0	1
1	0	0	1
1	1	1	1

Chapter 9

1. Let e_i represent the event "an error in transmission occurs on line i ($i = 1, 2, 3$)." Let c_i represent the event "a correct transmission occurs on line i." Then an erroneous transmission occurs in four cases. In one case, when e_1, e_2, and e_3 all occur. The probability of this case occurring is $.1 \times .1 \times .1 = .001$. In the other cases of erroneous transmission, (a) e_1, e_2, and c_3 occur, or (b) e_1, e_3, and c_2 occur, or (c) e_2, e_3, and c_1 occur. All three of these possibilities occur with probability .009. Since all four cases are mutually exclusive, the probability of an erroneous transmission is the sum of these probabilities or .028.

3. See Figure 16.

7. 499/990.

9. (a) See Figure 17. The numbers appearing in the first column of circles are the numbers appearing on die 1. In the second column of circles, the numbers are the numbers appearing on die 2. The possible sums are shown to the extreme right. Each chain has probability 1/16 of occurring. Since there is one chain with sum 2, the probability of 2 occurring is 1/16. Similarly, since there are three chains with a sum of 4, the probability of 4 occurring is 3/16, and so on.

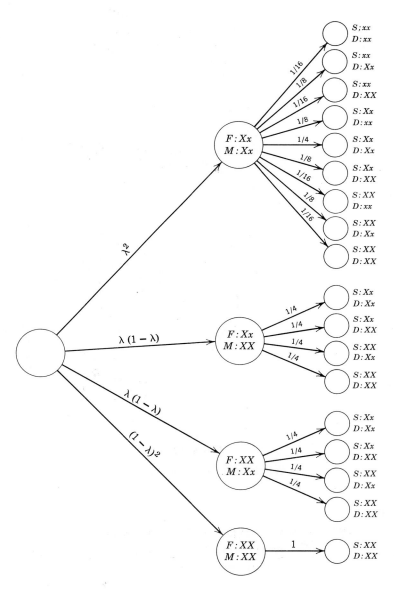

Figure 16

Solution to Exercise 3, Chapter 9

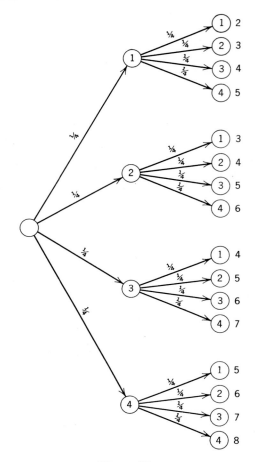

Figure 17

Solution to Exercise 9a, Chapter 9

(b)

$$P(\text{Win}) = P(\{5\}) + P(\{3\}) \cdot P(\{3\} \mid \{3\} \cup \{5\}) + P(\{4\})$$
$$\cdot P(\{4\} \mid \{4\} \cup \{5\}) + P(\{6\}) \cdot (\{6\} \mid \{6\} \cup \{5\})$$
$$+ P(\{7\}) \cdot P(\{7\} \mid \{7\} \cup \{5\})$$

$$= 1/4 + 1/8 \cdot \frac{1/8}{1/8 + 1/4} + 3/16 \cdot \frac{3/16}{3/16 + 1/4}$$

$$+ 3/16 \cdot \frac{3/16}{3/16 + 1/4} + 1/8 \cdot \frac{1/8}{1/8 + 1/4}$$

$$= 83/168$$

11. 2/5.

13. 5/11. This is "probably" less accurate because observation seems to indicate that each face of a fair die is equally likely to appear regardless of the number of dice tossed.

15. (a) See Figure 18. This is not an independent trials process, but it is a Markov process. (b) 2/3. (c) 1/3. (d) 1/3. (e) They are the same. The sum of all three digits is even, therefore if the sum of any two is even (or odd) then the third digit must also be even (or odd).

17. (a) See Figure 19. This is an independent trials process but not a Markov process as we have defined Markov processes. (b) 2/3. (c) 1/9. Three English words are possible: *BAT, TAB,* and *TAT.*

21. Since we do not consider *y* to be a vowel, the probability that the first letter chosen is a vowel is 4/11. The probability that it is a vowel in the first half of the alphabet is 3/11.

23.   L = 877

     M = 941

     I = I + I

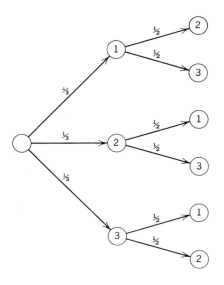

Figure 18

Solution to Exercise 15a, Chapter 9

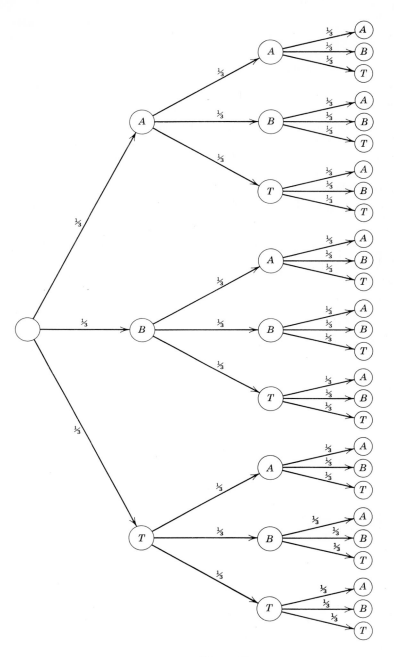

Figure 19

Solution to Exercise 17a, Chapter 9

```
      IF (I − L)  1,2,2
   2  I = I − L
   1  J = J + J
      IF (J − M)  3,4,4
   4  J = J − M
   3  N = I + J
```

The random number is N. The cycle is the l.c.m. of 876 and 940. This is 205,860. The cycle using 941 and 947 is 444,620, which is larger than the one using the program written here.

25.

```
        DIMENSION N(2),NN(2),NO(2),NW(100),NL(100)
        DO 30 I = 1,100
        NW(I) = 0
   30   NL(I) = 0
        NTOT = 0
        READ 100, I,J,NTEST
  100   FORMAT (I5,I5,I10)
        L = 947
        M = 941
   25   DO 7 K = 1,2
        I = I + I
        J = J + J
        IF (I − L)  1,2,2
   2    I = I − L
   1    IF (J − M)  3,4,4
   4    J = J − M
   3    N(K) = I + J
        IF (N(K) − 1000)  5,6,6
   6    N(K) = N(K) − 1000
   5    NN(K) = N(K)/6
```

```
 7   NO(K) = N(K) − 6 * NN(K) + 1
     NSUM = NO(1) + NO(2)
     NTOSS = 1
     IF (NSUM − 7)  9,8,9
 9   IF (NSUM − 11)  10,8,10
10   IF (NSUM − 2)  12,11,12
12   IF (NSUM − 3)  13,11,13
13   IF (NSUM − 12)  14,11,14
14   NPT = NSUM
27   DO 15 K = 1,2
     I = I + I
     J = J + J
     IF (I − L)  16,17,17
17   I = I − L
16   IF (J − M)  18,19,19
19   J = J − M
18   N(K) = I + J
     IF (N(K) − 1000)  20,21,21
21   N(K) = N(K) − 1000
20   NN(K) = N(K)/6
15   NO(K) = N(K) − 6 * NN(K) + 1
     NSUM = NO(1) + NO(2)
     NTOSS = NTOSS + 1
     IF (NSUM − 7)  26,11,26
26   IF (NSUM − NPT)  22,8,22
22   IF (NTOSS − 100)  27,27,23
 8   NW(NTOSS) = NW(NTOSS) + 1
     GO TO 23
11   NL(NTOSS) = NL(NTOSS) + 1
```

23 NTOT = NTOT + 1

IF (NTOT − NTEST) 25,24,24

24 NTIE = NTEST − NTOT

PRINT 31

31 FORMAT (24H②TOSSES④WINS②LOSSES)

DO 32 I = 1,100

PRINT 33,I,NW(I),NL(I)

33 FORMAT (I8,I8,I8)

32 CONTINUE

PRINT 34,NTIE

34 FORMAT (I5,23H①DRAWS①AFTER①100①TOSSES)

STOP

END

Using I = 400 and J = 401 as starting values (see READ statement), then in 495 games the number of wins and losses ending in a given number of tosses is summarized as follows:

Number of Tosses to End Game	Wins	Losses	Total Games
1	89	85	174
2	52	46	98
3	22	32	54
4	18	29	47
5	16	20	36
6	7	12	19
7	10	8	18
8	3	3	6
9	4	6	10
10	6	7	13
11	3	6	9
13	1	1	2
14	1	2	3
15	1	1	2
17	1	1	2
19	0	1	1
22	0	1	1
TOTAL	234	261	495

28. Choosing $p = 5$ and $x = 2$, we get the sequence 2, 4, 3, 1, 2, 4, 3, 1, ...

30. $2^1 = 0 \cdot 11 + 2$; $2^2 = 0 \cdot 11 + 4$; $2^3 = 0 \cdot 11 + 8$; $2^4 = 1 \cdot 11 + 5$; $2^5 = 2 \cdot 11 + 10$; $2^6 = 5 \cdot 11 + 9$; $2^7 = 11 \cdot 11 + 7$; $2^8 = 23 \cdot 11 + 3$; $2^9 = 46 \cdot 11 + 6$; $2^{10} = 93 \cdot 11 + 1$.

APPENDIX B
How FORTRAN Works

In this text we have assumed that the computer we are using "understands" FORTRAN. That is, if we punch FORTRAN statements on cards properly, our computer will read them and perform whatever commands it is given by the FORTRAN program. The day may not be far off when this will indeed happen, but in today's computers there are many intermediate steps which we have ignored.

Simply because we needed DIMENSION statements, you might have guessed from reading this text that there is more to the use and operation of a computer than we have let on. We used these statements to tell our computer how much of its memory to save for subscripted variables. Although we did not need to worry about the computer's memory or about its size, it is evident from the use of the DIMENSION statement that the memory and its size are important and deserve some attention from us.

FORTRAN is a language. It has a syntax, rules of punctuation, etc., like other languages. Of course, it is considerably less complex than any natural language such as English. More important, however, is the fact that statements in FORTRAN are *unambiguous*. There is no doubt about what each FORTRAN statement means or, for that matter, what an entire FORTRAN program means. In English or in any other natural language, it is not always clear what any given word, statement, or paragraph means.

The word FORTRAN itself is an abbreviation for the expression FORmula TRANSlator. As this full name implies, our FORTRAN programs are "translated" into another language — the particular computer's language — before any of the steps in the program is actually carried out. A program in the FORTRAN language is translated into a program in another language called **machine language**. In general, this machine language is different for each different computer. The two programs, one in FORTRAN language and one in machine language, are the same in the sense that they describe the same algorithm. They look very different, however, and you, without a great deal of study, may have trouble determining that they do indeed perform the same algorithm.

There is an analogy between such a translation and the translation from one natural language, such as English, to another natural language, such as French. Suppose we want to write a letter in French. If we do not understand French, we might write the letter in English and have it translated into French by someone who understands both languages. Anyone who reads French can then read our letter. Similarly, suppose we want to write a program in a computer's machine language but do not understand that language. We can write the program in FORTRAN and have it translated into machine language. Of course, whoever does the translating must "understand" both languages. It turns out that for each of the computers in Appendix E a program has been written which makes it possible for each of these computers to "understand" FORTRAN and to be able to translate from FORTRAN into its own machine language. This program is called a **FORTRAN compiler.** Unfortunately, it is also often referred to simply as "FORTRAN." Therefore, the word FORTRAN sometimes stands for a "language" and sometimes for a program which "translates."[1] When we mean the latter, we shall always refer to the FORTRAN compiler. The reader is warned, however, that not all textbooks do so. We emphasize that the FORTRAN compiler for one computer is quite different from the FORTRAN compiler for another computer. Each computer has its own separate and distinct FORTRAN compiler.

Before we can describe this translation process and the program which does the translation, we need to study the machine language of a computer. Any computer will suffice for our purposes, so in the interest of simplicity we invent an imaginary and elementary computer. We then write a simple program (adding 10 integers) in the machine language of our imaginary computer. Next we describe in detail how this computer can translate our simple program from a language which is not quite as sophisticated as FORTRAN into a program in its own machine language. Finally, we discuss what happens to a FORTRAN program when it is read into the computer and how it gets translated. We now describe

---

[1] Here is one ambiguity in the English language. As another example, recall from Chapter 2 the two different meanings for the word "programming."

our imaginary computer which has many of the capabilities of most modern computers.

A modern digital computer is composed of three basic parts: (1) input-output devices such as card readers, typewriters, magnetic tape units; (2) a memory; and (3) an arithmetic unit. We have called the instructions to carry out a given algorithm in a computer a **program**. The instructions in a program are recorded in the memory of the computer. Since in general only numbers can be recorded in the memory, the instructions are coded in terms of some number system. For example, the instruction "add" may be represented by $+1$. Of course, the arithmetic unit must be able to decode these instructions. Thus, when the arithmetic unit encounters a $+1$, it must understand that it is to perform an addition.

The memories of most computers are able to retain several numbers,[2] or **words** as they are usually called. This makes it possible to write *all* the instructions for the solution of a problem ahead of time and to store them in the memory. Computers with such memories are called **stored program computers**.

Let us suppose we have a stored program computer with a 1000-word memory, and that each word contains four decimal digits and a sign, $+$ or $-$. If we wish to add two numbers, we must tell the arithmetic unit what numbers we wish to add or, equivalently, where these two numbers are in the memory. To this end each word in the memory has a label or **address**. The addresses in our computer are numbers which run consecutively from 000 to 999, one for each word in the memory. If the arithmetic unit encounters the instruction $+1324$, it will decode this as "add the number that has the address 324 in memory to the number already in the arithmetic unit."

Let us now write a program to add 10 integers in our computer. We suppose that the ten integers are stored in the memory at ten consecutive addresses from 100 to 109. Let us suppose our computer has been constructed to execute the following instructions:

$+1xyz$ — *Add* the number in the memory location with the address "xyz" to the number in the arithmetic unit. Do not change the contents of the memory location with the address "xyz."

$-1xyz$ — *Subtract* the number in location "xyz" from the number in the arithmetic unit. Do not change the contents of the memory location with the address "xyz."

---

[2] In general, a number in a computer is made up of more than one digit.

+2000   *Clear* the arithmetic unit to all zeros.

−2xyz   *Save* the contents of the arithmetic unit in the memory at the location with address "xyz." Do not change the contents of the arithmetic unit.

+0000   *Stop* the computer.

We design our computer so that, when we push the "start" button, the computer takes its first instruction from the memory location with address 000. It then proceeds to addresses 001, 002, ..., and so on, interpreting each of these words as an instruction and executing them in order. The following program will add the ten integers and leave the result at the address 099.

Address in Memory	Contents of the Address
000	+2000
001	+1100
002	+1101
003	+1102
004	+1103
005	+1104
006	+1105
007	+1106
008	+1107
009	+1108
010	+1109
011	−2099
012	+0000

Let us analyze now what happens when we start our computer. The computer goes first to memory location 000 and picks up the number +2000. It decodes this instruction and clears the arithmetic unit to all zeros so that there is nothing left there from a previous computation. The computer then goes to memory location 001, takes the number there, +1100, and decodes it as the instruction "add the number in location 100 to the number in the arithmetic unit." Since the arithmetic unit contains zeros, the result of performing this instruction leaves the integer in memory location 100 in the arithmetic unit. We have now added the first of our 10 integers.

Next the computer goes to location 002, decodes the number there,

+1101, as "add the number in location 101 to the arithmetic unit." Thus the second integer which is stored in location 101 is added to the first integer, and their sum remains in the arithmetic unit. As the computer proceeds to the next instruction in location 003 and executes it, the third integer, which is stored in 102, is added to the sum of the first two and the new sum remains in the arithmetic unit.

Likewise, the instructions in 004 through 010 are taken in sequence and each tells the computer to add another integer to the integer already in the arithmetic unit. After the instruction in 010 has been performed, the sum of all 10 integers is in the arithmetic unit. The next instruction performed is the one at location 011. This number, −2099, is decoded as "save the contents of the arithmetic unit in memory location 099." After the computer does this, the sum is saved where we can later get it to print the sum or to do further calculations. The final instruction at 012 stops the computer.

We had to write one "add instruction" for each integer we wanted to add. If we had several hundred numbers to add, the repetition of the add instruction would be both tedious and wasteful. Fortunately, there is a way to avoid this repetition.

Notice that all the instructions (or words) contained in memory locations 001 to 010 are very similar if viewed as four-digit integers. In fact, each one can be obtained from the previous one by the "addition" of +0001. Since instructions are represented by numbers, there is no reason why arithmetic cannot be performed on the instructions themselves. Suppose, in fact, we add +0001 to the "add instruction" in memory location 001 after that instruction has been executed. Then this memory location would contain "+1101" which is precisely the instruction also in memory location 002. Thus, the computer might just as well take its next instruction from memory location 001 instead of from 002.

Previously, however, we said that, after our computer had executed the instruction in 001, it would go in turn to memory locations 002, 003, etc., for its instructions. If we had some way of making the computer go back to location 001 for its next instruction, there would no longer be any need at all for the instruction in location 002. Clearly, we could continue to add +0001 to the instruction in location 001 and generate all the instructions now in memory locations 002 to 010. Then, if we could also accomplish the trick of making the computer return to 001 for its instruction, we could eliminate from the program all the instructions from 002 through 010.

To this end the following instruction is appended to the list of instructions for our computer:

+3xyz   Take the next instruction from the address "xyz" in memory and then proceed from there to "xyz + 1," "xyz + 2," etc.

Another program to add the numbers starting in address 100 can now be written. Assume that the word with the address 099 contains all zeros initially.

Address	Contents
000	+2000
001	+1099
002	+1100
003	−2099
004	+2000
005	+1002
006	+1009
007	−2002
008	+3000
009	+0001

Let us look at this program in detail. Our computer first decodes the instruction in 000 and clears the arithmetic unit to all zeros. It then decodes the instruction in 001 and adds the contents of address 099 to the arithmetic unit. Since the contents of 099 are zero, we are merely adding zero to zero. This seems nonsensical now, but the purpose of this instruction will become clear as we progress. We next perform the operation in 002. This adds the contents of 100 to the arithmetic unit. Then we save that result in location 099.

We have saved the number because the next instruction at 004 clears the arithmetic unit to all zeros again. We need to clear out the arithmetic unit at this time so that we can proceed to perform arithmetic on the instructions. To this end the instruction at 005, which is executed next, adds the contents of location 002 to the zeros in the arithmetic unit. The arithmetic unit then contains the "number" +1100. Of course, this can be and has been decoded as an instruction, but we now treat it as a number. The next instruction at 006 adds the contents of location 009 to the arithmetic unit. When this instruction is completed, the arithmetic unit contains +1101.

We then save this number in location 002. At this point—just as the computer is about to go to location 008 for its next instruction—the memory of the computer contains

Address	Contents
000	+2000
001	+1099
002	+1101
003	−2099
004	+2000
005	+1002
006	+1009
007	−2002
008	+3000
009	+0001

This is identical with the memory's previous contents with the exception of the contents of address 002.

When the computer decodes the instruction at 008, it does no arithmetic at all but goes back to location 000 for its next instruction. It clears the arithmetic unit to all zeros, adds the contents of location 099 which contains the first integer, adds the contents of location 101 (the second integer) to it, and saves the result in 099. Location 099 then contains the sum of the first two integers. The instructions in locations 004 to 007 change the contents of location 002 to +1102. The instruction in 008 returns the computer to 000 for its next instruction.

When the sequence 000 to 003 is executed, the sum of the first two integers is picked up from location 099 (instruction at 001), the third integer is added to it (instruction at 002), and the sum of all three is saved in location 099 (instruction at 003). It is clear then that each time we execute the instructions at locations 000 to 003 another number is added to the sum.

In summary, then, the add instruction in memory location 002 is changed each time the instruction in location 007 is executed. The instructions lying in memory locations 004 through 006 determine this change. The instruction in location 008 returns the computer to the part of the program which performs the additions.

But this program has a serious difficulty. It will not stop after adding 10 numbers. It will continue to add numbers until it has added 900 of them and the instruction in address 002 becomes +2000. Instructions

002 and 003 will then clear the contents of the arithmetic unit and store all zeros in address 099. The next time the instruction having the address 002 is encountered, it will contain the instruction +2001 which we have not yet defined.

We need some way of stopping the computer after 10 numbers have been added. That is, we need to insert a counting process before the instruction in address 008 is executed.

> **Question.** What is the purpose of the instruction stored in the address 001 in memory? If it had been left out, what would the memory location with address 099 contain when the "jump" instruction at address 008 is being executed for the third time?

The counting process can be implemented in a number of ways. For example, a +0010 could be placed in some memory location which we call, for convenience, the "counter." Each time a +0001 is added to the "add instruction" in memory location 002, it also is subtracted from the counter. As long as this counter remains positive, the computer is allowed to continue operating. As soon as it becomes zero, however, the computer is stopped.

Another way of counting to 10 is to notice that we wish the program to continue until the instruction in 002 becomes +1109. Therefore, if we subtract +1110 from the "number" in location 002 and the result is less than zero, the program should continue. Otherwise, the program should stop.

In either of these counting processes we need some way of deciding whether a "number" or "instruction" is positive, negative, or zero. The following instructions, which we now include in our computer's list of instructions, accomplishes this.

+4xyz   (a) If the number in the arithmetic unit is *positive*, take the next instruction from the address "xyz" and proceed from there taking successive instructions from addresses "xyz + 1," "xyz + 2," etc.

           (b) If the number in the arithmetic unit is zero or negative, ignore this instruction and proceed.

−4xyz   (a) If the number in the arithmetic unit is *negative*, take the next instruction from address "xyz" and proceed from there.

           (b) If the number in the arithmetic unit is zero or positive, ignore this instruction and proceed.

Let us consider the first solution proposed where we have a counter originally set at 10 and subtract 1 from it after each addition is performed. Previously we assumed that the memory location with address 099 contained zeros when we pushed the "start" button. This is not a safe assumption, however, because the previous user of our computer may have left something there. Therefore, we put zeros in the memory location 099 ourselves at the outset.

Address	Contents
000	+2000
001	−2099
002	+2000
003	+1099
004	+1100
005	−2099
006	+2000
007	+1004
008	+1016
009	−2004
010	+2000
011	+1017
012	−1016
013	−2017
014	+4002
015	+0000
016	+0001
017	+0010

After we have made sure that location 099 contains all zeros, we add the first integer in memory location 100 to zero and save it in location 099 (instructions 002 to 005). We then add +0001 to the instruction in 004 and save the sum in location 004 (instructions 006 to 009).

Next we subtract +0001 from the counter in location 017 and save the result in the counter (instructions 010 to 013). Notice that the new value of the counter (+0009 the first time) is still in the arithmetic unit. A check of the definition of the save instruction (−2xyz) will assure you of this.

Thus the instruction at 014 sees if the arithmetic unit, which is the same as the counter, is positive or not. If it is, it returns the computer to location 002 and the computer proceeds through the instructions 002, 003, . . . , etc., in sequence. Only one of these instructions, the one at

004, has been changed. Eventually, of course, the counter becomes zero. When this happens, the instruction at 014 does not return the computer to 002, but lets it go on. The instruction at 015 then stops the computer.

Notice that the numbers at 016 and 017 are not instructions at all. They are numbers. The latter is the counter and the former is a number 1 which is used to modify the counter and to alter the instruction with the address 004.

It is clear that the program above could be used to add more than 10 numbers, indeed as many numbers as we wish, simply by changing the contents of address 017. We could therefore add 100 or more numbers with a program of 18 address locations.

> **Problem.** Write a program to add the 10 numbers in locations 100 to 109 using only 15 instructions. Use the second technique suggested above: subtract +1110 from the "number" which is the add instruction (see the word in location 004) and repeat the process if the result is less than zero.

Until about 1950, programs were written in machine language in much the same way as we have just done. It was at about that time that a programmer first thought of writing a program to do some of the bookkeeping of writing programs in order to make his job easier. There evolved a technique called **symbolic programming.**

Symbolic programming uses mnemonic codes instead of numeric ones. For example, the last program above would read

START	CLR	
	SAV	SUM
A	CLR	
	ADD	SUM
X	ADD	NUM
	SAV	SUM
	CLR	
	ADD	X
	ADD	ONE
	SAV	X
	CLR	
	ADD	CTR

	SUB	ONE
	SAV	CTR
	TRP	A
	STP	
ONE	CON	+0001
CTR	CON	+0010
SUM	EQU	099
NUM	EQU	100

The first 16 lines correspond exactly to the first 16 lines of the machine language program. The abbreviations are: CLR = clear, SAV = save, TRP = transfer if positive, STP = stop, CTR = counter, EQU = equals, CON = contains.

There are now three columns. The first identifies the memory location just as the numbers did in the address column previously. The second defines the instruction as the sign and the first digit in the second column did before. The third column is the address which was given by the last three digits in column two of the machine language program.

This symbolic program is punched on cards and read into the computer. The information read in this way is considered as "information" or "data" supplied to still another program. This second program will translate our symbolic program into a machine language program. The translator program is called a **symbolic assembly program** or sometimes simply an **assembler.**

We assume that the assembly program has been written already and is now in machine language. Moreover, it is stored in the memory of the computer when our symbolic program for adding 10 integers is read by the computer. In fact, it contains instructions which read our symbolic program into the computer.

One thing the assembly program contains is a table of instructions as follows:

$$ADD = +1$$
$$CLR = +2$$
$$SAV = -2$$
$$STP = +0$$
$$SUB = -1$$
$$TRP = +4$$

We shall see how it uses this table, which we call the **operation table,** shortly.

The first thing that the assembly program does is to assign successive memory locations to each instruction of the symbolic program and to make a second table which contains the memory locations corresponding to the symbols in the first column of the symbolic program. In our program START corresponds to 000. Because the next instruction has no symbol, 001 is not put in this table. However, A = 002 is put in the table. Proceeding in this way we get the following **symbol table:**

$$START = 000$$

$$A = 002$$

$$X = 004$$

$$ONE = 016$$

$$CTR = 017$$

The symbols SUM and NUM are treated differently. While our assembly program is assigning memory locations to the instructions in the program, it also checks the operation codes. If an instruction contains one of the operation codes in the operation table or if it contains a CON, the process described above is carried out. When it encounters EQU, it jumps to a set of instructions which add another entry to the symbol table. In particular, it adds the symbol on the left together with the number on the right in the same line of the symbol table. In our program SUM = 099 and NUM = 100 are added to the symbol table because of the two EQU codes. The symbol table now reads

$$START = 000$$

$$A = 002$$

$$X = 004$$

$$ONE = 016$$

$$CTR = 017$$

$$SUM = 099$$

$$NUM = 100$$

Having constructed the symbol table, we have completed *pass one* of the symbolic assembly program. As the name implies, we have "passed through" our symbolic program which adds 10 integers "once." During the pass, we examined each line and (a) made sure that it contained an instruction in the operation table or contained an EQU or a CON, (b) assigned a memory location to each instruction, and (c) constructed a symbol table.

The assembler now goes back and passes through each instruction of our symbolic program again. In this second pass, called *pass two*, each symbolic instruction is translated into a machine language instruction.

During pass two the first column in our symbolic program is ignored. The symbol in the second column is looked up in the operation table. For example, CLR is found to be equal to +2. Then the symbol in the third column is looked up in the symbol table. If nothing appears in the third column, three zeros are used. Thus the first line in our symbolic program becomes +2000, and it is assigned to memory location 000.

Next we proceed to the second instruction

SAV   SUM

From the operation table SAV = −2, and from the symbol table SUM = 099, so this becomes −2099. This machine language instruction is placed in the next memory location, which is 001. Proceeding in this way, we can translate each symbolic language instruction into one machine language instruction. We place each of these machine language instructions in succeeding memory locations.

Everything proceeds without difficulty until we reach either a CON or an EQU in column two. When we come across a CON, we do not use either table but merely put whatever appears in the third column in the next available memory location. For example, the STP resulted in +0000 being put in memory location 015. Therefore, when we look at ONE CON +0001, we put the third column, +0001, in the next memory location, which is 016. The next instruction in our symbolic program puts +0010 in memory location 017.

If an EQU is encountered in pass two, it is skipped over. These are only used in pass one in forming the symbol table.

Following the rules detailed above, we construct the machine language program used previously for adding 10 integers in precisely the same form as we wrote it earlier.[3]

---

[3] Actually the EQU operation code is not often used in practice in the way we described here. Generally the numbers to be added are read into a location which we refer to only by a symbol and the result is stored into a symbolic location. When we print the sum, then we print the contents of a symbolic location. The actual numerical locations are found in the symbol table where they were inserted by the assembler in a convenient way.

What we have described is an algorithm for translating from a symbolic program into a machine language program. It required that the symbolic program be examined twice. Many assemblers follow this type of algorithm.

The first assembler must be written in machine language. But, if we wanted to write a second one, we could write it in symbolic language and use our first assembler to translate it. In fact, we could write a succession of assemblers each being translated by its predecessor. This is indeed a common practice in computing and is called "boot strapping" since the succeeding assemblers are, so to speak, pulling themselves up by their own boot straps.

We turn now to the FORTRAN language and the FORTRAN compiler. This compiler is much more complicated than the assembler we have just described, and we cannot discuss it in the same amount of detail. We content ourselves with a general description and some words about what actually happens to a FORTRAN program when it is read into a computer.

First we note that our program to add 10 integers can be written in FORTRAN as follows:

        DIMENSION K(10)

        I = 0

        DO   1   J = 1,10

    1   I = I + K(J)

        STOP

where the 10 integers to be added are K(1), K(2), . . . , K(10). The sum is called I.

The FORTRAN program is read into the computer's memory in some coded form by a program called a **monitor**.[4] The monitor then jumps to the FORTRAN compiler. This compiler will then pass through the statements one or more times doing the following things. It will test to see if the syntax and the punctuation are correct. For example, it must make sure that for every left parenthesis there is a right parenthesis. When it sees a DO, it must check that it is followed by an integer, then an integer variable, then an = sign, and so on. It also finds extra

---

[4] We shall have more to say about monitors in a short while.

blank spaces and throws them away. It must assign memory locations to all variables such as I, J, K(1), . . . , K(10). It must also check that every statement number used in a statement appears somewhere on the left. For example, if we have a statement GO TO 20 but no statement is proceeded by a 20, an error has been made.

Whenever the FORTRAN compiler finds such errors, it prints out a message called a **diagnostic** and usually does not try to perform the steps in the algorithm of the FORTRAN program it has read. Unfortunately, many FORTRAN compilers print diagnostics which are somewhat cryptic. In the compiler's defense, however, it should be pointed out that not all errors are easy to trace to their cause.

The FORTRAN compiler then translates the FORTRAN program into a symbolic program using some of the translation ideas we mentioned earlier in describing an assembler. Once a symbolic program has been produced, the compiler calls on an assembler, which in turn produces the machine language program.

At this point the FORTRAN compiler jumps back to the monitor. The monitor starts to do the instructions in the program we have written. This is called **executing** the program. The instructions executed are now in the form of a machine language program. In more precise terms, the monitor simply transfers control (through a $+3$ or $+4$ or similar instruction) to the start of the translated program.

The STOP instruction is treated in a peculiar way by many FORTRAN compilers. Instead of inserting a $+0000$ in the machine language program, the compiler often inserts a "jump" instruction. This jump instruction sends control back to the monitor. Thus, when a machine language program has been executed and completed, the computer does not actually stop. Instead the monitor starts to read the next program in line and uses the FORTRAN compiler or the assembler to translate it. We avoid actually stopping the computer to save computer time, which may be quite expensive.

In summary, then, several FORTRAN programs and/or symbolic programs on cards can be placed in the card reader. The monitor, the FORTRAN compiler, and the assembler (all in machine language) are stored in the computer's memory. The computer operator starts the computer in such a way that it jumps into the monitor. The monitor (1) reads the first program and (2) jumps into either the FORTRAN compiler or the assembler, depending on the original language of the program just read. If the program is in FORTRAN, the FORTRAN compiler (1) finds any errors it can and prints out diagnostics, (2) finding no errors, translates the FORTRAN program into a symbolic program, (3) has the assembler translate the symbolic program into a machine language program, and (4) executes the machine language program. When the machine language program is completed, it jumps back to the monitor which reads another program.

A more detailed discussion of monitors, compilers, and assemblers must be left to more advanced texts.

The Sum of the First K Squares

The purpose of this appendix is to find the sum of the squares of the first K integers. That is, we want a formula which gives the value of the sum

$$1^2 + 2^2 + 3^2 + \cdots + (K-1)^2 + K^2$$

To find this we begin with the identity

$$(n+1)^3 = n^3 + 3n^2 + 3n + 1$$

This is true for every number n and if we take in succession the values $1, 2, 3, \ldots, (K-2), (K-1), K$ for n in this identity we get the equations

$$(1+1)^3 = 1^3 + 3 \cdot 1^2 + 3 \cdot 1 + 1$$

$$(2+1)^3 = 2^3 + 3 \cdot 2^2 + 3 \cdot 2 + 1$$

$$(3+1)^3 = 3^3 + 3 \cdot 3^2 + 3 \cdot 3 + 1$$

$$\cdot \cdot \cdot \cdot \cdot \cdot \cdot \cdot \cdot \cdot \cdot \cdot \cdot \cdot \cdot \cdot \cdot \cdot \cdot \cdot \cdot \cdot \cdot \cdot \cdot$$

$$(K-1)^3 = (K-2)^3 + 3 \cdot (K-2)^2 + 3 \cdot (K-2) + 1$$

$$K^3 = (K-1)^3 + 3 \cdot (K-1)^2 + 3 \cdot (K-1) + 1$$

$$(K+1)^3 = K^3 + 3 \cdot K^2 + 3K + 1$$

Now we add all these equations. The sum of all the left-hand sides must equal the sum of all the right-hand sides. We need not write this all out, for many terms on the two sides will be equal and so cancel each other. For instance, the term on the left in the first equation is 2^3 which is just equal to the first term on the right in the second equation. Therefore, they cancel out. Indeed, every term on the left but the last one will just equal the first term on the right in the next equation. Cancelling all these terms, all we are left with is the last term on the left, the first term of the first equation on the right, and all the second, third and fourth terms on the right. This gives us, upon adding all the equations,

$$(K + 1)^3 = 1^3 + 3[1^2 + 2^2 + 3^2 + \cdots + (K - 2)^2 + (K - 1)^2 + K^2]$$
$$+ 3[1 + 2 + 3 + \cdots + (K - 2) + (K - 1) + K] + K$$

Here we added all the 1 terms on the right to give just K on the right. Also we have factored 3 out of all the other terms and grouped together in one bracket all the squares to be added and in the other bracket all the first powers to be added. The term in the first bracket is what we wish to find. The term in the second bracket is the sum of the first K integers. We assume this sum to be known (see the problem below). The sum of the first K integers is

$$1 + 2 + 3 + \cdots + (K - 2) + (K - 1) + K = \frac{K(K + 1)}{2}$$

Making use of this fact, we find that the previous equation then becomes

$$(K + 1)^3 = 1 + 3[1^2 + 2^2 + \cdots + (K - 1)^2 + K^2] + \frac{3K(K + 1)}{2} + K$$

Solving for the term in brackets, we have

$$1^2 + 2^2 + \cdots + (K - 1)^2 + K^2 = \frac{(K + 1)^3}{3} - \frac{K + 1}{3} - \frac{K(K + 1)}{2}$$

Simplifying, we find the answer to be

$$1^2 + 2^2 + \cdots + (K - 1)^2 + K^2 = \frac{K(K + 1)(2K + 1)}{6}$$

Problem. Begin with the identity

$$(n + 1)^2 = n^2 + 2n + 1$$

and apply it as above for $n = 1, 2, 3, \ldots, (K - 2), (K - 1)$, K to prove that the sum of the first K integers is $K(K+1)/2$ as stated in the preceding proof.

Chronological List of Scientists

This appendix lists all the 26 mathematicians and scientists referred to in the footnotes in the text. The individuals are listed chronologically according to their date of *birth*. Their contribution to the topics discussed in this text are given below their names. These items are by no means all of their contributions to mathematics and computing, nor even necessarily their principal contribution. The reader is referred to the footnotes or to a history of mathematics for a full account of the work of these distinguished men. The page number shown on the right is the page where a footnote regarding each individual may be found.

Computing Systems
Usable with this Book

In this appendix we list 72 computing systems which are the products of 23 manufacturers. All these systems will successfully handle the FORTRAN programming described in this text (Chapter 3). The systems produced by American manufacturers are listed first in alphabetical order by the manufacturer's name. The Canadian and British manufacturers' systems follow.

The minimum size machine required to accommodate the FORTRAN in this text is listed in terms of the high-speed memory, number of tapes, etc. The memory size is given in words, characters (6 or 8 bits), or bytes (8 bits). The symbol K is either 1000 or $1024 = 2^7$ depending on the computer. The maximum size of the floating-point numbers and the integers which each system allows are given in the "range" columns. In addition, the number of digits in the mantissa of the floating-point numbers is given in the "precision" column. Sometimes the precision is given by an integer followed by a $+$ sign. For example, for the Advance 6000 series the precision is given as $11+$. This means that the number of digits in the mantissa of that system is at least 11 and may sometimes be one greater, 12. To understand why this is so, we need only consider a computer with four binary bits in the mantissa of its floating-point numbers. Numbers from 0 to 15 can be represented in 4 bits. Therefore, we can always get one digit of precision. For numbers less than 15, we get two digits of precision. However, for two-digit numbers between 16 and 99, we get only one digit of precision. Such a computer is said to have a precision of $1+$, since it has more than one digit of precision but does not always have two digits of precision.

The range and precision given here are the normal range and precision which will result if the programs described in this text are used precisely as written. In many cases it is possible to increase (or decrease) either the range or precision or both by appropriate changes in the programs. The individual FORTRAN manuals should be consulted if this point is of interest.

Fifteen of the systems are preceded by an asterisk. Those systems should use the READ and WRITE (or PUNCH) statements described in Section 3.8.* All other systems should use the READ and PRINT statements in Section 3.8.

There are three computing systems which will *not* accommodate the FORTRAN in this text. They are the PDP-5, the PDP-8, and the IBM 650. Both the PDP-5 and the PDP-8 allow only one subscript on a variable and only four symbols in a variable name. The IBM 650 does not have the FORMAT statements used here.

In addition, when using this text and an IBM 1620 computer, the GOTRAN system should not be used. GOTRAN has no FORMAT statements, allows only one subscript on a variable, does not allow multiplication or division with integers, and has several other restrictive rules. If the IBM 1620 computer is to be used, either FORTRAN or FORGO should be employed.

Computing Systems

System	Minimum FORTRAN System					Floating Point		Integers	Notes
	Memory	Tapes	Printer	Punch	Reader	Range	Precision	Range	
AMERICAN MANUFACTURERS									
Advanced Scientific Instruments									
ASI 210/2100	8K wds.	0	1	1	1	10^{76}	10	$10^6 - 1$	
ASI 6000 series	4K wds.	0	1	1	1	10^{76}	$11+$	$2^{23} - 1$	
Burroughs Corporation									
B 2500/B 3500	30K wds.	0	1	1	1	10^{99}	8	$10^8 - 1$	
B 5500	8K wds.	1	1	1	1	10^{69}	11	$2^{39} - 1$	
Control Data Corporation									
Bendix G-20	8K wds.	2	1	1	1	10^{63}	$12+$	$2^{21} - 1$	
*CDC-160	4K wds.	0	0	1	1	10^{32}	$8+$	$2^{11} - 1$	Use "apostrophe" instead of "asterisk." All FORMAT statements at beginning of program. Use two END cards.
CDC-160A	8K wds.	0	0	1	1	10^{32}	$8+$	$2^{22} - 1$	
CDC-160G	8K wds.	2	0	1	1	10^{32}	$8+$	$2^{22} - 1$	
CDC-1604/1604A	32K wds.	2	1	1	1	10^{308}	$10+$	$2^{47} - 1$	2 tapes may replace the printer and reader.
*CDC-1700	8K wds.	0	1	1	1	10^{38}	$6+$	$2^{15} - 1$	Reader and punch are paper tape.

Model	Memory								Notes
CDC 3100/3200/3300/3500	8K wds.	3	1	1	1	10^{308}	10+	$2^{23}-1$	1 drum can replace 4 tapes.
CDC 3400/3600/3800	32K wds.	4	1	1	1	10^{308}	10+	$2^{47}-1$	Requires large-capacity disc.
CDC 6400/6600	32K wds.	1	1	1	1	10^{322}	14+	$2^{59}-1$	
Decision Control, Inc., Data Machines Division									
*DATA 620	4K wds.	0	1	0	0	10^{38}	7	$2^{15}-1$	
Digital Equipment Corp.									
PDP-6	10K wds.	0	1	1	1	10^{38}	8+	$2^{35}-1$	
*PDP-7	8K wds.	1	1	1	0	10^{99}	10+	$2^{17}-1$	
PDP-9	8K wds.	1	1	1	0	10^{99}	10+	$2^{17}-1$	
PDP-10	8K wds.	1	1	0	0	10^{38}	8+	$2^{35}-1$	Tape is paper tape.
Electronics Associates, Inc.									
EAI 8400	8K wds.	0	1	1	1	10^{76}	7	$2^{16}-1$	Punch and reader are paper tape.
General Electric Company									
GE-215/225/235	8K wds.	0	1	1	1	10^{76}	9	$2^{19}-1$	
GE-400	8K wds.	4	1	1	1	10^{127}	8	$2^{23}-1$	
GE-600 series	64K wds.	6	1	1	1	10^{38}	8+	$2^{35}-1$	1 drum or disk.
Hewlett Packard, Dymec Division									
*HP-2116A	4K wds.	0	1	1	1	10^{38}	6+	$2^{15}-1$	Printer-punch-reader is ASR33 (teletype).
Honeywell Electronics Data Processing									
*Honeywell 200	16K char.	4	1	0	0	10^{99}	10	$2^{29}-1$	
*Honeywell 1200/2200/4200	32K char.	4	1	0	0	10^{616}	10+	$2^{20}-1$	

Computing Systems (Continued)

System	Minimum FORTRAN System					Floating Point		Integers	Notes
	Memory	Tapes	Printer	Punch	Reader	Range	Precision	Range	
AMERICAN MANUFACTURERS (Continued)									
Honeywell, Computer Control Division									
DDP-116	8K wds.	0	1	1	1	10^{38}	6+	$2^{15}-1$	
DDP-124	8K wds.	0	1	1	1	10^{76}	6+	$2^{23}-1$	
*DDP-516	8K wds.	0	1	0	0	10^{38}	6+	$2^{15}-1$	Printer is teletype.
International Business Machines Corp.									
*IBM System/360 Models 30, 40, 44, 50, 65, 67, 75	16K bytes	3	1	1	1	10^{75}	6+	$2^{31}-1$	3 tapes and punch can be replaced by 16K bytes of memory.
*IBM 1130	4K wds.	0	0	1	1	10^{38}	7	$2^{15}-1$	
IBM 1401	8K char.	0	1	1	1	10^{99}	8	$10^{5}-1$	
IBM 1410	20K char.	4	1	1	1	10^{99}	8	$10^{5}-1$	
*IBM 1440	12K char.	0	1	1	1	10^{99}	8	$10^{5}-1$	1 disk.
*IBM 1460	12K char.	4	1	1	1	10^{99}	8	$10^{5}-1$	1 disk can replace 4 tapes.
IBM 1620	20K char.	0	1	1	1	10^{99}	8	$10^{5}-1$	Using FORTRAN with FORMAT.
*IBM 1620	40K char.	0	1	1	1	10^{49}	8	$10^{6}-1$	Using FORGO. Integer exponents must be a constant or a single integer variable.

IBM 1620	20K char.	0	1	1	1	10^{50}	8	$10^5 - 1$	Using PDQ FORTRAN.
*IBM 1800	4K wds.	0	1	1	1	10^{38}	7	$2^{15} - 1$	1 drum.
IBM 704	4K wds.	4	1	1	1	10^{38}	8+	$2^{17} - 1$	Uses special END card.
IBM 705	40K char.	8	1	1	1	10^{99}	8	$10^{10} - 1$	
IBM 7010	40K char.	5	1	1	1	10^{99}	8	$10^5 - 1$	
IBM 7040/7044	8K wds.	3	1	1	1	10^{38}	8+	$2^{35} - 1$	
IBM 7070/7074	5K wds.	0	1	1	1	10^{49}	8	$10^{10} - 1$	
IBM 7080	80K char.	10	0	0	1	10^{99}	8	$10^{10} - 1$	
IBM 7090/7094	32K wds.	8	1	1	1	10^{38}	8+	$2^{35} - 1$	
National Cash Register Co.									
NCR 315	20K char.	3	1	0	1	10^{147}	12	$10^{12} - 1$	1 cram file can replace 3 tapes.
Philco Corporation									
Philco 2000	8K wds.	7	0	0	0	10^{616}	11	$2^{39} - 1$	
Radio Corporation of America									
RCA Spectra 70	65K bytes	5	1	0	1	10^{75}	6+	$2^{31} - 1$	Models 35, 45, 55
RCA 301	20K char.	4	1	1	1	10^{99}	8	$10^7 - 1$	
RCA 3301	60K wds.	6	1	1	1	10^{99}	8	$10^7 - 1$	
Raytheon Computer									
Raytheon 520	8K wds.	0	1	1	1	10^{99}	12	$2^{23} - 1$	
Scientific Data Systems									
SDS 92	8K wds.	0	1	0	1	10^{616}	6+	$2^{23} - 1$	
SDS 910/925, 920/930	4K wds.	1	1	0	1	10^{76}	11+	$2^{23} - 1$	
SDS 9300	16K wds.	3	1	1	1	10^{76}	11+	$2^{23} - 1$	

Computing Systems (Continued)

System	Minimum FORTRAN System					Floating Point		Integers	Notes
	Memory	Tapes	Printer	Punch	Reader	Range	Precision	Range	
AMERICAN MANUFACTURERS (Continued)									
Scientific Data Systems (Continued)									
SDS Sigma 2	8K wds.	0	1	1	1	10^{75}	6+	$2^{15}-1$	Reader and punch are paper tape.
SDS Sigma 7	4K wds.	0	1	0	1	10^{75}	6+	$2^{31}-1$	
Systems Engineering Laboratories, Inc.									
*SEL 810/840	8K wds.	0	1	1	1	10^{153}	11+	$2^{24}-1$	
UNIVAC Division of the Sperry Rand Corp.									
UNIVAC III	16K wds.	5	1	1	1	10^{49}	10	$10^{6}-1$	Requires 1004 processor.
UNIVAC 418	12K wds.	0	1	1	1	10^{38}	8	$2^{17}-1$	
UNIVAC 490 series	32K wds.	1	1	1	1	10^{38}	8+	$2^{29}-1$	1 drum.
UNIVAC 1050	16K char.	4	1	1	1	10^{49}	8	$10^{5}-1$	
UNIVAC 1107	32K wds.	0	1	1	1	10^{38}	8+	$2^{35}-1$	1 drum.
Westinghouse Electric Corp.									
PRODAC 250	8K wds.	0	1	1	1	10^{76}	6+	$2^{16}-1$	32K mass memory.
PRODAC 550	8K wds.	0	1	1	1	10^{46}	8+	$2^{17}-1$	32K drum.

582

CANADIAN AND BRITISH MANUFACTURERS

Elliott-Automation Computers Ltd.

Elliott 4120/4130	16K wds.	0	1	1	1	10^{76}	11	$2^{23}-1$	Punch and reader are paper tape.
Elliott 503	24K wds.	1	1	1	1	10^{76}	8	$2^{38}-1$	Punch and reader are paper tape.
Elliott 903B	8K wds.	0	0	1	1	10^{18}	7+	$2^{17}-1$	

English Electric-Leo-Marconi Computers, Ltd.

KDF 9	12K wds.	3	1	1	1	10^{76}	11+	$2^{39}-1$	Reader is paper tape.
*System 4-30	32K bytes	5	1	0	1	10^{256}	9	$10^{11}-1$	1 disk can replace 5 tapes.
System 4-50/4-70	65K bytes	5	1	1	1	10^{75}	17	$2^{31}-1$	1 disk can replace 5 tapes.

Ferranti-Packard Electric, Ltd.

FP 6000	16K wds.	0	0	1	1	10^{76}	11+	$2^{23}-1$	

International Computers and Tabulators, Ltd.

Atlas 1	30K wds.	0	1	1	1	10^{115}	11+	$2^{36}-1$	
Atlas 2	40K wds.	0	1	1	1	10^{115}	11+	$2^{36}-1$	
ICT 1500	20K wds.	4	1	1	1	10^{100}	7	$10^{7}-1$	
ICT 1900 series	4K wds.	0	1	1	1	10^{76}	11+	$2^{23}-1$	

Index